Everyday Mathematics®

The University of Chicago School Mathematics Project

Math Masters

The McGraw·Hill Companies

The University of Chicago School Mathematics Project (UCSMP)

Max Bell, Director, UCSMP Elementary Materials Component; Director, *Everyday Mathematics* First Edition; James McBride, Director, *Everyday Mathematics* Second Edition; Andy Isaacs, Director, *Everyday Mathematics* Third Edition; Amy Dillard, Associate Director, *Everyday Mathematics* Third Edition

Authors

Max Bell, John Bretzlauf, Amy Dillard, Robert Hartfield, Andy Isaacs, James McBride, Ann McCarty*, Kathleen Pitvorec, Peter Saecker, Robert Balfanz†, William Carroll†

**Third Edition only* *†First Edition only*

Technical Art
Diana Barrie

Teacher in Residence
Denise Porter

Contributors

Ann Brown, Sarah Busse, Terry DeJong, Craig Dezell, John Dini, James Flanders, Donna Goffron, Steve Heckley, Karen Hedberg, Deborah Arron Leslie, Sharon McHugh, Janet M. Meyers, Donna Owen, William D. Pattison, Marilyn Pavlak, Jane Picken, Kelly Porto, John Sabol, Rose Ann Simpson, Debbi Suhajda, Laura Sunseri, Jayme Tighe, Andrea Tyrance, Kim Van Haitsma, Mary Wilson, Nancy Wilson, Jackie Winston, Carl Zmola, Theresa Zmola

Photo Credits

Corbis, p. vi; Getty Images, cover, *center*, p. iii; ©Kelly Kalhoefer/Getty Images, cover, *top right*; ©Stuart Westmorland/CORBIS, cover, *bottom left*; Portrait of Galileo, FPG/Getty Images.

This material is based upon work supported by the National Science Foundation under Grant No. ESI-9252984. Any opinions, findings, conclusions, or recommendations expressed in this material are those of the authors and do not necessarily reflect the views of the National Science Foundation.

---

www.WrightGroup.com

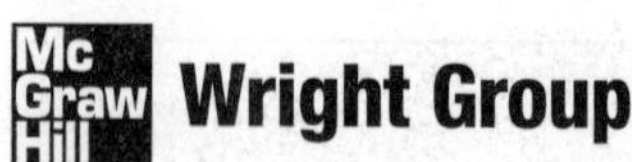

Printed in the United States of America.

Send all inquiries to:
Wright Group/McGraw-Hill
P.O. Box 812960
Chicago, IL 60681

ISBN 0-07-605278-8

3 4 5 6 7 8 9 QWV 12 11 10 09 08 07

The McGraw·Hill Companies

Contents

Teaching Masters 

Study Link Masters 

Unit 1

Unit 2

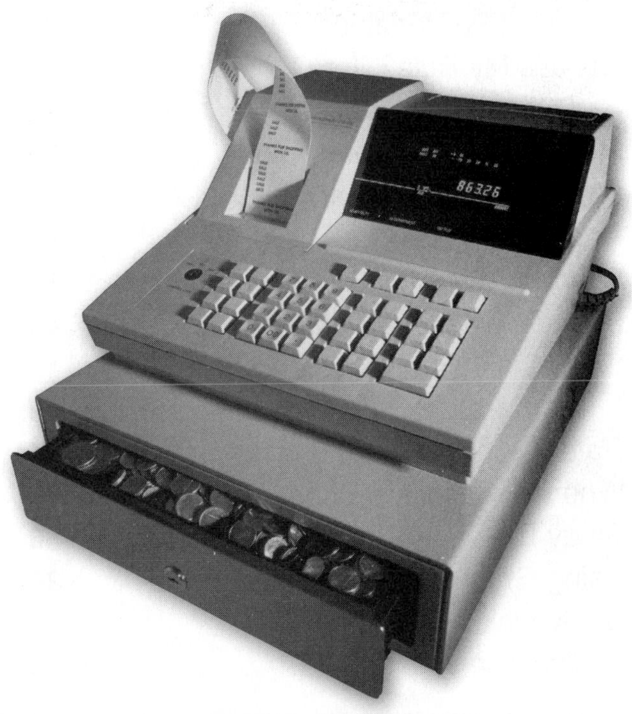

Unit 3

Unit 4

Unit 5

Unit 6

Unit 7

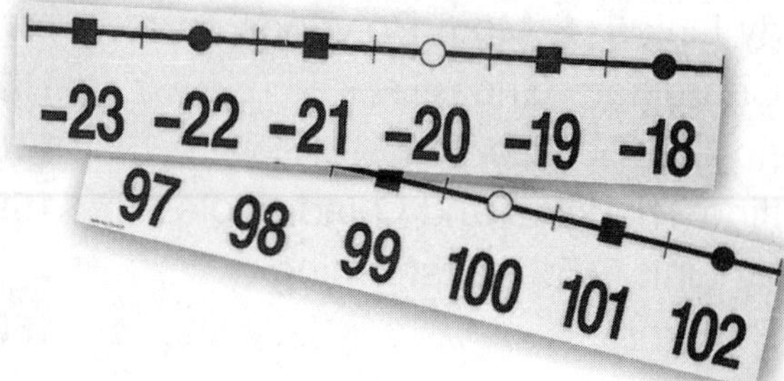

Unit 8

Unit 9

Unit 10

Project Masters

Teaching Aid Masters

Game Masters

Teaching Masters  and Study Link Masters 

Name Date Time

LESSON 5·3 **Sums of Angle Measures in Polygons**

A *diagonal* is a line segment that connects two vertices of a polygon and is *not* a side. You can draw diagonals from one vertex to separate polygons into triangles.

1. Draw diagonals from the given vertex to separate each polygon into triangles. Then complete the table.

Polygon	Number of Sides (n)	Number of Triangles	Sum of Angle Measures
Example: Quadrangle (diagonal)	4	2	2 ∗ 180° = 360°
Pentagon			____ ∗ ____ = ______°
Hexagon			____ ∗ ____ = ______°
Octagon			____ ∗ ____ = ______°
Decagon			____ ∗ ____ = ______°

2. a. Study your completed table. Use any patterns you notice to write a formula to find the sum of the angle measures in any polygon (n-gon).

Formula ____________________

b. Use the formula to find the sums of the angle measures in a

heptagon. ________° nonagon. ________° dodecagon. ________°

156

Name Date Time

STUDY LINK 1·13 **Unit 2: Family Letter**

Operations with Whole Numbers and Decimals

In Unit 2, your child will revisit operations with whole numbers and decimals from earlier grades and will continue strengthening previously developed number skills. We will work with estimation strategies, mental methods, paper-and-pencil algorithms, and calculator procedures with whole numbers. We will also develop techniques for working with decimal numbers.

In addition to standard and number-and-word notation, we will learn new ways to represent large and small numbers using exponential and scientific notation. Your child will realize that scientific notation, which is used by scientists and mathematicians, is an easier and more efficient way to write large numbers. For example, the distance from the Sun to the planet Pluto is 3,675,000,000 miles. In scientific notation, the same number is expressed as $3.675 * 10^9$.

To use scientific notation, your child will first need to know more about exponential notation, which is a way of representing multiplication of repeated factors. For example, $7 * 7 * 7 * 7$ can be written as 7^4. Similarly, 100,000, or $10 * 10 * 10 * 10 * 10$, is also 10^5.

Unit 2 also reviews multiplication and division of whole numbers. All these strategies will be extended to decimals. The partial-quotient algorithm used in fourth and fifth grade *Everyday Mathematics* to divide whole numbers will also be used to divide decimals to obtain decimal quotients. This algorithm is similar to the traditional long division method, but it is easier to learn and apply. The quotient is built up in steps using "easy" multiples of the divisor. The student doesn't have to get the partial quotient exactly right at each step. The example below demonstrates how to use the partial-quotient algorithm.

Example:

Partial-Quotient Algorithm

```
12) 3270 |        Partial Quotients
  − 2400 |  200 ←— 200 ∗ 12 = 2,400
     870 |         100 ∗ 12 = 1,200
   − 600 |   50 ←— 50 ∗ 12 = 600
     270 |         20 ∗ 12 = 240
   − 240 |   20 ↙  10 ∗ 12 = 120
      30 |          5 ∗ 12 = 60
    − 24 |____2 ←— 2 ∗ 12 = 24
       6    272
       ↑     ↑
 Remainder  Quotient
```

The partial-quotient algorithm is discussed on pages 22 and 23 in the *Student Reference Book.*

Please keep this Family Letter for reference as your child works through Unit 2.

37

Name Date Time

Unit 1: Family Letter

Introduction to *Sixth Grade Everyday Mathematics*®

The program we are using this year—*Everyday Mathematics*—offers students a broad background in mathematics. Some approaches in this program may differ from the ones you learned as a student. That's because we're using the latest research results and field-test experiences to teach students the math skills they'll need in the 21st century. Following are some program highlights:

- A problem-solving approach that uses mathematics in everyday situations
- Activities to develop confidence, self-reliance, and cooperation
- Repeated review of concepts throughout the school year to promote mastery
- Development of concepts and skills through hands-on activities
- Opportunities to communicate mathematically
- Frequent practice using games as alternatives to tedious drills
- Opportunities for home and school communication

Sixth Grade Everyday Mathematics emphasizes a variety of content.

Number Relations

- Recognizing place value in whole numbers and decimals
- Using exponential and scientific notation
- Finding factors and multiples
- Converting between fractions, decimals, and percents
- Ordering positive and negative numbers

Operations, Computation, and Mental Arithmetic

- Solving problems involving whole numbers, fractions, decimals, and positive and negative numbers
- Applying properties of addition, subtraction, multiplication, and division

Data and Chance

- Collecting, organizing, displaying, and analyzing data
- Identifying and comparing landmarks of data sets (mean, median, mode, and range)
- Using probability to represent and predict outcomes and analyze chance

Measurement, Measures, and Numbers in Reference Frames

- Measuring using metric and U.S. customary units
- Using formulas to calculate circumference, area, and volume
- Naming and plotting points on a coordinate grid

Geometry

- Measuring and drawing angles
- Understanding properties of angles
- Identifying and modeling similar and congruent figures
- Constructing figures with a compass and a straightedge
- Drawing to scale
- Exploring transformations of geometric shapes
- Experimenting with modern geometric ideas

Patterns, Functions, and Algebra

- Creating and extending numerical patterns
- Representing and analyzing functions
- Manipulating algebraic expressions
- Solving equations and inequalities
- Working with Venn diagrams
- Applying algebraic properties
- Working with ratios and proportions

Throughout the year, you will receive Family Letters telling you about each unit. Letters may include definitions and suggestions for at-home activities. Parents and guardians are encouraged to share ideas pertaining to these math concepts with their child in their home language. You and your child will experience an exciting year filled with discovery.

Building Skills Through Games

Games are as integral to the *Everyday Mathematics* program as Math Boxes and Study Links because they are an effective and interactive way to practice skills.

In this unit, your child will work on understanding place value of whole and decimal numbers, data landmarks, and order of operations by playing the following games.

Detailed game instructions for all sixth-grade games are provided in the *Student Reference Book.*

High-Number Toss (Whole Number and Decimal Versions) See *Student Reference Book,* pages 323 and 324.

Students practice reading and comparing whole numbers through hundred-millions and decimals through thousandths.

Landmark Shark See *Student Reference Book,* pages 325 and 326.

Students practice finding the mean, median, mode(s), and range of a set of numbers.

Name That Number See *Student Reference Book,* page 329.

Students practice writing number sentences using order of operations.

STUDY LINK 1•1 **Unit 1: Family Letter** *cont.*

Collection, Display, and Interpretation of Data

Everyday Mathematics will help your child use mathematics effectively in daily life. For example, the media—especially newspapers and magazines—use data. Employees and employers need to know how to gather, analyze, and display data to work efficiently. Consumers need to know how to interpret and question data presented to them so they can make informed choices. Citizens need to understand government data to participate in the running of their country.

In *Everyday Mathematics,* data provide a context for the development of numeric skills that, in traditional programs, would be developed in isolation. In Unit 1, your child will work with data displayed in stem-and-leaf plots, circle graphs, step graphs, broken-line graphs, bar graphs, and tables.

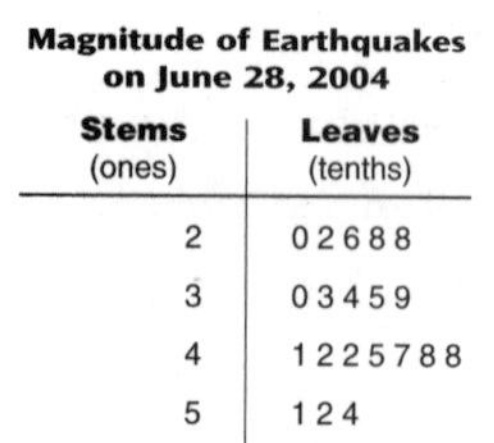

Magnitude of Earthquakes on June 28, 2004
Stems (ones)
Leaves (tenths)
2 | 0 2 6 8 8
3 | 0 3 4 5 9
4 | 1 2 2 5 7 8 8
5 | 1 2 4
6 | 8

Stem-and-leaf plot

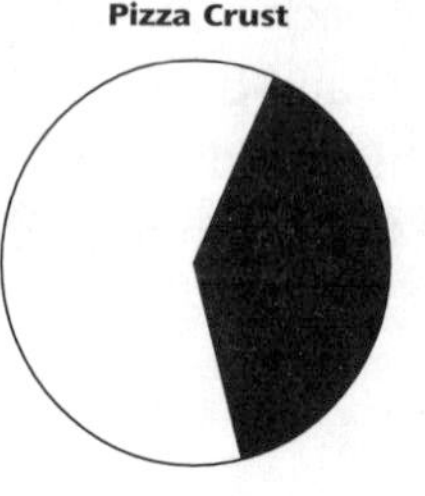

Circle graph

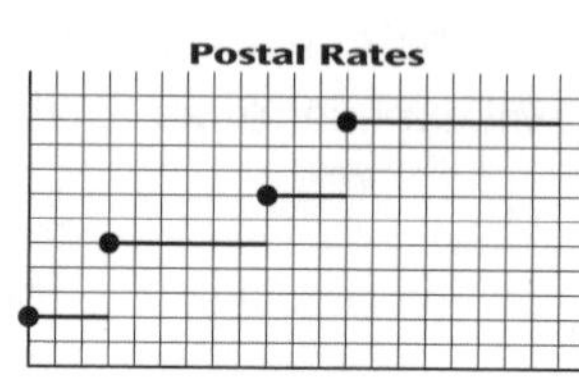

Step graph

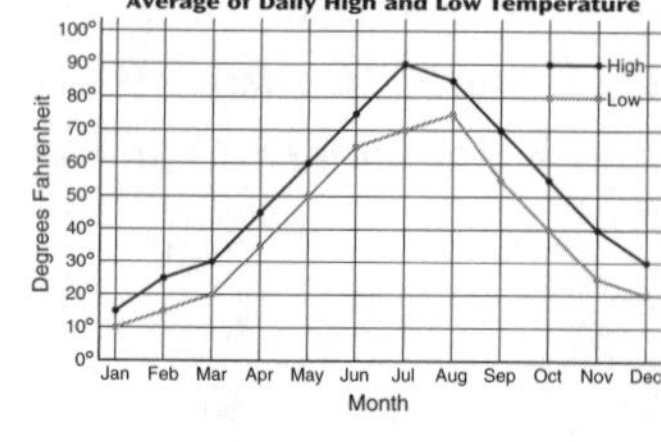

Broken-line graph

The displays above relate to earthquake magnitudes, preferred pizza crusts, postal rates, and temperatures. Real-world applications support and enrich other areas of mathematics as well.

Throughout Unit 1, your child will look for graphs and tables in newspapers and magazines and bring them to school with your permission. The class will think critically about the materials collected. Students will consider the following questions:

- What is the purpose of the graph or table?
- Is the display clear and attractive, or can it be improved?
- Does the display seem accurate, or is it biased?
- Can you draw conclusions or make predictions based on the information?

Finally, students will learn a new game, *Landmark Shark,* which will help them develop skill in finding landmarks of data in various data sets. Ask your child to teach you how to play this game.

This should be a stimulating year, and we invite you to share the excitement with us!

Please keep this Family Letter for reference as your child works through Unit 1.

STUDY LINK 1•1 **Unit 1: Family Letter** *cont.*

As You Help Your Child with Homework

As your child brings assignments home, you might want to go over the instructions together, clarifying them as necessary. Some of the answers listed below will guide you through the unit's Study Links.

Study Link 1•2

2. 90

5. Sample answers: Title: Weekly Allowance; Unit: Dollars

6. 90 **7.** 80 **8.** 120 **9.** 80

Study Link 1•3

2. a. 4.8 **b.** 2.8, 4.2, 4.8 **c.** 4.1

3. 80 **4.** 110 **5.** 500 **6.** 50

Study Link 1•4

1. Mia: 80; Nico: 80 **3.** Mia: 80; Nico: 75

4. Mia: 25; Nico: 45

6. $5.82 **7.** $30.27

8. $14.24 **9.** $20.50

Study Link 1•5

1. a. 38 **b.** 147.5 **c.** 149.2

2. a. 29 **b.** 149 **c.** 151.3

3. $9.01 **4.** $1,107.47

5. $45.87 **6.** $35.67

Study Link 1•6

2. 90°F **3.** About 25 minutes

4. Sample answers: **a.** About 100 minutes

b. The rate of cooling levels off to $2\frac{1}{2}$°F every 10 min.

5. a. no

b. The tea cools very quickly at first, but then the temperature drops slowly.

6. 1,728 **7.** 3,306 **8.** 4,484 **9.** 2,538

Study Link 1•7

2. 5 **3.** 2 **4.** 3 times **5.** 2 times

6. 2; 3 **8.** 6,613 **9.** 8,448 **10.** 10,872

11. 9, 711

Study Link 1•8

2. $1.29 **3. a.** $1.75

b. Sample answer: The price difference per ounce is $0.23. The price jumps another $0.23 for every additional part of an ounce.

5. 28 **6.** 45 **7.** 67 **8.** 55

Study Link 1•9

1. Answers vary.

3. men **4. a.** 89% **b.** 11%

5. 10% greater **6.** 60% greater

7. Sample answer: Because they don't know the person, they don't know how the stranger will react.

8. 24 **9.** 14 **10.** 32 **11.** 19

Study Link 1•10

1. Width (ft): 2; 3; 4; 6; 8; 9
Area (ft^2): 20; 27; 32; 36; 32; 27; 11

2. square

3. Length (yd): 24; 16; 12; 8; 6; 4; 2; 1
Perimeter (yd): 98; 52; 38; 32; 28; 32; 38; 98

4. a. 6 yd or 8 yd **b.** 8 yd or 6 yd **5.** $0.10

6. $4.00 **7.** $485.00 **8.** $2,050.00

Study Link 1•11

1. 165,000 **2.** 2003 and 2004

3. Sample answer: Yes. The population in 2005 would have to be 310,000 for the claim to be true.

4. $5.00 **5.** $90.00 **6.** $13,925.00 **7.** $0.89

Study Link 1•12

1. a. 30 min

b. 1 hr 20 min, or $1\frac{1}{3}$ hours, or 80 min

2. 2 hr 20 min, or $2\frac{1}{3}$ hours, or 140 min

3. Sample answer: Biased. There are other ways to get to work, so not all commuters are represented.

4. $70.00 **5.** $8.45 **6.** $25.92

Name Date Time

Tabbing the *Student Reference Book*

Some sections of the *Student Reference Book* appear in the table below.

1. Follow Steps 1–4. Then complete the table.

Step 1 Count out one stick-on note for each of the 5 section titles.

Step 2 Record a different section title on each stick-on note.

Step 3 Find the first page of each section. Make a tab for that section by attaching the appropriate stick-on note to the side of that first page.

Step 4 Record the page on which you placed each stick-on note.

Section Title	Page Number
Answer Key	
Contents (Table of Contents)	
Games	
Glossary	
Index	

Use your tabs and the table above to complete Problems 2–6.

2. Find and read the definition for **bar graph.**

3. Using your Index tab, find the page number(s) on which bar graphs are presented. Record the page number(s). ______________________

4. Turn to the page(s) you recorded in Problem 3. What mathematical topic appears in the color strip at the top of the page?

____

5. Study the Check Your Understanding problem at the bottom of the page. On what page can you find the answer to the problem?

____

To which tabbed section does this page belong? ______________________

6. Using your Contents tab, find the mathematical topic under which *bar graphs* is listed. (It should be the same as the one you recorded in Problem 4.)

What is the last page of this topic? ______________________

Name ______________________ Date ______________ Time ______________

LESSON 1·2

Survey Data

Math Message

									0
1	2	3	4	5	6	7	8	9	10
11	12	13	14	15	16	17	18	19	20
21	22	23	24	25	26	27	28	29	30
31	32	33	34	35	36	37	38	39	40

______

									0
1	2	3	4	5	6	7	8	9	10
11	12	13	14	15	16	17	18	19	20
21	22	23	24	25	26	27	28	29	30
31	32	33	34	35	36	37	38	39	40

______

									0
1	2	3	4	5	6	7	8	9	10
11	12	13	14	15	16	17	18	19	20
21	22	23	24	25	26	27	28	29	30
31	32	33	34	35	36	37	38	39	40

______

									0
1	2	3	4	5	6	7	8	9	10
11	12	13	14	15	16	17	18	19	20
21	22	23	24	25	26	27	28	29	30
31	32	33	34	35	36	37	38	39	40

______

									0
1	2	3	4	5	6	7	8	9	10
11	12	13	14	15	16	17	18	19	20
21	22	23	24	25	26	27	28	29	30
31	32	33	34	35	36	37	38	39	40

______

Name Date Time

STUDY LINK 1•2

Mystery Line Plots and Landmarks

1. Draw a line plot for the following spelling test scores.

100, 100, 95, 90, 92, 93, 96, 90, 94, 90, 97

2. The mode of the above data is ________.

3. Draw a line plot below that represents data with the following landmarks. Use at least 10 numbers.

range: 7 minimum: 6 median: 10 modes: 8 and 11

4. Describe a situation in which the data in the above line plot might occur.

____

____

5. Give the line plot a title and a unit.

Title ____

Unit ____

Practice

6. 540 ÷ 6 = ________

7. 7,200 ÷ 90 = ________

8. 84,000 ÷ 700 = ________

9. 400,000 ÷ 5,000 = ________

Name Date Time

LESSON 1·2

Outliers and Gaps

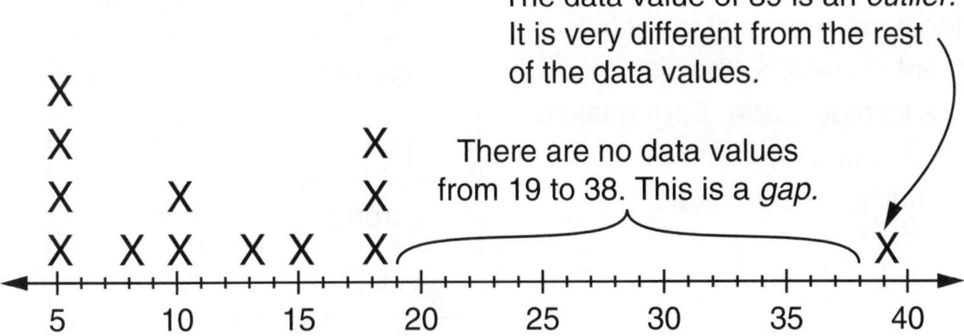

The data value of 39 is an *outlier.* It is very different from the rest of the data values.
There are no data values from 19 to 38. This is a *gap.*
X X X X X X X X X X X X X X
5 10 15 20 25 30 35 40

The effect of an outlier on the mean depends on the number of data values in the set and the size of the gap between the outlier and the other data values.

1. Find the mean and median for the data set above.

mean ________ median ________

2. Find the mean and median for the data set above without the outlier. Round each landmark to the nearest tenth.

mean without outlier ________ median without outlier ________

3. Explain the effect of the outlier on the mean of the set.

____

____

4. Suppose the outlier of the data set were 30 instead of 39.

a. Predict the value of the mean.

predicted mean ______________________

b. Now calculate the mean. Round it to the nearest tenth.

mean ________

Name Date Time

Stem-and-Leaf Plots

Every day, there are many earthquakes worldwide. Most are too small for people to notice. Scientists refer to the size of an earthquake as its magnitude. Earthquakes are classified in categories from minor to great, depending on magnitude.

Class	Magnitude
Great	8.0 or more
Major	7–7.9
Strong	6–6.9
Moderate	5–5.9
Light	4–4.9
Minor	3–3.9

The table below shows the magnitude of 21 earthquakes that occurred on June 28, 2004.

Magnitude of Earthquakes Occurring June 28, 2004										
4.2	5.2	2.8	4.8	3.9	2.0	3.3	4.8	4.5	3.5	2.2
2.6	3.4	6.8	3.0	4.7	2.8	4.2	4.1	5.4	5.1	

1. Construct a stem-and-leaf plot of the earthquake magnitude data.

2. Use your stem-and-leaf plot to find the following landmarks.

   a. range ________

   b. mode(s) ________

   c. median ________

Magnitude of Earthquakes Occurring on June 28, 2004

Stems (ones)	**Leaves** (tenths)

Practice

3. 6,400 ÷ 80 = ________

4. 121,000 ÷ 1,100 = ________

5. 3,000,000 ÷ 6,000 = ________

6. 600,000 ÷ 12,000 = ________

Name Date Time

Reviewing Stem-and-Leaf Plots

Students in Mr. Conley's sixth-grade class measured how far they could reach and jump. Each student stood with legs together, feet flat on the floor, and one arm stretched up as high as possible. **Arm reach** was then measured from top fingertip to floor.

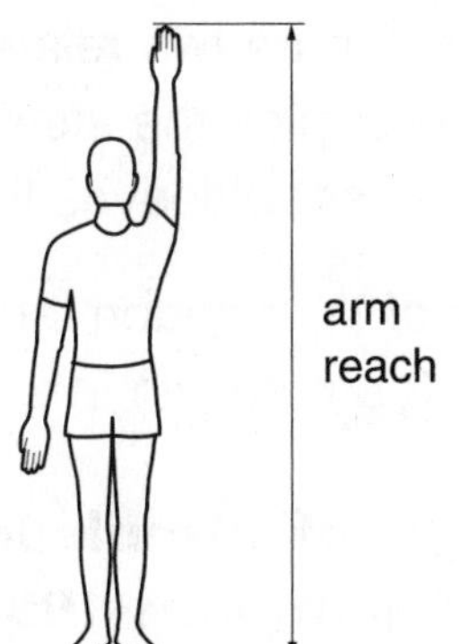

1. Using a tape measure, measure your arm reach in inches. Record this measurement.

_______ in.

In the **standing jump,** each student stood with knees bent and then jumped forward as far as possible. The distance was measured from the starting line to the point closest to where the student's heels came down.

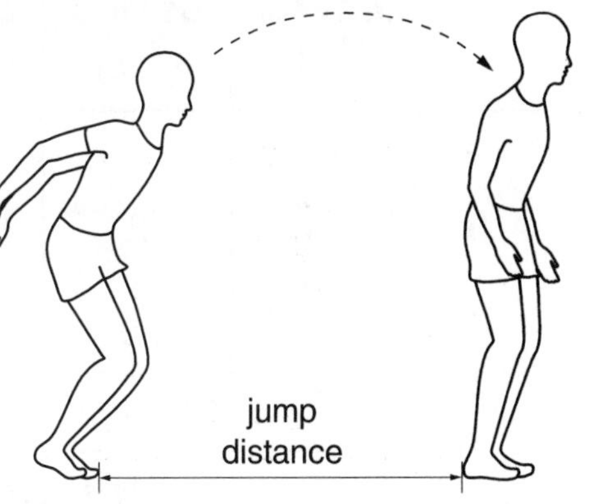

Students displayed their results using two different stem-and-leaf plots.

Plot 1
Unit: inches

Stems (10s)	**Leaves** (1s)
4	4 6 8
5	0 0 3 3 4 5 6 7 7 8 8 9
6	0 0 1 3 8 9

Plot 2
Unit: inches

Stems (10s)	**Leaves** (1s)
6	1 7
7	0 1 2 2 2 3 3 4 5 6 6 6 6 8 9 9
8	3 4 7

2. Use what you know about your arm reach to figure out which stem-and-leaf plot represents the class data for the standing jump.

a. Which plot do you think it is? Plot _______

b. Explain why you think so. _______________

____

____

____

Name Date Time

Back-to-Back Stem-and-Leaf Plots

You can compare two related sets of data in a **back-to-back stem-and-leaf plot.** In this type of plot, the stem is written in the center, with one set of leaves to the right and another set of leaves to the left.

The ages of Wimbledon tennis champions in the women's and men's singles from 1993–2003 are shown in the back-to-back stem-and-leaf plot below.

Ages of Wimbledon Tennis Champions 1993–2003

Women Leaves (1s)	**Stems** (10s)	**Men Leaves** (1s)
7	1	
4 3 2 2 1 1 0	2	1 2 2 3 4
7 6	2	5 6 7 8 9
	3	0

1. How many women champions were in their twenties? ___________

2. What is the mode age for women? ___________ For men? ___________

3. What is the median age for women? ___________ For men? ___________

Students' Heights (in centimeters)	
Girls' Heights	**Boys' Heights**
162, 126, 134, 145, 127, 134, 143, 159, 147, 169, 164, 171, 163, 171, 154, 157	154, 137, 162, 147, 145, 174, 132, 151, 170, 161, 166, 136, 168, 155, 153, 143

4. The data table above shows students' heights in centimeters. Make a back-to-back stem-and-leaf plot to display the data. Use the 2-digit stems provided.

Students' Heights

Girls Leaves (1s)	**Stems** (10s)	**Boys Leaves** (1s)
	12	
	13	
	14	
	15	
	16	
	17	

Name Date Time

Median and Mean

SRB 135–137

Mia's quiz scores are 75, 70, 75, 85, 75, 85, 80, 95, and 80.

Nico's quiz scores are 55, 85, 95, 100, 75, 75, 65, 95, and 75.

1. Find each student's mean score. Mia ________ Nico ________

2. Make a stem-and-leaf plot for each student's scores.

a. Mia's Quiz Scores

Stems (100s and 10s)	**Leaves** (1s)

b. Nico's Quiz Scores

Stems (100s and 10s)	**Leaves** (1s)

3. Find each student's median score. Mia ________ Nico ________

4. What is the range of scores for each student? Mia ________ Nico ________

5. Which landmark, mean or median, is the better indicator of each student's overall performance? Explain.

____

____

____

____

____

Practice

6. \$4.57 + \$1.25 = ________

7. \$14.49 + \$15.78 = ________

8. \$19.99 − \$5.75 = ________

9. \$39.25 − \$18.75 = ________

Name Date Time

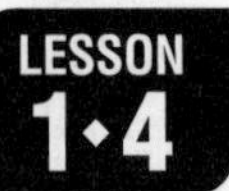

Defining the Mean

The table at the right shows the number of students absent from gym class during the week.

Day	Students Absent
Monday	6
Tuesday	2
Wednesday	5
Thursday	4
Friday	8

1. Place unit cubes on the line below to show the number of absent students for each day.

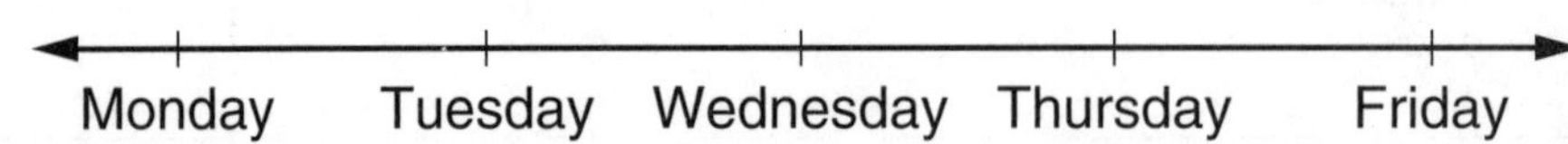

If you redistribute, or even out, the number of absent students so the number is the same for each day, you are finding the **mean.** The mean is a useful landmark when there are *not* one or two numbers that are far away from the rest of the data values (outliers).

2. Move the cubes on the line plot so that each day has the same number. After you've evened out the cubes, how many does each day have? ________

You can use a number sentence to model how you evened out the cubes. You started with $6 + 2 + 5 + 4 + 8 = 25$ cubes. Then you redistributed the cubes so that the total number of cubes (25) was the same for each of the 5 days, or $25 \div 5 = 5$.

3. Use the cubes to find the mean of the following number of absent students. Monday: 5; Tuesday: 0; Wednesday: 6; Thursday: 2; Friday: 7

Then write a number sentence to model what you did. ____________________

Name Date Time

Range, Median, and Mean

Heights were measured to the nearest centimeter for 12 boys and 12 girls. All of the students were 12 years old.

Boys' heights: 157, 150, 131, 143, 147, 169, 148, 147, 145, 163, 139, 151

Girls' heights: 146, 164, 138, 149, 145, 167, 150, 156, 143, 148, 149, 160

1. Make a stem-and-leaf plot for the boys' data. Then find the range, median, and mean of the boys' heights.

a. range ________

b. median ________

c. mean ________

Boys' Heights (cm)

Stems (10s)	**Leaves** (1s)

2. Make a stem-and-leaf plot for the girls' data. Then find the range, median, and mean of the girls' heights.

a. range ________

b. median ________

c. mean ________

Girls' Heights (cm)

Stems (10s)	**Leaves** (1s)

Practice

3. \$5.86 + \$3.15 = ____________

4. \$221.17 + \$886.30 = ____________

5. \$75.37 − 29.50 = ____________

6. \$124.35 − \$88.68 = ____________

Name Date Time

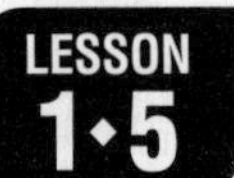

Calculating and Analyzing Landmarks

1. Write your seven-digit home phone number in the boxes below.

☐☐☐ - ☐☐☐☐

2. Using a marker, write each digit on a separate index card. These digits will make up your data set.

3. Arrange the digits in order from least to greatest.

4. Find the following landmarks for your data set. If you need a reminder about how to find landmarks, review pages 136 and 137 of the *Student Reference Book*.

range ______________

median ______________

mode ______________

mean ______________

5. Explain how the range, median, and mean change if you add the three numbers of your area code to your data set.

____

____

____

____

Name Date Time

LESSON 1•5 Mentally Calculating a Mean

Consider some of these strategies when calculating the mean of a data set.

- Look for easy combinations of numbers and add them.

Example: 12 + 18 = 30
(10 + 2) + (10 + 8) =
(10 + 2) + (8 + 10) =
10 + (2 + 8) + 10 =
10 + 10 + 10 = 30

- If the data set has 5 numbers, you can divide the sum of the numbers by 10 and then multiply that number by 2.

Example: If the sum of 5 test scores is 80, then the mean is
(80 ÷ 10) ∗ 2 = 8 ∗ 2 = 16.

- Multiply any mode(s) by the number of occurrences.

Example: For 20, 15, 20, 20, 10, the mode (20) occurs 3 times.
(20 ∗ 3) + 10 + 15 = (20 ∗ 3) + 25 = 85

1. Apply strategies like those above to mentally calculate the mean of the following temperatures: 43°F, 52°F, 37°F, 48°F, 40°F.

a. Record the sum of the temperatures. ____________

b. Record the mean. ____________

2. Mentally calculate the sum and mean for the following data sets. Then choose one of the data sets and write a number sentence to show the strategies you used to find your answers.

a. **Data Set A:** Number of letters in first names: 6, 9, 10, 4, 6

sum of letters = _______ mean number of letters = _______

b. **Data Set B:** Lengths of standing long jumps (inches): 22, 31, 28, 20, 29

sum of lengths = _______ mean length of jumps = _______

c. For Data Set __________, I used the following number sentences:

____

____

Name Date Time

The Climate in Omaha

Omaha, the largest city in Nebraska, is located on the eastern border of the state on the Missouri River.

Precipitation is moisture that falls as rain or snow. Rainfall is usually measured in inches; snowfall is usually translated into an equivalent amount of rain.

Average Number of Days in Omaha with At Least 0.01 Inch of Precipitation

	Jan	Feb	Mar	Apr	May	Jun	Jul	Aug	Sep	Oct	Nov	Dec
Number of days	7	6	7	10	12	11	9	9	9	7	5	7

These averages are the result of collecting data for more than 58 years.

1. Complete the following graph.
   First make a dot for each month to represent the data in the table.
   Then connect the dots with line segments. The result is called a **broken-line graph.**
   This type of graph is often used to show trends.

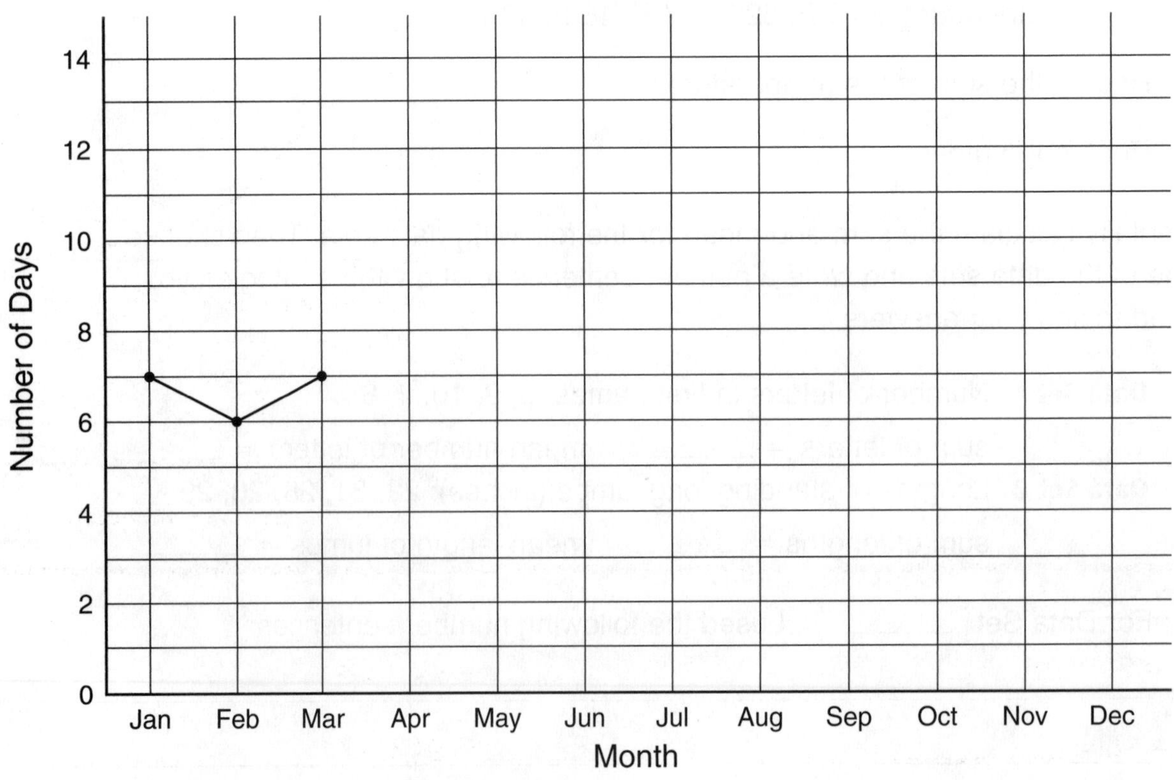

Source: *The Times Books World Weather Guide*

Name Date Time

Cooling Off

The graph shows how a cup of hot tea cools as time passes.

1. Use the graph to fill in the missing data in the table.

2. What is the tea's approximate temperature after 30 minutes? ________

3. About how many minutes does it take for the tea to cool to a temperature of 95°F?

____

4. a. About how many minutes do you think it will take the tea to cool to room temperature (70°F)?

____

____

b. Why do you think so?

____

____

____

Elapsed Time (minutes)	Temperature (°F)
0 (pour tea)	
10	
40	
	100
	115
5	

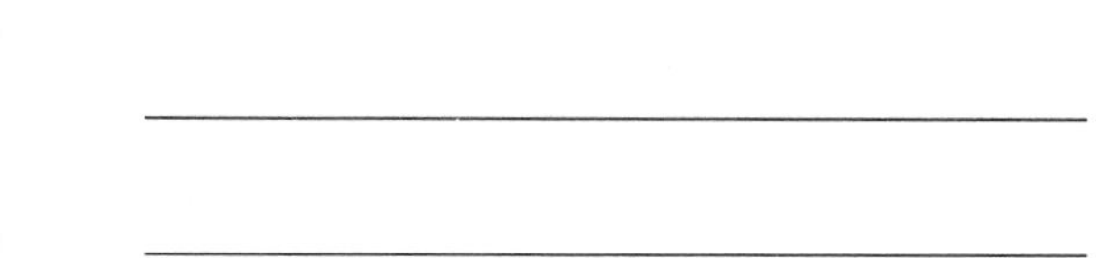

5. a. Does the tea cool at a constant rate? ________

b. Explain your answer.

____

____

____

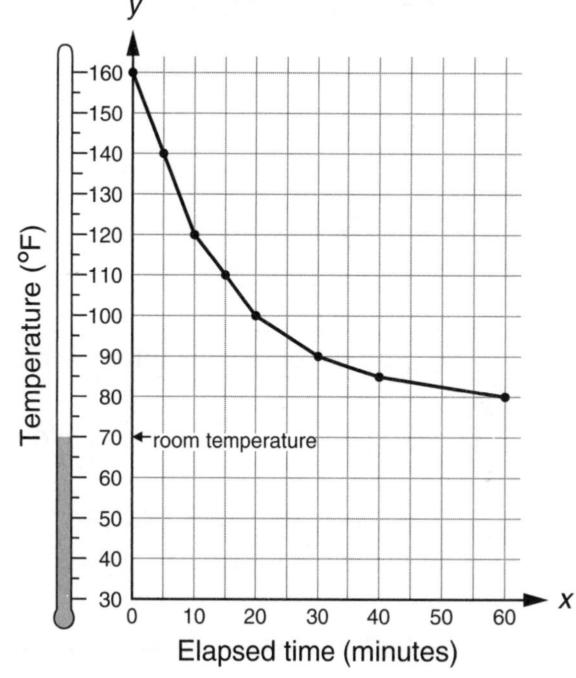

Practice

6. 32 ∗ 54 = ________

7. ________ = 87 ∗ 38

8. 59 ∗ 76 = ________

9. ________ = 94 ∗ 27

Name Date Time

Using Bar Graphs

Every week, Ms. Penczar gives a math quiz to her class of 15 students. The table below shows the class's average scores for a six-week period.

1. Draw a bar graph that shows the same information. Give the graph a title and label each axis.

Week	Class Average
1	68
2	66
3	79
4	89
5	91
6	88

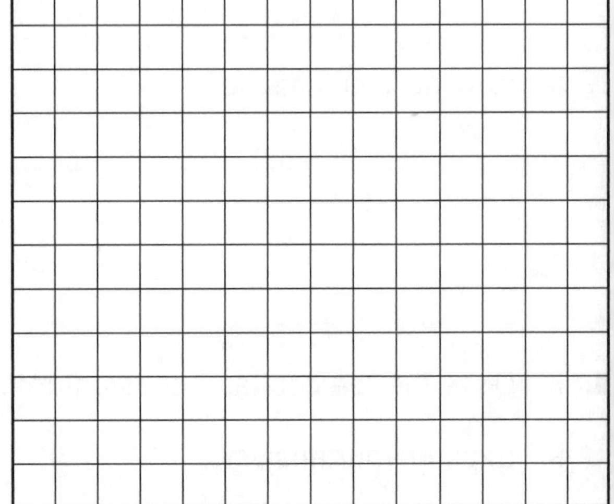

Use the graph you drew to answer the following questions.

2. The highest average score occurred in Week ________.

3. The lowest average score occurred in Week ________.

4. How many times did scores improve from one week to the next?

____

5. How many times did scores decline from one week to the next?

____

6. The greatest one-week improvement occurred between Week ________ and Week ________.

7. Name a possible set of scores for Ms. Penczar's 15 students that would result in the class average given for Week 2.

______ ______ ______ ______ ______ ______ ______ ______

______ ______ ______ ______ ______ ______ ______

Practice

8. 389 ∗ 17 = ____________

9. ____________ = 176 ∗ 48

10. 453 ∗ 24 = ____________

11. ____________ = 249 ∗ 39

Name Date Time

Reviewing Bar Graphs

A school board conducted a survey in which 70 ninth graders were asked how many hours they spend doing homework each day. The bar graph displays the survey results.

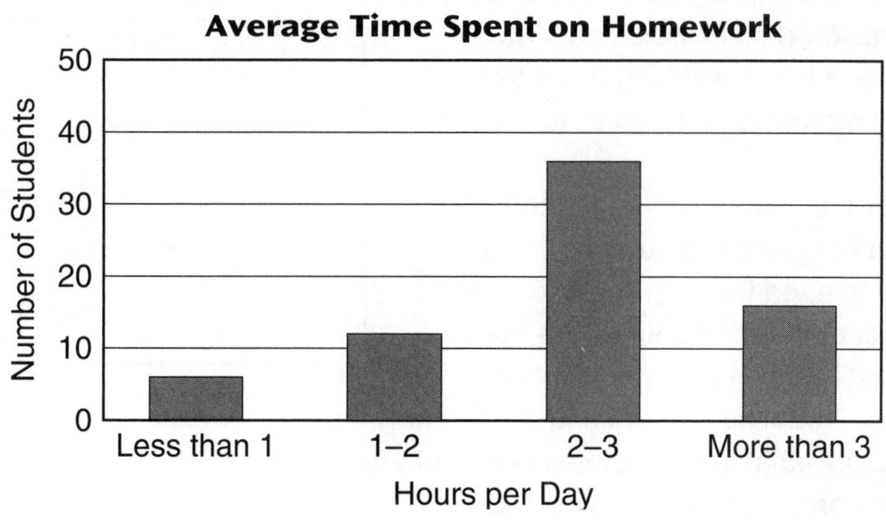

Decide whether each of the following statements about the survey results is true or false. If a statement is false, explain why.

1. All students spend some time each day doing homework. ________

____

____

2. About half of the students spend more than 3 hours on homework. ________

____

____

3. More than 15 students spend 1–2 hours per day on homework. ________

____

____

4. The number of students spending 2–3 hours on homework is about 3 times as many as the number of students who spend 1–2 hours on homework. ________

____

____

Name Date Time

The Cost of Mailing a Letter

The cost of mailing a first-class letter in the United States depends on how much the letter weighs. The table at the right shows first-class postal rates in 2004: 37 cents for a letter weighing 1 ounce or less; 60 cents for a letter weighing more than 1 ounce but not more than 2 ounces; and so on.

2004 First-Class Postal Rates

Weight (oz)	Cost
1	\$0.37
2	\$0.60
3	\$0.83
4	\$1.06
5	\$1.29
6	\$1.52

A step graph for these data has been started on page 23. Notice the placement of dots in the graph. For example, on the step representing 60 cents, the dot at the right end, above the 2, shows that it costs 60 cents to mail a letter weighing exactly 2 ounces. There is no dot at the left end of the step—that is, at the intersection of 1 ounce and 60 cents—because the cost of mailing a 1-ounce letter is 37 cents, not 60 cents.

1. Continue the graph for letters weighing up to 6 ounces.

2. Using the rates shown in the table, how much would it cost to send a letter that weighs $4\frac{1}{2}$ ounces? __________

Try This

3. a. Using the rates shown in the table, how much would it cost to mail a letter that weighs $6\frac{1}{2}$ ounces? __________

b. How did you determine your answer?

____

____

____

4. Continue the graph on page 23 to show the cost of mailing a first-class letter weighing more than 6 ounces, but not more than 7 ounces.

Practice

5. $\frac{252}{9} =$ ______ **6.** ______ $= 8\overline{)360}$ **7.** $\frac{469}{7} =$ ______ **8.** ______ $= 9\overline{)495}$

Name Date Time

The Cost of Mailing a Letter *continued*

Cost: $1.80, $1.70, $1.60, $1.50, $1.40, $1.30, $1.20, $1.10, $1.00, $0.90, $0.80, $0.70, $0.60, $0.50, $0.40, $0.30, $0.20, $0.10, $0.00

Ounces: 0, 1, 2, 3, 4, 5, 6, 7

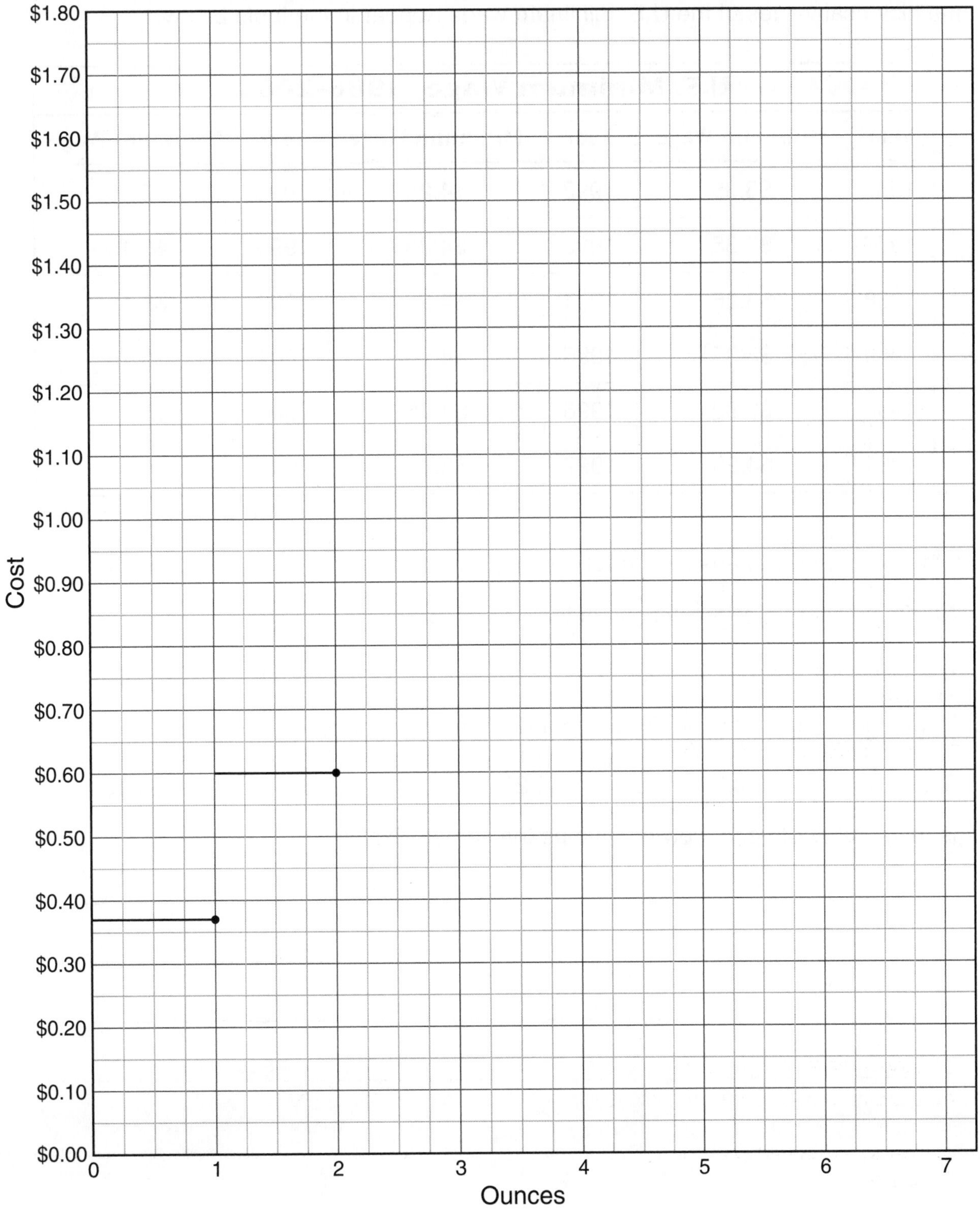

Name Date Time

Identifying Jumps in Data Values

Set by Congress, minimum wage is the minimum rate per hour that can be paid to workers. Some historical values of the U.S. minimum wage appear in the table below.

U.S. Minimum Wage, 1986–2003

Year	Minimum Wage	Year	Minimum Wage	Year	Minimum Wage
1986	$3.35	1992	$4.25	1998	$5.15
1987	$3.35	1993	$4.25	1999	$5.15
1988	$3.35	1994	$4.25	2000	$5.15
1989	$3.35	1995	$4.25	2001	$5.15
1990	$3.80	1996	$4.75	2002	$5.15
1991	$4.25	1997	$5.15	2003	$5.15

Source: Economic Policy Institute

Use the table above to answer the following questions.

1. Name the years at which a jump in the values occurs.

____

2. Name the number of years for which the minimum wage is

$3.35 ______ $3.80 ______ $4.25 ______ $4.75 ______ $5.15 ______

3. Is the number of years between jumps the same? Explain.

____

____

____

____

Name Date Time

Parking Lot Charges

1. A parking lot charges $3.00 for the first hour or fraction of an hour and $2.00 for each additional hour or fraction of an hour.

   a. Complete the table at the right.

   b. What is the cost of parking for $2\frac{1}{2}$ hours? ___________

Time	Cost
30 min	$3.00
1 hr	$3.00
$2\frac{1}{2}$ hr	
3 hr 59 min	
5 hr	
5 hr 15 min	

2. Draw a step graph of the parking lot charges. Remember: The parking lot charges $3.00 for the first hour or fraction of an hour and $2.00 for each additional hour or fraction of an hour.

3. What is the cost of parking for 1 hour and 15 minutes?

   ____

4. What is the cost of parking for 3 hours and 45 minutes?

   ____

Parking Lot Charges

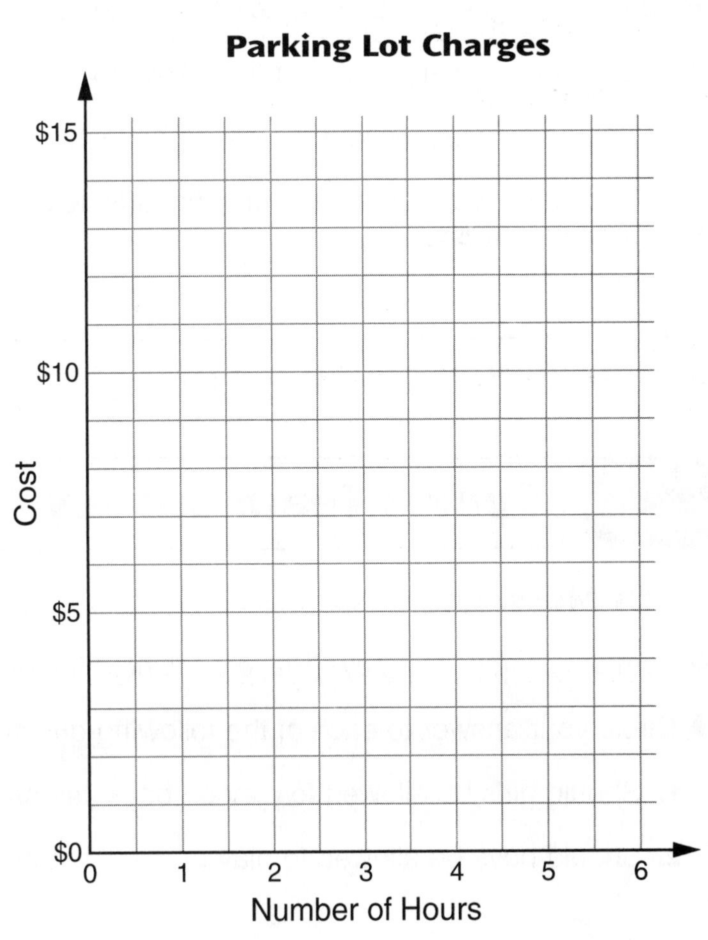

Name Date Time

LESSON 1·9 Sports Team Survey

Math Message

- I am a ____ girl ____ boy. (Place an X next to your gender.)
- Circle your answer to each of the following questions.

1. Should girls be allowed to play on boys' teams? yes no

2. Should boys be allowed to play on girls' teams? yes no

Name Date Time

LESSON 1·9 Sports Team Survey

Math Message

- I am a ____ girl ____ boy. (Place an X next to your gender.)
- Circle your answer to each of the following questions.

1. Should girls be allowed to play on boys' teams? yes no

2. Should boys be allowed to play on girls' teams? yes no

Name Date Time

LESSON 1·9 Sports Team Survey

Math Message

- I am a ____ girl ____ boy. (Place an X next to your gender.)
- Circle your answer to each of the following questions.

1. Should girls be allowed to play on boys' teams? yes no

2. Should boys be allowed to play on girls' teams? yes no

Name Date Time

LESSON 1•9 A Magazine Survey

An issue of a sports magazine for kids featured a readers' survey. In the survey, readers were asked to respond to the following three questions:

1. Should girls be allowed to play on boys' teams?
2. Should boys be allowed to play on girls' teams?
3. On how many organized sports teams do you play during a year?

Readers' responses are represented by the circle graphs below.

Question 1: Should girls be allowed to play on boys' teams?

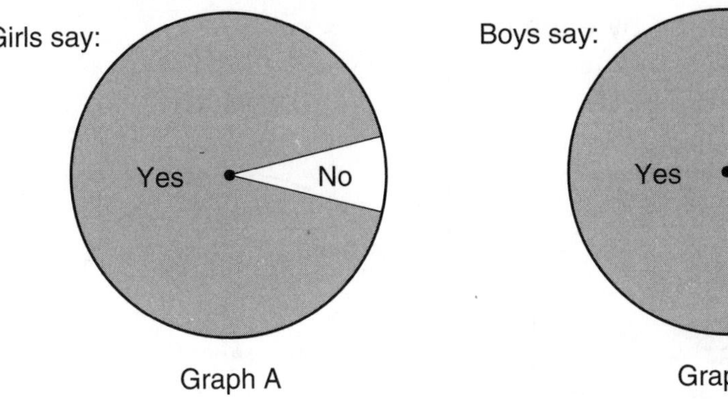

Graph A Graph B

Question 2: Should boys be allowed to play on girls' teams?

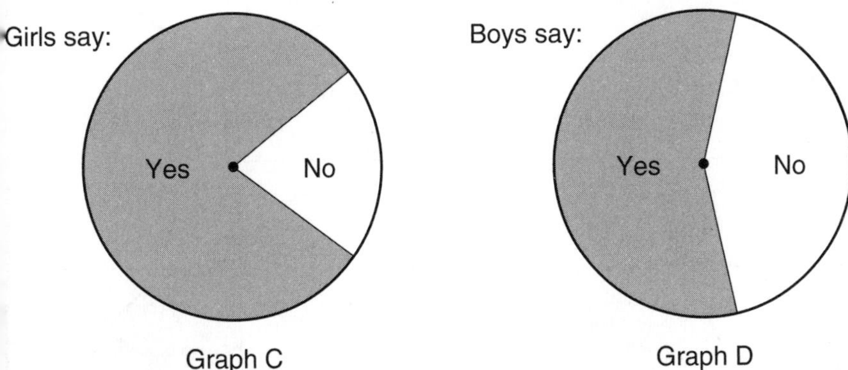

Graph C Graph D

Question 3: On how many organized sports teams do you play during a year?

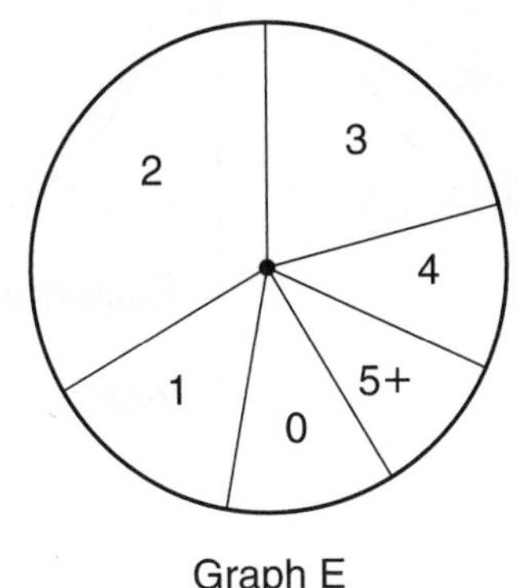

Graph E

Name Date Time

Analyzing Circle Graphs

1. Would you be willing to tell strangers that they had

smudges on their faces? yes no

food stuck between their teeth? yes no

dandruff? yes no

A marketing research company asked men and women these same questions. The results are summarized in the circle graphs below.

Use the legend to read the graphs. yes, would tell no, would not tell

2. Write estimates for the percents represented by each graph.

Smudge on Face

Women

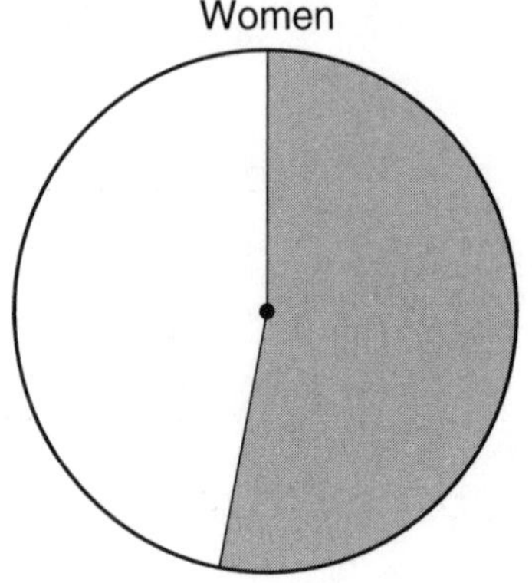

Estimates:

yes ______ no ______

Men

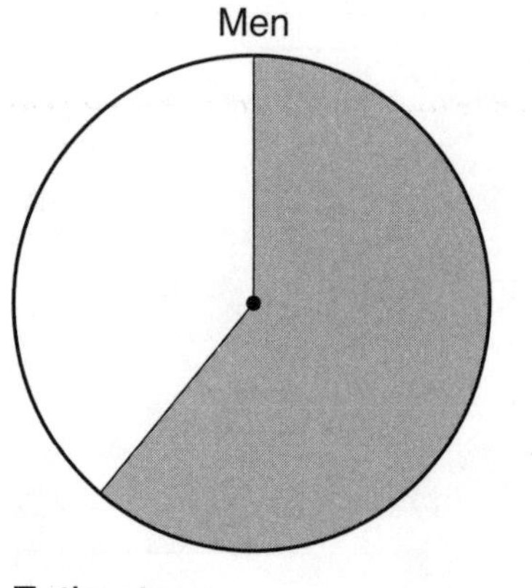

Estimates:

yes ______ no ______

Food in Teeth

Women

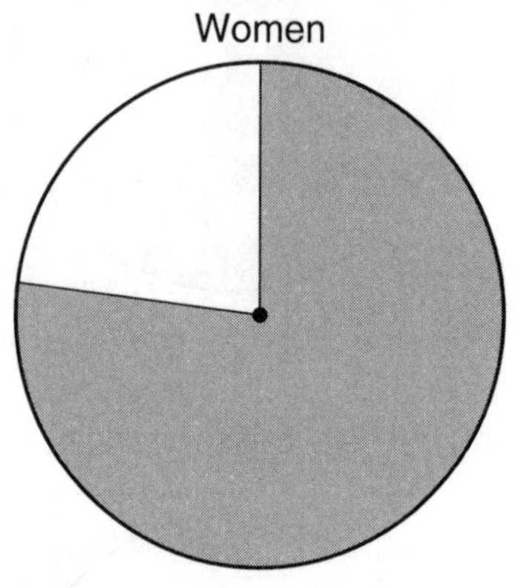

Estimates:

yes ______ no ______

Men

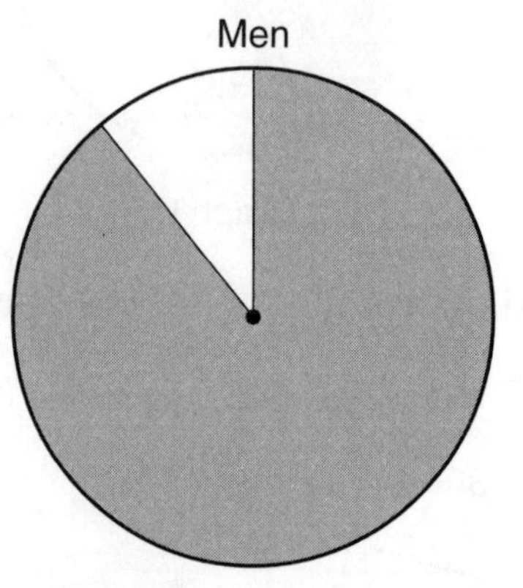

Estimates:

yes ______ no ______

Dandruff

Women

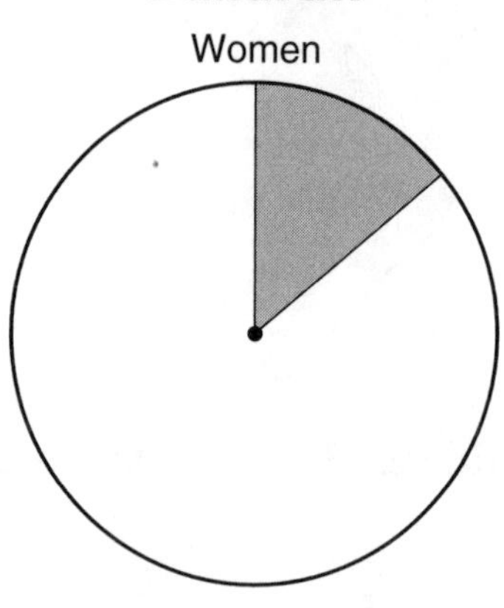

Estimates:

yes ______ no ______

Men

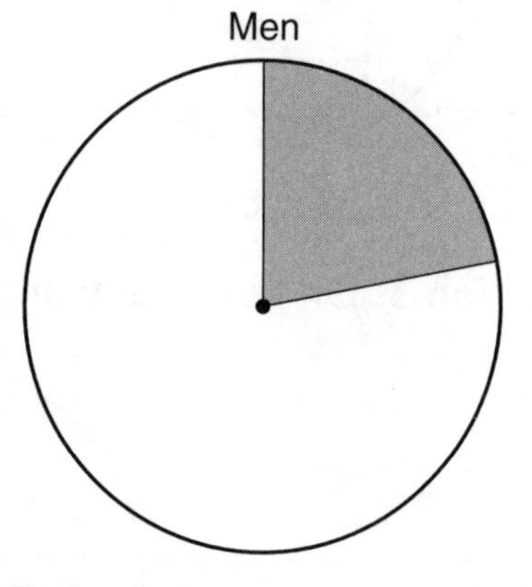

Estimates:

yes ______ no ______

Source: America by the Numbers

Name Date Time

Analyzing Circle Graphs *continued*

Cut out the Percent Circle at the right and poke a hole in the center with a pencil. Use the Percent Circle to find the percent represented by each sector mentioned in the questions below.

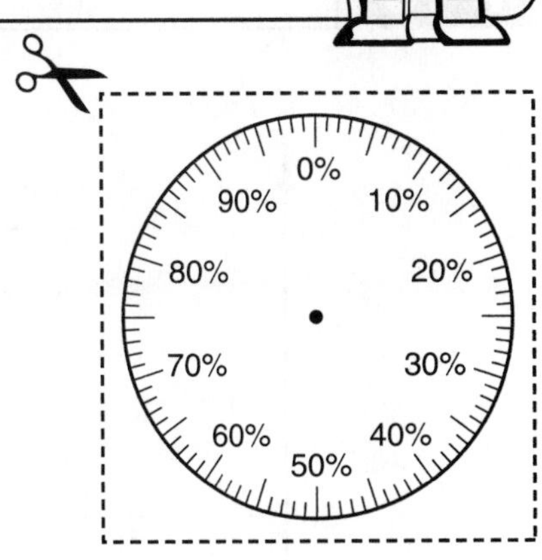

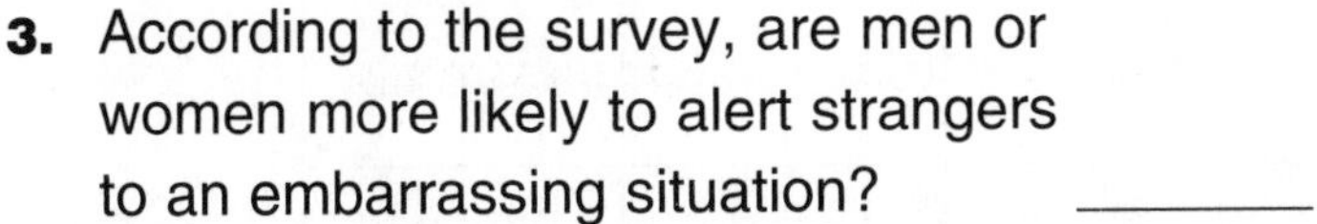

3. According to the survey, are men or women more likely to alert strangers to an embarrassing situation? ______

4. **a.** About what percent of men say they would tell strangers that they had food stuck between their teeth? ______

b. About what percent of men would not be willing to tell? ______

5. In the survey, how much greater is the percent of men who would be willing to alert strangers to smudges on their faces than the percent of women who would be willing to do so? ______

6. How much greater is the percent of women who would be willing to tell strangers about food in their teeth than the percent of women who would tell strangers about dandruff? ______

7. Why do you think people might be hesitant to alert strangers to such situations?

______

______

______

Practice

8. $\frac{336}{14} =$ ______

9. ______ $= 50\overline{)700}$

10. $\frac{992}{31} =$ ______

11. ______ $= 29\overline{)551}$

Name Date Time

Using a Graph to Find the Largest Area

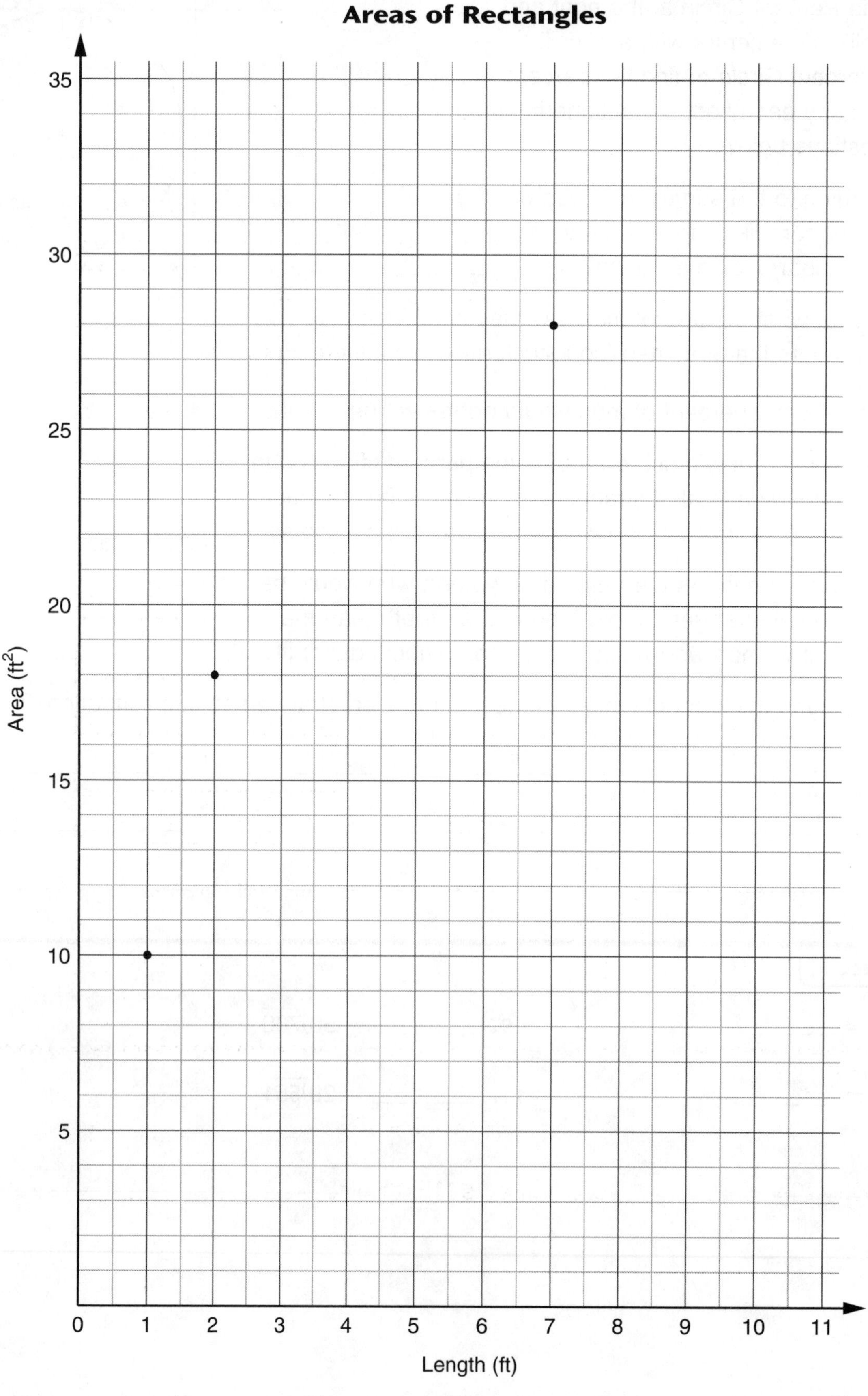

Areas of Rectangles

Name Date Time

Perimeter and Area

The student council is preparing the gym floor for the annual talent show. They will use 24 feet of tape to mark the seating area for the judges.

The table below lists the lengths of some rectangles with perimeters of 24 feet. Complete the table. You may want to draw the rectangles on grid paper. Let the side of each grid square represent 1 foot.

1.

Length (ft)	10	9	8	7	6	5	4	3	2	1
Width (ft)				5		7			10	11
Perimeter (ft)	24	24	24	24	24	24	24	24	24	24
Area (ft^2)				35		35			20	

2. How would you describe the rectangular region that will provide the largest seating area for the judges? ____________

The stage area for the talent show will be 48 square yards. The table below lists the lengths of some rectangles with areas of 48 yd^2. Complete the table.

3.

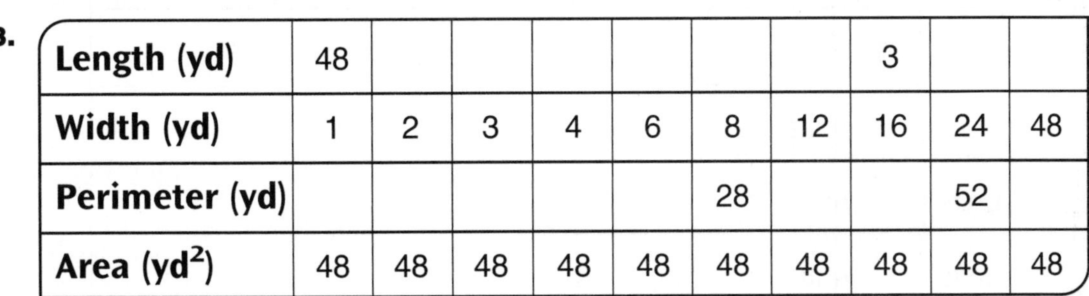

Length (yd)	48							3		
Width (yd)	1	2	3	4	6	8	12	16	24	48
Perimeter (yd)						28			52	
Area (yd^2)	48	48	48	48	48	48	48	48	48	48

4. What is the length and width of the rectangular region that will take the least amount of tape to mark off?

a. length ____________ **b.** width ____________

Practice

5. $0.01 * 10 = ____________

6. $0.40 * 10 = ____________

7. $48.50 * 10 = ____________

8. $205.00 * 10 = ____________

Name Date Time

Grid-Paper Perimeters

Work with a partner. Use page 408 for Problems 1 and 2.

Suppose one side of a centimeter square on the grid paper is 1 unit.

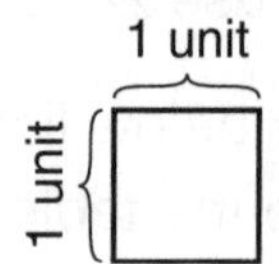

1. Use the lengths of the sides that appear in the first row of the table to draw a rectangle with a perimeter of 12 units.

2. Now make two different rectangles that also have perimeters of 12 units. Record the lengths of the sides for these rectangles. (*Remember:* A square is also a rectangle.)

3. Write a number sentence for the perimeter of the rectangle. For example, two possible number sentences for the first rectangle are 1 + 1 + 5 + 5 = 12 OR 2 * (1 + 5) = 12.

4. Complete the table.

Perimeter	Shorter Side	Longer Side	Number Sentence
12 units	1 unit	5 units	1 + 5 + 1 + 5 = 12 OR 2 * (1 + 5) = 12
12 units	___ units	___ units	
12 units	___ units	___ units	
14 units	___ units	___ units	
14 units	___ units	___ units	
14 units	___ units	___ units	
16 units	___ units	___ units	
16 units	___ units	___ units	
16 units	___ units	___ units	
16 units	___ units	___ units	

Use your completed table to complete Problems 5 and 6 on page 33.

Name Date Time

LESSON 1•10

Grid-Paper Perimeters *continued*

5. Look for a pattern or rule in the results of your table. Then apply this rule to find the lengths of the sides of a rectangle with a perimeter of 20 units without using your grid paper. Record the lengths of the shorter and longer sides of this rectangle and a number sentence for its perimeter.

shorter side _____ units longer side _____ units

number sentence ________________________________

6. What are the side lengths of the rectangle in your table that has the largest area?
(A = shorter side ∗ longer side)

shorter side _____ units longer side _____ units

Try This

7. Find the lengths of sides *x* and *y*. Then find the perimeter and area of the polygon.

a. x = ________ cm

b. y = ________ cm

c. perimeter = ________ cm

d. area = ________ cm^2

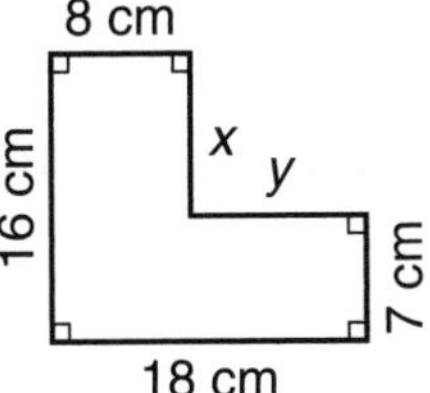

Name Date Time

The Population of River City

The way a graph is constructed affects how fairly the data are represented.

The mayor of River City is trying to convince the city council that the city needs more schools. She claims that the city's population has doubled since 1998. The mayor used the graph below to support her claim.

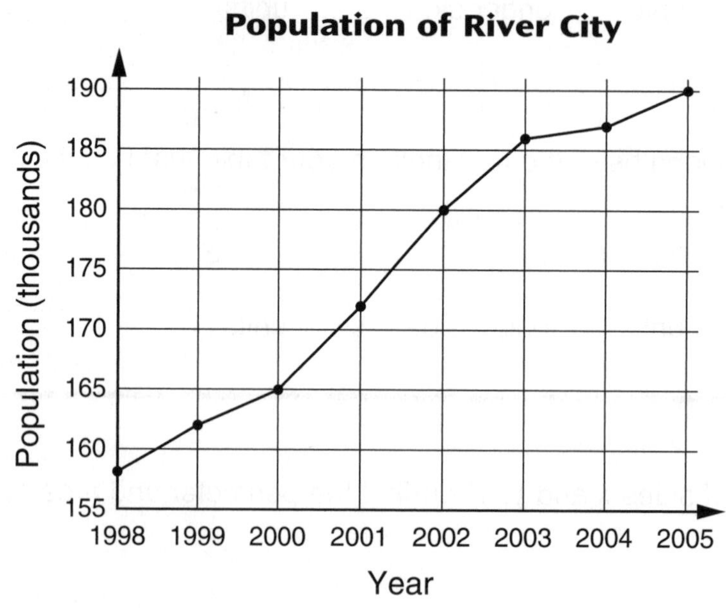

1. According to the graph, what was the population in 2000? ______________

2. Between which 2 years was the increase in population the least?

____

3. Is the mayor's claim misleading? Explain.

____

____

____

Practice

4. $0.05 ∗ 100 = ______________

5. $0.90 ∗ 100 = ______________

6. $139.25 ∗ 100 = ______________

7. ______________ ∗ 100 = $89.00

Name Date Time

Persuasive Graphs

Create a persuasive graph for one of the two situations below or make up a situation of your own. You want to present your case in a way most favorable to you and your cause. Be sure that your graph does not contain false information. Remember that you are merely presenting the information in a way that will be of the greatest benefit to you.

- ◆ You have been in charge of sales at the school store this year. Each month profits have increased—from $10 in September to $18 in June. You would like to have the same job again next year and want to show your principal why you are the best candidate for the position.
- ◆ For health reasons, you have been encouraging your uncle to lose weight. Over the past 8 weeks, he has gone from 300 pounds to 291 pounds. You are proud of your uncle and want to show him how much progress he has made.

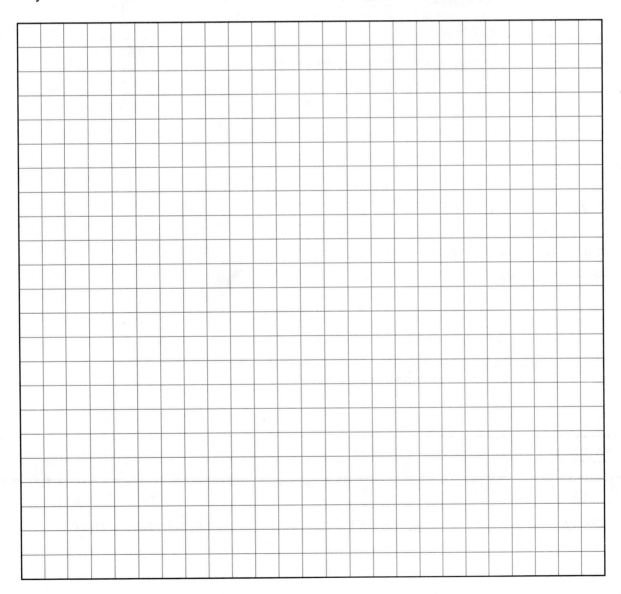

Name Date Time

Survey Results

A sample of 2,000 working adults was surveyed to determine how much time they spend performing certain weekly activities and how much time they would prefer to spend on these activities. For example, the average time adults spend on household chores is 4 hr 50 min, while the average time they prefer to do household chores is 2 hr 30 min.

The survey results are shown in the side-by-side bar graph below.

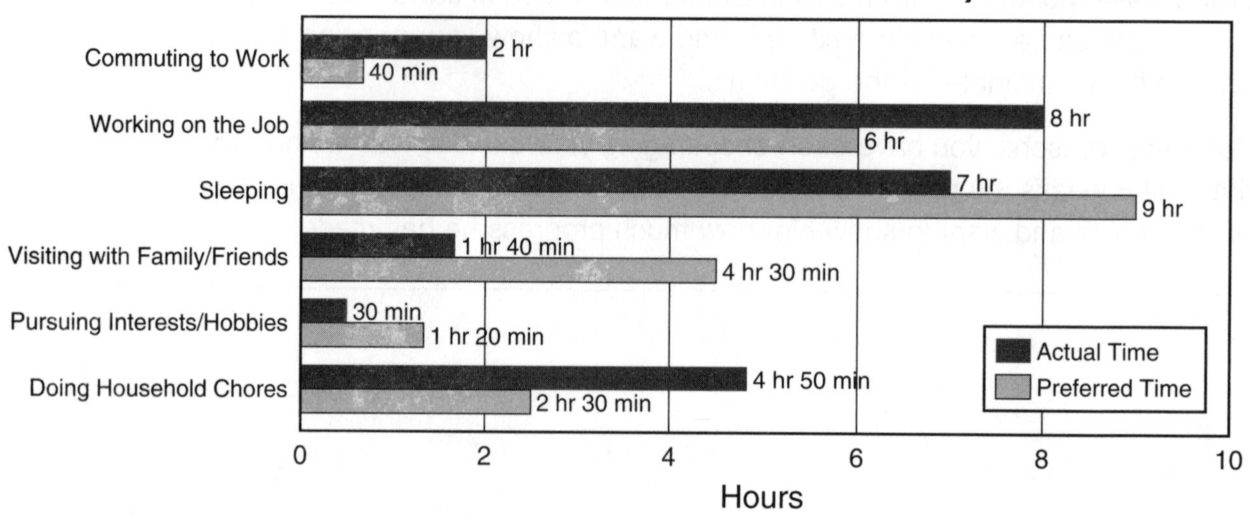

1. a. What is the actual time spent pursuing interests/hobbies? ___________

b. How much time would adults prefer to spend pursuing interests/hobbies?

____

2. What is the difference between the actual time and preferred time for doing household chores?

____

3. For this survey, researchers interviewed every 25th rider who boarded a commuter train on a Monday morning. Do you think this sampling method provides a random or biased sample? Explain.

____

____

Practice

4. $700.00 ÷ 10 = ________ **5.** $84.50 ÷ 10 = ________ **6.** $259.20 ÷ 10 = ________

Name Date Time

Unit 2: Family Letter

Operations with Whole Numbers and Decimals

In Unit 2, your child will revisit operations with whole numbers and decimals from earlier grades and will continue strengthening previously developed number skills. We will work with estimation strategies, mental methods, paper-and-pencil algorithms, and calculator procedures with whole numbers. We will also develop techniques for working with decimal numbers.

In addition to standard and number-and-word notation, we will learn new ways to represent large and small numbers using exponential and scientific notation. Your child will realize that scientific notation, which is used by scientists and mathematicians, is an easier and more efficient way to write large numbers. For example, the distance from the Sun to the planet Pluto is 3,675,000,000 miles. In scientific notation, the same number is expressed as $3.675 * 10^9$.

To use scientific notation, your child will first need to know more about exponential notation, which is a way of representing multiplication of repeated factors. For example, $7 * 7 * 7 * 7$ can be written as 7^4. Similarly, 100,000, or $10 * 10 * 10 * 10 * 10$, is also 10^5.

Unit 2 also reviews multiplication and division of whole numbers. All these strategies will be extended to decimals. The partial-quotient algorithm used in fourth and fifth grade *Everyday Mathematics* to divide whole numbers will also be used to divide decimals to obtain decimal quotients. This algorithm is similar to the traditional long division method, but it is easier to learn and apply. The quotient is built up in steps using "easy" multiples of the divisor. The student doesn't have to get the partial quotient exactly right at each step. The example below demonstrates how to use the partial-quotient algorithm.

Example:

Partial-Quotient Algorithm

Division	Partial quotients	Partial Quotients
12) 3270		
− 2400	200 ←	200 ∗ 12 = 2,400
870		100 ∗ 12 = 1,200
− 600	50 ←	50 ∗ 12 = 600
270	↙	20 ∗ 12 = 240
− 240	20	10 ∗ 12 = 120
30		5 ∗ 12 = 60
− 24	2 ←	2 ∗ 12 = 24
6 ↑ Remainder	272 ↑ Quotient	

The partial-quotient algorithm is discussed on pages 22 and 23 in the *Student Reference Book.*

Please keep this Family Letter for reference as your child works through Unit 2.

Vocabulary

Important terms in Unit 2:

dividend In division, the number that is being divided. For example, in $35 \div 5 = 7$, the dividend is 35.

dividend / divisor = quotient

$$\frac{\text{dividend}}{\text{divisor}} = \text{quotient}$$

divisor In division, the number that divides another number (the *dividend*). For example, in $35 / 5 = 7$, the divisor is 5.

exponent A small, raised number used in *exponential notation* to tell how many times the base is used as a *factor.* For example, in 5^3, the base is 5, the exponent is 3, and $5^3 = 5 * 5 * 5$. Same as *power.*

exponential notation A way of representing repeated multiplication by the same factor. For example, 2^3 is exponential notation for $2 * 2 * 2$. The *exponent* 3 tells how many times the base 2 is used as a factor.

factor (1) Each of two or more numbers in a product. For example, in $6 * 0.5$, 6 and 0.5 are factors. Compare to *factor of a counting number* n. (2) To represent a number as a product of factors. For example, factor 21 by rewriting as $7 * 3$.

number-and-word notation A notation consisting of the significant digits of a number and words for the place value. For example, 27 billion is number-and-word notation for 27,000,000,000.

power Same as *exponent.*

power of 10 (1) In *Everyday Mathematics,* a number that can be written in the form 10^a, where a is a counting number. That is, the numbers $10 = 10^1$, $100 = 10^2$, $1000 = 10^3$, and so on, that can be written using only 10s as factors. Same as positive power of 10. (2) More generally, a number that can be written in the form 10^a, where a is an integer. That is, all the positive and negative powers of 10 together, along with $10^0 = 1$.

precise Exact or accurate.

precise measures The smaller the scale of a measuring tool, the more *precise* a measurement can be. For example, a measurement to the nearest inch is more precise than a measurement to the nearest foot. A ruler with $\frac{1}{16}$-inch markings can be more precise than a ruler with only $\frac{1}{4}$-inch markings, depending on the skill of the person doing the measuring.

precise calculations The more accurate measures or other data are, the more *precise* any calculations using those numbers can be.

quotient The result of dividing one number by another number. For example, in $10 / 5= 2$, the quotient is 2.

remainder An amount left over when one number is divided by another number. For example, in $16 / 3 \rightarrow 5$ R1, the quotient is 5 and the remainder R is 1.

scientific notation A way of writing a number as the product of a *power of 10* and a number that is at least 1 and less than 10. Scientific notation allows you to write large and small numbers with only a few symbols. For example, in scientific notation, 4,300,000 is $4.3 * 10^6$, and 0.00001 is 1×10^{-5}. Scientific calculators display numbers in scientific notation. Compare to *standard notation* and expanded notation.

standard notation Our most common way of representing whole numbers, integers, and decimals. Standard notation is base-ten place-value numeration. For example, standard notation for three hundred fifty-six is 356. Same as decimal notation.

Do-Anytime Activities

Consider using the suggested real-life applications and games that not only promote your child's understanding of Unit 2 concepts, but also are easy, fun, and rewarding to do at home.

1. Encourage your child to incorporate math vocabulary in everyday speech. Help your child recognize the everyday uses of fractions and decimals in science, statistics, business, sports, print and television journalism, and so on.
2. Have your child help you measure ingredients when cooking or baking at home. This will usually involve working with fractional amounts. Furthermore, your child could assist you with adjusting the amounts for doubling a recipe or making multiple servings.
3. Extend your child's thinking about fractions and decimals to making connections with percents. By using money as a reference, you could help your child recognize that one-tenth is equal to $\frac{10}{100}$ or 10%, one-quarter is the same as 0.25, $\frac{25}{100}$, or 25%, and so on.
4. Ask your child to use mental math skills to help you calculate tips. For example, if the subtotal is \$25.00 and the tip you intend to pay is 15%, have your child first find 10% of \$25 (\$2.50) and then find 5% of \$25 by taking half the 10% amount (\$2.50 / 2 = \$1.25). Add \$2.50 and \$1.25 to get the tip amount of \$3.75.

Building Skills through Games

Several math games develop and reinforce whole number and decimal concepts in Unit 2. Detailed game instructions for all sixth-grade games are provided in the *Student Reference Book.* Encourage your child to play the following games with you at home.

Scientific Notation Toss See *Student Reference Book*, page 331.
Two players can play this game using a pair of 6-sided dice. Winning the game depends on creating the largest number possible using scientific notation. *Advanced Scientific Notation Toss*, mentioned at the bottom of page 331, adds more excitement to the original game.

Doggone Decimal See *Student Reference Book*, page 310.
In this game, two players compete to collect the greatest number of cards. You will need number cards, 4 index cards, 2 counters or coins, and a calculator. The skill practiced here is estimating products of whole and decimal numbers.

As You Help Your Child with Homework

As your child brings assignments home, you might want to go over the instructions together, clarifying them as necessary. The answers listed below will guide you through the unit's Study Links.

Study Link 2•1

1. a. 2 **b.** 5 **c.** 1 **d.** 6 **e.** 8 **f.** 0

2. a. 430,000 **b.** 90,105,000 **c.** 170,000,065 **d.** 9,500,243,000

3. a. (3 * 100,000) + (2 * 10,000) + (1 * 1,000)

4. a. 1,000 **b.** 1,000,000 **c.** 1,000,000,000

5. a. 48 million miles **b.** 25.7 million miles

6. a. 44,300,000,000 **b.** 6,500,000,000,000 **c.** 900,000 **d.** 70

7. 416,300 **8.** 230,000 **9.** 1,900,000

10. 7,000,000

Study Link 2•2

1. 38.469 **2.** 1.3406 **3.** eight-tenths

4. ninety-five hundredths **5.** five-hundredths

7. four and eight hundred two ten-thousandths

11. (1 * 0.01) + (3 * 0.001)

12. (1 * 100) + (9 * 1) + (3 * 0.1) + (5 * 0.01) + (2 * 0.001) + (7 * 0.0001)

13. 8.630 **14.** 0.368 **15.** *D* **16.** *A*

17. *C* **18.** *B* **19.** 0.63 **20.** 0.0168

21. 0.7402 **22.** 45.009 **23.** 0.5801

Study Link 2•3

1. 0.297 minutes **2.** 5.815 meters

3. 1.339 mph **4.** 1.38 goals

7. $0.71 **8.** 0.85 **9.** 1.5 **10.** $6.75

Study Link 2•4

1. 0.0049 **2.** 0.078 **3.** 3.0 **4.** 0.07

5. 150.0 **6.** 190 **7.** 3,760 **8.** 0.0428

9. a. 100 **b.** 10^{100} **10.** 0.000000001

11. 10^7 **12.** $5.25 **13.** $6.02 **14.** $9.11

Study Link 2•5

1. 2,001 **2.** 1,288 **3.** 11,904

4. a. 20.01 **b.** 20.01 **c.** 200.1

5. a. 1,190.4 **b.** 11.904 **c.** 11.904

7. $5.00 **8.** $11.00 **9.** 34.5 **10.** 0.07

Study Link 2•6

1. 24.3 **2.** 11.48 **3.** 0.827 **4.** 756.3

5. 18.012 **6.** 29.82 **7.** 49.92 **8.** 10.241

9. 76.7 miles; 11.8 * 6.5 = 76.7

12. $16.00 **13.** $11.00 **14.** 96 **15.** 24

Study Link 2•7

6. → 66 R6; $66\frac{6}{8}$ **7.** → 65 R1; $65\frac{1}{15}$ **8.** = 49

9. →18 R15; $18\frac{15}{46}$ **10.** → 158 R20; $158\frac{20}{38}$

11. →126 R42; $126\frac{42}{44}$

12. $3.98 **13.** $11.84 **14.** $74.94 **15.** $499.95

Study Link 2•8

1. Sample estimate: 2; Answer: 2.47

2. Sample estimate: 20; Answer: 19.7

5. 2.83 **6.** $7.20 **7.** 1.99 **8.** 4.22

Study Link 2•9

1. 12,400 **3.** 0.000008 **5.** $1.1802 * 10^{10}$

6. 0.00016 **7.** $4.3 * 10^{-3}$ **8.** 2,835,000

9. > **10.** = **11.** < **12.** >

13. 10 is raised to a negative power.

14. 7,624 **15.** 3.71 **16.** 900 **17.** 200

Study Link 2•10

1. 49 **3.** 64 **5.** 0.00001

7. 3^9 **9.** 11^{-3} **14.** $8^5 = 32,768$

Study Link 2•11

1. $3.6 * 10^{-3}$ **3.** $8 * 10^4$ **5.** 50,000

7. 48,100,000 **9.** $1 * 10^{-3}$; 0.001 **11.** $3.9 * 10^3$

13. $5.2 * 10^{-1}$ **16.** 6,763 – 3,929 = 2,834

17. 71,146 – 4,876 = 66,270

Name Date Time

Large Numbers

trillions			billions			millions			thousands			ones		
100,000,000,000,000	10,000,000,000,000	1,000,000,000,000	100,000,000,000	10,000,000,000	1,000,000,000	100,000,000	10,000,000	1,000,000	100,000	10,000	1,000	100	10	1

1. Write the digit in each place of the number 6,812,507,439.

a. millions ________ **b.** hundred thousands ________ **c.** ten millions ________

d. billions ________ **e.** hundred millions ________ **f.** ten thousands ________

2. Write each of the following numbers in standard form.

a. four hundred thirty thousand ____________________

b. ninety million, one hundred five thousand ____________________

c. one hundred seventy million, sixty-five ____________________

d. nine billion, five hundred million,
two hundred forty-three thousand ____________________

3. Write each number in expanded form. **Example:** 235 = (2 ∗ 100) + (3 ∗ 10) + (5 ∗ 1)

a. 321,000

____

b. 7,300,000,000,000

____

c. 2,510,709

____

4. Use extended facts to complete the following.

a. 1 million = 1,000 ∗ ____________________

b. 1 billion = 1,000 ∗ ____________________

c. 1 trillion = 1,000 ∗ ____________________

Name Date Time

Large Numbers *continued*

___ ___ ___ , ___ ___ ___ , ___ ___ ___ , ___ ___ ___ , ___ ___ ___

trillion billion million thousand

Because the orbits of the planets are elliptical in shape, the distance between two planets changes over time. The least distances of Mercury, Venus, Saturn, and Neptune from Earth appear in the table at the right. The distances are approximations.

Least Distance from Earth

Planet	Distance (in miles)
Mercury	48,000,000
Venus	25,700,000
Saturn	850,000,000
Neptune	2,680,000,000

5. Write each planet's least distance from Earth in number-and-word notation.

a. Mercury ______________________

b. Venus ______________________

c. Saturn ______________________

d. Neptune ______________________

6. Write the following numbers in standard notation.

a. 44.3 billion ______________________

b. 6.5 trillion ______________________

c. 0.9 million ______________________

d. 0.7 hundred ______________________

Practice

Round each number to the given place.

7. 416,254; hundreds

____

8. 234,989; ten thousands

____

9. 1,857,000; hundred thousands

____

10. 6,593,278; millions

____

Name Date Time

LESSON 2•1

Walking Away with a Billion Dollars

Suppose you inherit one billion dollars. The bank pays you the entire amount of money in $100 bills. About how much will your payment weigh in tons?

Use the information below to solve the problem.

- ◆ You can cover a sheet of paper with about six $100 bills.
- ◆ There are 500 sheets in a ream of paper.
- ◆ There are 10 reams in 1 carton of paper.
- ◆ One ream of paper weighs about 5 pounds.
- ◆ One ton equals 2,000 pounds.

Show all your work. Write an explanation that is clear and easy to follow.

Name Date Time

Writing Decimals

1. Build a numeral. Write:
9 in the thousandths place,
4 in the tenths place,
8 in the ones place,
3 in the tens place, and
6 in the hundredths place.

Answer:

__ __ . __ __ __

2. Build a numeral. Write:
3 in the tenths place,
6 in the ten-thousandths place,
4 in the hundredths place,
0 in the thousandths place, and
1 in the ones place.

Answer:

__ . __ __ __ __

Write the following numbers in words.

3. 0.8 ____________________

4. 0.95 ____________________

5. 0.05 ____________________

6. 0.067 ____________________

7. 4.0802 ____________________

Write a decimal place value in each blank space.

8. Bamboo grows at a rate of about 0.00004, or four ____________________, kilometer per hour.

9. The average speed that a certain brand of catsup pours from the mouth of the bottle is about 0.003, or three ____________________, mile per hour.

10. A three-toed sloth moves at a speed of about 0.068 to 0.098, or sixty-eight ____________________ to ninety-eight ____________________, mile per hour.

Name _______________ Date _______________ Time _______________

Writing Decimals *continued*

hundreds	tens	ones	**and**	tenths	hundredths	thousandths	ten-thousandths	hundred-thousandths	millionths
100	10	1	.	0.1	0.01	0.001	0.0001	0.00001	0.000001

Write each of the following numbers in expanded notation.

Example: 2.756 = (2 ∗ 1) + (7 ∗ 0.1) + (5 ∗ 0.01) + (6 ∗ 0.001)

11. 0.013 ____

12. 109.3527 ____

____

13. Using the digits 0, 3, 6, and 8, write the greatest decimal number possible.

___ . ___ ___ ___

14. Using the digits 0, 3, 6, and 8, write the least decimal number possible.

___ . ___ ___ ___

Try This

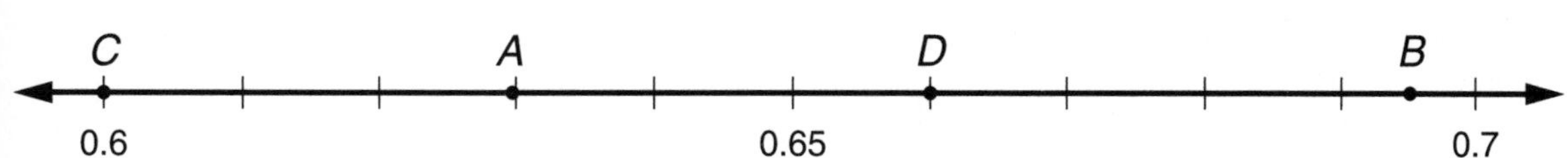

Name the point on the number line that represents each of the following numbers.

15. 0.66 ______ **16.** 0.6299 ______ **17.** 0.6 ______ **18.** 0.695 ______

19. Refer to the number line above. Round 0.6299 to the nearest hundredth. ________

Practice

20. 0.01 + 0.006 + 0.0008 = __________

21. 0.7 + 0.04 + 0.0002 = __________

22. __________ = 40 + 5 + 0.009

23. __________ = 0.50 + 0.080 + 0.00010

Name Date Time

LESSON 2·2

Modeling and Comparing Decimals

One way to compare decimals is to model them with base-10 grids.

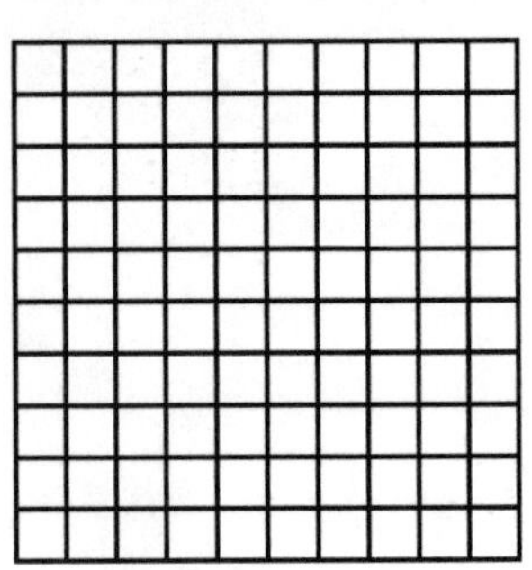

The flat is the whole, or 1.0.

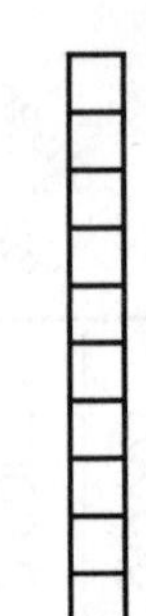

The long is worth 0.1.

The cube is worth 0.01.

The fractional part of the cube is worth 0.001.

Another way to compare decimals is to draw pictures.

The flat is the whole, or 1.0.

The long is worth 0.1.

The cube is worth 0.01.

The fractional part of the cube is worth 0.001.

1. Use decimal models to complete the following.

1.0 = 0.10 * _______ 0.10 = 0.01 * _______ 0.01 = 0.001 * _______

Model the decimal numbers in each pair. Draw a picture to record each model. Then compare the decimal numbers using <, >, or =.

2.

0.3 _______ 0.14

3.

1.56 _______ 1.562

4.

0.2 _______ 0.025

5. Model and record a decimal number that is between 0.41 and 0.42.

0.41 < _________ < 0.42

Name Date Time

Sports Records

Solve.

1. The fastest winning time for the New York Marathon (Tesfay Jifar of Ethiopia, 2001) is 2 hours, 7.72 minutes. The second fastest time is 2 hours, 8.017 minutes (Juma Ikangaa of Tanzania, 1989).

   How much faster was Jifar's time than Ikangaa's? ______________

2. In the 1908 Olympic Games, Erik Lemming of Sweden won the javelin throw with a distance of 54.825 meters. He won again in 1912 with a distance of 60.64 meters.

   How much longer was his 1912 throw than his 1908 throw?

   ____

3. Driver Buddy Baker (Oldsmobile, 1980) holds the record for the fastest winning speed in the Daytona 500 at 177.602 miles per hour. Bill Elliott (Ford, 1987) has the second fastest speed at 176.263 miles per hour.

   How much faster is Baker's speed than Elliott's?

   ____

4. The highest scoring World Cup Soccer Final was in 1954. Teams played 26 games and scored 140 goals for an average of 5.38 goals per game. In 1950, teams played 22 games and scored 88 goals for an average of 4 goals per game.

   What is the difference between the 1954 and the 1950 average goals per game?

   ____

5. 46.09 + 123.047 Estimate ________

   46.09 + 123.047 = ______________

6. 0.172 + 4.5 Estimate ________

   0.172 + 4.5 = ______________

Practice

Solve mentally.

7. \$0.36 + \$0.29 + \$0.64 + ______________ = \$2.00

8. 7.03 + ______________ + 14.05 + 13.07 = 35

9. 9.225 + 8.5 + 5.775 + ______________ = 25

10. \$3.69 + ______________ + \$8.31 + \$6.25 = \$25

Name Date Time

LESSON 2•3 Modeling Subtraction of Decimals

You can model subtraction of decimals using base-10 grids or pictures. For example, to solve 1.237 – 0.645, first represent 1.237, adjust by trading, and then subtract.

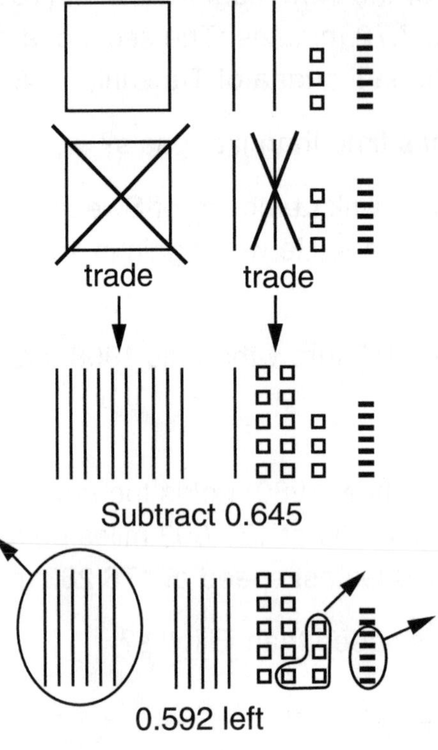

Use base-10 grids or pictures to find each difference. Show your work.

1. 3.6 − 2.973 = ____________

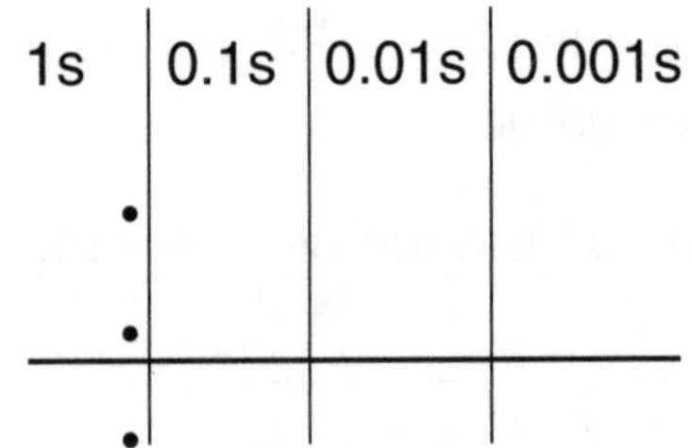

2. 2.0 − 0.761 = ____________

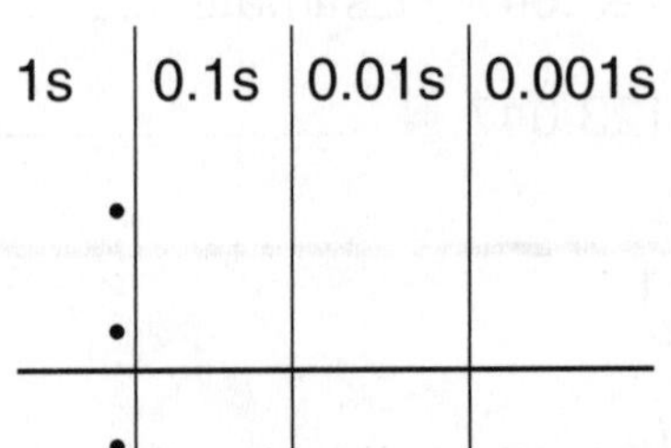

3. 1.7 − 0.083 = ____________

1s	0.1s	0.01s	0.001s
.			
.			
.			

Name Date Time

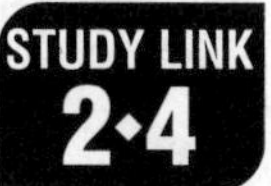

Multiplying by Powers of 10

Some Powers of 10									
10^4	10^3	10^2	10^1	10^0	.	10^{-1}	10^{-2}	10^{-3}	10^{-4}
10 ∗ 10 ∗ 10 ∗ 10	10 ∗ 10 ∗ 10	10 ∗ 10	10	1	.	$\frac{1}{10}$	$\frac{1}{10} * \frac{1}{10}$	$\frac{1}{10} * \frac{1}{10} * \frac{1}{10}$	$\frac{1}{10} * \frac{1}{10} * \frac{1}{10} * \frac{1}{10}$
10,000	1,000	100	10	1	.	0.1	0.01	0.001	0.0001

Multiply.

1. 4.9 ∗ 0.001 = ____________

2. ____________ = 7.8 ∗ 0.01

3. $30 * 10^{-1}$ = ____________

4. ____________ = $7 * 10^{-2}$

5. $0.15 * 10^3$ = ____________

6. ____________ = 1.9 ∗ 100

7. $37.6 * 10^2$ = ____________

8. $42.8 * 10^{-3}$ = ____________

9. Mathematician Edward Kasner asked his 9-year-old nephew to invent a name for the number represented by 10^{100}. The boy named it a *googol.* Later, an even larger number was named—a *googolplex.* This number is represented by 10^{googol}, or $10^{10^{100}}$.

a. How many zeros are in the standard form of a googol, or 10^{100}? ____________

b. One googolplex is 1 followed by how many zeros? ____________

10. The speed of computer memory and logic chips is measured in nanoseconds. A nanosecond is one-billionth of a second, or 10^{-9} second. Write this number in standard form. ____________

11. Light travels about 1 mile in 0.000005 seconds. If a spacecraft could travel at this speed, it would travel almost 10^6 miles in 5 seconds. About how far would this spacecraft travel in 50 seconds? ____________ miles

Practice

Mentally calculate your change from $10.

12. Cost: $4.75; Change: ____________

13. Cost: $3.98; Change: ____________

14. Cost: $0.89; Change: ____________

15. Cost: $8.46; Change: ____________

Name Date Time

"What's My Rule?"

For each problem, complete the table and find the rule. Use Problem 4 to write your own "What's My Rule?" problem.

1. *Rule:* ______________________

____

in	out
$10	$100
$25	
	$1,450
$7,985	
	$2,300,000

2. *Rule:* ______________________

____

in	out
$0.10	
$3.00	$30.00
	$500.00
$88.50	
$235.75	

3. *Rule:* ______________________

____

in	out
$0.90	$0.09
$5.00	$0.50
	$2.00
$760	
$1,000	

4. *Rule:* ______________________

____

in	out

Name Date Time

Multiplying Decimals: Part 1

Multiply.

1. $\begin{array}{r} 23 \\ * \ 87 \\ \hline \end{array}$

2. $\begin{array}{r} 56 \\ * \ 23 \\ \hline \end{array}$

3. $\begin{array}{r} 124 \\ * \ 96 \\ \hline \end{array}$

4. Use your answer for Problem 1 to place the decimal point in each product.

a. 2.3 ∗ 8.7 = ______________

b. 23 ∗ 0.87 = ______________

c. 2.3 ∗ 87 = ______________

5. Use your answer for Problem 3 to place the decimal point in each product.

a. 124 ∗ 9.6 = ______________

b. 1.24 ∗ 9.6 = ______________

c. 12.4 ∗ 0.96 = ______________

Two new U.S. nickels were issued in 2004. A likeness of Thomas Jefferson remained on the front of the nickels. The reverse side featured images commemorating either the Louisiana Purchase or the Lewis and Clark expedition.

6. A U.S. nickel is 1.95 mm thick.

a. Estimate the height of a stack of 25 nickels. Estimate __________ mm

b. Calculate the actual height of the stack in mm. __________ mm

c. How much is a stack of 25 nickels worth? __________

Practice

Multiply by 0.10 to find 10% of each number.

7. 10% of $50.00 = __________

8. 10% of $110.00 = __________

9. 10% of 345 = __________

10. 10% of 0.70 = __________

Name Date Time

Estimating and Calculating Cost

Suppose you have $25.00 to spend on snacks for your basketball team. You need to purchase 25 pieces of fruit and 25 beverages. The table below shows the food items available and the cost of each item.

Fruit	Cost	Beverages	Cost
Banana	$0.42	Fruit punch	$0.65
Apple	$0.28	Orange juice	$0.50
Orange	$0.41	Bottled water	$0.75

1. Make a table of the items you will buy, how many of each item, and the cost. Remember that you can spend up to $25.00 but not more than $25.00. Your table might have four columns with these headings: Food Item, Number of Items, Cost per Item, and Subtotals.

2. Explain how you decided which items to buy and how many of each item.

Name Date Time

Whole Number Multiplication

Use your favorite multiplication algorithm to find the following products. Show your work in the computation grid below or on a separate sheet of paper.

1. 16 * 17 = ____________

2. 32 * 45 = ____________

3. ____________ = 4 * 186

4. ____________ = 89 * 51

5. ____________ = 724 * 6

6. 26 * 32 = ____________

7. 9 * 5,668 = ____________

8. ____________ = 37 * 487

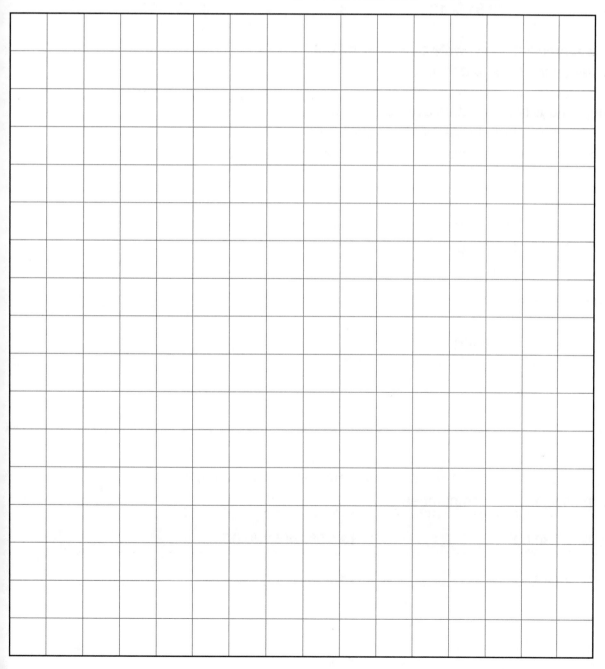

Name Date Time

Multiplying Decimals: Part 2

Place a decimal point in each problem.

SRB 37–39

1. 2 4 3 $*$ 7.06 = 171.558
2. 16.4 $*$ 0.7 = 1 1 4 8
3. 8 2 7 $*$ 9.5 = 7.8565
4. 7 5 6 3 $*$ 5.1 = 3,857.13

Multiply. Show your work on a separate sheet of paper or on the back of this page.

5. ______________ = 2.28 $*$ 7.9
6. ______________ = 49.7 $*$ 0.6
7. ______________ = 3.84 $*$ 13
8. ______________ = 0.19 $*$ 53.9

Solve each problem. Then write a number model.
(*Hint: Change fractions to decimals.*)

9. Janine rides her bike at an average speed of 11.8 miles per hour. At that speed, about how many miles can she ride in $6\frac{1}{2}$ hours? ______________

   Number Model ______________________________

10. Kate types at an average rate of 1.25 pages per quarter hour. If she types for $2\frac{3}{4}$ hours, about how many pages can she type? ______________

    Number Model ______________________________

11. Find the area in square meters of a rectangle with length 1.4 m and width 2.9 m. ______________

    Number Model ______________________________

Practice

Multiply mentally by 0.10 to find 10%. Then mentally calculate the percent that has been assigned to each number.

12. 20% of \$80.00 = ______________
13. 5% of \$220.00 = ______________
14. 15% of 640 = ______________
15. 30% of 80 = ______________

Name Date Time

A Mental Multiplication Strategy

The same strategy was used to solve both example problems below.
This strategy can also be used to multiply numbers mentally.

Example 1:

16 ∗ 2.5

16 / 2 ↓ 2.5 ∗ 2 ↓

8 ∗ 5

16 ∗ 2.5 = 8 ∗ 5 = 40

Example 2:

72 ∗ 0.125

72 / 2 ↓ 0.125 ∗ 2 ↓

36 ∗ 0.25

36 / 2 ↓ 0.25 ∗ 2 ↓

18 ∗ 0.50

72 ∗ 0.125 = 18 ∗ 0.50 = 9

1. Explain the strategy.

____

____

2. Use the strategy to solve the problems below. Show your work.

a. 16 ∗ 1.5 = ________ **b.** 18 ∗ 3.5 = ________

c. 20 ∗ 0.75 = ________ **d.** 0.125 ∗ 16 = ________

3. Solve these problems mentally.

a. 8 ∗ 7.5 = ________ **b.** 24 ∗ 1.25 = ________

4. Make up two problems that can be solved using a mental multiplication strategy.

a. ______________________ **b.** ______________________

Name Date Time

LESSON 2•6

Modeling Decimal Multiplication

You can use an area model to find a product.

Example: 0.3 * 0.5

Shade 0.3 of the grid this way: ▨

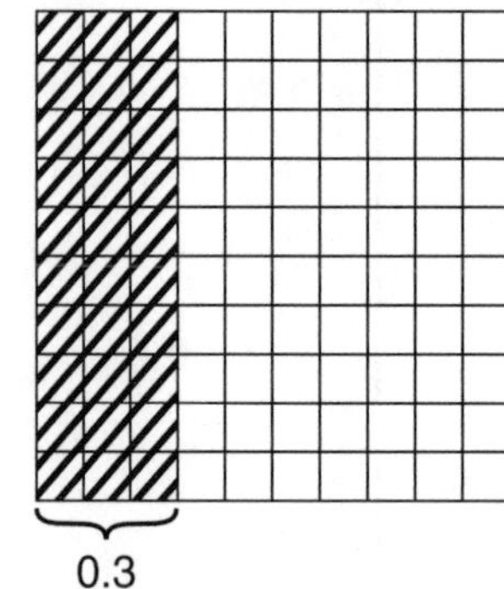

Next, shade 0.5 of the grid this way: ▧

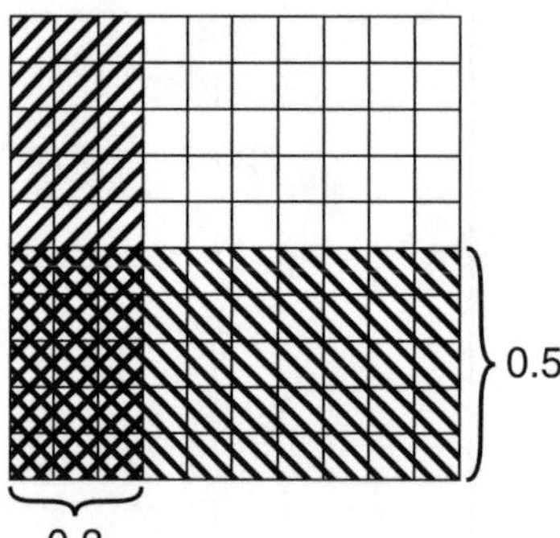

The product is the area that is double-shaded this way: ▩

Since 0.15 of the grid is double-shaded,

0.3 * 0.5 = 0.15.

Shade each factor. Then find the product.

1. 0.9 * 0.4

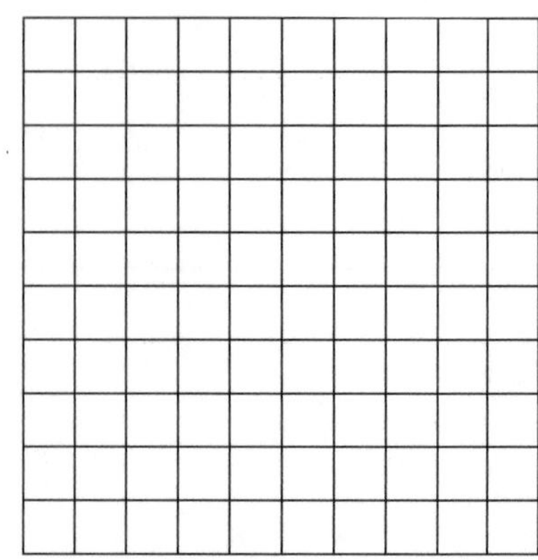

0.9 * 0.4 = ________

2. 0.7 * 0.6

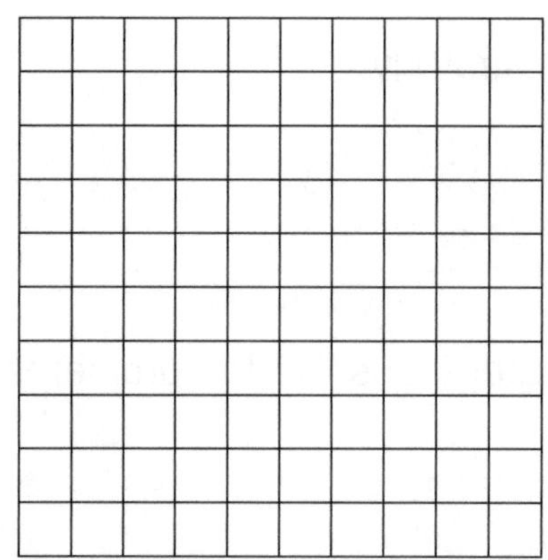

0.7 * 0.6 = ________

3. 0.5 * 0.5

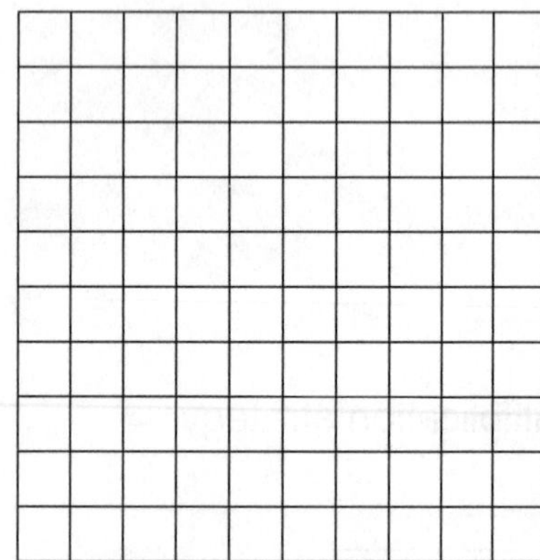

0.5 * 0.5 = ________

4. Write your own problem.

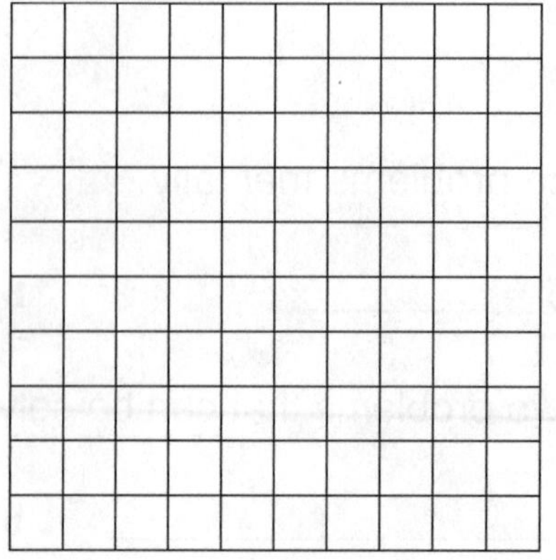

_______ * _______ = _______

Name Date Time

Dividing Numbers

3 Ways to Write a Division Problem

$246 \div 12 \rightarrow 20\text{ R}6$ $\quad 12\overline{)246} \rightarrow 20\text{ R}6$ $\quad 246 / 12 \rightarrow 20\text{ R}6$

2 Ways to Express a Remainder

$12\overline{)246} \rightarrow 20\text{ R}6$ $\quad 12\overline{)246} = 20\frac{6}{12}$, or $20\frac{1}{2}$

When estimating quotients, use "close" numbers that are easy to divide.

Example: 346 / 12 Estimate _35_ How I estimated: _350 / 10 = 35_

1. 234 / 6 Estimate ______ How I estimated: ______
2. 659 / 12 Estimate ______ How I estimated: ______
3. 512 / 9 Estimate ______ How I estimated: ______
4. 1,270 / 7 Estimate ______ How I estimated: ______
5. 728 / 34 Estimate ______ How I estimated: ______

Solve using a division algorithm. Show your work on a separate sheet of paper or a computation grid.

6. $8\overline{)534}$ ______
7. 976 / 15 ______
8. $980 \div 20$ ______
9. $46\overline{)843}$ ______
10. 6,024 / 38 ______
11. $5{,}586 \div 44$ ______

Practice

Multiply mentally.

12. 2 notebooks at $1.99 each = ______
13. 4 pens at $2.96 each = ______
14. 3 books at $24.98 each = ______
15. 5 gifts at $99.99 each = ______

Name Date Time

STUDY LINK 2·8

Dividing Decimals

For each problem, follow the steps below. Show your work on a separate sheet of paper or a computation grid.

- Estimate the quotient. Use numbers that are close to the numbers given and that are easy to divide. Write your estimate. Then write a number sentence to show how you estimated.
- Ignore any decimal points. Divide as if the numbers were whole numbers.
- Use your estimate to insert a decimal point in the final answer.

1. 19.76 ÷ 8 Estimate ____________

____
How I estimated

Answer ____________

2. 78.8 / 4 Estimate ____________

____
How I estimated

Answer ____________

3. 85.8 / 13 Estimate ____________

____
How I estimated

Answer ____________

4. 51.8 / 7 Estimate ____________

____
How I estimated

Answer ____________

5. Find 17 ÷ 6. Give the answer as a decimal with 2 digits after the decimal point.

____

6. Five people sent a $36 arrangement of flowers to a friend. Divide $36 into 5 equal shares. How much is 1 share, in dollars and cents?

____

Practice

Divide mentally to find the price for 1 pound (lb).

7. $3.98 for 2 lb = $__________ per 1 lb

8. $16.88 for 4 lb = $__________ per 1 lb

9. $45.80 for 5 lb = $__________ per 1 lb

10. $299.10 for 10 lb = $__________ per 1 lb

Name Date Time

STUDY LINK 2·9

Using Scientific Notation

Write each number in standard notation.

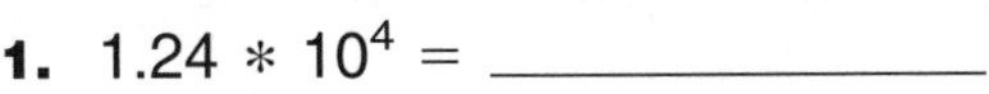

1. $1.24 * 10^4 =$ ______________

2. $3.5 * 10^{-3} =$ ______________

3. $8 * 10^{-6} =$ ______________

4. $7.061 * 10^8 =$ ______________

Change the numbers given in standard notation to scientific notation. Change the numbers given in scientific notation to standard notation.

5. Light travels about 11,802,000,000, or ______________, inches per second.

6. A bacterium can travel across a table at a speed of $1.6 * 10^{-4}$,

or ______________, km per hour.

7. One dollar bill has a thickness of 0.0043, or ______________, inches.

8. The mass of 1 million pennies is approximately $2.835 * 10^6$,

or ______________, grams.

Use $<$, $>$, or $=$ to compare each pair of numbers.

9. 10^{-2} _____ 10^{-3}

10. $1.23 * 10^{-3}$ _____ $\frac{1.23}{1,000}$

11. $9.87 * 10^5$ _____ $1.2 * 10^6$

12. $5.4 * 10^{-1}$ _____ $9.6 * 10^{-4}$

13. Explain how you can tell whether a number written in scientific notation is less than 1.

____

Practice

Solve mentally.

14. $3,625 + 3,999 =$ _______

15. $8.7 - 4.99 =$ _______

16. $4 * 225 =$ _______

17. $100,000 / 500 =$ _______

18. $683 - 298 =$ _______

19. $387 + 499 =$ _______

Name Date Time

LESSON 2•9 Ground Areas of Buildings

The approximate ground areas of some famous buildings are given below in scientific notation. To the left of the photograph of each building is its ground plan. Convert the scientific notation to standard notation.

1. Great Pyramid of Giza
(Egypt; c. 2580 B.C.)*

$5.7 * 10^5$, or _______________, ft^2

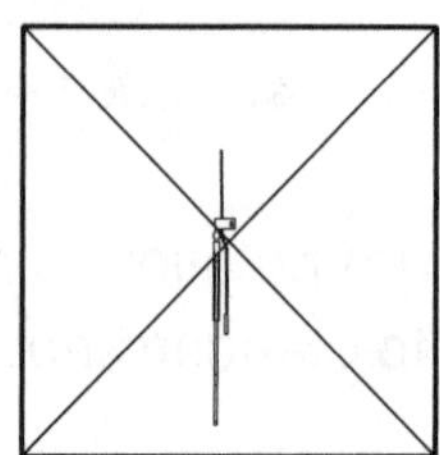

2. Roman Colosseum
(Rome, Italy; 70–224)*

$2.5 * 10^5$, or _______________, ft^2

3. St. Peter's Basilica
(Vatican City; 1506–1626)*

$3.9 * 10^5$, or _______________, ft^2

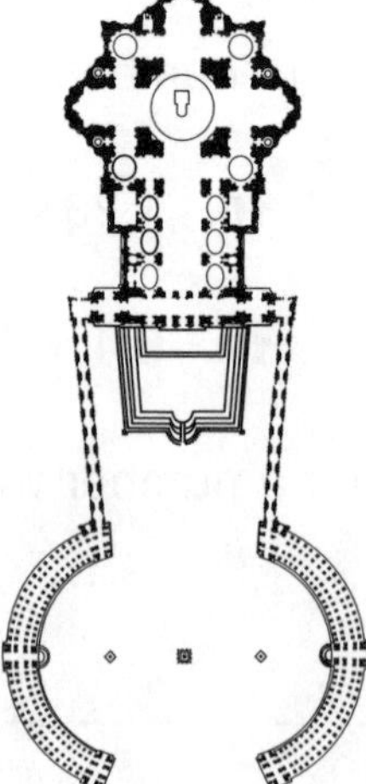

4. Taj Mahal
(Agra, India; 1636–1653)*

$9.8 * 10^4$, or _______________, ft^2

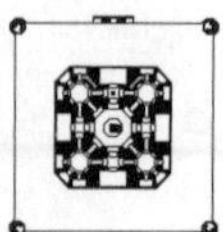

*Location and date(s) of construction

LESSON 2•9 Ground Areas of Buildings *continued*

5. Pentagon
(Arlington, Virginia,
United States; 1941–1943)*

$1.3 * 10^6$, or ______________, ft^2

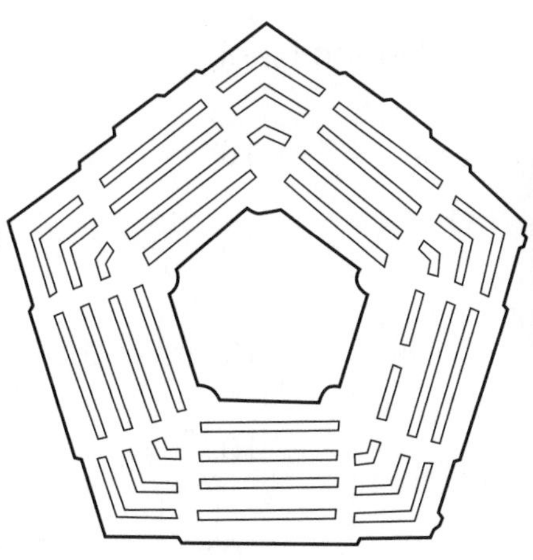

*Location and dates of construction

Source: Comparisons

6. Use the information in Problems 1–5 to write two comparisons.

a. Ratio comparison (The area of one building is *x* times larger [or smaller] than the area of another building.)

____

____

____

b. Difference comparison (The area of one building is *x* square feet more [or less] than the area of another building.)

____

____

____

7. Try to find out the ground area of a large building, such as your school, a shopping mall, an historic landmark, a sports arena, or a factory. How does that building's ground area compare to the ground area of each building pictured in Problems 1–5?

____

____

____

Name Date Time

LESSON 2·9 Patterns and Powers of 10

Use any patterns you notice to fill in the blanks.

$10^5 =$ ______________	$10^0 = 1$
$10^{\square} = 10{,}000$	$10^{-1} = 0.1$
$10^3 = 1{,}000$	$10^{\square} = 0.01$
$10^{\square} = 100$	$10^{-3} =$ ______________
$10^1 =$ ______________	$10^{\square} = 0.0001$

What do you notice about the number of digits after the decimal point and the negative powers of 10?

____

Name Date Time

LESSON 2·9 Patterns and Powers of 10

Use any patterns you notice to fill in the blanks.

$10^5 =$ ______________	$10^0 = 1$
$10^{\square} = 10{,}000$	$10^{-1} = 0.1$
$10^3 = 1{,}000$	$10^{\square} = 0.01$
$10^{\square} = 100$	$10^{-3} =$ ______________
$10^1 =$ ______________	$10^{\square} = 0.0001$

What do you notice about the number of digits after the decimal point and the negative powers of 10?

____

Name Date Time

STUDY LINK 2•10

Exponential Notation

Use your calculator to write each number in standard notation.

SRB 6

1. $7^2 =$ ______
2. $(0.25)^2 =$ ______
3. $4^3 =$ ______
4. $(0.41)^3 =$ ______
5. $10^{-5} =$ ______
6. $(2.5)^{-3} =$ ______

Use digits to write each number in exponential notation.

7. three to the ninth power ______
8. eight to the seventh power ______
9. eleven to the negative third power ______
10. five-tenths to the negative sixth power ______

Write each number as a product of repeated factors.

Example: $5^3 = 5 * 5 * 5$

11. $(\frac{1}{2})^5 =$ ______
12. $10^{-2} =$ ______
13. $10^{-6} =$ ______

14. You can find the total number of different 4-digit numbers that can be made using the digits 1 through 9 by raising the number of choices for each digit (9) to the number of digits (4), or 9^4.

    Based on this pattern, how many different 5-digit numbers could you make from the digits 1 through 8? ______

Practice

Solve mentally.

15. $15.32 - 1.88 =$ ______
16. 7,200 / 90 = ______
17. $4.98 + 3.99 =$ ______
18. $8 * 525 =$ ______

Name Date Time

LESSON 2·10

Binary Numbers

The table below shows how to write whole numbers 1 through 10 as binary numbers. A binary number is written with a subscripted *two* to distinguish it from a base-ten number.

		Powers of 2						
		2^6	2^5	2^4	2^3	2^2	2^1	2^0
Base-Ten Number	**Binary Number**	64	32	16	8	4	2	1
1	1_{two}							$1 * 2^0$
2	10_{two}						$1 * 2^1$	$0 * 2^0$
3	11_{two}						$1 * 2^1$	$1 * 2^0$
4	100_{two}					$1 * 2^2$	$0 * 2^1$	$0 * 2^0$
5	101_{two}					$1 * 2^2$	$0 * 2^1$	$1 * 2^0$
6	110_{two}					$1 * 2^2$	$1 * 2^1$	$0 * 2^0$
7	111_{two}					$1 * 2^2$	$1 * 2^1$	$1 * 2^0$
8	1000_{two}				$1 * 2^3$	$0 * 2^2$	$0 * 2^1$	$0 * 2^0$
9	1001_{two}				$1 * 2^3$	$0 * 2^2$	$0 * 2^1$	$1 * 2^0$
10	1010_{two}				$1 * 2^3$	$0 * 2^2$	$1 * 2^1$	$0 * 2^0$

To write a binary number as a base-ten number, first write the binary number in expanded notation. Then convert to standard form.

Example:

$$\begin{aligned} 11111_{two} &= (1 * 2^4) + (1 * 2^3) + (1 * 2^2) + (1 * 2^1) + (1 * 2^0) \\ &= (1 * 16) + (1 * 8) + (1 * 4) + (1 * 2) + (1 * 1) \\ &= 16 + 8 + 4 + 2 + 1 \\ &= 31 \end{aligned}$$

Use the table and example above to write each binary number as a base-ten number.

1. 1011_{two} = ________ **2.** 101110_{two} = ________ **3.** 1110101_{two} = ________

4. 111101_{two} = ________ **5.** 1000001_{two} = ________ **6.** 1111111_{two} = ________

Try This

Use patterns in the table to write the binary number for each number.

7. 21 = ______________ **8.** 68 = ______________ **9.** 100 = ______________

Name Date Time

Scientific Notation

Write the following numbers in scientific notation.

1. 0.0036 ____________

2. 0.0007 ____________

3. 80,000 ____________

4. 600 thousand ____________

Write the following numbers in standard notation.

5. $5 * 10^4$ ____________

6. $4.73 * 10^9$ ____________

7. $4.81 * 10^7$ ____________

8. $8.04 * 10^{-2}$ ____________

Write the next two numbers in each pattern.

9. $1 * 10^{-1}$; 0.1; $1 * 10^{-2}$; 0.01; ____________; ____________

10. 0.01, 0.002, 0.0003, ____________, ____________

Solve the following problems. Write each answer in scientific notation.

11. $(4 * 10^3) - 10^2 =$ ____________

12. $10^3 - (2 * 10^1) =$ ____________

13. $(5 * 10^{-1}) + 0.02 =$ ____________

14. $(7 * 10^4) - 10^3 =$ ____________

15. Use a calculator to complete the table.

Problem	Calculator Display	Scientific Notation	Standard Notation
$5{,}000{,}000^2$			
$90^4 - 300^2$			
$20^3 + 30^2$			
$10^4 * 10^4$			
$5^{20} / 5^{16}$			

Practice

Find the missing digits to complete each number sentence.

16. ☐,☐63 – 3,9☐9 = 2,83☐

17. 71,☐4☐ – 4,8☐6 = 6☐,270

Name Date Time

Practicing Calculator Skills

Use your calculator to complete the table.

Problem	Scientific Notation	Standard Notation
$100,000^3$	$1 * 10^{15}$	1,000,000,000,000,000
$20,000^5$		
$30^8 + 30^8$		
$800^4 - 400^2$		
$10^7 * 10^7$		
$\frac{70^{12}}{70^4}$		

Name Date Time

Practicing Calculator Skills

Use your calculator to complete the table.

Problem	Scientific Notation	Standard Notation
$100,000^3$	$1 * 10^{15}$	1,000,000,000,000,000
$20,000^5$		
$30^8 + 30^8$		
$800^4 - 400^2$		
$10^7 * 10^7$		
$\frac{70^{12}}{70^4}$		

Name Date Time

Unit 3: Family Letter

Variables, Formulas, and Graphs

In Unit 3, students will be introduced to variables—symbols such as *x*, *y*, and *m*—that stand for a specific number or any number in a range of values. The authors of *Everyday Mathematics* believe that work with variables is too important to be delayed until high-school algebra courses. The problem "Solve $3x + 40 = 52$" might be difficult for some high-school students because they see it as merely symbol manipulation. Problems such as these are posed to *Everyday Mathematics* students as puzzles that can be unraveled by asking, "What number makes the equation true?" *I need to add 12 to 40 to get 52. Three times what number yields 12? The answer is* $x = 4$.

In addition to being used in algebraic equations, variables are also used to describe general patterns, to form expressions that show relationships, and to write rules and formulas. Unit 3 will focus on these three uses of variables.

In this unit, your child will work with "What's My Rule?" tables like the one below (introduced in early grades of *Everyday Mathematics*). He or she will learn to complete such tables following rules described in words or by algebraic expressions. Your child will also determine rules or formulas from information given in tables and graphs.

Rule: $y = (4 * x) + -3$

x	*y*
5	17
2	
0	
	37

In addition, your child will learn how to name cells in a spreadsheet and write formulas to express the relationships among spreadsheet cells. If you use computer spreadsheets at work or at home, you may want to share your experiences with your child. The class will play *Spreadsheet Scramble,* in which students practice computation and mental addition of positive and negative numbers. Encourage your child to play a game at home. See the *Practice through Games* section of this letter for some suggestions.

	A	B	C	D	E	F
1						**Total**
2						
3						
4						
5	**Total**					

Please keep this Family Letter for reference as your child works through Unit 3.

Math Tools

Your child will be using **spreadsheets,** a common mathematics tool for the computer. The spreadsheet, similar to the one shown here, gets its name from a ledger sheet for financial records. Such sheets were often large pages, folded or taped, that were *spread* out for examination.

Class picnic ($$)

	A	B	C	D
1		budget for class picnic		
2				
3	quantity	food items	unit price	cost
4	6	packages of hamburgers	2.79	16.74
5	5	packages of hamburger buns	1.29	6.45
6	3	bags of potato chips	3.12	9.36
7	3	quarts of macaroni salad	4.50	13.50
8	4	bottles of soft drinks	1.69	6.76
9			subtotal	52.81
10			8% tax	4.23
11			total	57.04

Vocabulary

Important terms in Unit 3:

algebraic expression An expression that contains a variable. For example, if Maria is 2 inches taller than Joe, and if the variable *m* represents Maria's height, then the algebraic expression $m - 2$ represents Joe's height.

cell In a spreadsheet, a box formed where a column and a row intersect. A *column* is a section of cells lined up vertically. A *row* is a section of cells lined up horizontally.

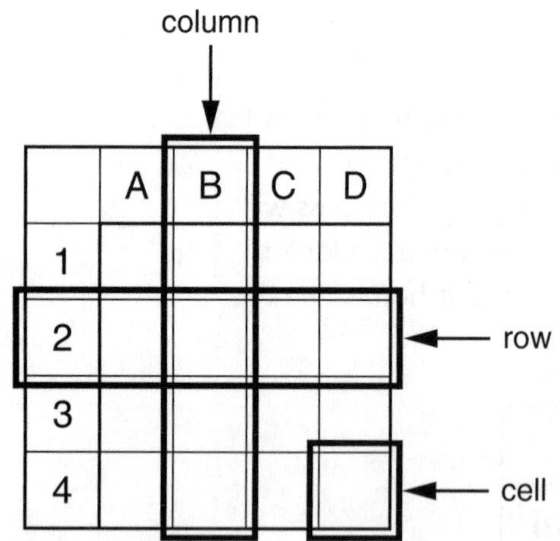

formula A general rule for finding the value of something. A formula is often written using letters, called *variables,* that stand for the quantities involved. For example, the formula for the area of a rectangle may be written as $A = b * h$, where *A* represents the area of the rectangle, *b* represents its base, and *h* represents its height.

general pattern In *Everyday Mathematics,* a number model for a pattern or rule.

special case In *Everyday Mathematics,* a specific example of a *general pattern*. For example, $6 + 6 = 12$ is a special case of $y + y = 2y$ and $9 = 4.5 * 2$ is a special case of $A = l * w$. Same as instance of a pattern.

time graph A graph representing a story that takes place over time. For example, the time graph below shows the trip Mr. Olds took to drive his son to school. The line shows the increases, decreases, and constant rates of speed that Mr. Olds experienced during the 13-minute trip.

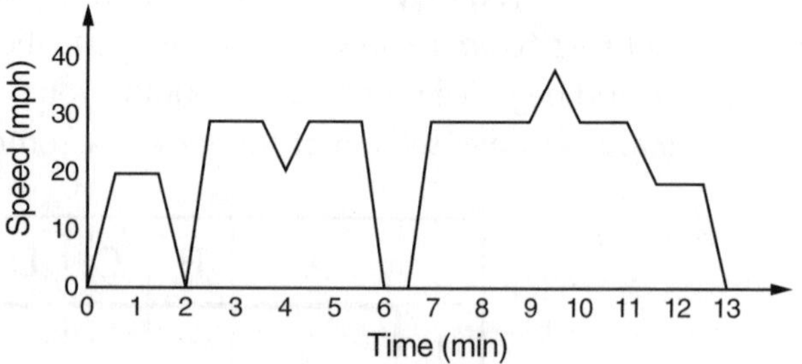

variable A letter or symbol that represents a number. A variable can represent one specific number, or it can stand for many different numbers.

Do-Anytime Activities

Try these ideas to help your child with the concepts taught in this unit.

1. If you are planning to paint or carpet a room, consider having your child measure and calculate the area using the area formula for rectangular surfaces: Area = base ∗ height. If the room is irregular in shape, divide it into rectangular regions, find the area of each region, and add all the areas to find the total area. If a room has a cathedral ceiling, imagine a line across the top of the wall to form a triangle. Your child can use the area formula for triangles: Area = $\frac{1}{2}$ ∗ (base ∗ height), to calculate the area of the triangle.

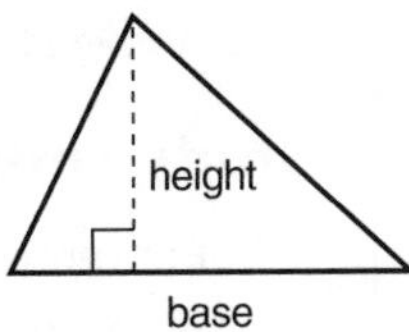

2. If you use a spreadsheet program on a home computer, help your child learn how to use it. You might help your child set up a spreadsheet to keep track of his or her math scores and to figure out the mean.
3. Practice renaming fractions, which is a prerequisite skill for Unit 4. **Examples:**

Rename as Fractions	Rename as Mixed or Whole Numbers
$3\frac{1}{2} = \frac{7}{2}$	$\frac{33}{5} = 6\frac{3}{5}$
$8\frac{1}{3} = \frac{25}{3}$	$\frac{25}{5} = 5$

Building Skills through Games

The concepts learned in Unit 3 will be reinforced through several math games included in this unit that are fun to play in class and at home. Detailed game instructions for all sixth-grade games are available in the games section of the *Student Reference Book.* Here is a list and a brief description of some of the games in this unit:

Getting to One See *Student Reference Book,* page 321
Two players can play this game using a calculator. The object of the game is to divide a number by a mystery number and to find the mystery number in as few tries as possible. Players apply place-value concepts of decimal numbers to determine which numbers to play.

***Division Top-It* (Advanced Version)** See *Student Reference Book,* page 336
Two to four people can play this game using number cards 1 through 9. Players apply place-value concepts, division facts, and estimation strategies to generate whole-number division problems that will yield the largest quotient.

As You Help Your Child with Homework

As your child brings assignments home, you may want to go over the instructions together, clarifying them as necessary. Some of the answers listed below will guide you through the unit's Study Links.

Study Link 3•1

Sample answers (1–7):

1. a. The sum of any number and 0 is equal to the original number.
b. 36.09 + 0 = 36.09; 52 + 0 = 52

2. (2 ∗ 24) + 24 = 3 ∗ 24; (2 ∗ 10) + 10 = 3 ∗ 10

3. 100 + 0.25 = 0.25 + 100; 0.5 + 0.25 = 0.25 + 0.5

4. $x^2 * x^3 = x^5$ **5.** $s * 0.1 = \frac{s}{10}$ **6.** $m^0 = 1$

7. 10 **8.** 100, 0.25 **9.** 20

10. 75, 100 **11.** 80, 0.80 **12.** 70, 0.70

Study Link 3•2

Sample answers (1–7):

1. (6 ∗ 2) ∗ 3 = 6 ∗ (2 ∗ 3); (6 ∗ 1) ∗ 5 = 6 ∗ (1 ∗ 5)

2. $12 \div (\frac{6}{2}) = (2 * 12) \div 6$; $10 \div (\frac{4}{2}) = (2 * 10) \div 4$

3. $\frac{10}{5} = 10 * \frac{1}{5}$; $\frac{3}{4} = 3 * \frac{1}{4}$

4. $a - b = a + (-b)$ **5.** $\frac{m}{n} = \frac{m * 3}{n * 3}$

6. $\frac{s}{t} = \frac{s \div 2}{t \div 2}$ **7.** $\frac{c}{d} * \frac{1}{2} = \frac{c * 1}{d * 2}$

8. 2.5 **9.** 1.06 **10.** 1.00

Study Link 3•3

1. $x - 7$ **2.** $d + 2.5$ **3.** $\frac{c}{12}$, $c \div 12$, or $\frac{1}{12}c$

4. 2 ∗ *h*, or 2*h*; 8 **5.** 3*r* + 8, or (3 ∗ *r*) + 8; 44

6. 275 **7.** 35 **8.** 0.5

Study Link 3•4

1. a. Subtract 0.22 from *m*.
b. $n = m - 0.22$

2. a. Multiply *r* by $\frac{1}{2}$ or divide *r* by 2.
b. $r * 0.5 = t$

3. $q = (2 * p) - 2$

4. 15 **5.** 210 **6.** 1,760 **7.** 29,040

Study Link 3•5

1. *in:* $6\frac{1}{2}$; *out:* $10\frac{1}{2}$, $9\frac{1}{2}$, 3, $-\frac{1}{2}$

2. *in:* 6, $\frac{1}{4}$; *out:* 48, 1.2, 2 **3.** *in:* 7, 0; *out:* 0, 18

4. Divide the *in* number by 3; $d = b \div 3$

5. Answers vary. **6.** –3 **7.** –12 **8.** –3 **9.** 10

Study Link 3•6

1. Perimeter (in.): 4, 8, 12, 16, 20; Area (in.^{2}): 1, 4, 9, 16, 25

3. 10 in. **4.** 17 in. **6.** $2\frac{1}{4}$ in.^{2}

7. $10\frac{1}{2}$ in.^{2} **8.** 54.45 **9.** 4.2

Study Link 3•7

1. January **2.** $115.95 **3.** A5 **4.** C3

5. Column E: $118.75; $152.95; $2,625.00

6. E3 = B3 + C3 + D3 **7.** E5 = B5 + C5 + D5

8. $128.75 **9.** 144 **10.** 9 **11.** 73.96 **12.** 17

Study Link 3•8

1. –6 **2.** 4 **3.** 1 **4.** −6 **5.** 8

6. 2 **7.** −15 **8.** −5 **9.** −13 **10.** −12

11. 0, −2, −9
a. Sample answer: Add −6 to *x*.
b. $x + (-6) = y$

12. a. 25 **b.** 32 **c.** 50 **d.** −19

13. a. $\frac{1}{10}$ **b.** $\frac{1}{2}$ **c.** 2 **d.** −9

Study Link 3•9

1. Sample answer: People are getting on the Ferris wheel.

2. 125 sec **3.** 170 sec **4.** 4 times **5.** 40 sec

Study Link 3•10

1. Jenna's Profit: $3, $6, $9, $12, $15; Thomas's Profit: $6, $8, $10, $12, $14

2. $18, $16 **3.** Jenna **4.** Jenna's

5. $3, $2 **6.** (4,12)

7. a. 81 **b.** 8,000 **c.** 76 **d.** 875 **e.** 3

Name Date Time

General Patterns and Special Cases

1. You are describing a general number pattern for a special case when you write a rule for a "What's My Rule?" table.

Write a rule for each table shown below.

in	out
8	13
11	16
20	25
105	110

Rule: ______________________

in	out
12	4
21	7
60	20
300	100

Rule: ______________________

2. You are writing special cases for a general number pattern when you complete a "What's My Rule?" table.

Complete.

Rule: Add the opposite of the number. $(x + -x = 0)$

in	out
3	0
25	
−7	
−53	

Rule: Divide by the number. $(y \div y = 1)$

in	out
8	1
9	
$\frac{1}{4}$	
100	

Use the values from the table above to write special cases for the following general number patterns:

$x + -x = 0$.

Special cases

Example: $3 + -3 = 0$

____

____

____

$y \div y = 1$.

Special cases

Example: $8 \div 8 = 1$

____

____

____

Name Date Time

LESSON 3•1

Number Patterns

Triangular, square, and rectangular numbers are examples of number patterns that can be shown by geometric arrangements of dots. Study the number patterns shown below.

Triangular Numbers

1st 2nd 3rd 4th

Square Numbers

1st 2nd 3rd 4th

Rectangular Numbers

1st 2nd 3rd 4th

1. Use the number patterns to complete the table.

Number of Dots in Arrangement										
	1st	**2nd**	**3rd**	**4th**	**5th**	**6th**	**7th**	**8th**	**9th**	**10th**
Triangular Number	1	3	6	10						
Square Number	1	4	9	16						
Rectangular Number	2	6	12	20						

2. What is the 11th triangular number? ________

How does the 11th triangular number compare to the 10th triangular number?

____

Name Date Time

LESSON 3•1

Number Patterns *continued*

3. Describe what you notice about the sum of 2 triangular numbers that are next to each other in the table.

____

____

4. Add the second square number and the second rectangular number; the third square number and the third rectangular number. What do you notice about the sum of a square number and its corresponding rectangular number?

____

____

5. Describe any other patterns you notice.

____

____

6. You can write triangular numbers as the sum of 4 triangular numbers when repetitions are allowed. For example: $6 = 1 + 1 + 1 + 3$

Find 3 other triangular numbers that can be written as sums of *exactly* 4 triangular numbers.

____ = ____ + ____ + ____ + ____

____ = ____ + ____ + ____ + ____

____ = ____ + ____ + ____ + ____

Name Date Time

Variables in Number Patterns

1. Following are 3 special cases representing a general pattern.

$17 + 0 = 17$ $-43 + 0 = -43$ $\frac{7}{8} + 0 = \frac{7}{8}$

a. Describe the general pattern in words.

____

____

b. Give 2 other special cases for the pattern.

______________ ______________

For each general pattern, give 2 special cases.

2. $(2 * m) + m = 3 * m$

______________ ______________

3. $s + 0.25 = 0.25 + s$

______________ ______________

For each set of special cases, write a general pattern.

4. $3^2 * 3^3 = 3^5$

$5^2 * 5^3 = 5^5$

$13^2 * 13^3 = 13^5$

____

5. $7 * 0.1 = \frac{7}{10}$

$3 * 0.1 = \frac{3}{10}$

$4 * 0.1 = \frac{4}{10}$

____

6. $2^0 = 1$

$146^0 = 1$

$(\frac{1}{2})^0 = 1$

____

Practice

Complete.

7. $\frac{1}{10} = \frac{\square}{100} = 0.10$

8. $\frac{1}{4} = \frac{25}{\square} = 0.\square$

9. $\frac{1}{5} = \frac{\square}{100} = 0.20$

10. $\frac{3}{4} = \frac{\square}{\square} = 0.75$

11. $\frac{4}{5} = \frac{\square}{100} = 0.\square$

12. $\frac{7}{10} = \frac{\square}{100} = 0.\square$

Name Date Time

STUDY LINK 3•2

General Patterns with Two Variables

For each general pattern, write 2 special cases.

1. $(6 * b) * c = 6 * (b * c)$ ______________________

____

2. $a \div \frac{b}{2} = (2 * a) \div b$ ______________________

____

3. $\frac{x}{y} = x * \frac{1}{y}$ ______________________

(y is not 0) ______________________

For each set of special cases, write a number sentence with 2 variables to describe the general pattern.

4. $7 - 5 = 7 + (-5)$

$12 - 8 = 12 + (-8)$

$9 - 1 = 9 + (-1)$

General pattern:

____

5. $\frac{4}{6} = \frac{4 * 3}{6 * 3}$

$\frac{1}{2} = \frac{1 * 3}{2 * 3}$

$\frac{2}{5} = \frac{2 * 3}{5 * 3}$

General pattern:

____

6. $\frac{6}{10} = \frac{6 \div 2}{10 \div 2}$

$\frac{4}{12} = \frac{4 \div 2}{12 \div 2}$

$\frac{2}{4} = \frac{2 \div 2}{4 \div 2}$

General pattern:

____

7. $\frac{1}{5} * \frac{1}{2} = \frac{1 * 1}{5 * 2}$

$\frac{2}{3} * \frac{1}{2} = \frac{2 * 1}{3 * 2}$

$\frac{3}{4} * \frac{1}{2} = \frac{3 * 1}{4 * 2}$

General pattern:

____

Practice

Write each fraction as a decimal.

8. $\frac{250}{100} =$ ________

9. $\frac{106}{100} =$ ________

10. $\frac{100}{100} =$ ________

LESSON 3·2

True and Not True Special Cases

For each of the following, write one special case for which the sentence is true. Then write one special case for which the sentence is not true.

1. $m * n = m + n$

True ______________________

Not true ______________________

2. $\frac{a}{2} + b = a + b$

True ______________________

Not true ______________________

For each of the following, write at least 2 special cases for which the sentence is true. Circle each sentence that you think expresses a general pattern that is always true.

3. $a^2 = 2 * a$

____

____

4. If a is not 0, then $\frac{a^m}{a^n} = a^{m-n}$

____

____

5. $(a + b) * (a - b) = a^2 - b^2$

____

____

Name Date Time

STUDY LINK 3•3

General Patterns with Two Variables

Write an algebraic expression for each situation. Use the suggested variable.

1. Kayla has x CDs in her music collection. If Miriam has 7 fewer CDs than Kayla, how many CDs does Miriam have? ______ CDs

2. Chaz ran 2.5 miles more than Nigel. If Nigel ran d miles, how far did Chaz run? ______ miles

3. If a car dealer sells c automobiles each year, what is the average number of automobiles sold each month?

   ______ automobiles

First translate each situation from words into an algebraic expression. Then solve the problem that follows.

4. The base of a rectangle is twice the length of the height. If the height of the rectangle is h inches, what is the length of the base?

   ______ inches

   If the height of the rectangle is 4 inches, what is the length of the base?

   ______ inches

Try This

5. Monica has 8 more than 3 times the number of marbles Regina has. If Regina has r marbles, how many marbles does Monica have?

   ______ marbles

   If Regina has 12 marbles, how many does Monica have? ______ marbles

Practice

6. 2.75 m = ______ cm
7. 3.5 cm = ______ mm
8. 500 m = ______ km

Name Date Time

"What's My Rule?" for Geometric Patterns

1. When you cut a circular pizza, each cut goes through the center.

Cuts	Pieces
1	2
2	4
3	
4	
	12
	16

1 cut

2 cuts

3 cuts

Fill in the missing numbers in the table. Then write an algebraic expression that describes how many pieces you have when you make *c* cuts.

_______________ pieces

2. Fold a sheet of paper in half. Now fold it in half again. And again. And again, until you can't make another fold.

After each fold, count the number of rectangles into which the paper has been divided. Fill in the missing numbers in the table. Write an algebraic expression to name the number of rectangles you have after you have folded the paper *k* times.

_______________ rectangles

Folds	Rectangle
0	1
1	2
2	
3	
4	
5	
6	

3. Below are the first 4 designs in a pattern made with square blocks. Draw Design 5 in this pattern.

Design 1

Design 2

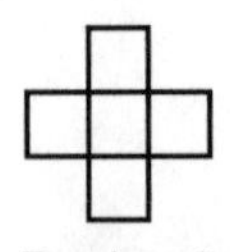
Design 3

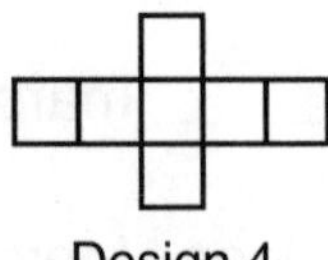
Design 4

Design 5

4. How many square blocks will there be in

a. Design 10? _______________

b. Design *n*? _______________

Name Date Time

LESSON 3•3

More Algebraic Expressions

Write each word phrase as an algebraic expression.

1. t increased by 5 ____________________

2. the product of w and 3 ____________________

3. 7 less than g ____________________

4. m halved ____________________

5. k shared equally by 8 people ____________________

6. 24 less than x tripled ____________________

7. b decreased by 12 ____________________

Evaluate each expression when $y = 9.05$.

8. $y + 4.98$ __________ 9. $y - 8.9$ __________ 10. $y * 10^2$ __________

Write an algebraic expression for each situation. Then solve the problem that follows.

11. Talia earns d dollars per week.

    How much does Talia earn in 10 weeks? ____________________ dollars

    If Talia earns $625.75 per week,
    how much does she earn in 10 weeks? ____________________ dollars

12. Michelle is 5 years younger than Ruby, who is r years old. Kyle is twice as old as Michelle.

    a. Using Ruby's age, r, write an expression for:

    Michelle's age ______________ years old

    Kyle's age ______________ years old

    b. Suppose Ruby is 12 years old. Find:

    Michelle's age ______________ years old

    Kyle's age ______________ years old

Name Date Time

"What's My Rule?" Part 1

1. a. State in words the rule for the "What's My Rule?" table at the right.

____

b. Which formula describes the rule? Fill in the circle next to the best answer.

Ⓐ $n = m - 0.22$ Ⓑ $m + n = 0.22$ Ⓒ $m = n - 0.22$

m	***n***
4.56	4.34
10	9.78
0.01	−0.21
$\frac{24}{100}$	0.02
7.80	7.58

2. a. State in words the rule for the "What's My Rule?" table at the right.

____

b. Which formula describes the rule? Fill in the circle next to the best answer.

Ⓐ $r - 0.25 = t$ Ⓑ $t + 0.12 = r$ Ⓒ $r * 0.5 = t$

r	***t***
20	10
15	7.5
1	0.5
1.5	0.75
3.4	1.7

3. Which formula describes the rule for the "What's My Rule?" table at the right? Fill in the circle next to the best answer.

Ⓐ $q - 13 = p$ Ⓑ $q = (2 * p) - 2$ Ⓒ $q = 2 * (p - 2)$

p	***q***
7	12
10	18
1	0
15	28
30	58

Practice

4. 180 in. = ____________ feet

5. $3\frac{1}{2}$ minutes = ____________ seconds

6. 5,280 ft = ____________ yards

7. $5\frac{1}{2}$ miles = ____________ feet

Name Date Time

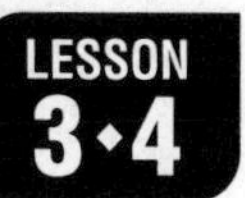

Special Cases for Formulas

A formula is an example of a general pattern. When you substitute values for the variables in a formula, you are writing a special case for the formula.

Area Formulas

Example:

To find the area of a rectangle, use the formula $A = b * h$.

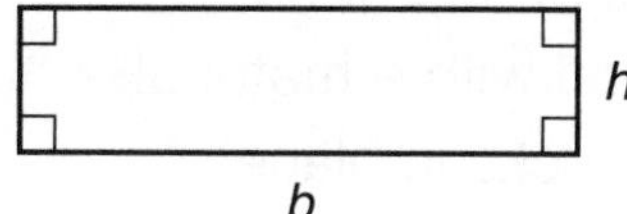

Write a special case for the formula using $b = 12$ cm and $h = 3$ cm.

First substitute only the value of b. $A =$ **12 cm** $* h$

Next substitute the value of h. $A = 12$ cm $*$ **3 cm**

Now find the value of A and write the special case.

36 cm² $= 12$ cm $* 3$ cm

1. To find the area of a triangle, use the formula $A = \frac{1}{2} * (b * h)$.

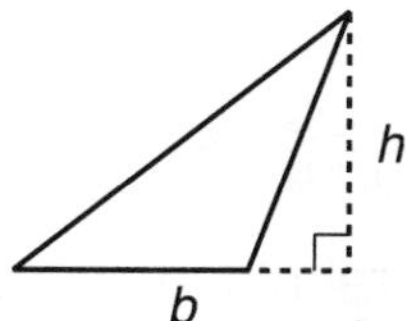

Find the value of A and write a special case for the formula using $b = 4.5$ cm and $h = 4.8$ cm.

________ $\text{cm}^2 = \frac{1}{2} *$ (________ cm $*$ ________ cm)

2. To find the area of a square, use the formula $A = s^2$.

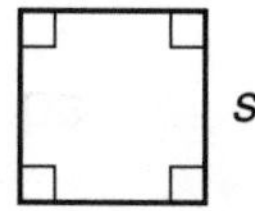

Find the value of A and write a special case for the formula using $b = 2.5$ ft and $h = 2.5$ ft.

________ $\text{ft}^2 =$ ________ ft^2

Name Date Time

LESSON 3•4

Formula for a Brick Wall

Suppose you were going to build a brick wall. It would be useful to estimate the number of bricks you would need. You could do this if you had a formula for estimating the number of bricks for any size wall.

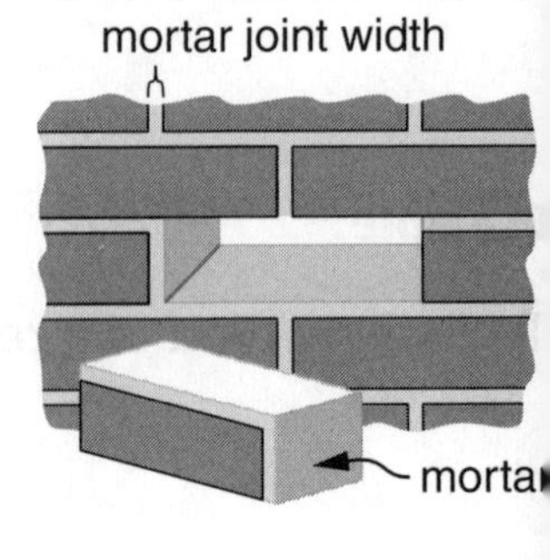

Study the following information. Then follow the instructions for measuring an actual brick wall. Try to devise a formula for estimating the number of bricks needed to build any size wall.

- A brick wall is built by putting layers of bricks on top of one another. The space between the bricks is filled with a material called *mortar,* which hardens and holds the bricks in place. The mortar between the bricks forms the *mortar joint.*
- A standard building brick is $2\frac{1}{4}$ inches by 8 inches by $3\frac{3}{4}$ inches. The face that is $2\frac{1}{4}$ inches by 8 inches is the part of the brick that is visible in a wall.

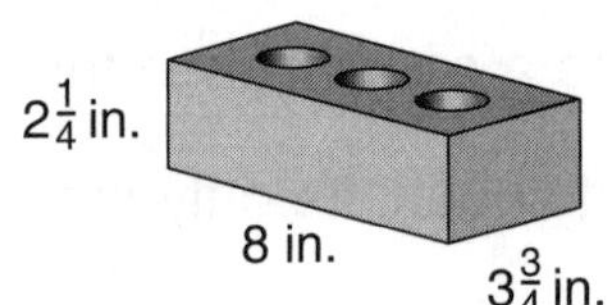

Equivalents: 1 ft = 12 in. 1 ft^2 = 12 in. $*$ 12 in. = 144 in.^{2}

1. Find a brick wall in your school, home, or neighborhood. Using a ruler or tape measure, measure the length and height of the wall or part of the wall. Count the bricks in the area you measured.

a. Length ______ (unit) **b.** Height ______ (unit) **c.** Number of bricks ______

d. Measure the width of the mortar joint in several places. Decide on a typical value for this measurement.

The mortar joints are each about ______ inch(es) wide.

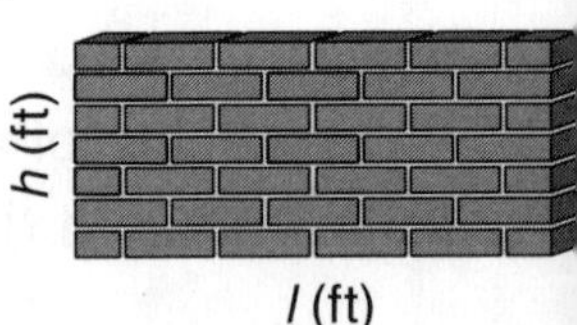

2. Devise a formula for calculating the number of bricks needed to build a wall. Let *l* stand for the length of the wall in feet. Let *h* stand for the height of the wall in feet. Let *N* stand for the estimated number of bricks needed to build the wall.

a. The area of this wall (the side you see) is ______ square feet.

b. My formula for the estimated number of bricks: $N =$ ______

3. Test your formula. Use the length and width you measured in Problem 1. Does the formula predict the number of bricks you counted?

______

Name Date Time

STUDY LINK 3•5

"What's My Rule?" Part 2

1. *Rule:* Subtract the *in* number from $11\frac{1}{2}$.

in	out
n	$11\frac{1}{2} - n$
1	
2	
$8\frac{1}{2}$	
	5
12	

2. *Formula:* $r = 4 * s$

in	out
s	r
12	
	24
0.3	
	1
$\frac{1}{2}$	

3. *Rule:* Triple the *in* number and add −6.

in	out
x	$(3x) + (-6)$
1	−3
2	
	15
8	
	−6

4. For the table below, write the rule in words and as a formula.

Rule: ____________________

Formula: ____________________

in	out
b	d
1.5	0.5
$6\frac{3}{4}$	$2\frac{1}{4}$
24	8
81	27
9.75	3.25

5. Make up your own.

Rule: ____________________

Formula: ____________________

in	out
x	y

Practice

6. $3 + -6 =$ ________

7. $-17 + 5 =$ ________

8. $8 + (-2) + (-9) =$ ________

9. $5 + 3 + (-5) + 7 =$ ________

Name Date Time

Rates

Solve the rate problems. You can use tables similar to "What's My Rule?" tables to help you find the answers, if needed.

1. Renee reads 30 pages per hour.

a. At this rate, how many pages can she read in 3 hours? ______ (unit)

b. Would she be able to read a 220-page book in 7 hours? ______

Hours	Pages
1	30
2	
3	

2. Wilson was paid $105 to cut 7 lawns. At this rate, how much was he paid per lawn? ______

Lawns	Dollars
7	105
6	
5	

3. Gabriel blinks 80 times in 5 minutes.

a. At this rate, how many times does he blink in 2 minutes? ______ (unit)

b. In 4 minutes? ______ (unit)

Minutes	Blinks
5	80
4	
3	

4. Michael can bake 9 batches of cookies in 3 hours.

At this rate, how many batches can he bake in 2 hours? ______ (unit)

Hours	Batches
3	9
2	
1	

5. Elizabeth can run 5 miles in $\frac{2}{3}$ of an hour.

At this rate, how long does it take her to run 1 mile?

______ (unit)

Hours	Miles
$\frac{2}{3}$	5
$\frac{1}{3}$	
1	

Name Date Time

LESSON 3·6

When an Object Is Dropped

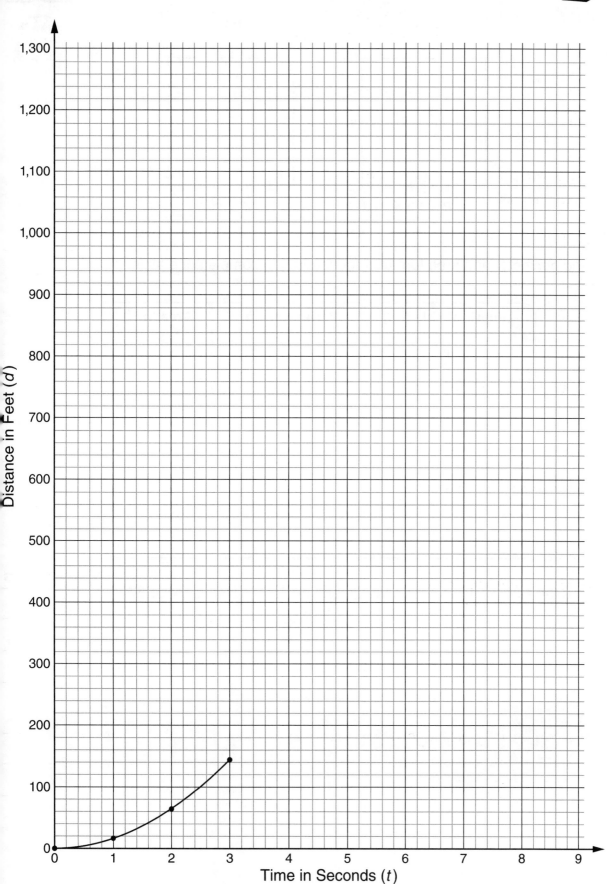

Distance in Feet (d)

1,300
1,200
1,100
1,000
900
800
700
600
500
400
300
200
100
0

0 1 2 3 4 5 6 7 8 9

Time in Seconds (t)

Name Date Time

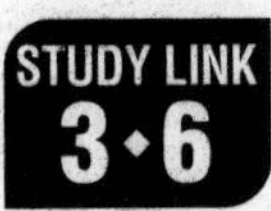

Area and Perimeter

SRB 212, 214, 215

Perimeter

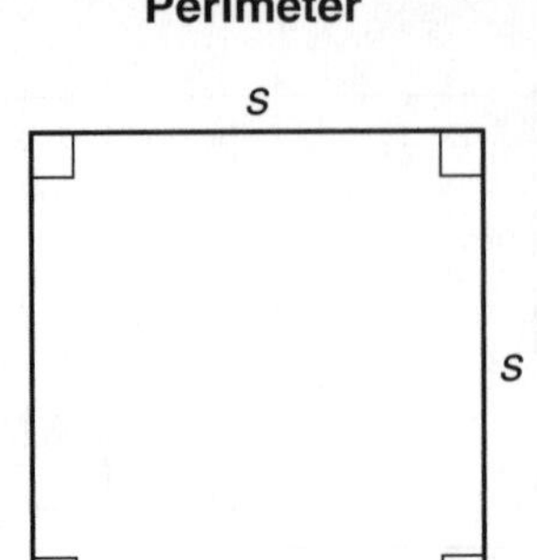

$P = 4 * s$

Area

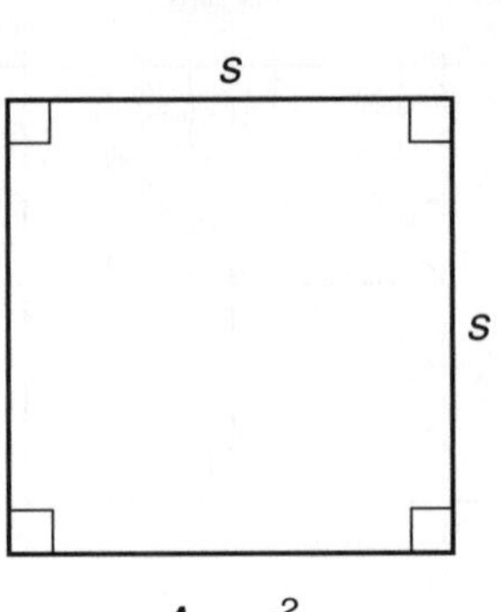

$A = s^2$

1. Use the perimeter and area formulas for squares to complete the table.

Length of side (in.)	Perimeter (in.)	Area (in.^{2})
1		
2		
3		
4		
5		

Use the table above to complete the graphs on *Math Masters,* page 87.

Name Date Time

Area and Perimeter *continued*

2. Graph the perimeter data from the table on page 86. Use the grid at the right.

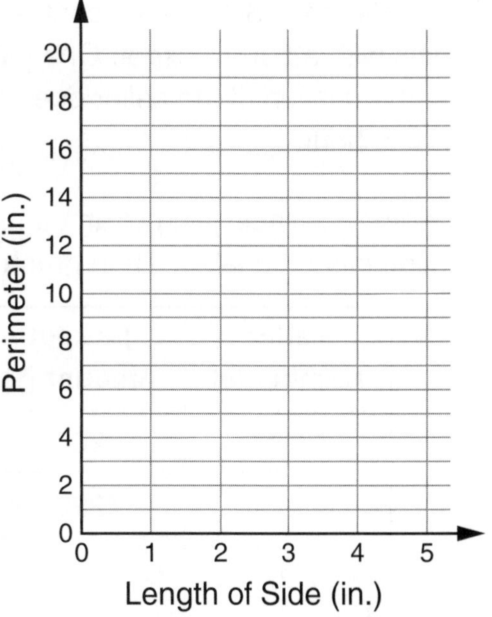

Use the graph you made in Problem 2 to answer the following questions.

3. If the length of the side of a square is $2\frac{1}{2}$ inches, what is the perimeter of the square?

____
(unit)

4. If the length of the side of a square is $4\frac{1}{4}$ inches, what is the perimeter of the square?

____
(unit)

5. Graph the area data from the table on page 86. Use the grid at the right.

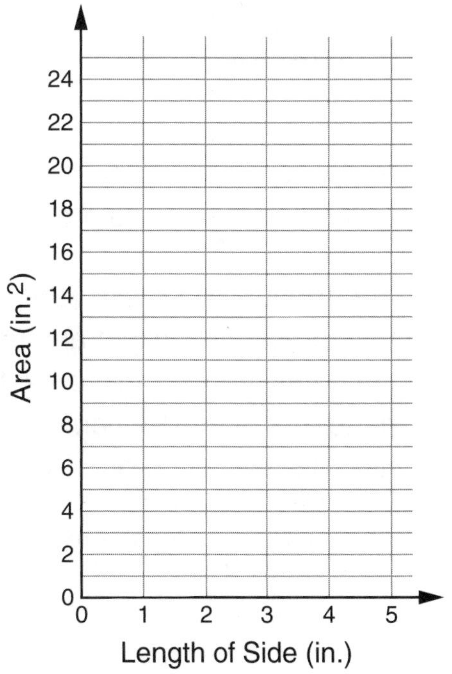

Use the graph you made in Problem 5 to answer the following questions.

6. If the length of the side of a square is $1\frac{1}{2}$ inches, what is the approximate area of the square?

About __________
(unit)

7. If the length of the side of a square is $3\frac{1}{4}$ inches, what is the approximate area of the square?

About __________
(unit)

Practice

Find the missing dimension for each rectangle.

8. $b = 5.5$ cm; $h = 9.9$ cm; $A =$ __________ cm^2

9. $b = 36$ in.; $h =$ __________ in.; $A = 151.2$ $in.^2$

Name Date Time

Using Graphs to Make Predictions

Radio station WSUM has a contest in which listeners call in to win money. The contest begins with a $200 jackpot. One caller each hour can win the jackpot by correctly answering a math question. If the caller does not give a correct answer, $25 is added to the jackpot for the next hour.

1. Some available jackpot amounts for callers appear in the table below. Complete the table. Then graph the data values from the table.

Caller Number (n)	Jackpot Amount ($)
1	200
2	225
3	
	275
5	

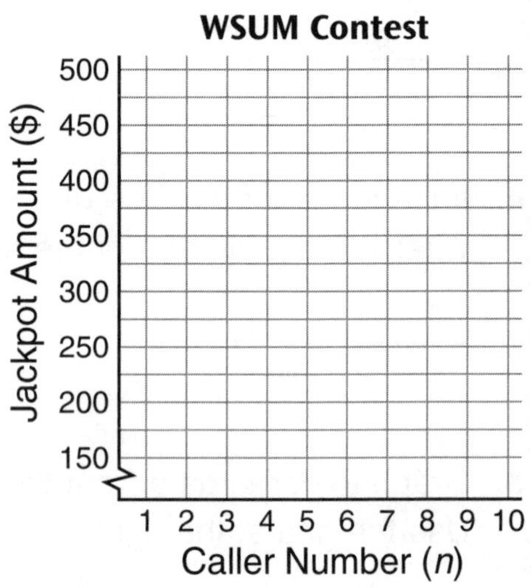

2. Suppose you were the eighth caller to WSUM and you answered correctly. Extend your graph to predict the amount of money you would win. ____________

3. The formula $(n - 1) * \$25 + \$200$ can be used to express the jackpot amount for any caller. Use this formula to complete the table below. Refer to page 247 of the *Student Reference Book* if you need to review the order of operations.

Rule: $(n - 1) * \$25 + \$200$

in	out
n	$(n - 1) * \$25 + \$200$
2	$225
4	
15	
	$825
101	

Try This

Predict the number of the caller who would win a jackpot of $1,000,000. Use the formula $(n - 1) * \$25 + \$200$ to check your prediction.

Name Date Time

STUDY LINK 3•7

Spreadsheet Practice

Ms. Villanova keeps a spreadsheet of her monthly expenses. Use her spreadsheet to answer the questions below.

	A	B	C	D	E
1		January	February	March	**Total**
2	Groceries	\$125.25	\$98.00	\$138.80	\$362.05
3	Phone Bill	\$34.90	\$58.50	\$25.35	
4	Car Expenses	\$25.00	\$115.95	\$12.00	
5	Rent	\$875.00	\$875.00	\$875.00	

1. What is shown in cell B1? ______________

2. What is shown in cell C4? ______________

3. Which cell contains the word *Rent?* ______________

4. Which cell contains the amount \$58.50? ______________

5. Ms. Villanova used column E to show the total for each row. Find the missing totals and enter them on the spreadsheet.

6. Write a formula for calculating E3 that uses cell names. ______________________

7. Write a formula for calculating E5 that uses cell names. ______________________

8. Ms. Villanova found that she made a mistake in recording her March phone bill. Instead of \$25.35, she should have entered \$35.35. After she corrects her spreadsheet, what will the new total be in cell E3?

____

Practice

Find the missing dimension for each square.

9. $s = 12$ cm; $A =$ __________ cm^2

10. $s =$ __________ in.; $A = 81$ $in.^2$

11. $s = 8.6$ mm; $A =$ __________ mm^2

12. $s =$ __________ ft; $A = 289$ ft^2

Name Date Time

STUDY LINK 3·8

Adding Positive and Negative Numbers

Solve.

1. $b + 9 = 3$; $b =$ ________

2. $-5 + a = -1$; $a =$ ________

3. $m + (-5) = -4$; $m =$ ________

4. $k + 3 = -3$; $k =$ ________

Add.

5. $13 + (-5) =$ ________

6. $(-10) + 12 =$ ________

7. ________ $= (-7) + (-8)$

8. ________ $= (-15) + 10$

9. $(-4) + (-9) =$ ________

10. ________ $= 7 + (-19)$

11. Complete the "What's My Rule?" table.

x	y
8	2
4	−2
2	−4
	−6
	−8
	−15

a. Give the rule for the table in words.

____

b. Circle the formula that describes the rule.

$x + 6 = y$ $x * (-6) = y$ $x + (-6) = y$ $\frac{x}{6} = y$

Practice

12. Evaluate when $k = 5$.

a. k^2 ________ **b.** 2^k ________ **c.** $10k$ ________ **d.** $-24 + k$ ________

13. Evaluate when $x = -1$.

a. 10^x ________ **b.** 2^x ________ **c.** $(\frac{1}{2})^x$ ________ **d.** $x + (-8)$ ________

Name Date Time

Spreadsheet Scramble Problems

Study the completed *Spreadsheet Scramble* game mat at the right.

Player 1 gets 1 point each for F3, F4, and C5.

Player 2 gets 1 point each for F2 and E5.

Player 1 wins the game, 3 points to 2 points.

Notice that if the numbers in cells C2 and B4 were interchanged and new totals were calculated, Player 2 would win the game, 4 points to 2 points.

	A	B	C	D	E	F
1						Total
2		−1	−6	3	−5	−9
3		4	2	−4	6	+8
4		−3	5	1	−2	+1
5	Total	0	+1	0	−1	

	A	B	C	D	E	F
1						Total
2		−1	−6	3	−5	−9
3		4	2	−4	6	+8
4		−3	5	1	−2	+1
5	Total	0	+1	0	−1	

→

	A	B	C	D	E	F
1						Total
2		−1	−3	3	−5	−6
3		4	2	−4	6	+8
4		−6	5	1	−2	−2
5	Total	−3	+4	0	−1	

Can you switch the values of two other cells so that Player 2 would win the game?

1. Which cells would you interchange?

____

2. What would be the new score of the game?

Player 1 __________ Player 2 __________

3. Fill in the new game mat.

	A	B	C	D	E	F
1						Total
2						
3						
4						
5	Total					

Name Date Time

A Time Story

Satya runs water into his bathtub. He steps into the tub, sits down, and bathes. He gets out of the tub and drains the water. The graph shows the height of the water in the tub at different times.

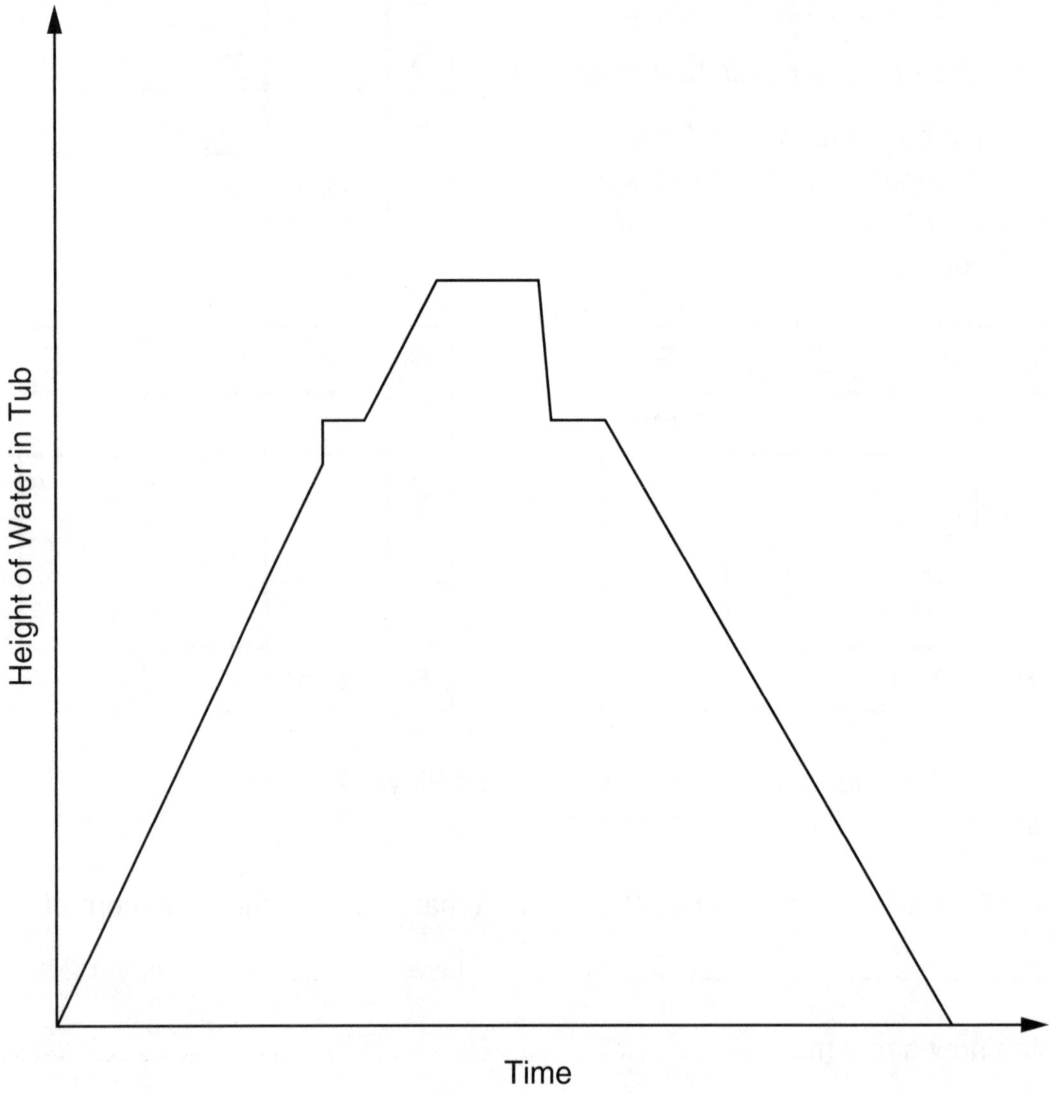

Height of Water in Tub

Time

Name Date Time

STUDY LINK 3•9

Ferris Wheel Time Graph

The time graph below shows the height of Rose's head from the ground as she rides a Ferris wheel. Use the graph to answer the following questions.

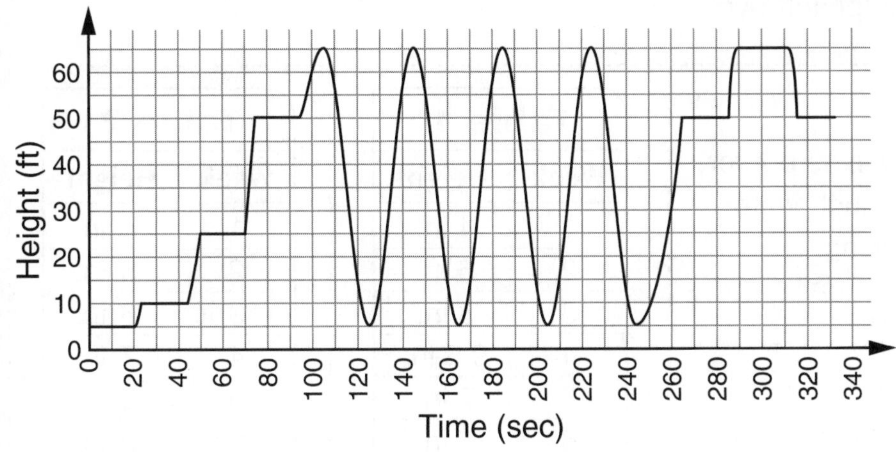

1. Explain what is happening from 0 to 95 seconds. ______________________

____

2. How long is Rose on the Ferris wheel before she is back to the position from which she started? About ______ (unit)

3. After the Ferris wheel has been completely loaded, about how long does the ride last before unloading begins? ______ (unit)

4. After the Ferris wheel has been loaded, how many times does the wheel go around before unloading begins? ______ (unit)

5. When the ride is in full swing, approximately how long does one complete revolution of the wheel take? ______ (unit)

Try This

6. Rose takes another ride. After 130 seconds, the Ferris wheel comes to a complete stop because of an electrical failure. It starts moving again 2 minutes later. Complete the graph to show this event.

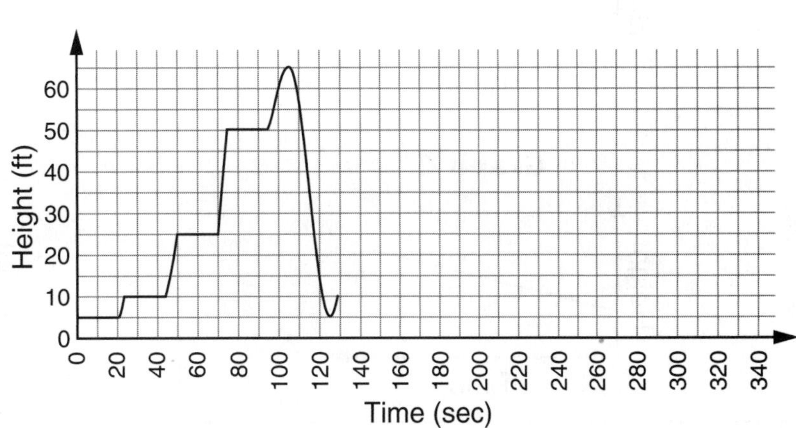

Name Date Time

LESSON 3•9

Matching Events, Tables, and Graphs

Cut out the situations, tables, and graphs. After you match each situation with one table and one graph, tape or glue them onto a separate sheet of paper. When you are finished, you will have one table and one graph left over.

A fern was growing rapidly in its pot for a while until it didn't get enough water. The fern then stopped growing.

A fern was growing slowly in its pot due to a lack of sunlight. When the fern was moved to a nearby windowsill, it began to grow more rapidly.

A fern was growing rapidly in its pot for a while until it was knocked over and a dog bit off the top. It stopped growing for a while before it eventually began to grow again.

Table 1

Week	Height
1	4 in.
2	6 in.
3	8 in.
4	9.5 in.
5	7 in.
6	7 in.
7	8 in.

Table 2

Week	Height
1	4 in.
2	5 in.
3	6 in.
4	7 in.
5	8 in.
6	9 in.
7	10 in.

Table 3

Week	Height
1	4 in.
2	4.5 in.
3	5 in.
4	5.5 in.
5	6 in.
6	8 in.
7	10 in.

Table 4

Week	Height
1	4 in.
2	6 in.
3	8 in.
4	10 in.
5	12 in.
6	12 in.
7	12 in.

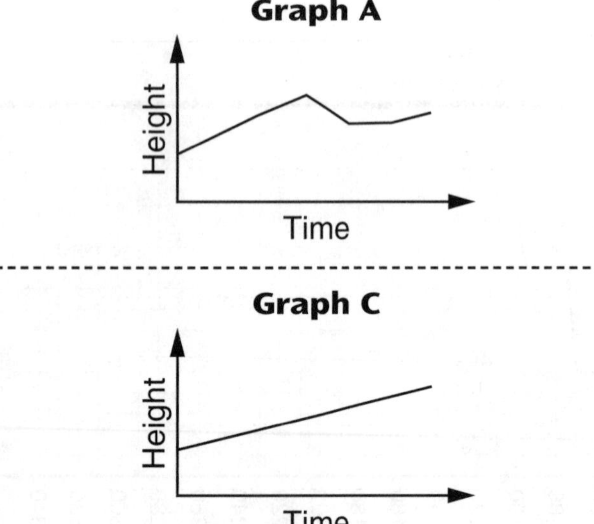

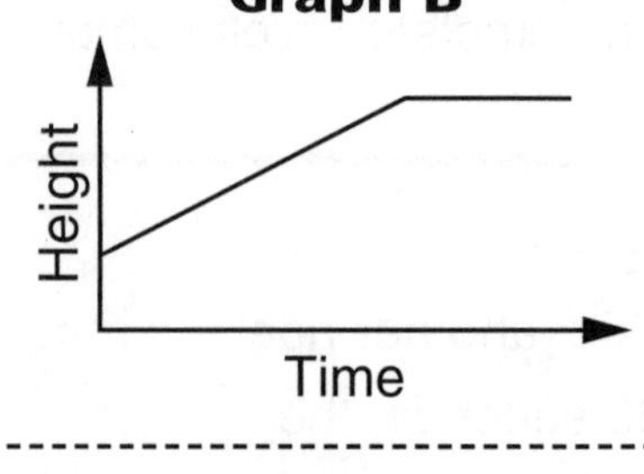

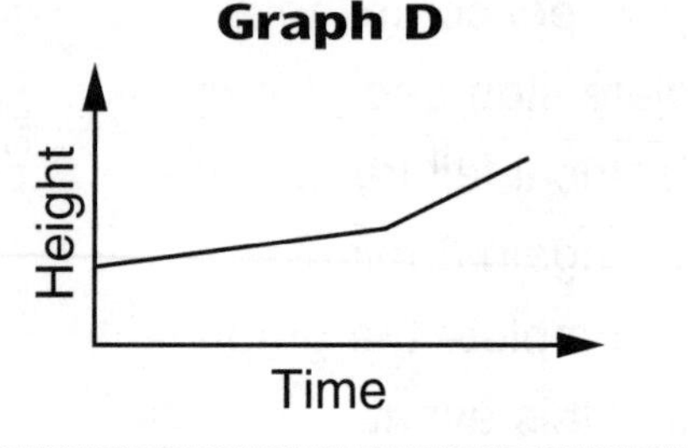

Name Date Time

Mystery Graphs

Make a mystery graph on the grid below. Be sure to label the horizontal and vertical axes. Describe the situation that corresponds to your graph on the lines provided.

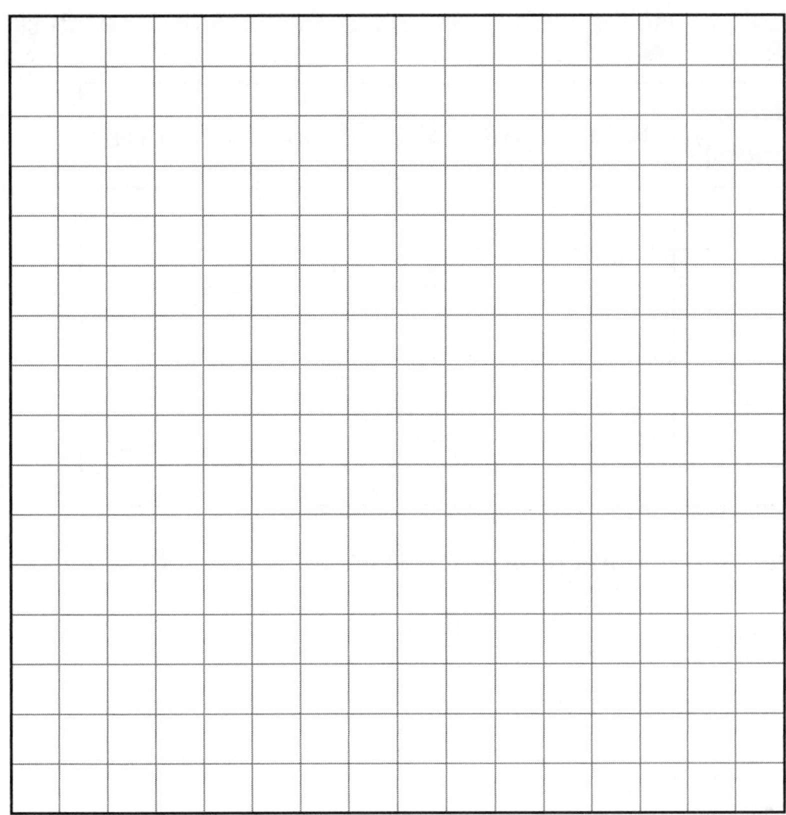

Name Date Time

Comparing Pet-Sitting Profits

Jenna and Thomas like to pet-sit for their neighbors. Jenna charges \$3 per hour. Thomas charges \$6.00 for the first hour and \$2 for each additional hour.

1. Complete the table below. Use the table to graph the profit values for each sitter.

Time (hours)	Jenna's Profit (\$)	Thomas's Profit (\$)
1		
2		
3		
4		
5		

2. Extend both line graphs to find the profit each sitter will make for 6 hours.

Jenna (6 hours) __________ Thomas (6 hours) __________

3. Which sitter, Jenna or Thomas, earns more money for jobs of 5 hours or more? ______________

4. Which line graph rises more quickly? ______________

5. Complete each statement. For every hour that passes, Jenna's profit increases by _________; Thomas's profit increases by _________.

6. At what point do the line graphs intersect?

____

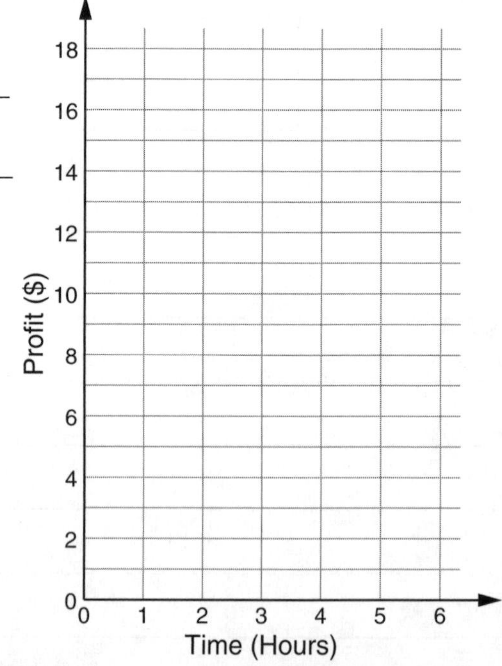

Practice

7. Evaluate when $m = 3$.

a. m^4 ______ **b.** 20^m ______ **c.** $4^m + 4m$ ______ **d.** $10^m - 5^m$ ______ **e.** $\frac{m^3}{m^2}$ ______

Name Date Time

Reviewing Rules, Tables, and Graphs

Rule: ______________________

____

____

in	out

(Label for *y*-axis) ______________________

0

0

(Label for *x*-axis) ______________________

Name Date Time

Rate of Change Experiment

Using a metric measuring cup, pour 100 mL of water into each of 4 bottles of different shapes. Each time you add water to a bottle, measure the height of the water level in centimeters. On a separate sheet of paper, make a table to record each change in volume and water height. Use your table to make a graph for each bottle on the grids below.

Bottle 1

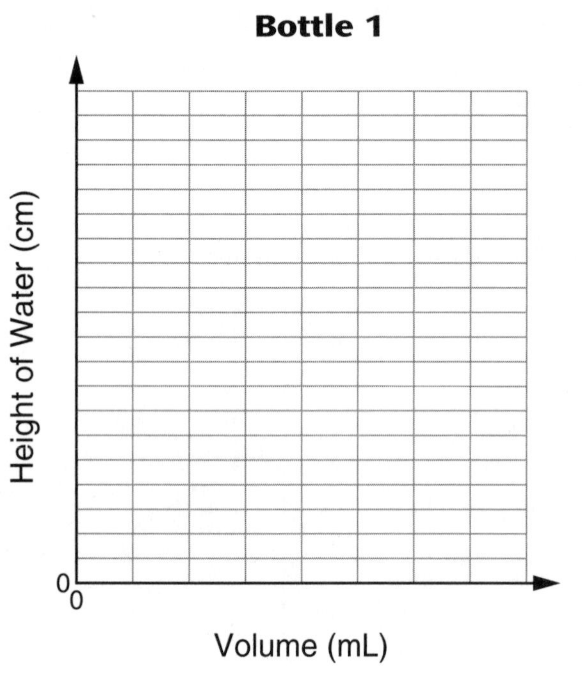

Bottle 2

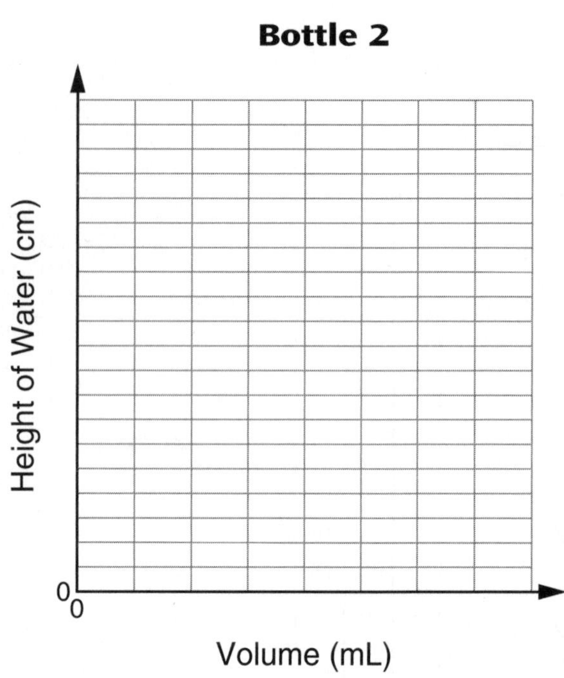

Bottle 3

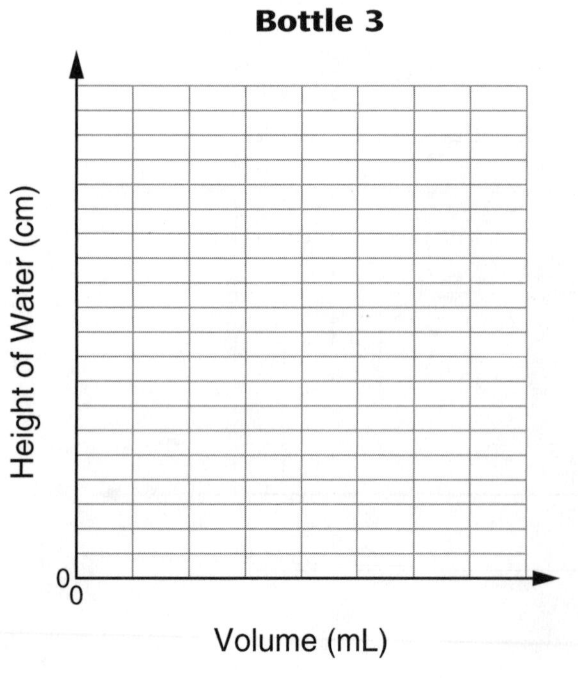

Bottle 4

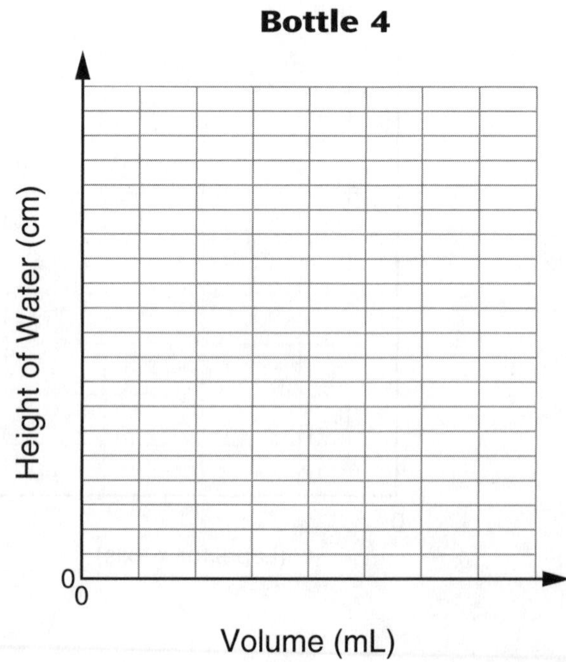

Name Date Time

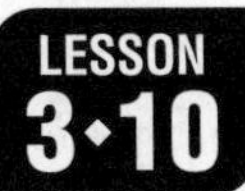

The Shape of Change

Assume the bottles are filled with water at a constant rate. Match the graphs with their bottles. Write the letter of the graph under the bottle it represents.

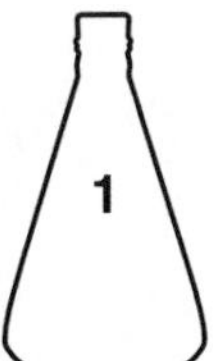

______

______

______

______

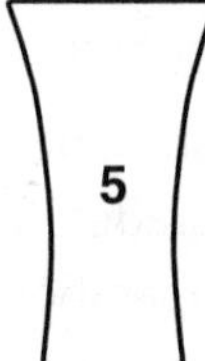

______

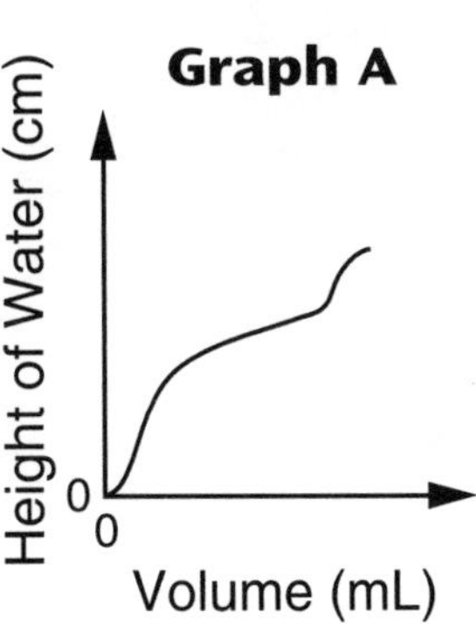

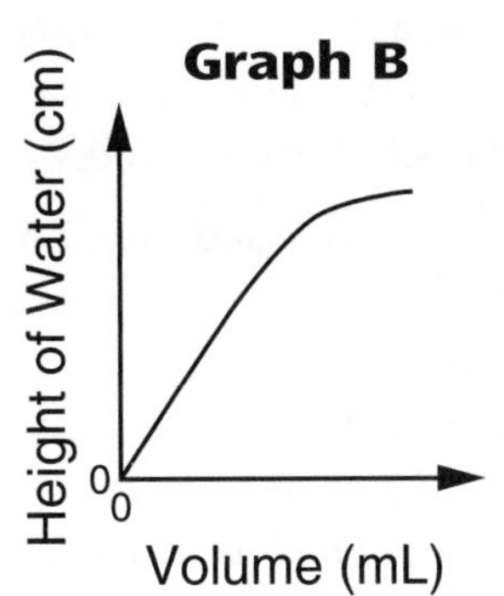

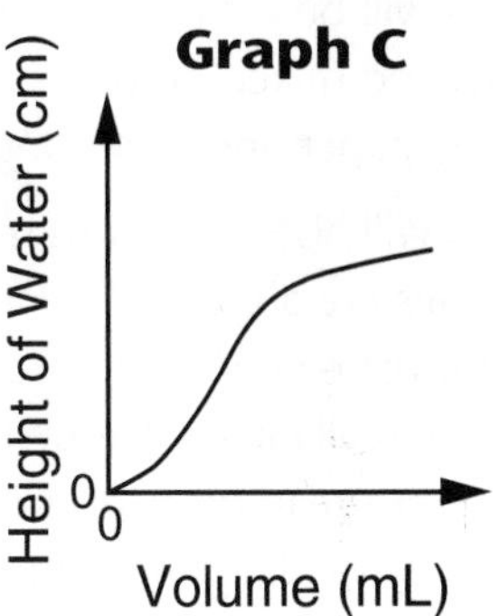

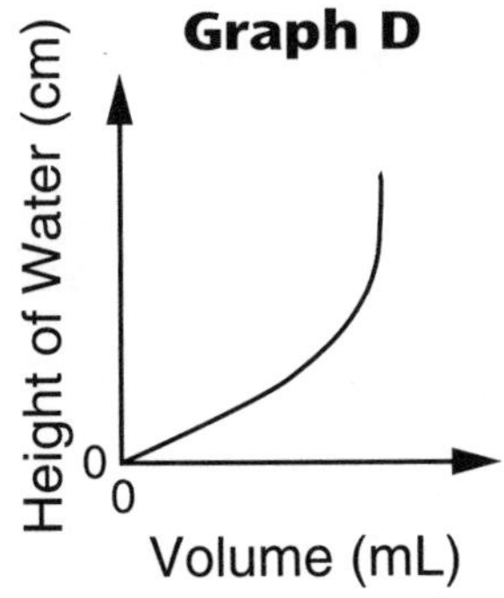

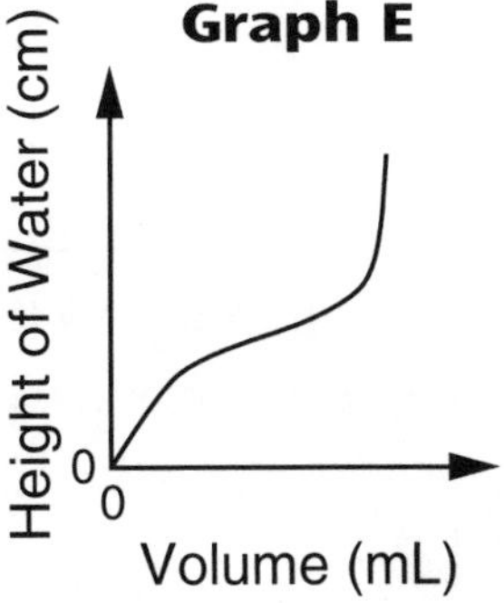

Name Date Time

Unit 4: Family Letter

Rational Number Uses and Operations

One reason for studying mathematics is that numbers in all their forms are an important part of our everyday lives. We use decimals when we are dealing with measures and money, and we use fractions and percents to describe parts of things.

Students using *Everyday Mathematics* began working with fractions in the primary grades. In *Fifth Grade Everyday Mathematics,* your child worked with equivalent fractions, operations with fractions, and conversions between fractions, decimals, and percents.

In Unit 4, your child will revisit these concepts and apply them. Most of the fractions with which your child will work (halves, thirds, fourths, sixths, eighths, tenths, and sixteenths) will be fractions that they would come across in everyday situations—interpreting scale drawings, following a recipe, measuring distance and area, expressing time in fractions of hours, and so on.

Students will be exploring methods for solving addition and subtraction problems with fractions and mixed numbers. They will look at estimation strategies, mental computation methods, paper-and-pencil algorithms, and calculator procedures.

Students will also work with multiplication of fractions and mixed numbers. Generally, verbal cues are a poor guide as to which operation (+, −, ∗, /) to use when solving a problem. For example, *more* does not necessarily imply addition. However, *many of* and *part of* generally involve multiplication. At this point in the curriculum, your child will benefit from reading and understanding $\frac{1}{2} * 12$ as *one-half of 12,* rather than *one-half times 12;* or reading and understanding $\frac{1}{2} * \frac{1}{2}$ as *one-half of one-half,* rather than *one-half times one-half.*

Finally, students will use percents to make circle graphs to display the results of surveys and to learn about sales and discounts.

Jambalaya Recipe

4 ounces each of chicken and sausage

4 cups peppers

$\frac{3}{4}$ cup rice

$1\frac{2}{3}$ cups chopped onions

$1\frac{1}{2}$ tablespoons chopped thyme

$\frac{1}{8}$ teaspoon salt

Please keep this Family Letter for reference as your child works through Unit 4.

Math Tools

The **Percent Circle,** on the Geometry Template, is used to find the percent represented by each part of a circle graph and to make circle graphs. The Percent Circle is similar to a full-circle protractor with the circumference marked in percents rather than degrees. This tool allows students to interpret and make circle graphs before they are ready for the complex calculations needed to make circle graphs with a protractor.

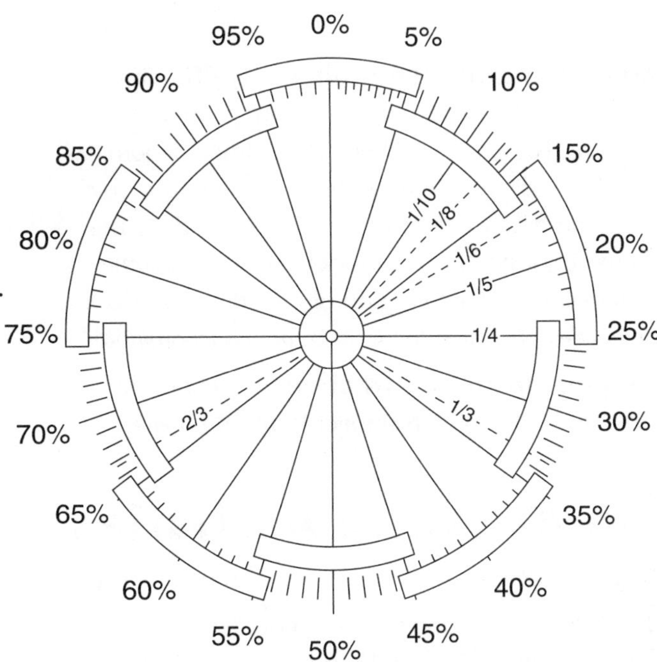

Vocabulary

Important terms in Unit 4:

common denominator A nonzero number that is a multiple of the denominators of two or more fractions. For example, the fractions $\frac{1}{2}$ and $\frac{2}{3}$ have common denominators 6, 12, 18, and other multiples of 6. Fractions with the same denominator already have a common denominator.

common factor A factor of two or more counting numbers. For example, 4 is a common factor of 8 and 12.

discount The amount by which a price of an item is reduced in a sale, usually given as a fraction or percent of the original price, or a percent off. For example, a $4 item on sale for $2 is discounted by 50%, or $\frac{1}{2}$. A $10.00 item at "10% off!" costs $9.00, or $\frac{1}{10}$ less than the usual price.

equivalent fractions Fractions with different denominators that name the same number.

greatest common factor (GCF) The largest factor that two or more counting numbers have in common. For example, the common factors of 24 and 36 are 1, 2, 3, 4, 6, and 12, and their greatest common factor is 12.

improper fraction A fraction whose numerator is greater than or equal to its denominator. For example, $\frac{4}{3}$, $\frac{5}{2}$, $\frac{4}{4}$, and $\frac{24}{12}$ are improper fractions. In *Everyday Mathematics,* improper fractions are sometimes called top-heavy fractions.

interest A charge for the use of someone else's money. Interest is usually a percentage of the amount borrowed.

least common denominator (LCD) The least common multiple of the denominators of every fraction in a given collection. For example, the least common denominator of $\frac{1}{2}$, $\frac{4}{5}$, and $\frac{3}{8}$ is 40.

least common multiple (LCM) The smallest number that is a multiple of two or more given numbers. For example, common multiples of 6 and 8 include 24, 48, and 72. The least common multiple of 6 and 8 is 24.

mixed number A number that is written using both a whole number and a fraction. For example, $2\frac{1}{4}$ is a mixed number equal to $2 + \frac{1}{4}$.

percent (%) Per hundred, for each hundred, or out of a hundred. $1\% = \frac{1}{100} = 0.01$. For example, *48% of the students in the school are boys* means that out of every 100 students in the school, 48 are boys.

proper fraction A fraction in which the numerator is less than the denominator. A proper fraction is between -1 and 1. For example, $\frac{3}{4}$, $-\frac{2}{5}$, and $\frac{21}{24}$ are proper fractions. Compare to *improper fraction. Everyday Mathematics* does not emphasize these distinctions.

quick common denominator (QCD) The product of the denominators of two or more fractions. For example, the quick common denominator of $\frac{3}{4}$ and $\frac{5}{6}$ is 4 ∗ 6, or 24. In general, the quick common denominator of $\frac{a}{b}$ and $\frac{c}{d}$ is $b * d$. As the name suggests, this is a quick way to get a *common denominator* for a collection of fractions, but it does not necessarily give the *least common denominator.*

simplest form of a fraction A fraction that cannot be renamed in simpler form. Also called "lowest terms." A mixed number is in simplest form if its fractional part is in simplest form. Simplest form is not emphasized in *Everyday Mathematics* because other equivalent forms are often equally or more useful. For example, when comparing or adding fractions, fractions with a common denominator are likely to be easier to work with than fractions in simplest form.

Do-Anytime Activities

Try these ideas to help your child with the concepts taught in this unit.

1. Consider allowing your sixth grader to accompany you on shopping trips when you know there is a sale. Have him or her bring a calculator to figure out the sale price of items. Ask your child to show you the sale price of the item and the amount of the discount. If your child enjoys this activity, you might extend it by letting him or her calculate the total cost of an item after tax has been added to the subtotal. One way to calculate the total cost is simply to multiply the subtotal by 1.08 (for 8% sales tax). For example, the total cost of a $25 item on which 8% sales tax is levied would be $25 * 1.08 = 25 * (1 + 0.08) = (25 * 1) + (25 * 0.08) = 25 + 2 = 27$, or $27.
2. On grocery shopping trips, point out to your child the decimals printed on the item labels on the shelves. These often show unit prices (price per 1 ounce, price per 1 gram, price per 1 pound, and so on), reported to three or four decimal places. Have your child round the numbers to the nearest hundredth (nearest cent).
3. Your child's teacher may display a Fractions, Decimals, Percents Museum in the classroom and expect students to contribute to this exhibit. Help your child look for examples of the ways in which printed advertisements, brochures, and newspaper and magazine articles use fractions, decimals, and percents.

Building Skills through Games

In Unit 4, your child will work on his or her understanding of rational numbers by playing games like the ones described below.

Fraction Action, Fraction Friction See *Student Reference Book,* page 317
Two or three players gather fraction cards that have a sum as close as possible to 2, without going over. Students can make a set of 16 cards by copying fractions onto index cards.

Frac-Tac-Toe See *Student Reference Book,* pages 314–316
Two players need a deck of number cards with 4 each of the numbers 0–10; a game board, a 5-by-5 grid that resembles a bingo card; a *Frac-Tac-Toe* Number-Card board; markers or counters in two different colors, and a calculator. The different versions of *Frac-Tac-Toe* help students practice conversions between fractions, decimals, and percents.

As You Help Your Child with Homework

As your child brings assignments home, you may want to go over the instructions together, clarifying them as necessary. The answers listed below will guide you through some of this unit's Study Links.

Study Link 4•1

Sample answers for problems 1–16.

1. $\frac{8}{10}$ **2.** $\frac{14}{20}$ **3.** $\frac{2}{8}$ **4.** $\frac{4}{6}$

5. $\frac{10}{8}$ **6.** $\frac{4}{4}$ **7.** $\frac{3}{4}$ **8.** $\frac{1}{5}$

9. $\frac{1}{4}$ **10.** $\frac{5}{2}$ **11.** $\frac{1}{5}$ **12.** $\frac{2}{3}$

13. $\frac{2}{6}, \frac{3}{9}, \frac{4}{12}$ **14.** $\frac{3}{4}, \frac{15}{20}, \frac{150}{200}$ **15.** $\frac{6}{1}, \frac{12}{2}, \frac{18}{3}$

16. $\frac{24}{10}, \frac{36}{15}, \frac{48}{20}$ **17.** $\frac{1}{2}$ **18.** $\frac{2}{3}$

19. $\frac{1}{5}$ **20.** $\frac{2}{5}$ **21.** $\frac{3}{8}$ **22.** $\frac{2}{7}$

23. $x = 3$ **24.** $y = 12$ **25.** $m = 30$

26. $27\frac{1}{4}$ **27.** $29\frac{1}{5}$ **28.** $29\frac{2}{7}$

Study Link 4•2

1. $>$ **2.** $>$ **3.** $<$ **4.** $<$

5. $>$ **6.** $<$ **7.** $\frac{1}{3}, \frac{2}{5}, \frac{12}{25}$

8. $\frac{1}{12}, \frac{1}{5}, \frac{1}{3}, \frac{2}{5}, \frac{7}{14}, \frac{6}{10}, \frac{15}{16}, \frac{49}{50}$

9. 9.897 **10.** 3.832 **11.** 0.823 **12.** 4.357

Study Link 4•3

1. $\frac{1}{2}$ **2.** $1\frac{1}{16}$ **3.** $2\frac{13}{20}$ **4.** $\frac{2}{3}$

5. $\frac{11}{12}$ **6.** $1\frac{1}{6}$ **7.** $1\frac{8}{45}$ **8.** 2

9. $\frac{3}{8}$ **10.** $1\frac{4}{15}$ **11.** $\frac{1}{3}$ **12.** $\frac{1}{2}$

13. $1\frac{3}{4}$ **14.** $\frac{1}{10}$ **15.** 2.7 **16.** 0.58

17. 1.98

Study Link 4•4

1. a. Sample answer: They may have added only the numerators.

b. Sample answer: Both fractions are close to 1, so their sum should be close to 2.

2. $1\frac{1}{4}$ inches

3. Sample answer: He can use three $\frac{1}{2}$-cup measures and one $\frac{1}{4}$-cup measure.

4. $4\frac{1}{2}$ **5.** $1\frac{3}{4}$ **6.** $2\frac{1}{3}$

7. $1\frac{7}{4}, \frac{11}{4}$ **8.** 90 **9.** 246 **10.** 432

11. 315

Study Link 4•5

1. a. $8\frac{1}{2}$ in. **b.** $1\frac{1}{2}$ in.; $\frac{1}{4}$ in.

2. a. $2\frac{1}{2}$ bushels **b.** 30 quarts

3. 4 **4.** $\frac{2}{3}$ **5.** $5\frac{1}{6}$ **6.** $\frac{5}{9}$

7. $1\frac{5}{8}$ **8.** 6 **9.** $6\frac{3}{5}$ **10.** $1\frac{5}{12}$

11. $2\frac{11}{20}$ **12.** 14 **13.** 17.9 **14.** $21.99

15. 20

Study Link 4•6

1. $\frac{6}{20}$ **2.** $\frac{15}{63}$ **3.** $\frac{15}{8}$ or $1\frac{7}{8}$ **4.** $\frac{11}{48}$

5. $\frac{35}{48}$ **6.** $\frac{21}{100}$ **7.** $\frac{14}{45}$

8. $\frac{32}{7}$ or $4\frac{4}{7}$ **9.** $\frac{96}{11}$, or $8\frac{8}{11}$ **10.** $\frac{1}{5}$ of the points

11. $2\frac{1}{4}$ cups **12.** $\frac{7}{12}$ of the sixth graders

13. a. $\frac{1}{2}$ the girls **b.** 6 girls

14. 9 **15.** 0.1 **16.** 0.1

Unit 4: Family Letter *cont.*

Study Link 4•7

1. $\frac{9}{5}$ 2. $\frac{18}{6}$ 3. $\frac{17}{3}$ 4. $\frac{7}{2}$

5. 3 6. $4\frac{1}{8}$ 7. $2\frac{1}{2}$ 8. $6\frac{2}{3}$

9. 3 10. $4\frac{1}{5}$ 11. $2\frac{1}{12}$ 12. $5\frac{4}{9}$

13. $7\frac{31}{32}$ 14. 20 15. 28 16. 63

17. 63

Study Link 4•8

1. $\frac{8}{10}$, 80% 2. $\frac{75}{100}$, 75% 3. $\frac{30}{100}$, $\frac{3}{10}$

4. 0.5 5. 0.75 6. 0.25 7. 1.8

8. $\frac{2}{5}$ 9. $\frac{1}{10}$ 10. $\frac{17}{25}$ 11. $\frac{1}{4}$

12. 50% 13. 25% 14. 60% 15. 95%

16. $\frac{50}{100}$, $\frac{1}{2}$ 17. $\frac{40}{100}$, $\frac{2}{5}$ 18. $\frac{100}{100}$, 1 19. $\frac{180}{100}$, $1\frac{4}{5}$

Study Link 4•9

1. 65% 2. 33.4% 3. 2% 4. 40%

5. 270% 6. 309% 7. 0.27 8. 0.539

9. 0.08 10. 0.60 11. 1.80 12. 1.15

13. 0.88, 88% 14. 0.42, 42%

Study Link 4•10

Problems 1–4 are circle graphs.

Study Link 4•11

1. Table entries: 150, 100, 125, 125 students
2. Table entries: 18, 12, 15, 15 students
3. **a.** 3.3 **b.** 8.8 **c.** 22

Name Date Time

Equivalent Fractions

Find an equivalent fraction by multiplying.

1. $\frac{4}{5}$ ______

2. $\frac{7}{10}$ ______

3. $\frac{1}{4}$ ______

4. $\frac{2}{3}$ ______

5. $\frac{5}{4}$ ______

6. $\frac{2}{2}$ ______

Find an equivalent fraction by dividing.

7. $\frac{9}{12}$ ______

8. $\frac{20}{100}$ ______

9. $\frac{4}{16}$ ______

10. $\frac{30}{12}$ ______

11. $\frac{10}{50}$ ______

12. $\frac{16}{24}$ ______

Write 3 equivalent fractions for each number.

13. $\frac{1}{3}$ ______________

14. $\frac{75}{100}$ ______________

15. 6 ______________

16. $\frac{12}{5}$ ______________

Write each fraction in simplest form.

17. $\frac{8}{16}$ ______

18. $\frac{6}{9}$ ______

19. $\frac{3}{15}$ ______

20. $\frac{10}{25}$ ______

21. $\frac{6}{16}$ ______

22. $\frac{14}{49}$ ______

Find the missing numbers.

23. $\frac{1}{5} = \frac{x}{15}$

$x =$ ______

24. $\frac{2}{3} = \frac{y}{18}$

$y =$ ______

25. $\frac{15}{25} = \frac{m}{50}$

$m =$ ______

Practice

Divide. Express the remainder as a fraction in simplest form.

26. $24\overline{)654}$

27. $25\overline{)730}$

28. $14\overline{)410}$

Name Date Time

Factor Rainbows

When listing the factors of a number, you need to be certain that you have included all the factors in your list. Creating a **factor rainbow** is one way to do this. A factor rainbow is an organized list of factor pairs.

Example: factor rainbow for 24

Every number is divisible by 1. Because 1 ∗ 24 = 24, use an arc to show that 1 and 24 are paired.

1 24

Now try dividing by 2. Because 2 ∗ 12 = 24, use an arc to pair 2 and 12.

1 2 12 24

Continue your divisibility tests by moving to 3, which is the next factor greater than 2. 24 is divisible by 3, so 3 ∗ 8 = 24. Pair 3 and 8.

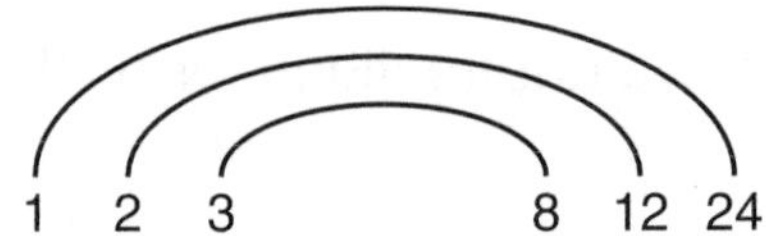

From the arcs you have drawn, you can see that all remaining factors must be between 3 and 8. Try dividing 24 by 4. Because 4 ∗ 6 = 24, use an arc to pair 4 and 6.

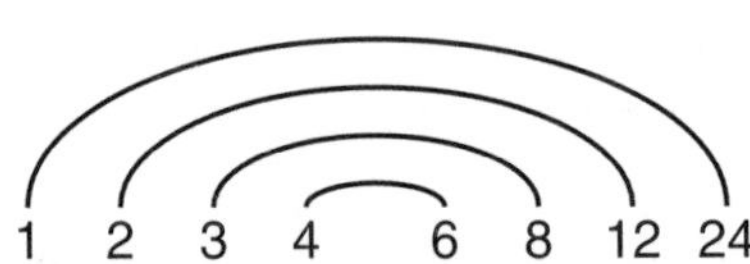

Any remaining factors must be between 4 and 6. The only whole number between 4 and 6 is 5. Notice that 5 does not divide into 24 evenly, so your rainbow is complete.

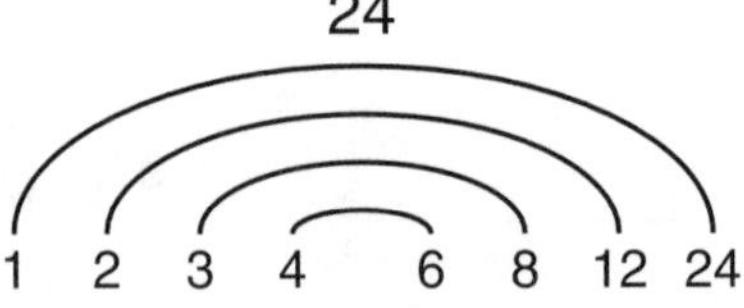

Use the example above when completing the factor rainbow for 36. Because 36 is a square number, one of the factors (6) is paired with itself.

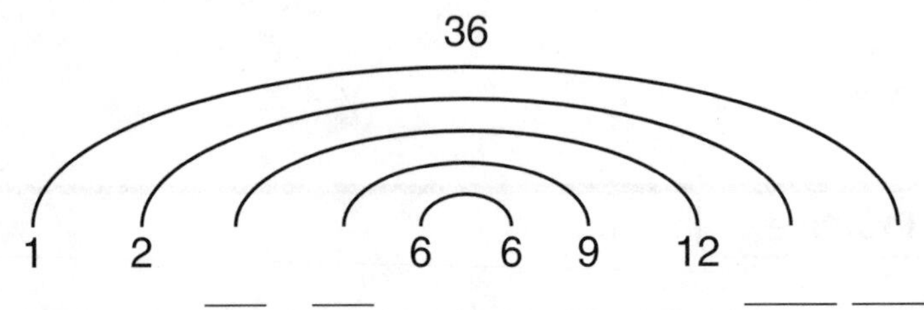

Name Date Time

Factor Rainbows *continued*

Use the examples on page 106 to help you complete the factor rainbow for each number.

1. factor rainbow for 18

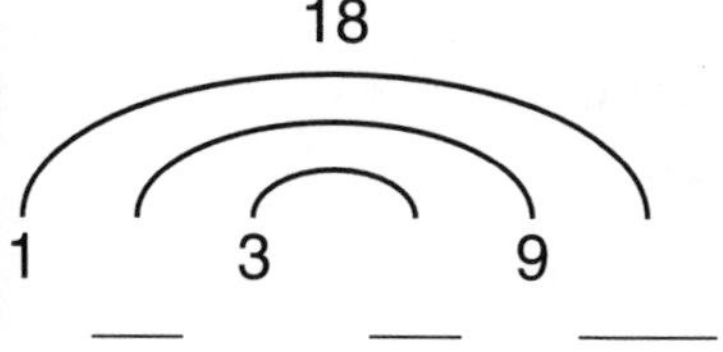

2. factor rainbow for 48

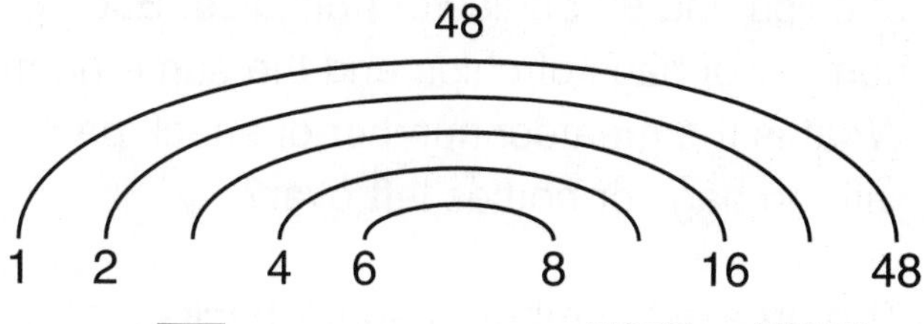

3. factor rainbow for 12

4. factor rainbow for 32

5. factor rainbow for 40

6. factor rainbow for 64

Name Date Time

Applications of the GCF

Some real-world problems involve finding the greatest common factor (GCF) of a set of numbers.

Solve.

1. Tyrone is preparing snack packs for the class field trip. He has 60 bags of chips and 90 bottles of fruit juice. Each pack should have the same number of bags of chips and the same number of bottles of fruit juice. What is the greatest number of snack packs that Tyrone can make with no bags or bottles left over?

   The greatest number of snack packs that he can make is ______.

   Each snack pack will have ______ bags of chips and

   ______ bottles of fruit juice.

2. Carla has 30 blue beads, 60 red beads, and 72 white beads. What is the maximum number of friends to whom Carla can give the same number of beads and have no beads left over?

   The maximum number of friends to get beads is ______.

   Each friend will get ______ blue beads, ______ red beads,

   and ______ white beads.

3. Ms. Mendis wants to split her class into groups for a bridge-building contest. There are 32 students in her class. She has 16 bottles of wood glue, 1,200 craft sticks, and 24 jars of paint. What is the greatest number of groups that Ms. Mendis can make so each group gets the same number of supplies and no supplies are left over?

   The greatest number of groups that she can make is ______.

   Each group will get ______ bottles of wood glue, ______ craft sticks,

   and ______ jars of paint.

Name Date Time

STUDY LINK 4•2

Comparing and Ordering Fractions

Write <, >, or = to make a true number sentence. For each problem that you did not solve mentally, show how you got the answer.

1. $\frac{4}{5}$ ______ $\frac{2}{5}$

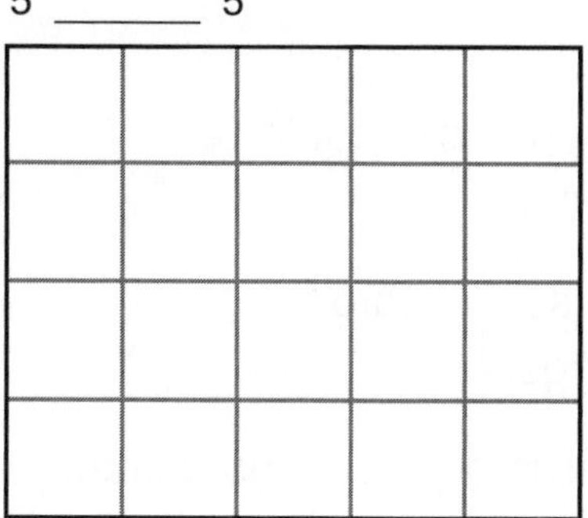

2. $\frac{3}{8}$ ______ $\frac{1}{3}$

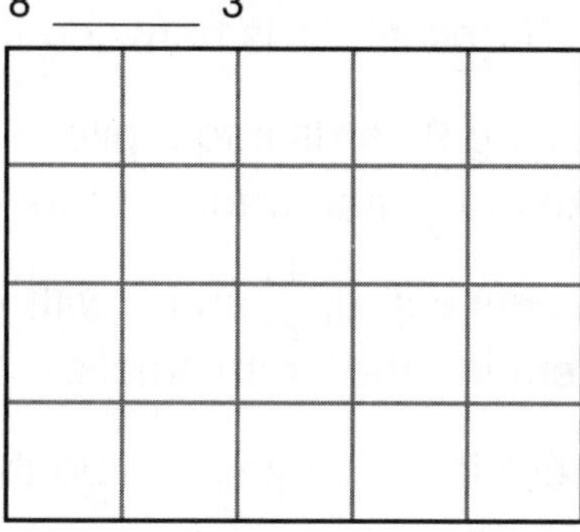

3. $\frac{3}{4}$ ______ $\frac{17}{20}$

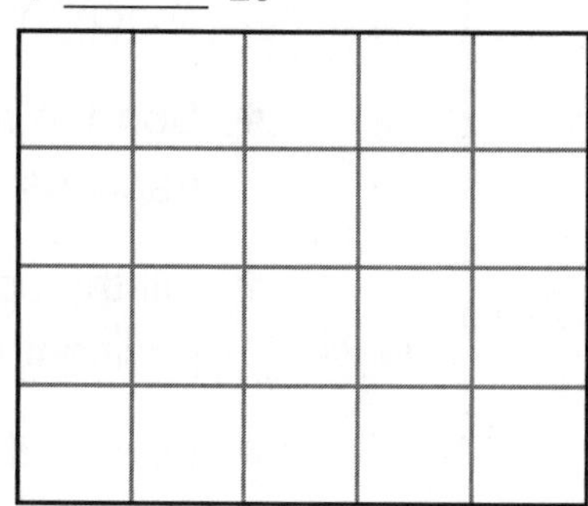

4. $\frac{19}{20}$ ______ $\frac{99}{100}$

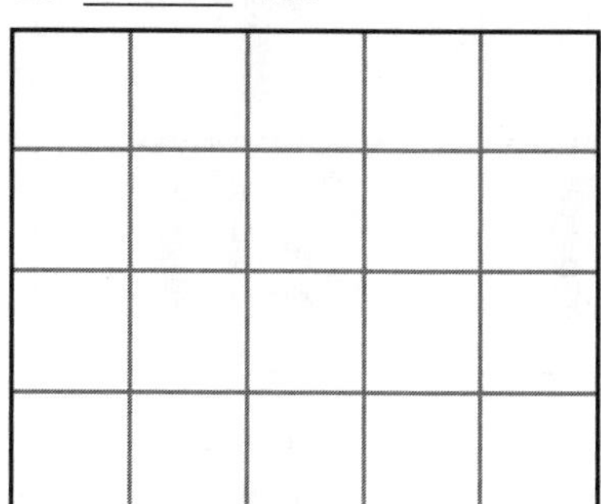

5. $\frac{4}{7}$ ______ $\frac{4}{10}$

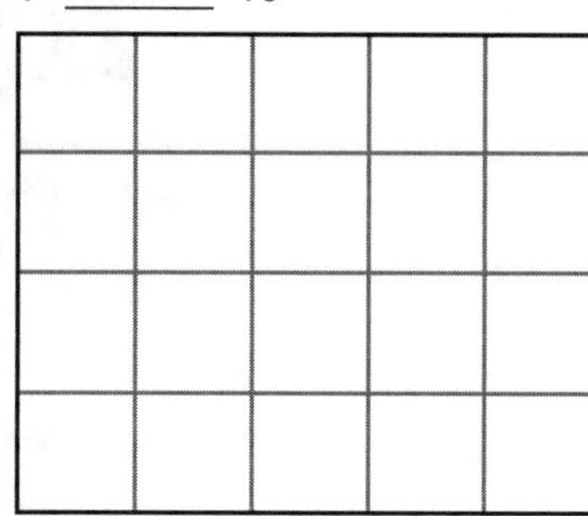

6. $\frac{2}{3}$ ______ $\frac{7}{9}$

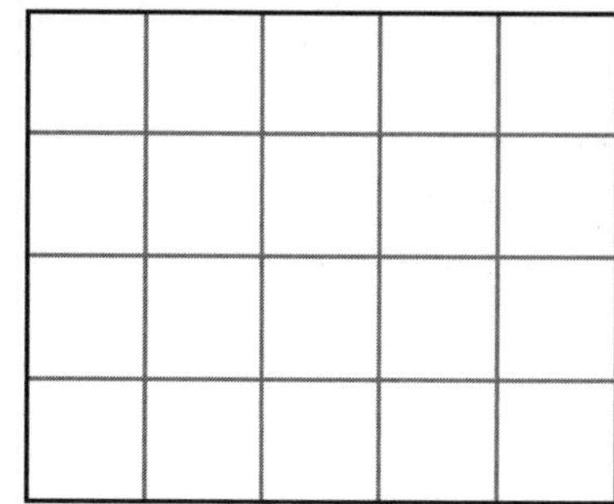

7. Circle each fraction that is less than $\frac{1}{2}$. $\frac{3}{6}$ $\frac{6}{10}$ $\frac{1}{3}$ $\frac{2}{5}$ $\frac{6}{11}$ $\frac{12}{25}$

8. Write the fractions in order from smallest to largest.

$\frac{1}{3}$ $\frac{15}{16}$ $\frac{7}{14}$ $\frac{1}{5}$ $\frac{2}{5}$ $\frac{49}{50}$ $\frac{6}{10}$ $\frac{1}{12}$

______ ______ ______ ______ ______ ______ ______ ______

Practice

9. 13.987 − 4.09 = __________

10. 5.9 − 2.068 = __________

11. 0.9 − 0.077 = __________

12. 8 − 3.643 = __________

Name Date Time

Benchmark Fractions

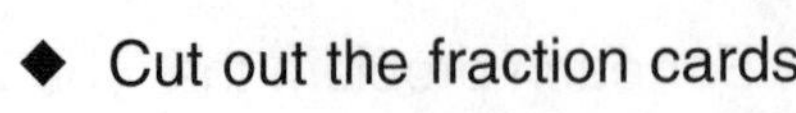

- Cut out the fraction cards.
- Remove the benchmark cards 0, $\frac{1}{2}$, and 1. Arrange these benchmark cards in order from left to right, leaving enough space to place fraction cards between them.
- Sort the remaining 9 cards into 3 piles—fractions closest to 0, fractions closest to $\frac{1}{2}$, and fractions closest to 1.
- Fill the space between 0, $\frac{1}{2}$, and 1 with your sorted cards, positioning them in order from smallest to largest.
- Record the order in which you placed the cards on the number line.

Number line: 1, $\frac{1}{2}$, 0

$\frac{1}{2}$	$\frac{48}{100}$	$\frac{1}{20}$
$\frac{1}{5}$	$\frac{3}{4}$	$\frac{6}{10}$
$\frac{1}{4}$	$\frac{1}{3}$	$\frac{9}{10}$
0	$\frac{2}{3}$	1

Name Date Time

LESSON 4•3

Fractions of a Square

Math Message

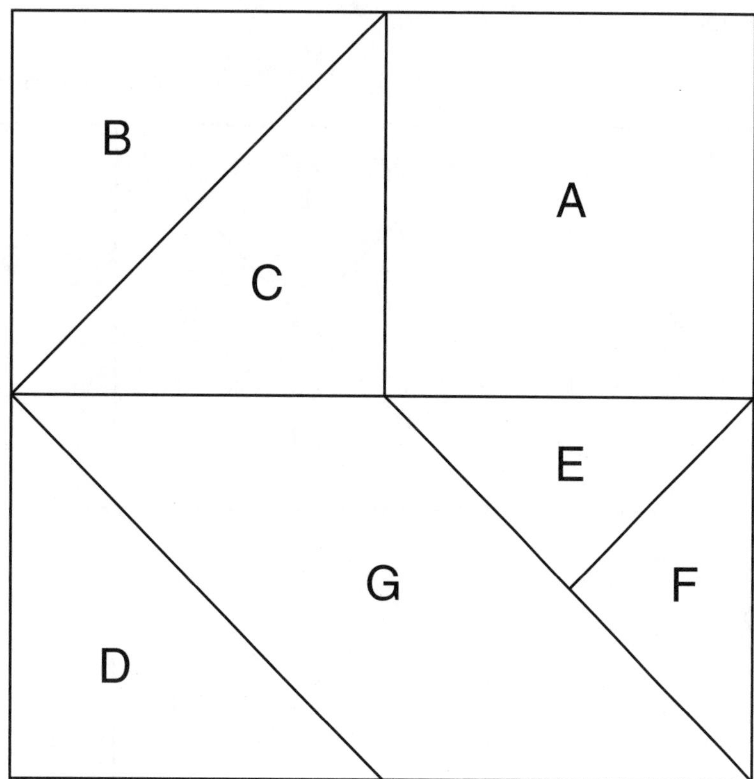

1. What fraction of the large square is …

   a. Square A? ________ b. Triangle B? ________

   c. Triangle E? ________ d. Parallelogram G? ________

2. What fraction of the large square are the following pieces, when put together? Write a number sentence to show your answer.

   a. Triangles B and C ________________

   b. Triangles E and F ________________

   c. Square A and Triangle C ________________

   d. Square A and Triangle E ________________

   e. Triangles E and B ________________

   f. Square A and Parallelogram G ________________

   g. Triangles D, E, and F and Parallelogram G

   ____

Name Date Time

Fractions of a Square *continued*

Cut out each shape.

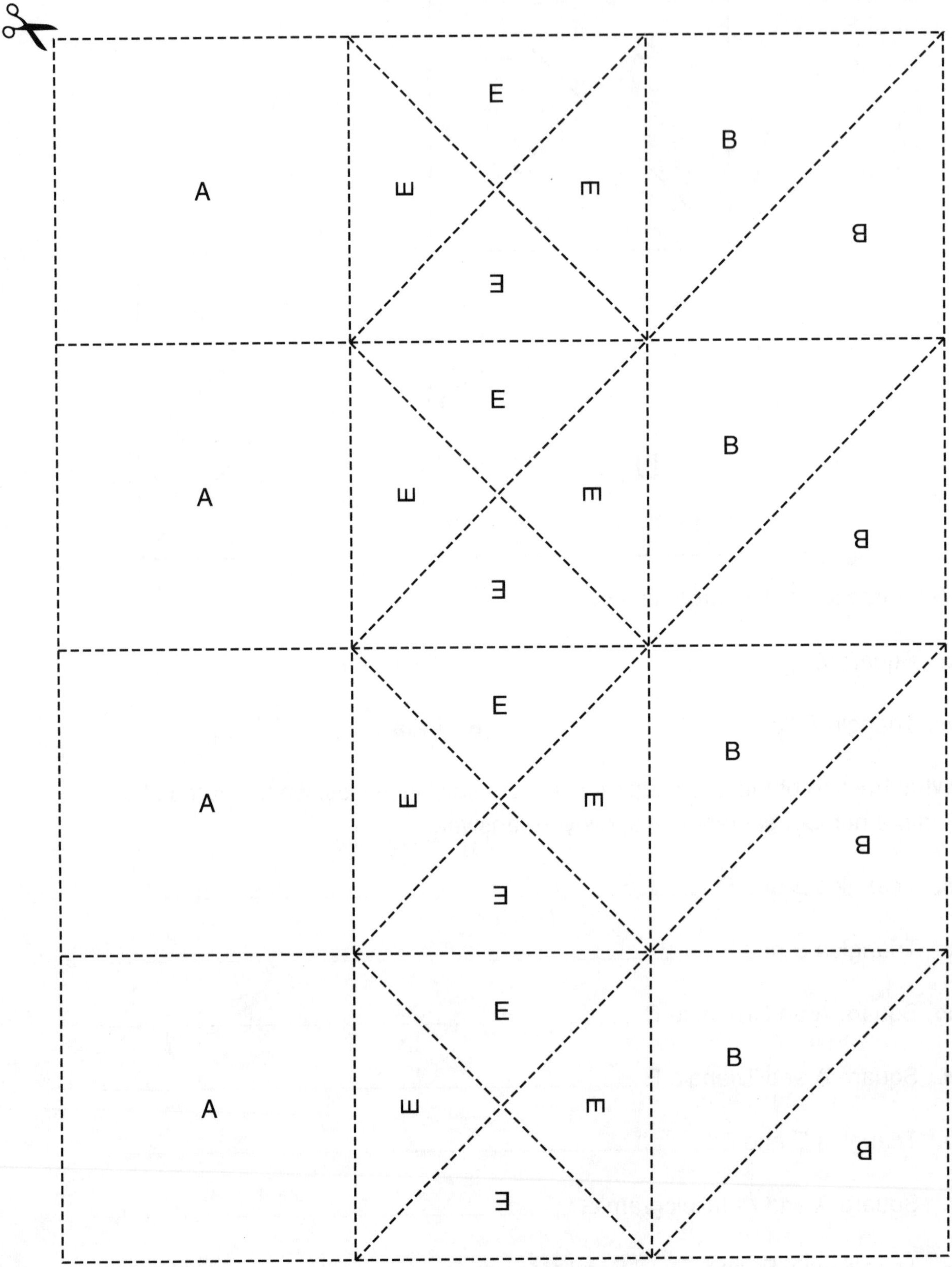

A E E E E B B

A E E E E B B

A E E E E B B

A E E E E B B

Name Date Time

Fractions of a Square *continued*

Cut out each shape.

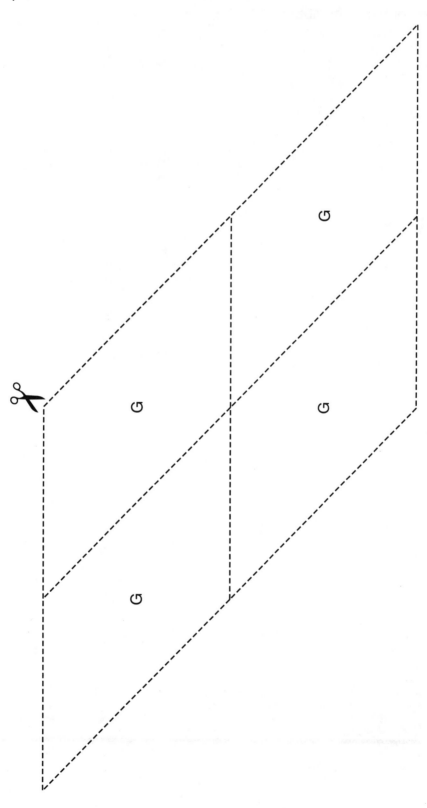

G

G

G

G

Name Date Time

STUDY LINK 4•3

Adding and Subtracting Fractions

Add or subtract. Write each answer in simplest form. If possible, rename answers as mixed numbers or whole numbers.

1. $\frac{1}{3} + \frac{1}{6} =$ ________

2. $\frac{3}{4} + \frac{5}{16} =$ ________

3. $\frac{9}{4} + \frac{2}{5} =$ ________

4. $\frac{2}{9} + \frac{4}{9} =$ ________

5. $\frac{1}{6} + \frac{3}{4} =$ ________

6. $\frac{5}{12} + \frac{3}{4} =$ ________

7. $\frac{7}{9} + \frac{2}{5} =$ ________

8. $\frac{5}{4} + \frac{3}{4} =$ ________

9. $\frac{7}{8} - \frac{2}{4} =$ ________

10. $\frac{5}{3} - \frac{2}{5} =$ ________

11. $\frac{11}{12} - \frac{7}{12} =$ ________

12. $\frac{4}{5} - \frac{3}{10} =$ ________

13. $\frac{15}{8} - \frac{3}{24} =$ ________

14. $\frac{3}{5} - \frac{1}{2} =$ ________

Practice

Solve mentally.

15. 3 − 0.30 = ________ **16.** 0.60 − 0.02 = ________ **17.** 2 − 0.02 = ________

Name Date Time

Using Fraction Strips to Add and Subtract

You can use fraction strips to find common denominators, sums, and differences. Study the examples below and then solve the problems.

Example 1: Solve. $\frac{1}{2} + \frac{1}{3} = \frac{\square}{6}$

Step 1 Use fraction strips to model both fractions.

$\frac{1}{2}$		$\frac{1}{3}$

Step 2 Rename each fraction using a common denominator.

$\frac{1}{2}$				$\frac{1}{3}$	
$\frac{1}{6}$	$\frac{1}{6}$	$\frac{1}{6}$		$\frac{1}{6}$	$\frac{1}{6}$

Step 3 Write the sum.

$\frac{3}{6} + \frac{2}{6} = \frac{5}{6}$

Use your fraction strips to find each of the following sums.

1. $\frac{1}{4} + \frac{2}{3} = \frac{\square}{12}$

2. $\frac{7}{12} + \frac{1}{3} = \frac{\square}{12}$

3. $\frac{3}{4} + \frac{1}{8} = \frac{\square}{\square}$

Example 2: Solve. $\frac{2}{3} - \frac{1}{4} = \frac{\square}{12}$

Step 1 Use fraction strips to model both fractions. Rename each fraction using a common denominator.

$\frac{1}{3}$				$\frac{1}{3}$			
$\frac{1}{12}$	$\frac{1}{12}$	$\frac{1}{12}$	$\frac{1}{12}$	$\frac{1}{12}$	$\frac{1}{12}$	$\frac{1}{12}$	$\frac{1}{12}$

$\frac{1}{4}$		
$\frac{1}{12}$	$\frac{1}{12}$	$\frac{1}{12}$

Step 2 Remove fraction strips to find the difference.

$\frac{1}{3}$				$\frac{1}{3}$			
$\frac{1}{12}$	$\frac{1}{12}$	$\frac{1}{12}$	$\frac{1}{12}$	$\frac{1}{12}$	$\frac{1}{12}$	$\frac{1}{12}$	$\frac{1}{12}$

$\frac{1}{4}$							
$\frac{1}{12}$	$\frac{1}{12}$	$\frac{1}{12}$	$\frac{1}{12}$	$\frac{1}{12}$	$\frac{1}{12}$	$\frac{1}{12}$	$\frac{1}{12}$

Step 3 Write the difference.

$\frac{2}{3} - \frac{1}{4} = \frac{5}{12}$

Use fraction strips to find each of the following differences.

4. $\frac{1}{2} - \frac{1}{3} = \frac{\square}{6}$

5. $\frac{7}{8} - \frac{1}{4} = \frac{\square}{8}$

6. $\frac{1}{3} - \frac{1}{4} = \frac{\square}{\square}$

Name Date Time

Paper Pool

Paper Pool is played on a rectangular grid. An imaginary ball is hit from the lower left pocket of the rectangular grid at a 45° angle. The ball travels at a 45° angle along the diagonals of the squares making up the grid. When the ball hits a side of the grid, it bounces off that side at a 45° angle and continues to travel along a diagonal that has not already been crossed. Play ends when the ball lands in any of the corner pockets. The length of the ball's path is found by counting the number of diagonals of the individual squares that the ball crosses before landing in a pocket.

3. Ball hits a pocket and play ends.

4. Because the ball crossed the diagonals of 12 squares before landing in a pocket, the length of its path is 12 units.

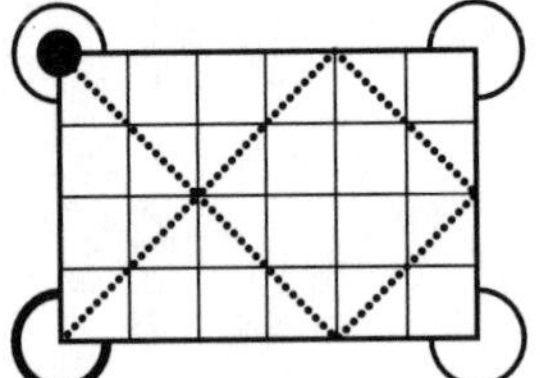

2. Ball hits side(s) and bounces off at a 45° angle.

1. Ball is hit from lower left pocket and travels at a 45° angle across the diagonals of the grid squares.

Length of ball's path: 12 units
Dimensions of grid: 4 units by 6 units

---

1. Draw the path of the ball on each rectangular grid below. Then record the length of the ball's path.

a.

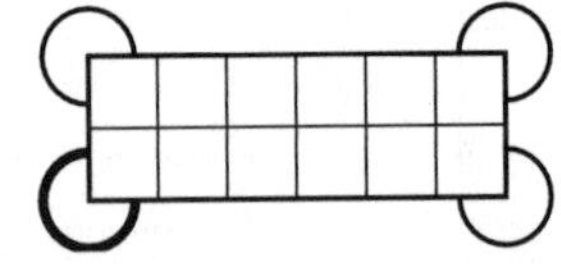

Length of ball's path: ______ units

b.

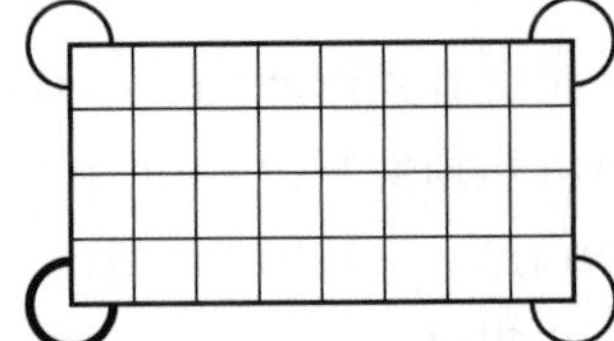

Length of ball's path: ______ units

c.

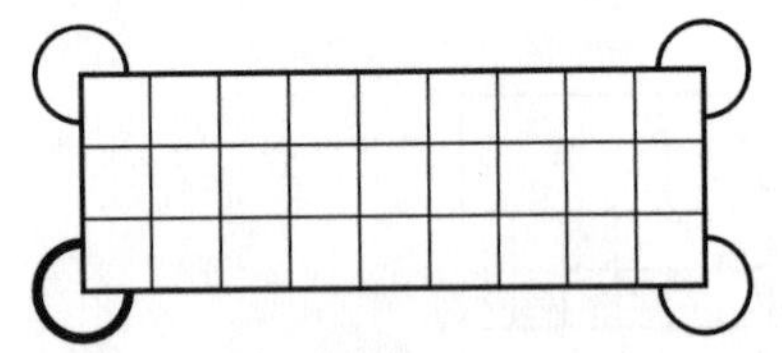

Length of ball's path: ______ units

d.

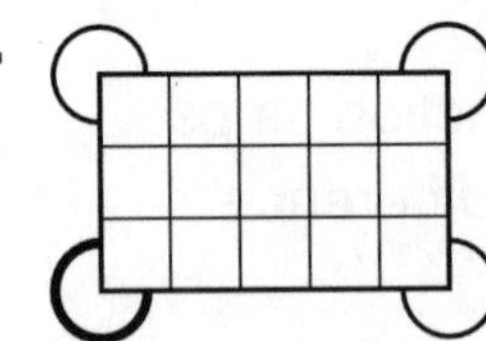

Length of ball's path: ______ units

2. For each grid in Problem 1, compare the length of the ball's path to the dimensions of the grid. For example, the length of the ball's path for a 4 × 6 grid is 12. Describe any patterns you notice.

____

____

____

Name Date Time

LESSON 4•4

Math Message

Cut out the ruler below. Use it to measure line segment *AB* to the nearest $\frac{1}{16}$ inch.

A ——————————————————— *B*

length of $\overline{AB}$ = ________

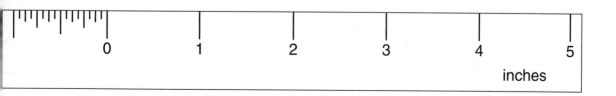

0 1 2 3 4 5

inches

Name Date Time

LESSON 4•4

Math Message

Cut out the ruler below. Use it to measure line segment *AB* to the nearest $\frac{1}{16}$ inch.

A ——————————————————— *B*

length of $\overline{AB}$ = ________

0 1 2 3 4 5

inches

Name Date Time

+, – Fractions and Mixed Numbers

1. In a national test, eighth-grade students answered the problem shown in the top of the table at the right. Also shown are the 5 possible answers they were given and the percent of students who chose each answer.

a. What mistake do you think the students who chose C made?

____

____

b. Explain why B is the best estimate.

____

____

____

Estimate the answer to $\frac{12}{13} + \frac{7}{8}$. You will not have enough time to solve the problem using paper and pencil.	
Possible Answers	**Percent Who Chose This Answer**
A. 1	7%
B. 2	24%
C. 19	28%
D. 21	27%
E. I don't know.	14%

2. A board is $6\frac{3}{8}$ inches long. Verna wants to cut enough so that it will be $5\frac{1}{8}$ inches long. How much should she cut? ______________ (unit)

3. Tim is making papier-mâché. The recipe calls for $1\frac{3}{4}$ cups of paste. Using only $\frac{1}{2}$-cup, $\frac{1}{4}$-cup, and $\frac{1}{3}$-cup measures, how can he measure the correct amount?

____

____

Add or subtract. Write your answers as mixed numbers in simplest form. Show your work on the back of the page. Use number sense to check whether each answer is reasonable.

4. $3\frac{1}{4} + 1\frac{1}{4} =$ ________ **5.** $4 - 2\frac{1}{4} =$ ________ **6.** $1\frac{2}{3} + \frac{2}{3} =$ ________

7. Circle the numbers that are equivalent to $2\frac{3}{4}$.

$1\frac{7}{4}$ $\frac{6}{4}$ $\frac{3}{7}$ $\frac{11}{4}$

Practice

Solve mentally.

8. 5 * 18 = ________ **9.** 6 * 41 = ________ **10.** 9 * 48 = ________ **11.** 7 * 45 = ________

Name Date Time

Fraction Counts and Conversions

Most calculators have a function that lets you repeat an operation, such as adding $\frac{1}{4}$ to a number. This is called the constant function. To use the constant function of your calculator to count by $\frac{1}{4}$s, follow one of the key sequences below, depending on the calculator you are using.

Calculator A	Calculator B
Press: (Op1) (+) (1) (n) (4) (d) (Op1) (Op1) (Op1) (Op1) (Op1) (Op1)	Press: (1) (b/c) (4) (+) (+) (0) (=) (=) (=) (=) (=)
Display: 5 $1\frac{1}{4}$	Display: K $\frac{5}{4}$
Press: ($U\frac{n}{d} \leftrightarrow \frac{n}{d}$)	Press: ($a^{b/c} \leftrightarrow d/c$)
Display: $\frac{5}{4}$	Display: $1\frac{1}{4}$

1. Using a calculator, start at 0 and count by $\frac{1}{4}$s to answer the following questions.

   a. How many counts of $\frac{1}{4}$ are needed to display $\frac{6}{4}$? ________

   b. How many counts of $\frac{1}{4}$ are needed to display $1\frac{1}{2}$? ________

2. Use a calculator to convert mixed numbers to improper fractions or whole numbers.

   a. $2\frac{3}{4}$ = ________
   b. $1\frac{7}{4}$ = ________
   c. $2\frac{4}{4}$ = ________
   d. $3\frac{12}{4}$ = ________

3. How many $\frac{1}{4}$s are between the following numbers?

   a. $\frac{3}{4}$ and 2 ________
   b. $\frac{6}{4}$ and $2\frac{3}{4}$ ________
   c. $1\frac{3}{4}$ and 4 ________
   d. 3 and $4\frac{1}{2}$ ________

Name Date Time

Math Message

Add or subtract. Be ready to explain your solution strategies for Problems 6 and 8.

1. $2\frac{1}{5} + 3\frac{3}{5}$

2. $6\frac{3}{8} + 5\frac{7}{8}$

3. $10\frac{7}{9} - 4\frac{1}{9}$

4. $5\frac{1}{4} - 3\frac{3}{4}$

5. $2\frac{2}{8} + 3\frac{1}{8}$

6. $2\frac{1}{4} + 3\frac{1}{8}$

7. $2\frac{7}{12} - 1\frac{6}{12}$

8. $2\frac{7}{12} - 1\frac{1}{2}$

Name Date Time

Math Message

Add or subtract. Be ready to explain your solution strategies for Problems 6 and 8.

1. $2\frac{1}{5} + 3\frac{3}{5}$

2. $6\frac{3}{8} + 5\frac{7}{8}$

3. $10\frac{7}{9} - 4\frac{1}{9}$

4. $5\frac{1}{4} - 3\frac{3}{4}$

5. $2\frac{2}{8} + 3\frac{1}{8}$

6. $2\frac{1}{4} + 3\frac{1}{8}$

7. $2\frac{7}{12} - 1\frac{6}{12}$

8. $2\frac{7}{12} - 1\frac{1}{2}$

Name Date Time

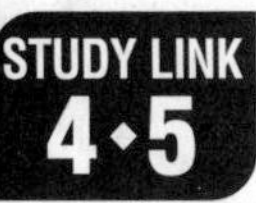

Mixed-Number Practice

1. Answer the following questions about the rectangle shown at the right. Include units in your answers.

$2\frac{3}{4}$ in.

$1\frac{1}{2}$ in.

   a. What is the perimeter? ________

   b. If you were to trim this rectangle so that it was a square measuring $1\frac{1}{4}$ inches on a side, how much would you cut

   from the base? ________ from the height? ________

2. Michael bought 1 peck of Empire apples, 1 peck of Golden Delicious apples, a $\frac{1}{2}$-bushel of Red Delicious apples, and $1\frac{1}{2}$ bushels of McIntosh apples.

1 peck = $\frac{1}{4}$ bushel

   a. How many bushels of apples did he buy in all? ________

   b. Michael estimates that he can make about 12 quarts of applesauce per bushel of apples. About how many quarts of applesauce can he make from the apples he bought? ________

Add or subtract. Show your work and estimates on the back of the page.

3. $2\frac{1}{3} + 1\frac{2}{3} =$ ________
4. $6\frac{1}{3} - 5\frac{2}{3} =$ ________
5. $4\frac{1}{2} + \frac{2}{3} =$ ________
6. $6 - 5\frac{4}{9} =$ ________
7. $4\frac{3}{8} - 2\frac{3}{4} =$ ________
8. $3\frac{1}{4} + 2\frac{3}{4} =$ ________
9. $9 - 2\frac{2}{5} =$ ________
10. $4\frac{1}{4} - 2\frac{5}{6} =$ ________
11. $5\frac{1}{4} - 2\frac{7}{10} =$ ________

Practice

Solve mentally.

12. $1\frac{1}{2} + 4\frac{2}{3} + 2\frac{1}{2} + 5\frac{1}{3} =$ ________
13. 4.5 + 3.4 + 7.5 + 2.5 = ________
14. \$2.35 + \$9.60 + \$8.05 + \$1.99 = ________
15. $5\frac{5}{8} + 3\frac{3}{4} + 2\frac{1}{4} + 8\frac{3}{8} =$ ________

Date Time

Representing Mixed Numbers

Picture	Number	Sum	[illegible]	[illegible]	[illegible]
Example:	$1\frac{1}{3}$	$1 + \frac{1}{3}$	$\frac{3}{3} + \frac{1}{3}$	$\frac{4}{3}$	$4 \div 3$
1.			$\frac{6}{6} + \frac{5}{6}$		$11 \div 6$
2.					
3.					
4.			$\frac{12}{4} + \frac{3}{4}$		$15 \div 4$
5.					

Name Date Time

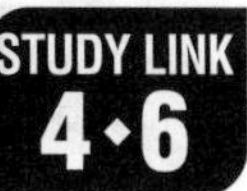

Fraction Multiplication

Use the fraction multiplication algorithm below to solve the following problems.

Fraction Multiplication Algorithm

$$\frac{a}{b} * \frac{c}{d} = \frac{a * c}{b * d}$$

1. $\frac{3}{5} * \frac{2}{4} =$ ________

2. $\frac{3}{7} * \frac{5}{9} =$ ________

3. $5 * \frac{3}{8} =$ ________

4. ________ $= \frac{11}{12} * \frac{1}{4}$

5. $\frac{5}{6} * \frac{7}{8} =$ ________

6. $\frac{3}{10} * \frac{7}{10} =$ ________

7. ________ $= \frac{2}{5} * \frac{7}{9}$

8. $\frac{4}{7} * 8 =$ ________

9. $12 * \frac{8}{11} =$ ________

10. South High beat North High in basketball, scoring $\frac{4}{5}$ of the total points. Rachel scored $\frac{1}{4}$ of South High's points. What fraction of the total points did Rachel score? ________

11. Josh was making raisin muffins for a party. He needed to triple the recipe, which called for $\frac{3}{4}$ cup raisins. How many cups of raisins did he need? ________

12. At Long Middle School, $\frac{7}{8}$ of the sixth graders live within 1 mile of the school. About $\frac{2}{3}$ of those sixth graders walk to school. None who live a mile or more away walk to school. About what fraction of the sixth graders walk to school? ________

13. **a.** For Calista's 12th birthday party, her mom will order pizza. $\frac{3}{4}$ of the girls invited like vegetables on their pizza. However, $\frac{1}{3}$ of those girls won't eat green peppers. What fraction of all the girls will eat a green-pepper-and-onion pizza? ________

b. If 12 girls are at the party (including Calista), how many girls will not eat a green-pepper-and-onion pizza? ________

Practice

Solve.

14. $12 * 0.75 =$ ______

15. $0.2 * 0.5 =$ ______

16. $0.4 * 0.25 =$ ______

Name Date Time

Modeling Fraction Multiplication

You can use an area model to find a product.

Example: $\frac{1}{4} * \frac{1}{3}$

Shade $\frac{1}{4}$ of the grid this way: ▨

Shade $\frac{1}{3}$ of the grid this way: ▧

The product is the area that is double-shaded. ▩

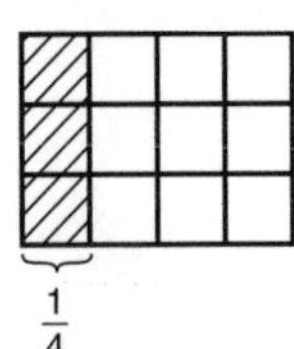

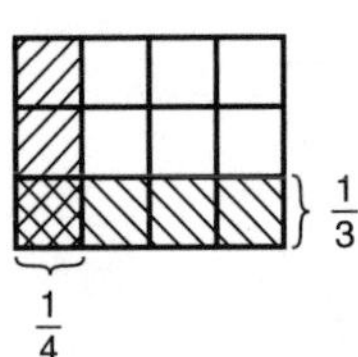

Since $\frac{1}{12}$ of the grid is double-shaded,

$\frac{1}{4} * \frac{1}{3} = \frac{1}{12}$.

Shade each factor and then find the product.

1.

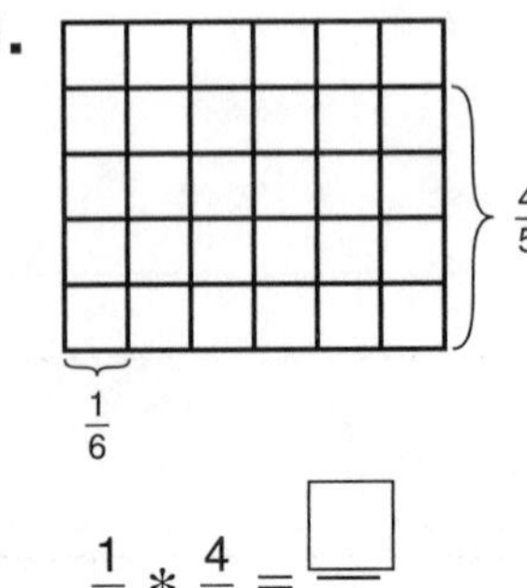

$\frac{1}{6} * \frac{4}{5} = \frac{\square}{30}$

2.

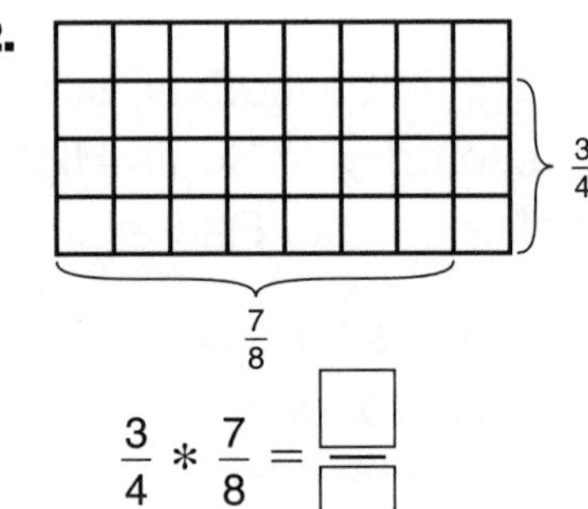

$\frac{3}{4} * \frac{7}{8} = \frac{\square}{\square}$

3.

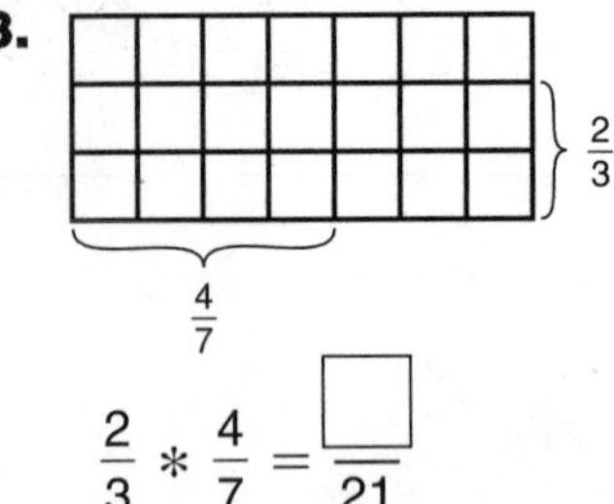

$\frac{2}{3} * \frac{4}{7} = \frac{\square}{21}$

4.

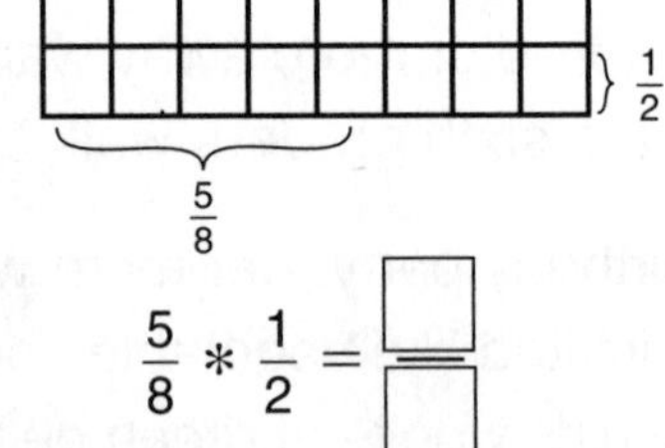

$\frac{5}{8} * \frac{1}{2} = \frac{\square}{\square}$

5. Which of the following represents a general pattern for the special cases in Problems 1–4? Circle the best answer.

A $\frac{a}{b} * \frac{c}{d} = \frac{a * b}{c * d}$

B $\frac{a}{b} * \frac{c}{d} = \frac{a * d}{c * d}$

C $\frac{a}{b} * \frac{c}{d} = \frac{a * c}{b * d}$

D $\frac{a}{b} * \frac{c}{d} = \frac{a + c}{b + d}$

Name Date Time

A Nature Hike Problem

Pavan, Jonathan, Nisha, and Gloria walked on the sixth-grade nature hike. They finished $\frac{1}{2}$ the length of the trail in the first hour. Then they slowed down. In the second hour, they walked $\frac{1}{2}$ the distance that was left. In the third hour, they moved even more slowly and walked only $\frac{1}{2}$ the remaining distance.

If they continue slowing down at this rate, what fraction of the trail will they walk in their fourth hour of hiking? __________

Explain or show how you solved the problem.

Name Date Time

LESSON 4·6

A Nature Hike Problem

Pavan, Jonathan, Nisha, and Gloria walked on the sixth-grade nature hike. They finished $\frac{1}{2}$ the length of the trail in the first hour. Then they slowed down. In the second hour, they walked $\frac{1}{2}$ the distance that was left. In the third hour, they moved even more slowly and walked only $\frac{1}{2}$ the remaining distance.

If they continue slowing down at this rate, what fraction of the trail will they walk in their fourth hour of hiking? __________

Explain or show how you solved the problem.

Date _____ Time _____

ath Message

wing mixed numbers as fractions.

_____ **2.** $2\frac{3}{8}$ = _____ **3.** $5\frac{7}{8}$ = _____

_____ **5.** $4\frac{3}{10}$ = _____ **6.** $2\frac{3}{16}$ = _____

wing fractions as mixed numbers.

_____ **8.** $\frac{17}{3}$ = _____ **9.** $\frac{27}{4}$ = _____

_____ **11.** $\frac{24}{5}$ = _____ **12.** $\frac{34}{9}$ = _____

how your work on the back of the page.
ed to explain how you found your answer. $3\frac{3}{8} * 1\frac{2}{5}$ = _____

Date _____ Time _____

ath Message

ving mixed numbers as fractions.

_____ **2.** $2\frac{3}{8}$ = _____ **3.** $5\frac{7}{8}$ = _____

_____ **5.** $4\frac{3}{10}$ = _____ **6.** $2\frac{3}{16}$ = _____

ving fractions as mixed numbers.

_____ **8.** $\frac{17}{3}$ = _____ **9.** $\frac{27}{4}$ = _____

_____ **11.** $\frac{24}{5}$ = _____ **12.** $\frac{34}{9}$ = _____

how your work on the back of the page.
ed to explain how you found your answer. $3\frac{3}{8} * 1\frac{2}{5}$ = _____

Name Date Ti

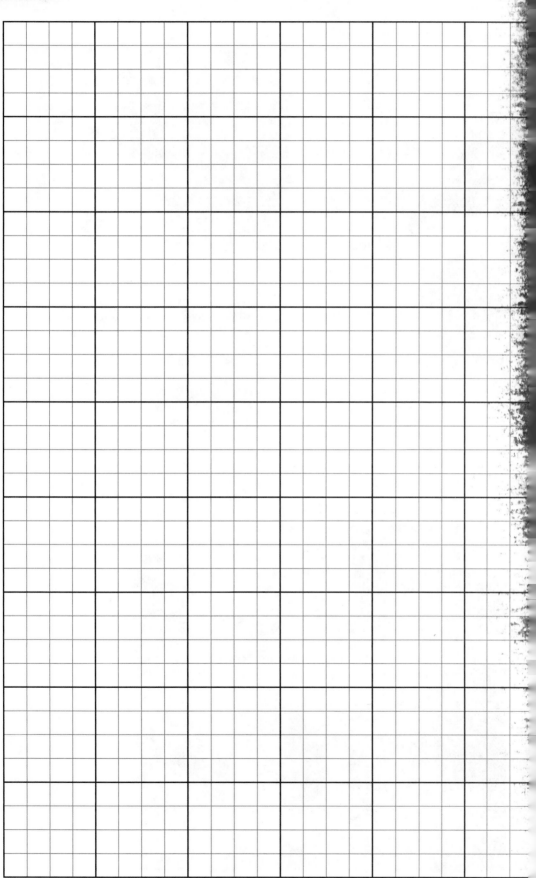

A Photo Album Page

Name Date Time

LESSON 4•7

Album Photos

$2\frac{1}{2}$ in.

$4\frac{1}{8}$ in.

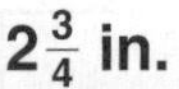

$2\frac{3}{4}$ in.

$2\frac{1}{8}$ in.

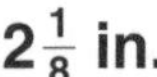

$2\frac{1}{8}$ in.

$2\frac{1}{8}$ in.

4 in.

$3\frac{5}{8}$ in.

Name Date Time

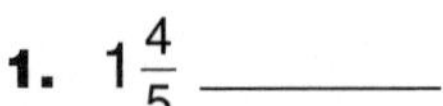

Multiplying Mixed Numbers

Rename each mixed number as a fraction.

SRB 71 72 90

1. $1\frac{4}{5}$ ________ 2. $2\frac{6}{6}$ ________ 3. $5\frac{2}{3}$ ________ 4. $3\frac{1}{2}$ ________

Rename each fraction as a mixed number or whole number.

5. $\frac{12}{4}$ ________ 6. $\frac{33}{8}$ ________ 7. $\frac{15}{6}$ ________ 8. $\frac{20}{3}$ ________

Multiply. Write each answer in simplest form. If possible, write answers as mixed numbers or whole numbers.

9. $5 * \frac{3}{5} =$ ________

10. $2\frac{1}{3} * 1\frac{4}{5} =$ ________

11. $\frac{5}{6} * 2\frac{1}{2} =$ ________

12. $1\frac{1}{6} * 4\frac{2}{3} =$ ________

13. $3\frac{3}{4} * 2\frac{1}{8} =$ ________

14. $7\frac{1}{2} * 2\frac{2}{3} =$ ________

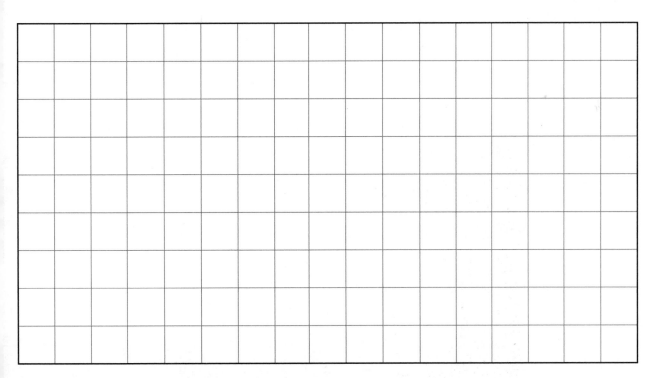

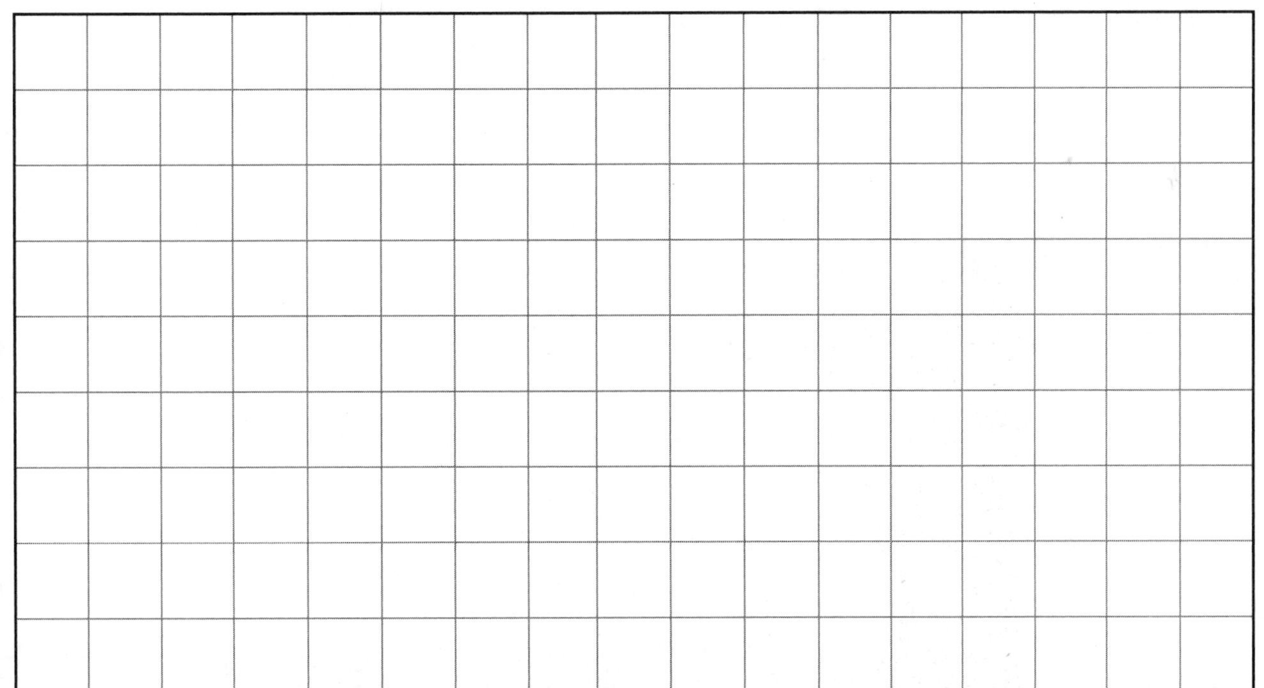

Practice

Solve mentally.

15. $8 * 3.5 =$ ________ 16. $12 * 5.25 =$ ________ 17. $4.2 * 15 =$ ________

Name Date Time

LESSON 4•7 Modeling Multiplication

An area model can help you keep track of partial products.

The area of each smaller rectangle represents a partial product.

Example: $2 * 4\frac{3}{4}$

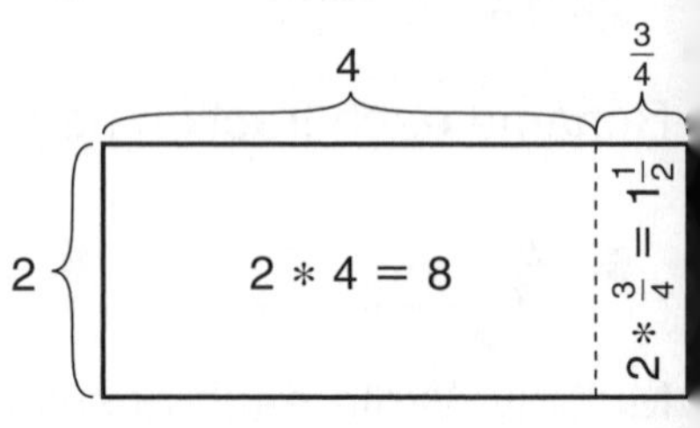

Find the area of each smaller rectangle.

$$2 * (4 + \tfrac{3}{4}) = (2 * 4) \quad + \quad (2 * \tfrac{3}{4})$$

$$2 * 4 = \mathbf{8} \qquad 2 * \tfrac{3}{4} = \mathbf{1\tfrac{1}{2}}$$

Then add the two areas to find the area of the largest rectangle. $\mathbf{8} + \mathbf{1\frac{1}{2}} = \mathbf{9\frac{1}{2}}$

So, $2 * 4\frac{3}{4} = 9\frac{1}{2}$

Find the area of each smaller rectangle. Then add the areas.

1. $2\frac{1}{4} * 5 = (2 + \frac{1}{4}) * 5$

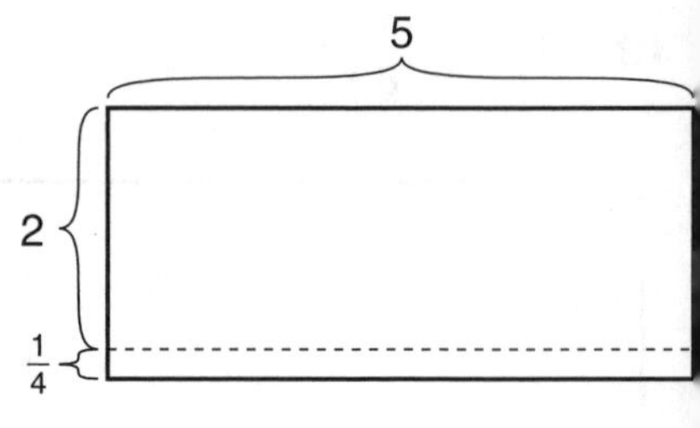

$2 * 5 =$ ________ $\qquad \frac{1}{4} * 5 =$ ________

So, $2\frac{1}{4} * 5 =$ ________

2. $2\frac{2}{3} * 3\frac{3}{4} = (2 + \frac{2}{3}) * (3 + \frac{3}{4})$

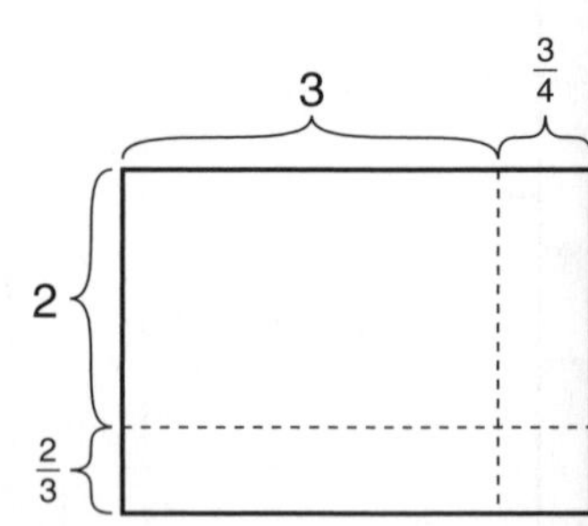

$2 * 3 =$ ________ $\qquad 2 * \frac{3}{4} =$ ________

$\frac{2}{3} * 3 =$ ________ $\qquad \frac{2}{3} * \frac{3}{4} =$ ________

So, $2\frac{2}{3} * 3\frac{3}{4} =$ ________

3. $1\frac{7}{8} * 3\frac{1}{2} = (1 + \frac{7}{8}) * (3 + \frac{1}{2})$

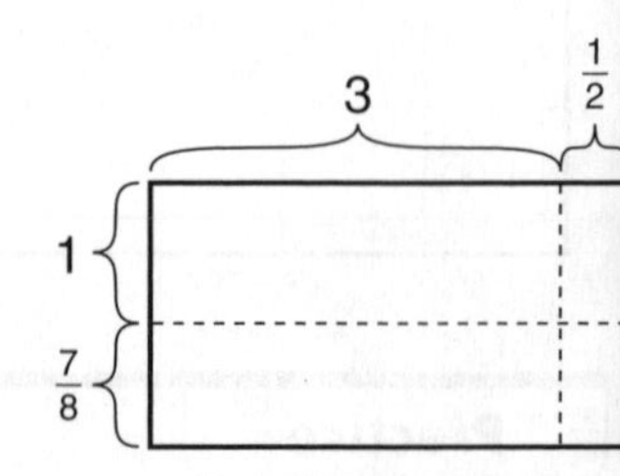

$1 * 3 =$ ________ $\qquad 1 * \frac{1}{2} =$ ________

$\frac{7}{8} * 3 =$ ________ $\qquad \frac{7}{8} * \frac{1}{2} =$ ________

So, $1\frac{7}{8} * 3\frac{1}{2} =$ ________

Name Date Tim

Buying an Aquarium

Robert wants to buy an aquarium for his bedroom.

Use the dimensions below to figure out whether Robert has enough floor space f free-standing aquarium after his furniture is in the room. Ignore doors and windo with only total floor space. Robert will need enough space to walk around his fu Drawing a floor plan might help.

How much floor space is available after Robert places the furniture but before he buys the aquarium?

____

Does Robert have enough space for the aquarium?

____

	Length (ft)	Width (ft)
Room	$9\frac{1}{2}$	$9\frac{3}{4}$
Desk	$3\frac{1}{4}$	$2\frac{1}{2}$
Bed	$6\frac{1}{4}$	$3\frac{3}{4}$
Dresser	$3\frac{1}{4}$	$2\frac{1}{4}$
Bookcase	$1\frac{1}{4}$	$3\frac{1}{2}$
Aquarium	2	1

Name Date Time

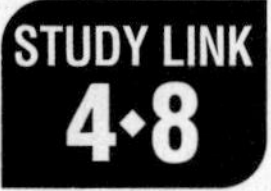

Fractions, Decimals, and Percents

Fill in the missing numbers below. Then shade each large square to represent all three of the equivalent numbers below it. Each large square is worth 1.

1. 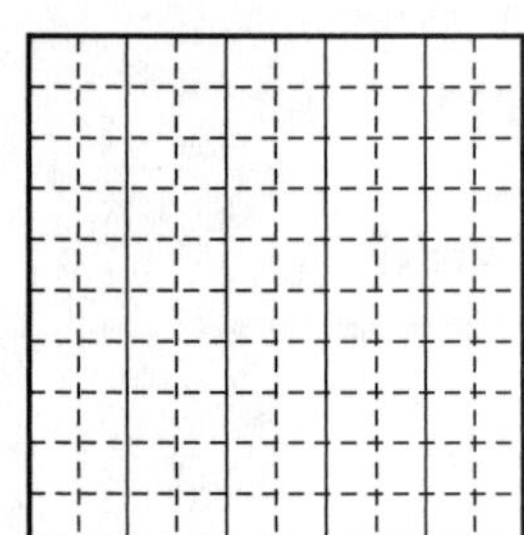

$\frac{4}{5} = \frac{\square}{10} =$ _____%

2. 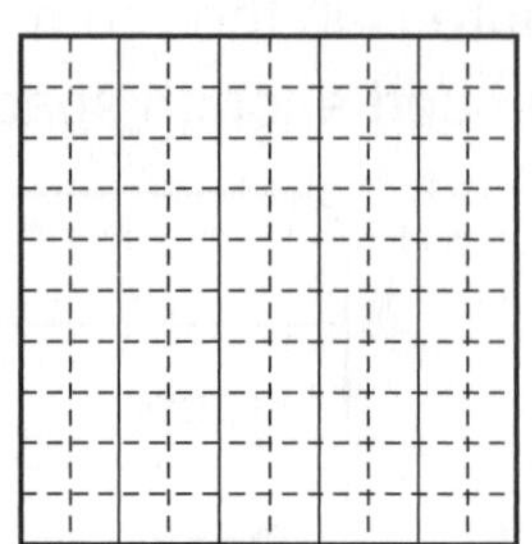

$\frac{6}{8} = \frac{\square}{100} =$ _____%

3. 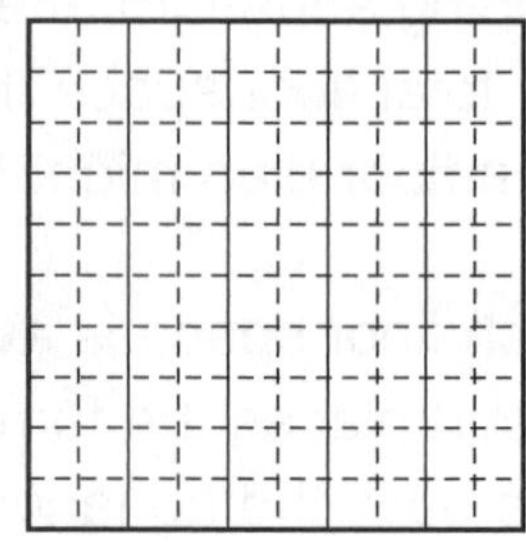

$30\% = \frac{\square}{100} = \frac{\square}{10}$

Rename the fractions as decimals.

4. $\frac{7}{14} =$ _____ **5.** $\frac{6}{8} =$ _____ **6.** $\frac{5}{20} =$ _____ **7.** $1\frac{4}{5} =$ _____

Rename the decimals as fractions in simplest form.

8. 0.4 = _____ **9.** 0.10 = _____ **10.** 0.68 = _____ **11.** 0.25 = _____

Rename the fractions as percents.

12. $\frac{25}{50} =$ _____ **13.** $\frac{6}{24} =$ _____ **14.** $\frac{18}{30} =$ _____ **15.** $\frac{19}{20} =$ _____

Rename the percents as fractions in simplest form.

16. $50\% = \frac{\square}{100} =$ _____ **17.** $40\% = \frac{\square}{100} =$ _____

18. $100\% = \frac{\square}{100} =$ _____ **19.** $180\% = \frac{\square}{100} =$ _____

Experiment

People often don't realize that fractions, decimals, and percents are numbers. To them, numbers are whole numbers like 1, 5, or 100. Try the following experiment: Ask several adults to name four numbers between 1 and 10. Then ask several children. Keep a record of all responses on the back of this page. How many named fractions, decimals, or percents? Now ask the same people to name four numbers between 1 and 3. Report your findings.

Name Date Time

LESSON 4·8

Renaming Fractions

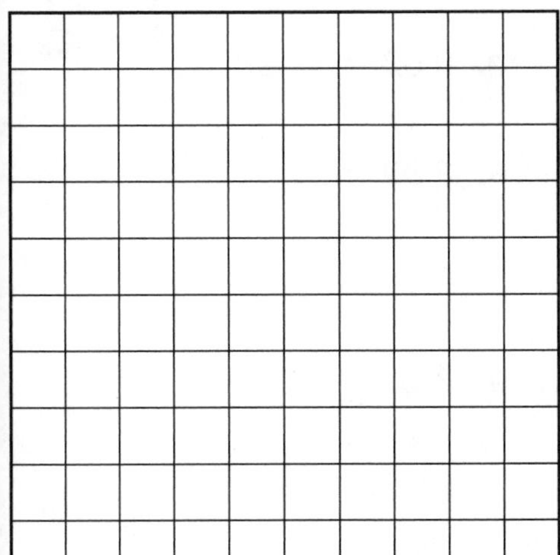

Fraction: $\frac{\square}{100}$

Decimal: ______

Percent: ______%

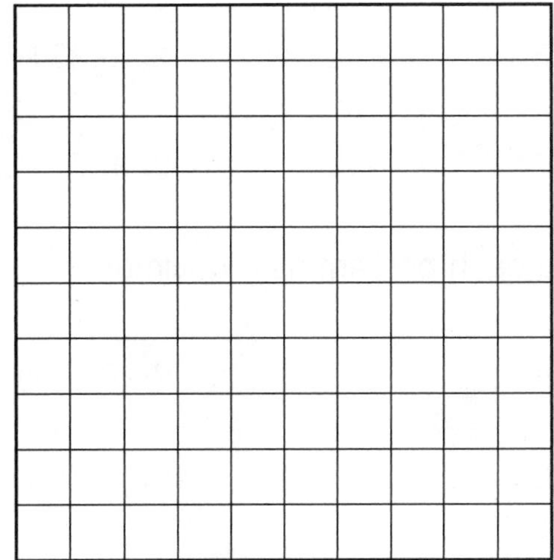

Fraction: $\frac{\square}{100}$

Decimal: ______

Percent: ______%

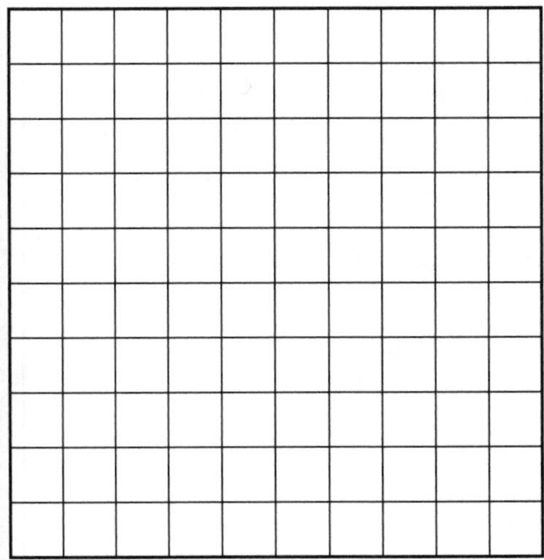

Fraction: $\frac{\square}{100}$

Decimal: ______

Percent: ______%

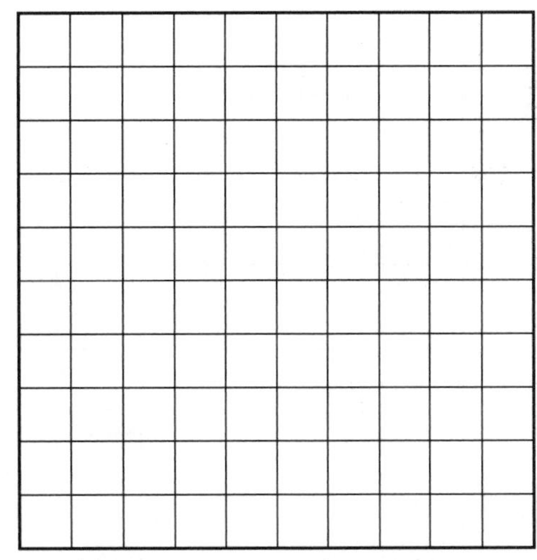

Fraction: $\frac{\square}{100}$

Decimal: ______

Percent: ______%

Name Date Time

Decimals, Percents, and Fractions

SRB 59 60

Rename each decimal as a percent.

1. 0.65 = ________ **2.** 0.334 = ________ **3.** 0.02 = ________

4. 0.4 = ________ **5.** 2.7 = ________ **6.** 3.09 = ________

Rename each percent as a decimal.

7. 27% = ________ **8.** 53.9% = ________ **9.** 8% = ________

10. 60% = ________ **11.** 180% = ________ **12.** 115% = ________

Use division to rename each fraction as a decimal to the nearest hundredth. Then rename the decimal as a percent.

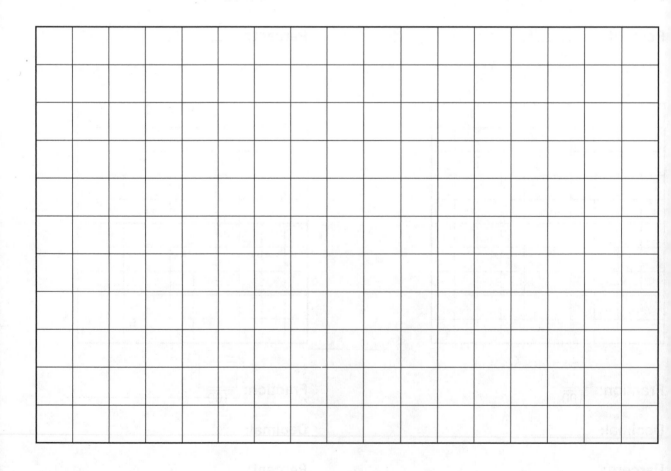

13. $\frac{7}{8}$ = 0.________ = ________% **14.** $\frac{5}{12}$ = 0.________ = ________%

Name Date Time

LESSON 4•9

Fractions, Decimals, and Percents

Write each fraction or decimal as a percent.

1. $\frac{11}{50}$ = ________ **2.** $\frac{3}{5}$ = ________ **3.** $\frac{7}{8}$ = ________

4. 0.45 = ________ **5.** 0.745 = ________ **6.** 0.0925 = ________

Write each percent as a decimal.

7. 65% = ________ **8.** 4% = ________ **9.** 9.2% = ________

10. $15\frac{1}{2}$% = ________ **11.** 20% = ________ **12.** 2% = ________

13. Enter your results from Problems 11 and 12 on the appropriate lines below. Then complete the pattern.

200%	20%	2%	0.2%	0.02%	0.002%
________	________	________	________	________	________

Percents Greater Than and Less Than 1%

You can apply the meaning of *percent* and a power-of-10 strategy to rename percents greater than or less than 1 percent as equivalent decimals.

Example: Write 125% as a decimal. 125% means 125 *per hundred.* or $\frac{125}{100}$ = 125 ÷ 100 = 1.**25**.	**Example:** Write 0.15% as a decimal. 0.15% means 0.15 *per hundred.* or $\frac{0.15}{100}$ = 0.15 ÷ 100 = 0.**00**.15

Write each percent as a decimal.

14. 375% = ________ **15.** 278% = ________ **16.** $400\frac{1}{2}$% = ________

17. 0.165% = ________ **18.** 0.03% = ________ **19.** 0.005% = ________

Name Date Time

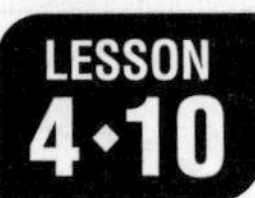

Math Message

1. Find the equivalent decimal and percent for each of the fractions in the table below. Use a mental math and/or paper-and-pencil strategy to complete the table.

Fraction	Decimal	Percent
$\frac{1}{10}$		
$\frac{1}{4}$		
$\frac{13}{25}$		
$\frac{6}{30}$		
$\frac{51}{75}$		

2. There were 90 questions on the math final exam. Max correctly answered 72 questions. What percent of the questions did he answer correctly? ______

Name Date Time

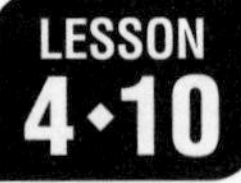

Math Message

1. Find the equivalent decimal and percent for each of the fractions in the table below. Use a mental math and/or paper-and-pencil strategy to complete the table.

Fraction	Decimal	Percent
$\frac{1}{10}$		
$\frac{1}{4}$		
$\frac{13}{25}$		
$\frac{6}{30}$		
$\frac{51}{75}$		

2. There were 90 questions on the math final exam. Max correctly answered 72 questions. What percent of the questions did he answer correctly? ______

Name Date Time

Circle Graphs

Use estimation to make a circle graph displaying the data in each problem. (*Hint:* For each percent, think of a simple fraction that is close to the value of the percent. Then estimate the size of the sector for each percent.) Remember to graph the smallest sector first.

1. According to the 2000 Census, 21.2% of the U.S. population was under the age of 15, 12.6% was age 65 or older, and 66.2% was between the ages of 15 and 64.

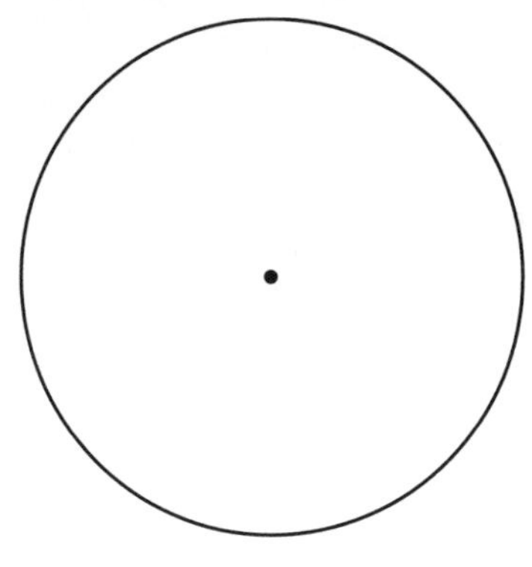

2. In 2004, NASA's total budget was $15.4 billion. 51% was spent on Science, Aeronautics, and Exploration. 48.8% was spent on Space Flight Capabilities, and 0.2% was spent on the Inspector General.

NASA Budget

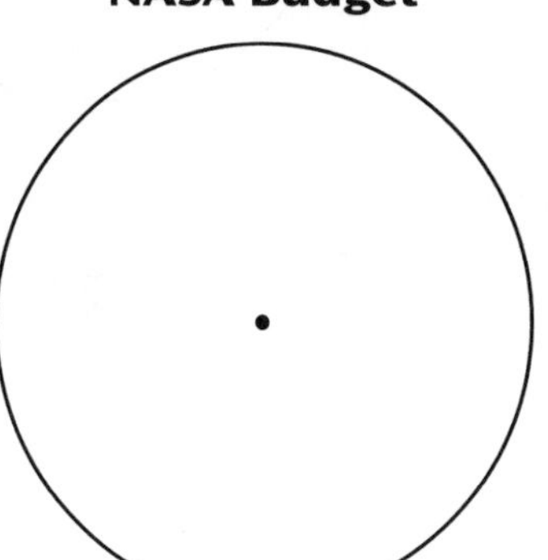

3. 98.3% of households in the United States have at least one television.

Households with TV

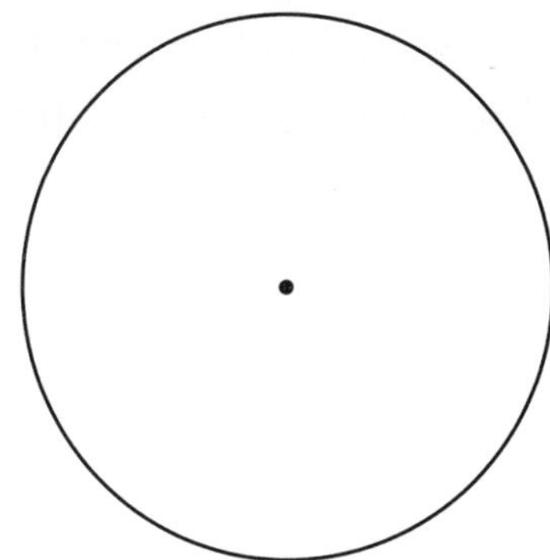

4. The projected school enrollment for the United States in 2009 is 72 million students. 23.2% will be in college, 22.9% will be in high school, and 53.9% will be in Grades Pre-K–8.

U.S. School Enrollment

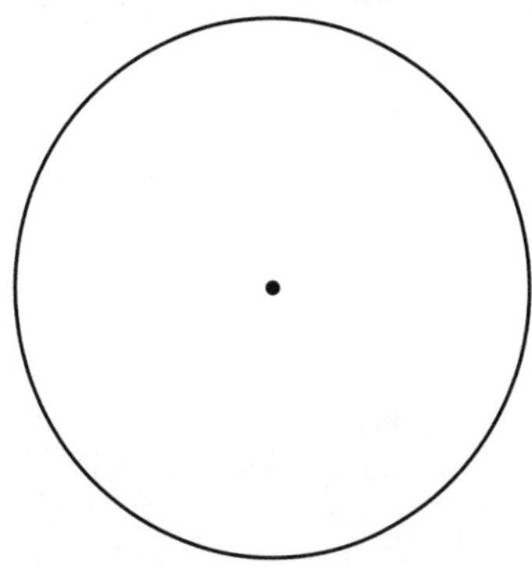

Name Date Time

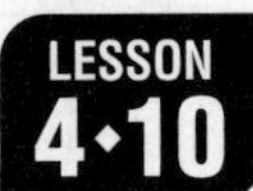

Estimating and Measuring Sector Size

Shade the circles below to represent your estimate of the given percent or fraction. Then check your estimates using the Percent Circle on the Geometry Template.

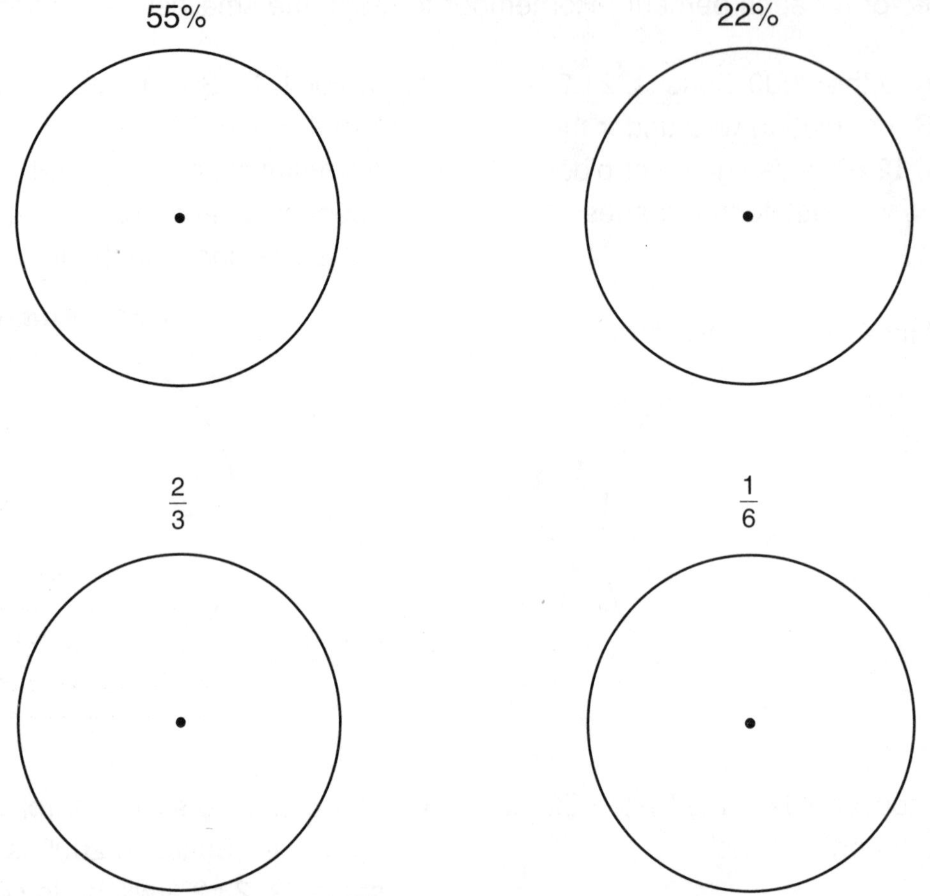

Starting with the smallest sector, use the Percent Circle to create a circle graph that shows 10% blue, 4% red, 60% green, and 26% yellow. Label each sector with the percent it represents.

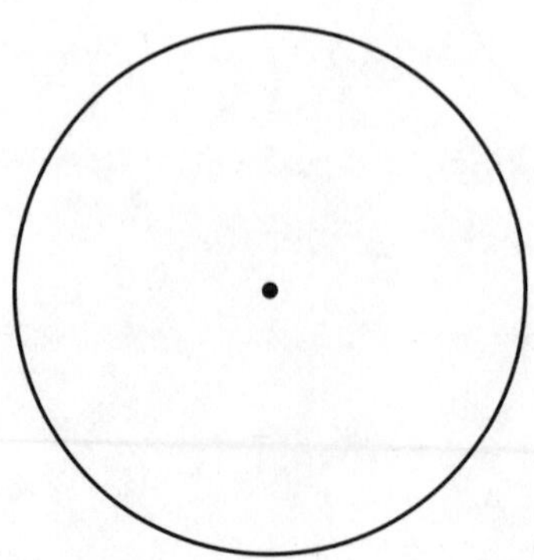

Name Date Time

Percent Problems

The results of a survey about children's weekly allowances are shown at the right.

Amount of Allowance	Percent of Children
$0	30%
$1–$4	20%
$5	25%
$6 or more	25%

1. Lincoln School has about 500 students. Use the survey results to complete this table.

Amount of Allowance	Predicted Number of Students at Lincoln
$0	
$1–$4	
$5	
$6 or more	

2. The sixth grade at Lincoln has about 60 students. Use the survey results to complete this table.

Amount of Allowance	Predicted Number of Sixth-Grade Students at Lincoln
$0	
$1–$4	
$5	
$6 or more	

A rule of thumb for changing a number of meters to yards is to add the number of meters to 10% of the number of meters.

Examples: 5 m is about 5 + (10% of 5), or 5.5, yd.
10 m is about 10 + (10% of 10), or 11, yd.

3. Use this rule of thumb to estimate how many yards are in the following numbers of meters.

a. 3 m is about 3 + (10% of 3), or ________, yd.

b. 8 m is about 8 + (10% of 8), or ________, yd.

c. 20 m is about 20 + (10% of 20), or ________, yd.

Name Date Time

Modeling Fractional Parts of a Number

You can use a diagram to model fractional parts of a number.

Example: Find $\frac{4}{5}$ of \$150.

First, think about \$150 being divided equally among 5 people.

\$150 ← Total amount

\$30	\$30	\$30	\$30	\$30	← Amounts for each $\frac{1}{5}$
$\frac{1}{5}$	$\frac{1}{5}$	$\frac{1}{5}$	$\frac{1}{5}$	$\frac{1}{5}$	← Fractional parts

One Way

$\frac{1}{5}$ of \$150 = \$30

$\frac{4}{5}$ of \$150

$= 4 * (\frac{1}{5}$ of \$150)

$= 4 *$ \$30 = \$120

$\frac{4}{5}$ of \$150 = \$120

Another Way

$\frac{5}{5}$ of \$150 = \$150

$\frac{1}{5}$ of \$150 = \$30

$\frac{5}{5} - \frac{1}{5} = \frac{4}{5}$

\$150 − \$30 = \$120

---

1. Use the diagram to find the amounts.

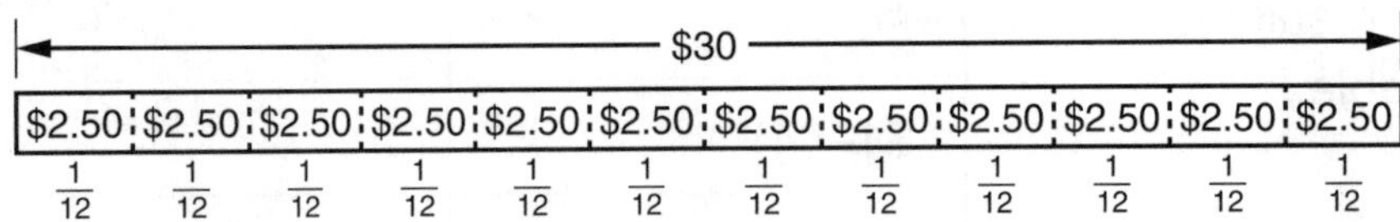

$\frac{3}{12}$ of \$30 = ________ $\frac{9}{12}$ of \$30 = ________ $\frac{1}{3}$ of \$30 = ________

$\frac{2}{3}$ of \$30 = ________ $\frac{1}{6}$ of \$30 = ________ $\frac{5}{12}$ of \$30 = ________

$\frac{7}{12}$ of \$30 = ________ $\frac{1}{4}$ of \$30 = ________ $\frac{5}{6}$ of \$30 = ________

2. Complete the diagram below. Then find the amounts.

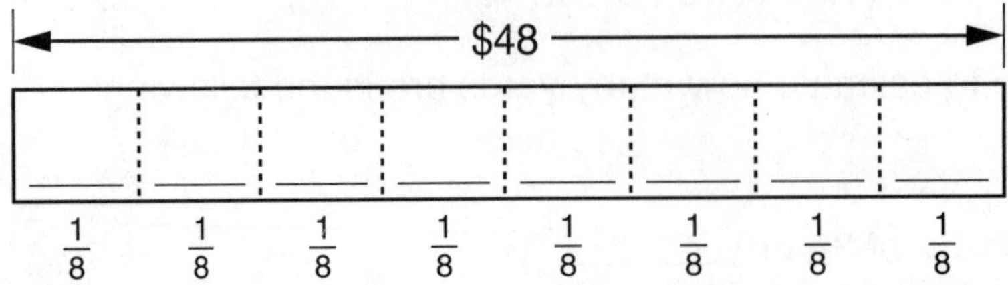

$\frac{1}{8}$ of \$48 = ________ $\frac{7}{8}$ of \$48 = ________ $\frac{3}{8}$ of \$48 = ________

$\frac{1}{4}$ of \$48 = ________ $\frac{1}{2}$ of \$48 = ________ $\frac{3}{4}$ of \$48 = ________

Name Date Time

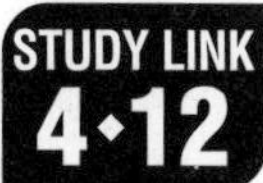

Unit 5: Family Letter

Geometry: Congruence, Constructions, and Parallel Lines

In *Fourth* and *Fifth Grade Everyday Mathematics,* students used a compass and straightedge to construct basic shapes and create geometric designs. In Unit 5 of *Sixth Grade Everyday Mathematics,* students will review some basic construction techniques and then devise their own methods for copying triangles and quadrilaterals and for constructing parallelograms. The term *congruent* will be applied to their copies of line segments, angles, and 2-dimensional figures. Two figures are congruent if they have the *same size* and the *same shape.*

Another approach to congruent figures in Unit 5 is through isometry transformations. These are rigid motions that take a figure from one place to another while preserving its size and shape. Reflections (flips), translations (slides), and rotations (turns) are basic isometry transformations (also known as rigid motions). A figure produced by an isometry transformation (the image) is congruent to the original figure (the preimage).

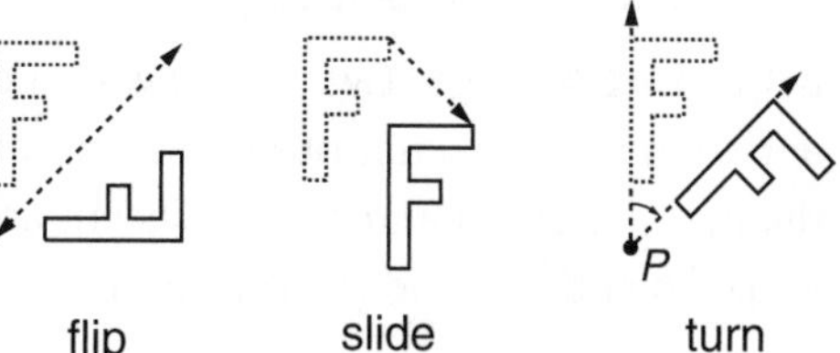

Students will continue to work with the Geometry Template, a tool that was introduced in *Fifth Grade Everyday Mathematics.* The Geometry Template contains protractors and rulers for measuring and cutouts for drawing geometric figures. Students will review how to measure and draw angles using the full-circle and half-circle protractors.

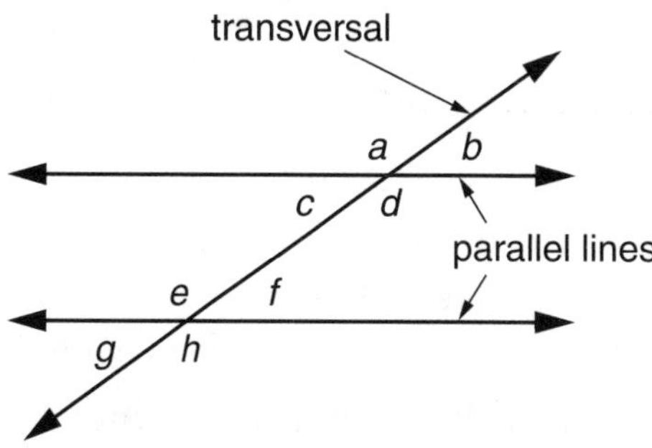

If the measure of any one angle is given, the measures of all the others can be found without measuring.

Students will also use a protractor to construct circle graphs that represent data collections. This involves converting the data to percents of a total, finding the corresponding degree measures around a circle, and drawing sectors of the appropriate size.

Measures often can be determined without use of a measuring tool. Students will apply properties of angles and sums of angles to find unknown measures in figures similar to those at the right.

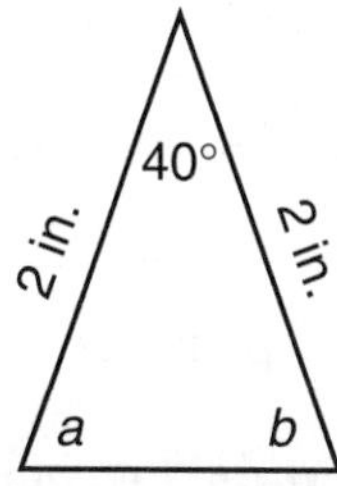

The sum of the angles in a triangle is 180°. Angles *a* and *b* have the same measure, 70°.

One lesson in Unit 5 is a review and extension of work with the coordinate grid. Students will plot and name points on a 4-quadrant coordinate grid and use the grid for further study of geometric shapes.

Please keep this Family Letter for reference as your child works through Unit 5.

Math Tools

Your child will use a compass and a straightedge to construct geometric figures. A compass is used to draw a circle, or part of a circle, called an arc. A straightedge is used only to draw straight lines, not for measuring. The primary difference between a compass-and-straightedge construction and a drawing or sketch of a geometric figure is that measuring is not allowed in constructions.

Vocabulary

Important terms in Unit 5:

adjacent angles Two angles with a common side and vertex that do not otherwise overlap. In the diagram, angles *a* and *b* are adjacent angles. So are angles *b* and *c, d* and *a*, and *c* and *d*.

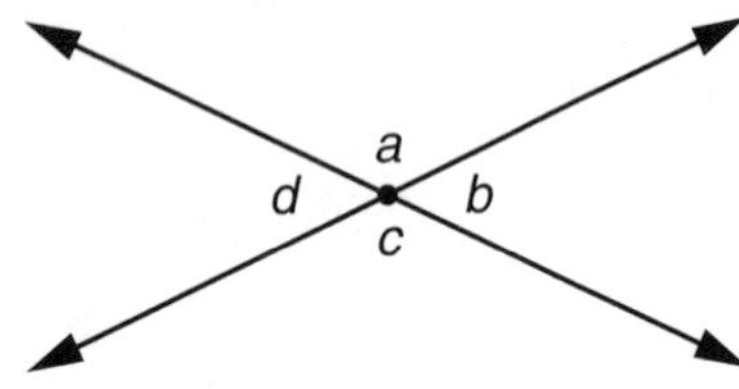

congruent Figures that have exactly the same size and shape are said to be congruent to each other. The symbol ≅ means "is congruent to."

line of reflection (mirror line) A line halfway between a figure (preimage) and its reflected image. In a reflection, a figure is flipped over the line of reflection.

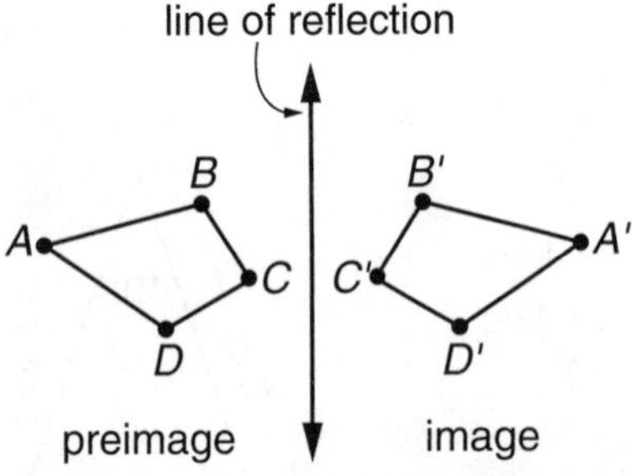

ordered pair Two numbers, or coordinates, used to locate a point on a rectangular coordinate grid. The first coordinate *x* gives the position along the horizontal axis of the grid, and the second coordinate *y* gives the position along the vertical axis. The pair is written (*x*,*y*).

reflection (flip) The flipping of a figure over a line (line of reflection) so its image is the mirror image of the original (preimage).

reflex angle An angle measuring between 180° and 360°.

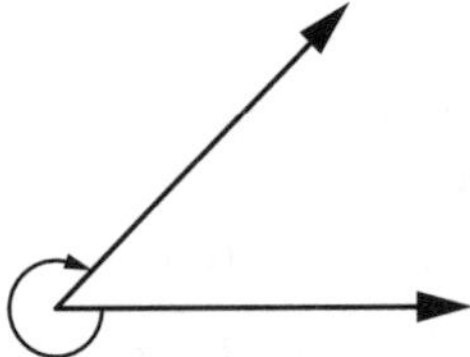

rotation (turn) A movement of a figure around a fixed point or an axis; a turn.

supplementary angles Two angles whose measures add to 180°. Supplementary angles do not need to be adjacent.

translation (slide) A transformation in which every point in the image of a figure is at the same distance in the same direction from its corresponding point in the figure. Informally called a slide.

vertical (opposite) angles The angles made by intersecting lines that do not share a common side. Same as opposite angles. Vertical angles have equal measures. In the diagram, angles 1 and 3 are vertical angles. They have no sides in common. Similarly, angles 4 and 2 are vertical angles.

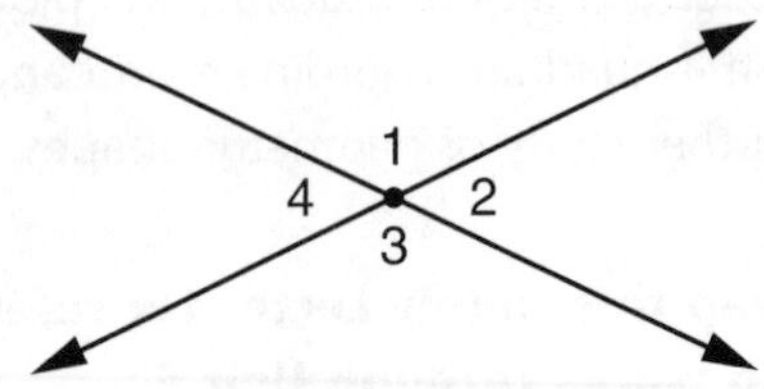

Do-Anytime Activities

To work with your child on the concepts taught in this unit, try these interesting and engaging activities:

1. While you are driving in the car together, ask your child to look for congruent figures, for example, windows in office buildings, circles on stoplights, or wheels on cars and trucks.
2. Look for apparent right angles or any other type of angles: acute (less than 90°) or obtuse (between 90° and 180°). Guide your child to look particularly at bridge supports to find a variety of angles.
3. Triangulation lends strength to furniture. Encourage your child to find corner triangular braces in furniture throughout your home. Look under tables, under chairs, inside cabinets, or under bed frames. Have your child count how many examples of triangulation he or she can find in your home.

Building Skills through Games

In Unit 5, students will work on their understanding of geometry concepts by playing games such as those described below.

Angle Tangle See *Student Reference Book,* page 306
Two players need a protractor, straightedge, and blank paper to play *Angle Tangle*. Skills practiced include estimating angle measures as well as measuring angles.

Polygon Capture See *Student Reference Book*, page 330
Players capture polygons that match both the angle property and the side property drawn. Properties include measures of angles, lengths of sides, and number of pairs of parallel sides.

Students will review concepts from previous units by playing games such as:

2-4-8 and 3-6-9 *Frac-Tac-Toe* (Decimal Versions) See *Student Reference Book*, pages 314–316
Two players need a deck of number cards with four each of the numbers 0–10; a gameboard; a 5 × 5 grid that resembles a bingo card; a *Frac-Tac-Toe* Number-Card board; markers or counters in two different colors; and a calculator. The two versions, *2-4-8 Frac-Tac-Toe* and *3-6-9 Frac-Tac-Toe,* help students practice conversions between fractions and decimals.

As You Help Your Child with Homework

As your child brings assignments home, you may want to go over the instructions together, clarifying them as necessary. The answers listed below will guide you through some of the Unit 5 Study Links.

Study Link 5•1

2. a. $\angle H$ **b.** $\angle J$

c. $\angle D$ **d.** $\angle ABC$, $\angle GFE$, $\angle L$

3b. 180 **3c.** 360

Study Link 5•2

1. $m\angle y = 120°$ **2.** $m\angle x = 115°$

3. $m\angle c = 135°$ $m\angle a = 45°$ $m\angle t = 135°$

4. $m\angle q = 120°$ $m\angle r = 80°$ $m\angle s = 70°$

5. $m\angle a = 120°$ $m\angle b = 60°$ $m\angle c = 120°$

$m\angle d = 40°$ $m\angle e = 140°$ $m\angle f = 140°$

$m\angle g = 80°$ $m\angle h = 100°$ $m\angle i = 100°$

6. $m\angle w = 90°$ $m\angle a = 75°$ $m\angle t = 105°$

$m\angle c = 75°$ $m\angle h = 105°$

7. 12 **8.** 30 **9.** 110

Study Link 5•3

2. a. 1,920,000 adults **b.** 3,760,000 adults

3. −7, 0, 0.07, 0.7, 7

4. 0.06, $\frac{1}{10}$, 0.18, 0.2, 0.25, 0.75, $\frac{4}{5}$, $\frac{4}{4}$

Study Link 5•4

Sample answers for 1–3:

1. Vertex *C:* (1,2)

2. Vertex *F:* (5,10) Vertex *G:* (3,7)

3. Vertex *J:* (2,1) **4.** Vertex *M:* (−2,−3)

5. Vertex *Q:* (8,−3)

Study Link 5•5

1. 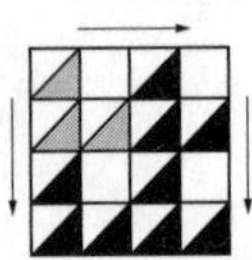

2. 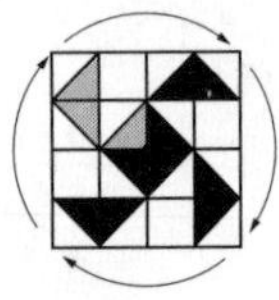

3. 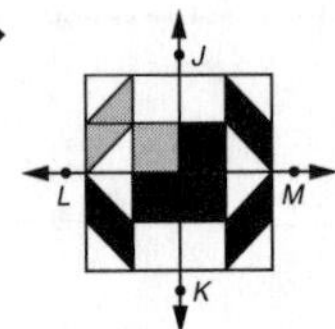

4. 64 **5.** 243 **6.** 1 **7.** 64

Study Link 5•7

1. $m\angle r = 47°$ $m\angle s = 133°$ $m\angle t = 47°$

2. $m\angle NKO = 10°$

3. $m\angle a = 120°$ $m\angle b = 120°$ $m\angle c = 60°$

4. $m\angle a = 57°$ $m\angle c = 114°$ $m\angle t = 57°$

5. $m\angle x = 45°$ $m\angle y = 45°$ $m\angle z = 135°$

6. $m\angle p = 54°$

7. 0.0027 **8.** 0.12 **9.** 0.0049 **10.** 0.225

Study Link 5•8

2. *A'*: (−2,−7) *B'*: (−6,−6)

C': (−8,−4) *D'*: (−5,−1)

3. *A''*: (2,1) *B''*: (6,2)

C'': (8,4) *D''*: (5,7)

4. *A'''*: (1,−2) *B'''*: (2,−6)

C''': (4,−8) *D'''*: (7,−5)

5. 0.3 **6.** 0.143 **7.** 0.0359

Study Link 5•9

3. Sample answers: All of the vertical angles have the same measure; all of the angles along the transversal and on the same side are supplementary; opposite angles along the transversal are equal in measure.

Study Link 5•10

1. a. 50°; $\angle YZW$ plus the 130° angle equals 180°, so $\angle YZW = 50°$. Because opposite angles in a parallelogram are equal, $\angle X$ also equals 50°.

b. 130°; $m\angle YZW = 50°$ and $\angle Y$ and $\angle Z$ are consecutive angles. Because consecutive angles of parallelograms are supplementary, $\angle Y = 130°$.

2. Opposite sides of a parallelogram are congruent.

3. 110°; Adjacent angles that form a straight angle are supplementary.

4. square **5.** rhombus

Name Date Time

Angles

1. Measure each angle to the nearest degree. Write the measure next to the angle.

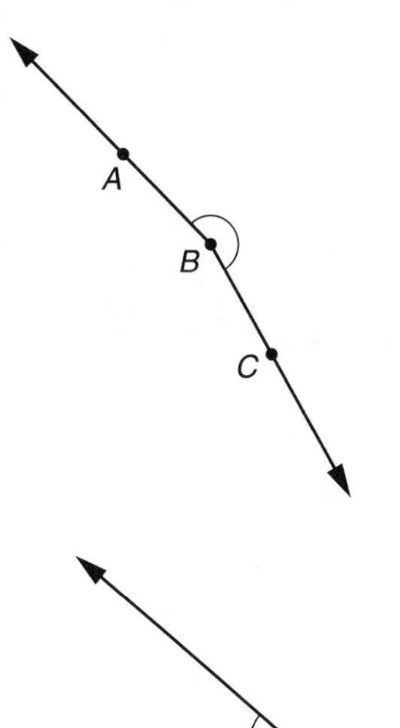

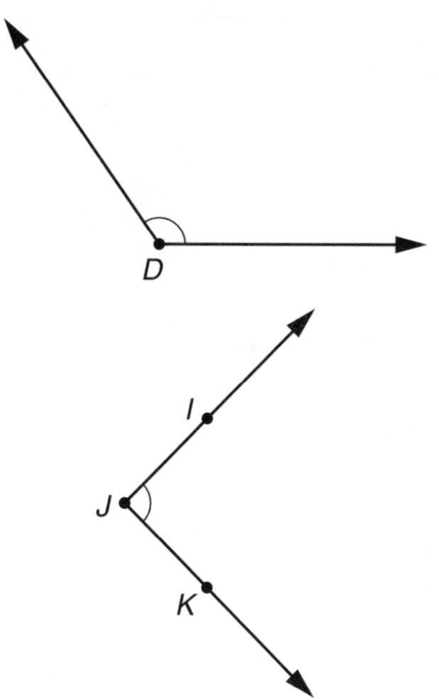

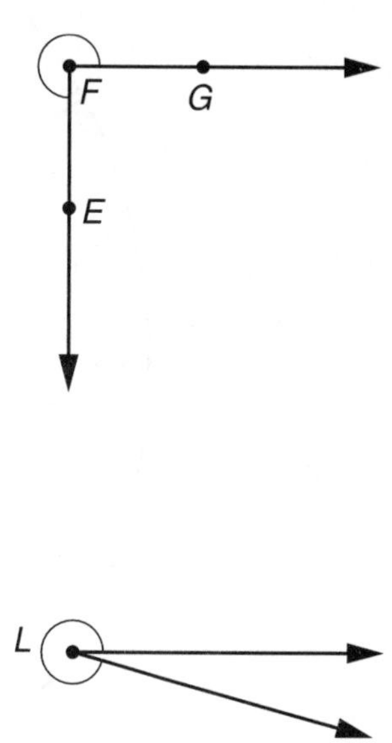

2. a. Which angle above is an acute angle? ________

   b. A right angle? ________ c. An obtuse angle? ________

   d. Which angles above are reflex angles? ____________________

3. a. Measure each angle in triangle *ADB* at the right.

   b. Find the sum of the 3 angle measures. ________ °

   c. Use Problem 3b to calculate the sum of the interior angle measures in quadrangle *ABCD*. ________ °

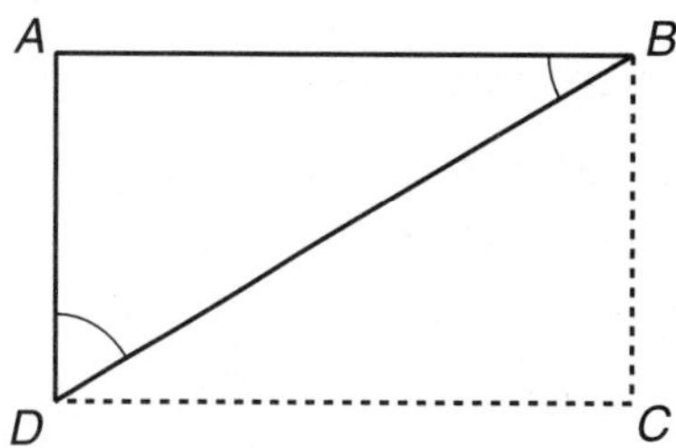

Try This

4. Find the measure of $\angle KLM$. Then draw an angle that is 60% of the measure of $\angle KLM$ on the reverse side of this paper. Label it as $\angle NOP$.

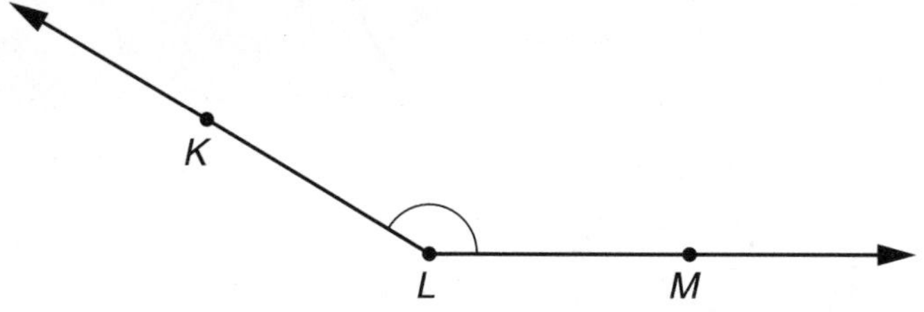

Name Date Time

LESSON 5•1 Making an Angle Measurer

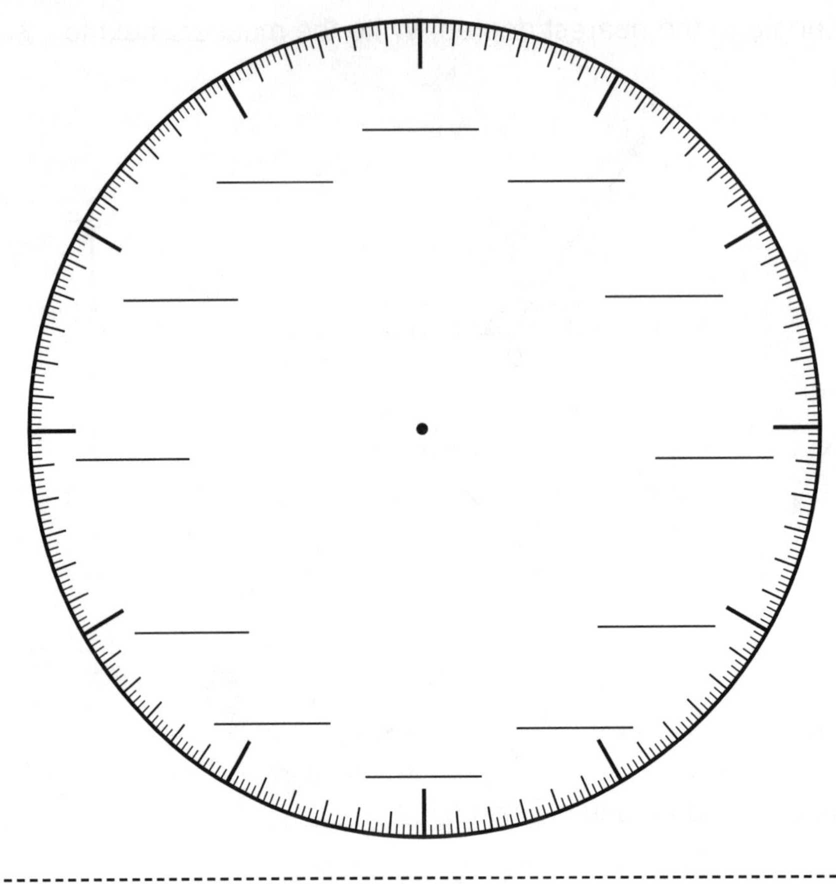

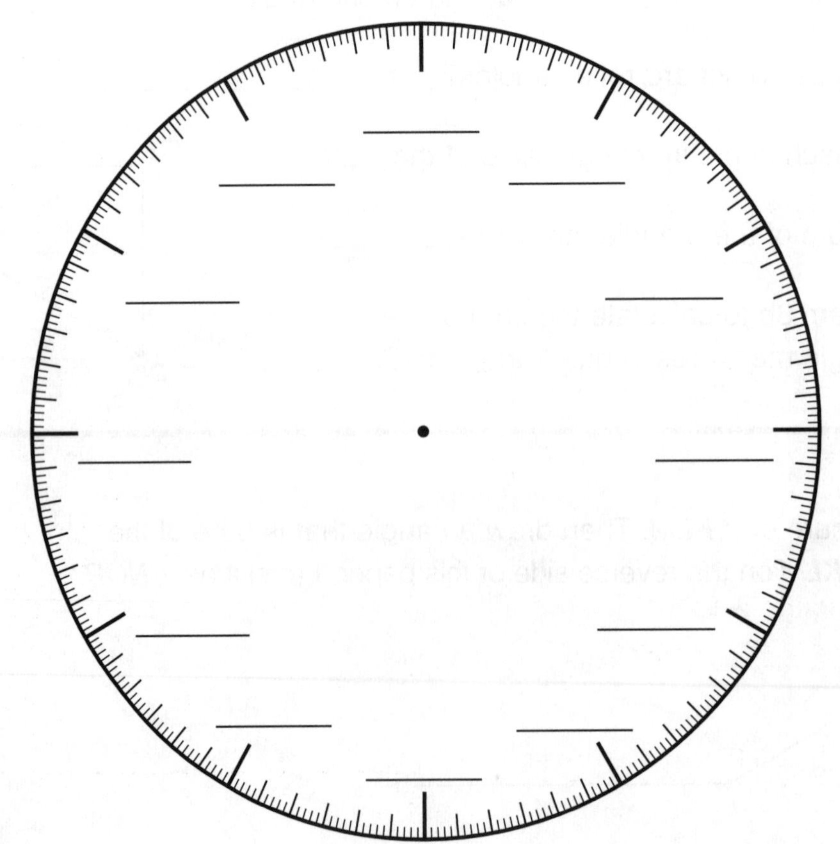

Name Date Time

Constructing a Hexagon

Follow the directions below to draw hexagon *ABCDEF*. Line segment *AF* at the bottom of the page is one of the sides of the hexagon. The completed drawing should be a convex hexagon. Use your Geometry Template and a pencil with a sharp point.

1. Draw a 130° angle with its vertex at point *A*. One side of the angle is $\overline{AF}$. Draw a point on the other side that is 5 centimeters from point *A*. Label this point *B*.

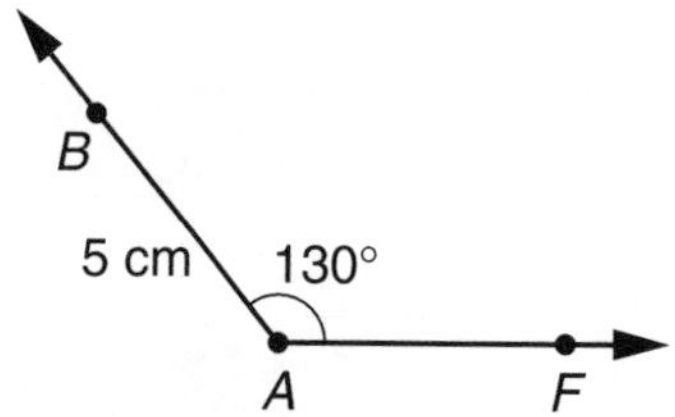

2. Draw a 115° angle with its vertex at point *B*. One side of the angle is $\overline{AB}$. Draw a point on the other side that is $1\frac{1}{2}$ inches from point *B*. Label it point *C*.

3. Draw a 145° angle with its vertex at point *C*. One side of the angle is $\overline{BC}$. Draw a point on the other side that is 6.5 centimeters from point *C*. Label it point *D*.

4. Draw a 90° angle with its vertex at point *D*. One side of the angle is $\overline{CD}$. Draw a point on the other side that is $2\frac{3}{4}$ inches from point *D*. Label it point *E*. Then draw $\overline{EF}$ to complete the hexagon.

5. What is the measure of $\angle E$? ________

of $\angle F$? ________

6. What is the length of $\overline{EF}$ to the nearest $\frac{1}{8}$ inch?

____

7. What is the sum of the measures of the angles of your hexagon?

____

The closer this sum is to 720°, the more accurate your drawing is.

A F

Name Date Time

STUDY LINK 5•2

Angle Relationships

SRB 163 233

Find the following angle measures. Do not use a protractor.

1.

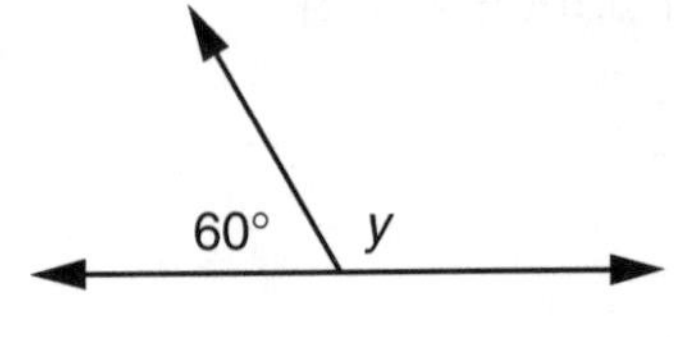

m∠y = ________

2.

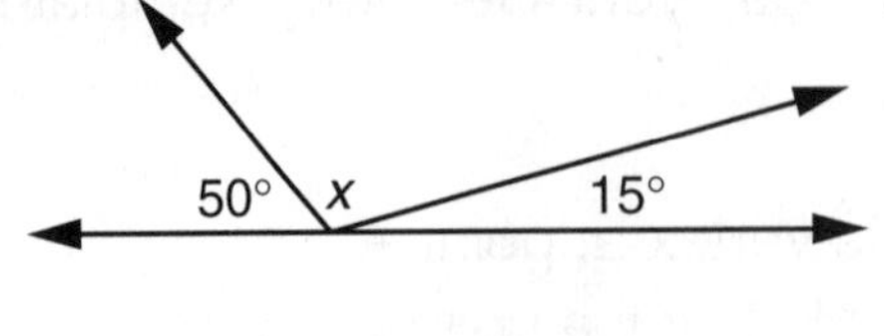

m∠x = ________

3.

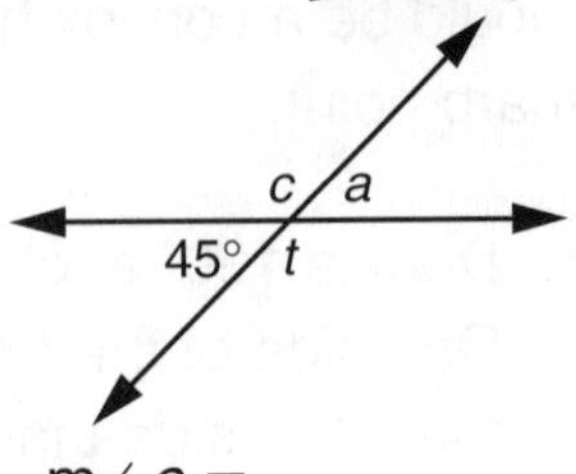

m∠c = ________

m∠a = ________

m∠t = ________

4. m∠q = ________ m∠r = ________ m∠s = ________

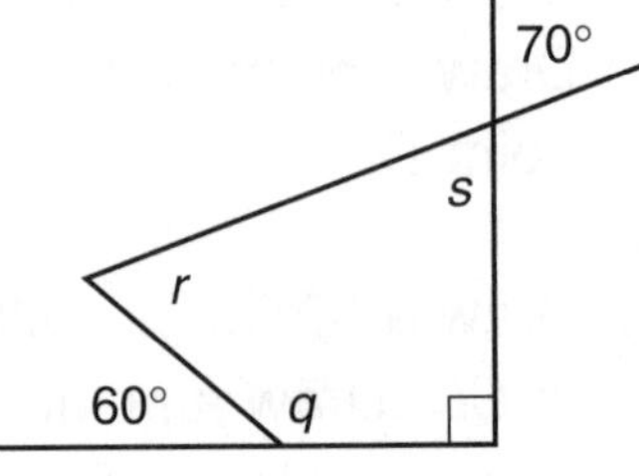

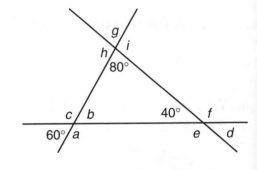

5. m∠a = ________ m∠b = ________

m∠c = ________ m∠d = ________

m∠e = ________ m∠f = ________

m∠g = ________ m∠h = ________

m∠i = ________

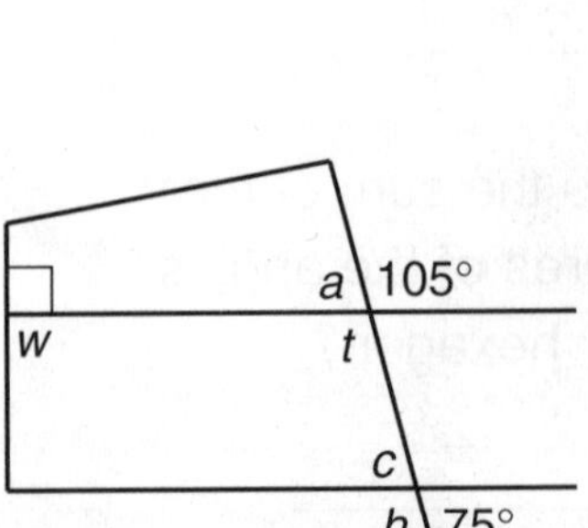

6. m∠w = ________ m∠a = ________

m∠t = ________ m∠c = ________

m∠h = ________

Practice

7. $\frac{3}{4}$ of 16 = ________ **8.** $\frac{3}{5}$ of 50 = ________ **9.** $\frac{1}{3}$ of 330 = ________

Name Date Time

Angle Measures: Triangles and Quadrangles

Cut out any or all of the triangles and quadrangles on this page.

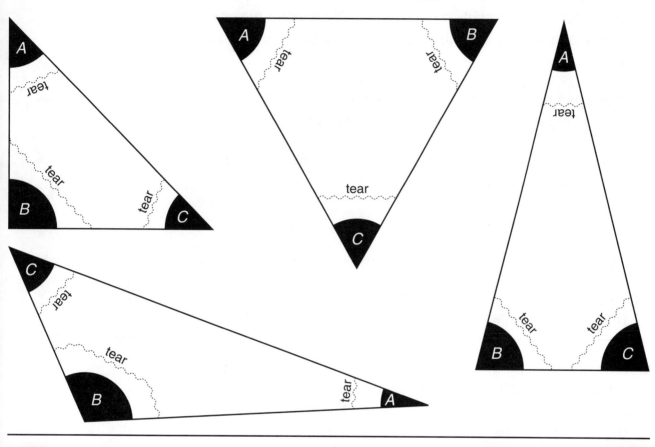

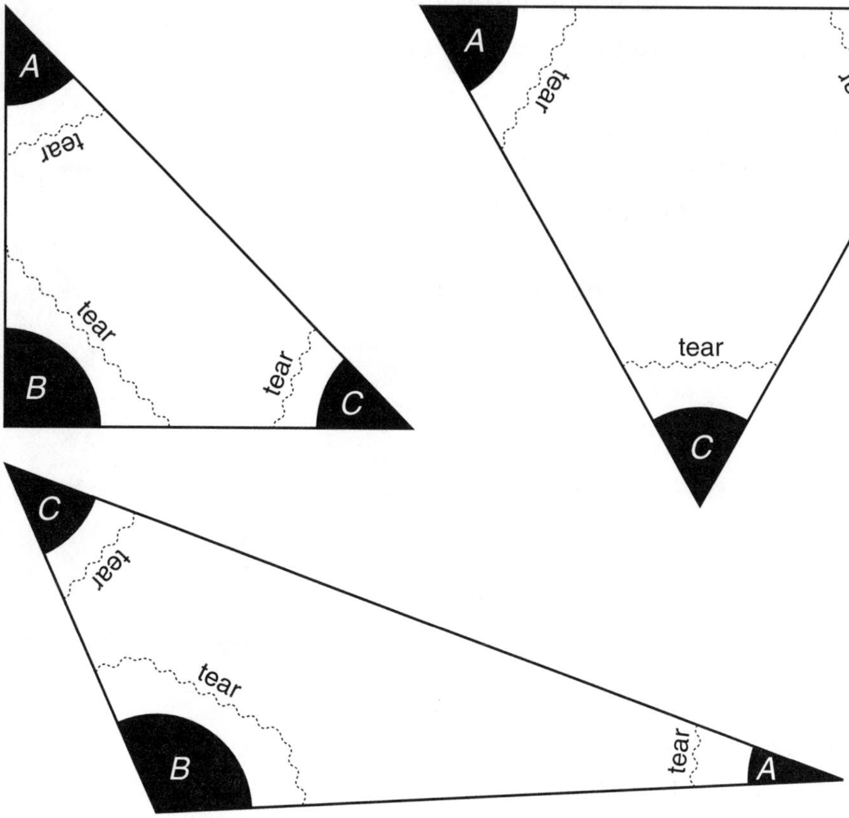

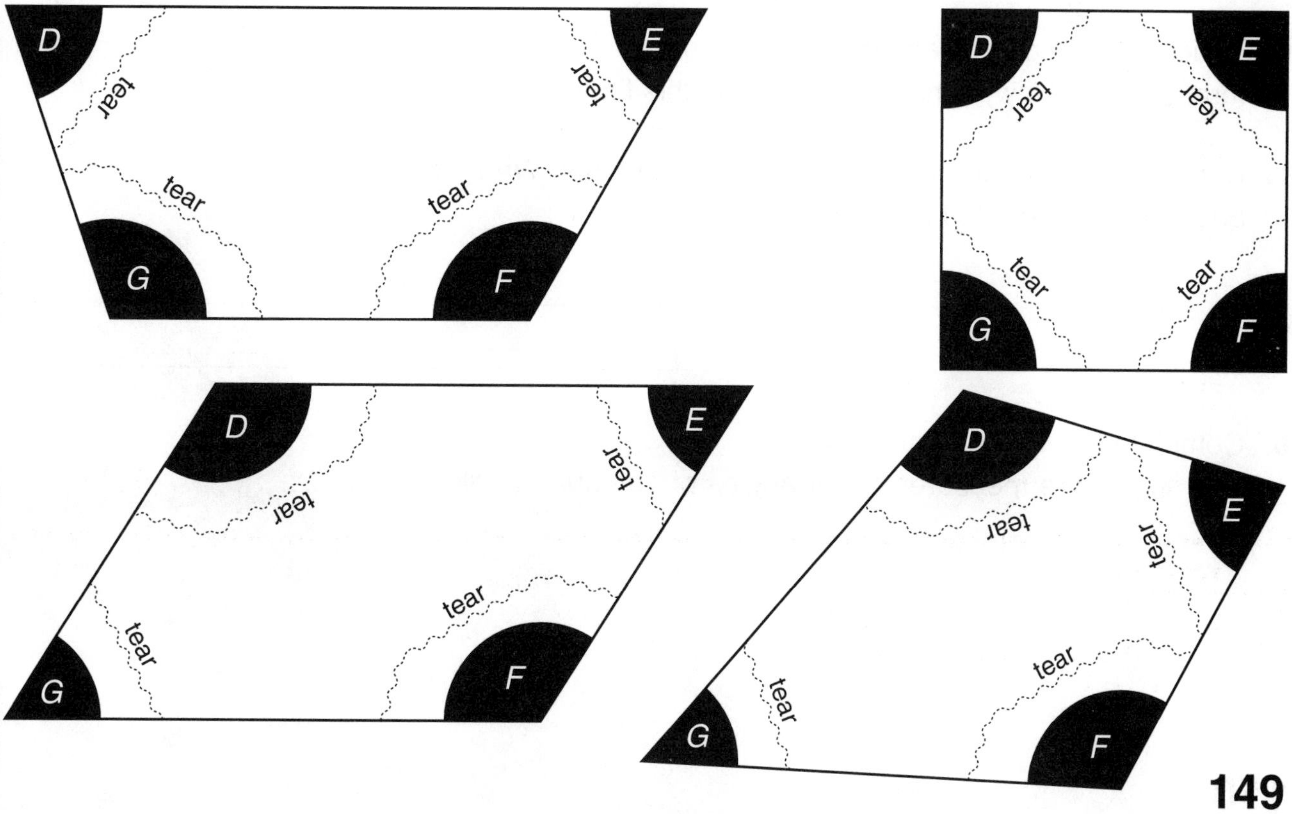

A tear B tear C tear

A tear B tear C tear

A tear B tear C tear

C tear B tear A tear

D tear E tear G tear F tear

D tear E tear G tear F tear

D tear E tear G tear F tear

D tear E tear G tear F tear

Name Date Time

LESSON 5•2

Finding Sums of Angle Measures

1. Cut out one of the triangles on *Math Masters*, page 149. Carefully cut or tear off each angle. Use point P at the right to position the angles so they touch but do not overlap. The shaded regions should form a semicircle. Use tape or glue to hold the angles in place.

•
P

2. Notice that the combined shaded regions form an angle. How many degrees does this angle measure? ________

3. Compare your results with those of other students. What do your triangles seem to have in common?

____

____

4. Complete the following statement.
The sum of the measures of the angles of any triangle is ________°.

---

5. Cut out one of the quadrangles on *Math Masters*, page 149. Carefully cut or tear off each angle. Use point Q at the right to position the angles so they touch but do not overlap. The shaded regions should form a circle. Use tape or glue to hold the angles in place.

•
Q

6. Notice that the combined shaded regions form a figure. How many degrees are in this figure? ________

7. Compare your results with those of other students. What do your quadrangles seem to have in common?

____

____

8. Complete the following statement.
The sum of the measures of the angles of any quadrangle is ________°.

Name Date Time

Applying Angle Relationships

1. Extend each side of the regular pentagon in both directions to form a star. The first extension has been done for you. Then use what you know about angle relationships to find and label the measures of each interior angle in your completed star.

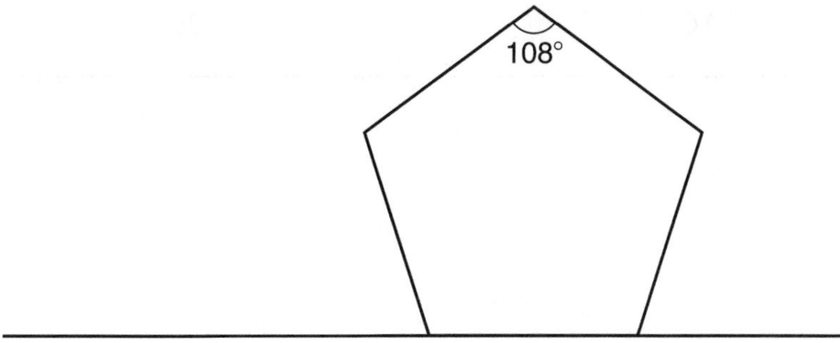

2. Describe the angle relationships you used to determine the measures of the interior angles.

____

____

____

____

Name Date Time

LESSON 5•3 Graphing Votes

Candidate	Percent of Votes Received	Degree Measure of Sector (to nearest degree)
Connie	28%	$\underline{0.28} * 360° = 100.8° \approx \underline{101°}$
Josh		______ $* 360° \approx$ ______
Manuel		______ $* 360° \approx$ ______
Total	**100%**	**360°**

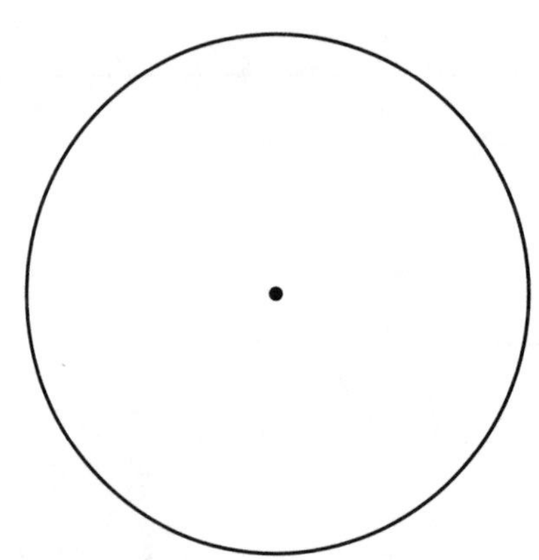

Name Date Time

LESSON 5•3

Pet Survey

Kind of Pet	Number of Pets	Fraction of Total Number of Pets	Decimal Equivalent (to nearest thousandth)	Percent of Total Number of Pets	Degree Measure of Sector
Dog	8	$\frac{8}{24}$	0.333	$33\frac{1}{3}\%$	$\frac{1}{3}$ * 360° = 120°
Cat	6				____ * 360° = ____
Guinea pig or hamster	3				____ * 360° = ____
Bird	3				____ * 360° = ____
Other	4				____ * 360° = ____

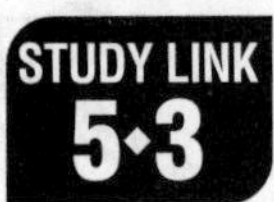

Circle Graphs

1. The table below shows a breakdown, by age group, of adults who listen to classical music.

a. Calculate the degree measure of each sector to the nearest degree.

b. Use a protractor to make a circle graph. Do *not* use the Percent Circle. Write a title for the graph.

Age	Percent of Listeners	Degree Measure
18–24	11%	
25–34	18%	
35–44	24%	
45–54	20%	
55–64	11%	
65+	16%	

Source: USA Today, Snapshot

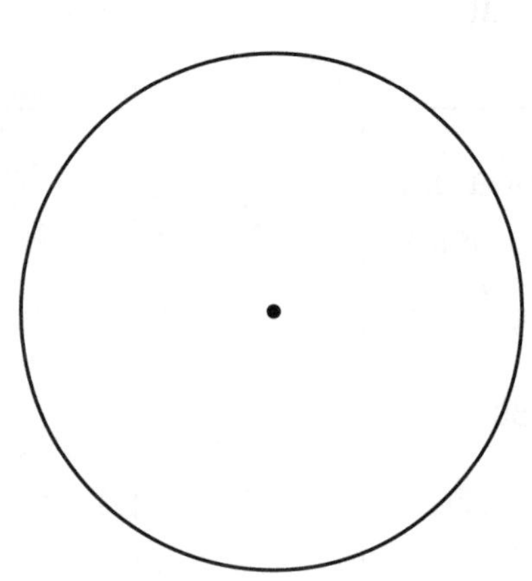

2. On average, about 8 million adults listen to classical music on the radio each day.

a. Estimate how many adults between the ages of 35 and 44 listen to classical music on the radio each day.

About ______________ (unit)

b. Estimate how many adults at least 45 years old listen to classical music on the radio each day.

About ______________ (unit)

Practice

Order each set of numbers from least to greatest.

3. 7, 0.07, −7, 0.7, 0 ______________

4. 0.25, 0.75, 0.2, $\frac{4}{5}$, $\frac{4}{4}$, 0.06, 0.18, $\frac{1}{10}$

____

Name Date Time

LESSON 5·3

Fractions of 360°

Shade each fractional part. Then record the number of degrees in each shaded region.

1. Shade $\frac{1}{2}$ of the circle.

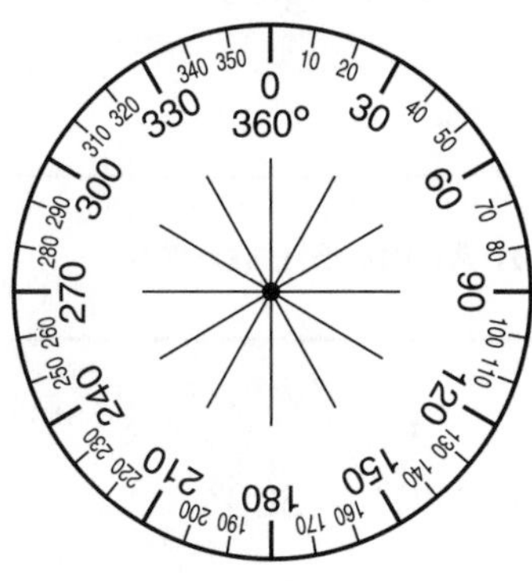

$\frac{1}{2}$ of 360° = ________ °

2. Shade $\frac{1}{4}$ of the circle.

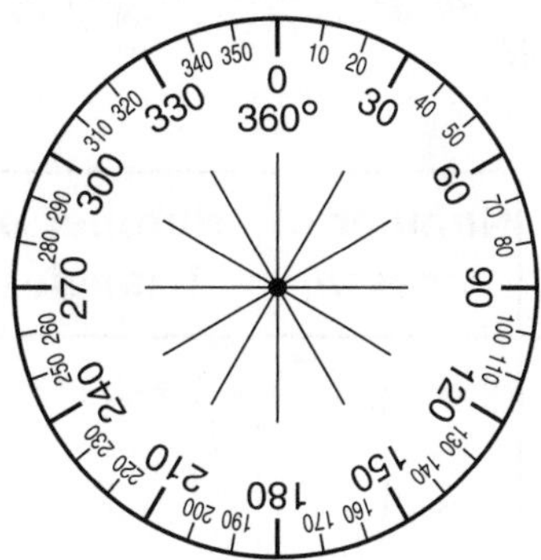

$\frac{1}{4}$ of 360° = ________ °

3. Shade $\frac{1}{6}$ of the circle.

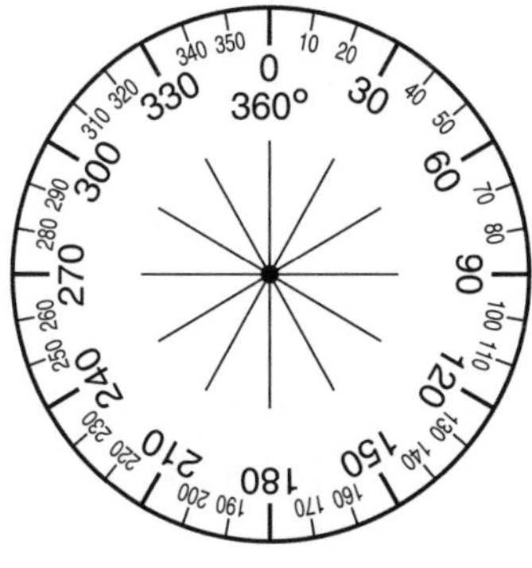

$\frac{1}{6}$ of 360° = ________ °

4. Shade $\frac{1}{3}$ of the circle.

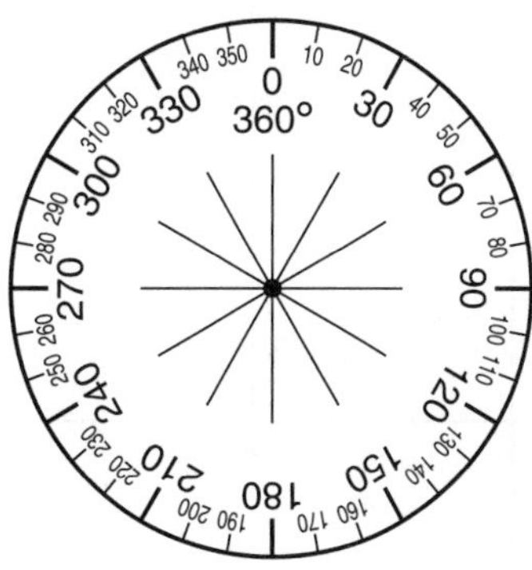

$\frac{1}{3}$ of 360° = ________ °

5. Shade $\frac{1}{12}$ of the circle.

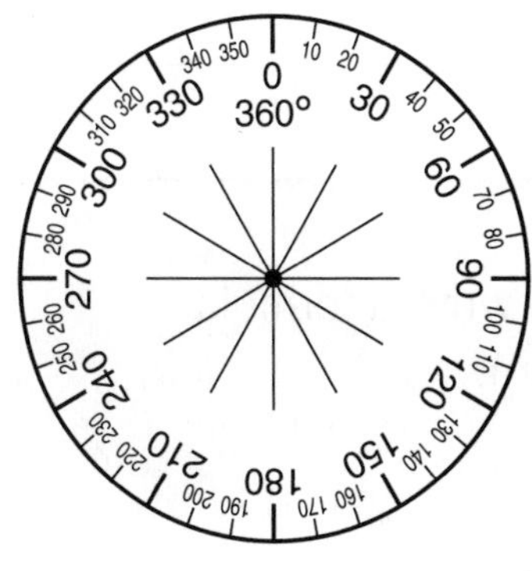

$\frac{1}{12}$ of 360° = ________ °

6. Shade $\frac{3}{4}$ of the circle.

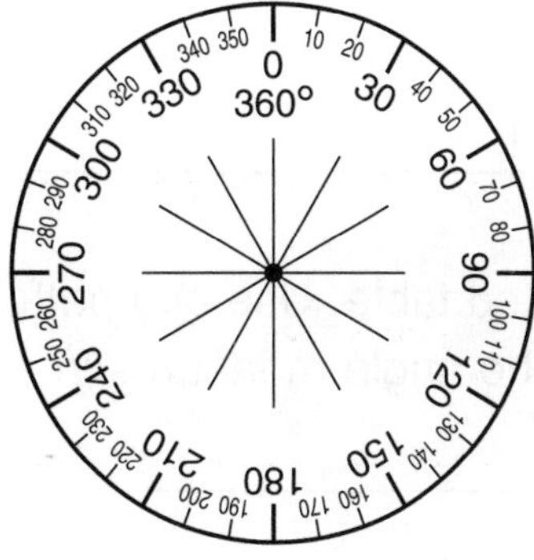

$\frac{3}{4}$ of 360° = ________ °

Name Date Time

Sums of Angle Measures in Polygons

A *diagonal* is a line segment that connects two vertices of a polygon and is *not* a side. You can draw diagonals from one vertex to separate polygons into triangles.

1. Draw diagonals from the given vertex to separate each polygon into triangles. Then complete the table.

Polygon	Number of Sides (n)	Number of Triangles	Sum of Angle Measures
Example: Quadrangle (diagonal)	4	2	$2 * 180° = 360°$
Pentagon			____ * ____ = ______°
Hexagon			____ * ____ = ______°
Octagon			____ * ____ = ______°
Decagon			____ * ____ = ______°

2. a. Study your completed table. Use any patterns you notice to write a formula to find the sum of the angle measures in any polygon (n-gon).

Formula ______________________

b. Use the formula to find the sums of the angle measures in a

heptagon. ________° nonagon. ________° dodecagon. ________°

Name Date Time

More Polygons on a Coordinate Grid

For each polygon described below, some vertices are plotted on the grid. Either one vertex or two vertices are missing.

- Plot and label the missing vertex or vertices on the grid. (There may be more than one place you can plot a point.)
- Write an ordered number pair for each vertex you plot.
- Draw the polygon.

1. Right triangle *ABC* Vertex *C:* (_______,_______)

2. Parallelogram *DEFG* Vertex *F:* (_______,_______) Vertex *G:* (_______,_______)

3. Scalene triangle *HIJ* Vertex *J:* (_______,_______)

4. Kite *KLMN* Vertex *M:* (_______,_______)

5. Square *PQRS* Vertex *Q:* (_______,_______)

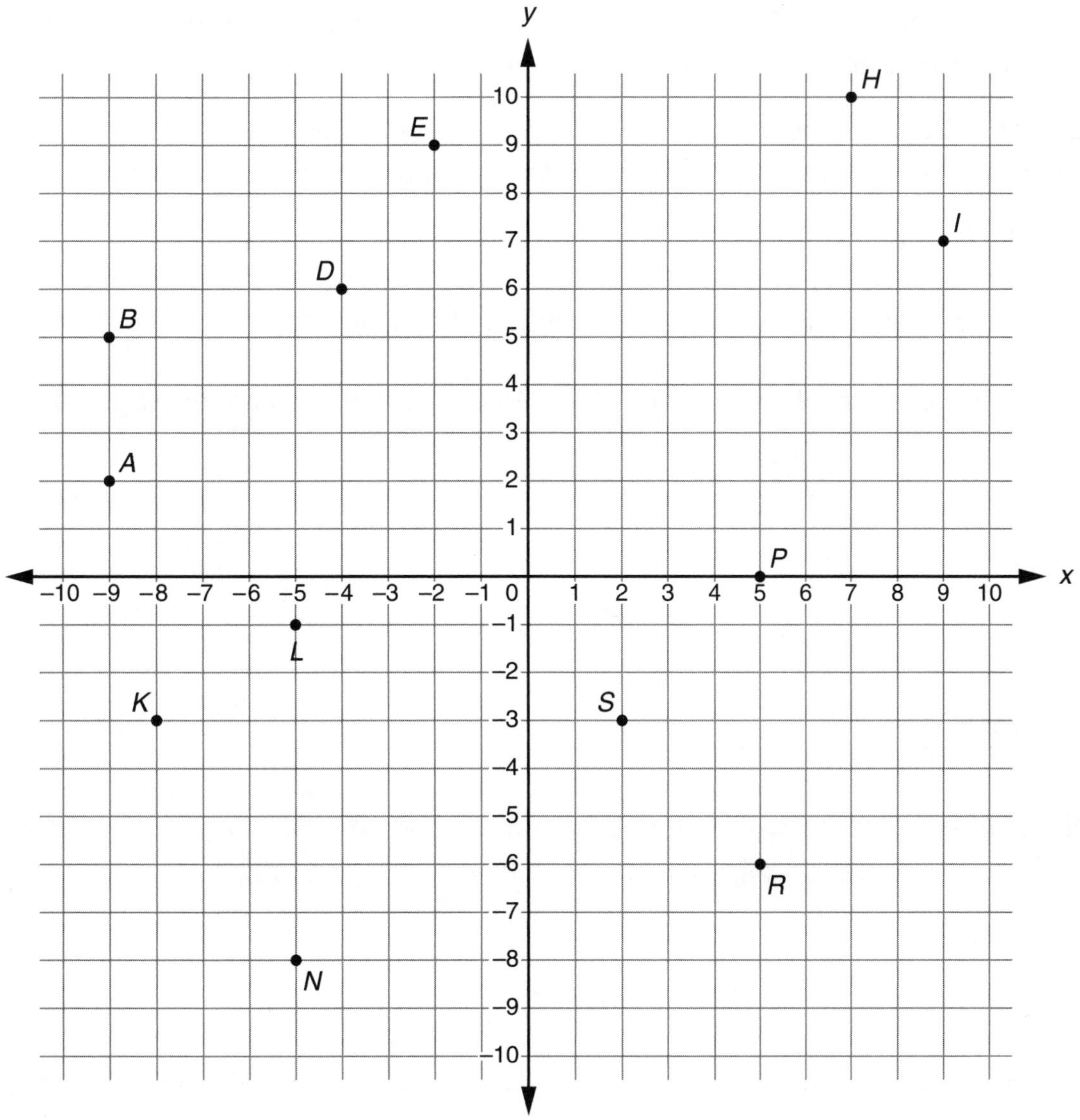

Name Date Time

X and O—Tic-Tac-Toe

Materials ☐ 4 each of number cards 0–10 (from the Everything Math Deck, if available)

☐ Coordinate Grid (*Math Masters,* p. 417)

Players 2

Object of the game To get 4 Xs or Os in a row, column, or diagonal on the coordinate grid.

Directions

1. Shuffle the cards and place the deck facedown on the playing surface.
2. In each round:
   - Player 1 draws 2 cards from the deck and uses the cards in any order to form an ordered pair. The player marks this ordered pair on the grid with an X and places the 2 cards in the discard pile.
   - Player 2 draws the next 2 cards from the deck and follows the same procedure, except that he or she uses an O to mark the ordered pair.
   - Players take turns drawing cards to form ordered pairs and marking the ordered pairs on the coordinate grid. If the 2 possible points that the player can make have already been marked, the player loses his or her turn.
3. The winner is the first player to get 4 Xs or 4 Os in a row, column, or diagonal.

Name Date Time

LESSON 5•4

Plotting Triangles and Quadrangles

Plot each of the described triangles and quadrangles on *Math Masters*, page 417. Record the coordinates of each vertex in the table below.

	Description	Coordinates of Each Vertex
Example:	Square with side measuring 3 units	(6,−6); (6,−3); (9,−3); (9,−6)
1.	A rhombus that is *not* a square, which has at least one vertex with a negative *x*-coordinate and a positive *y*-coordinate	
2.	An isosceles triangle that has an area of 2 square units	
3.	A rectangle that has a perimeter of 16 units	
4.	A right scalene triangle that has each vertex in a different quadrant	
5.	A kite that has one vertex at the origin	
6.	A parallelogram that has an area of 18 square units and one side on the *y*-axis	
7.	An obtuse scalene triangle that has at least two vertices with a negative *x*-coordinate and a negative *y*-coordinate	
8.	Write your own description.	

Name Date Time

Transforming Patterns

A pattern can be translated, reflected, or rotated to create many different designs. Consider the pattern at the right.

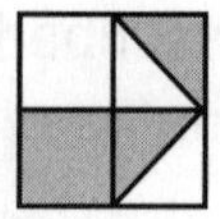

The following examples show how the pattern can be transformed to create different designs:

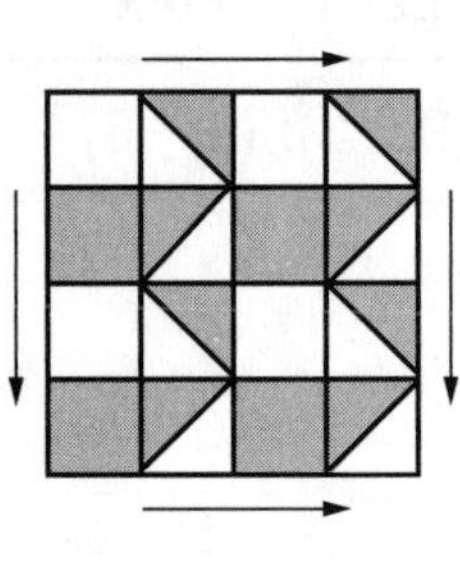

Translations

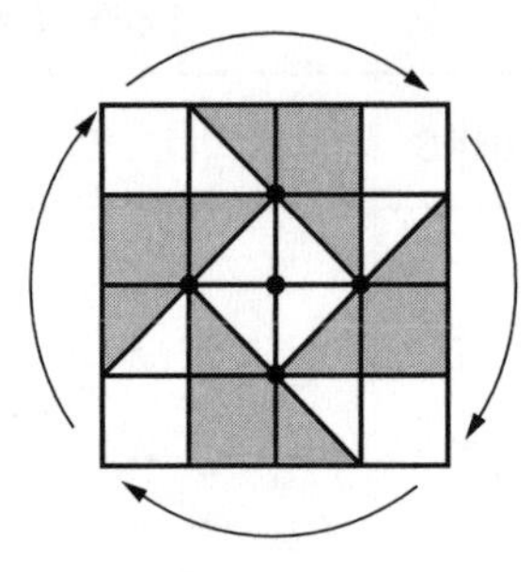

Rotations

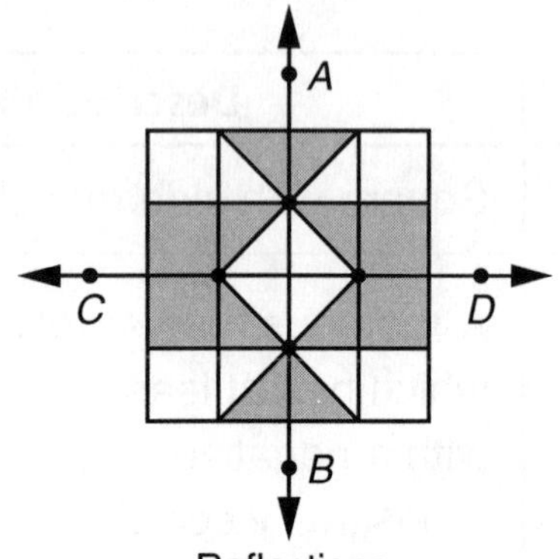

Reflections

1. Translate the pattern at the right across 2 grid squares. Then translate the resulting pattern (the given pattern and its translation) down 2 grid squares.

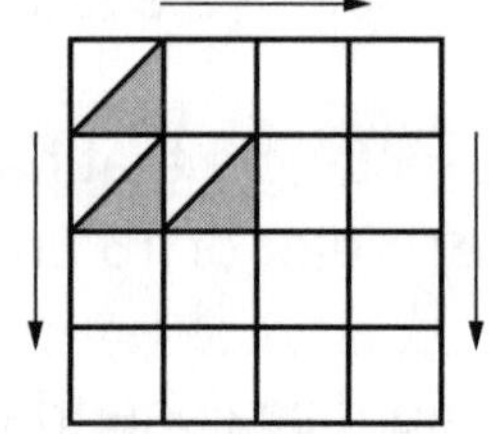

2. Rotate the given pattern clockwise 90° around point X. Repeat 2 more times.

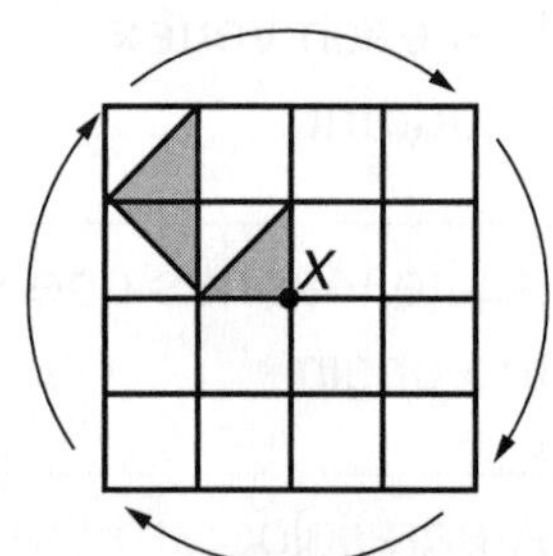

3. Reflect the given pattern over line JK. Reflect the resulting pattern (the given pattern and its reflection) over line LM.

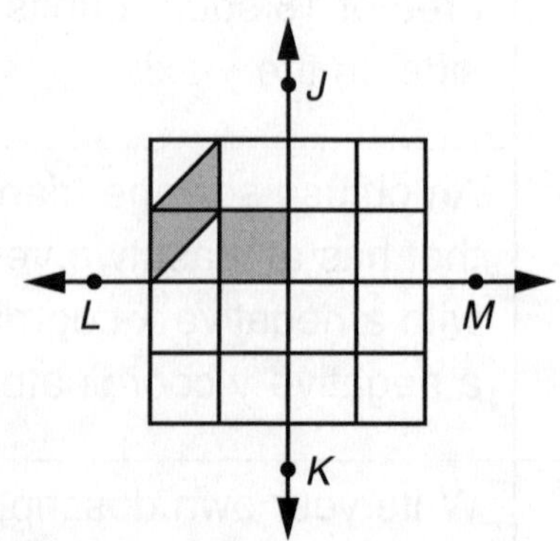

Practice

4. 2^6 = ________

5. 3^5 = ________

6. 7^0 = ________

7. 4^3 = ________

Name Date Time

Degrees and Directions of Rotation

When a figure is rotated, it is turned a certain number of degrees around a particular point. A figure can be rotated clockwise or counterclockwise.

Position a trapezoid pattern block on the center point of the angle measurer as shown at the right. Then rotate the pattern block as indicated and trace it in its new position.

Example: Rotate 90° clockwise.

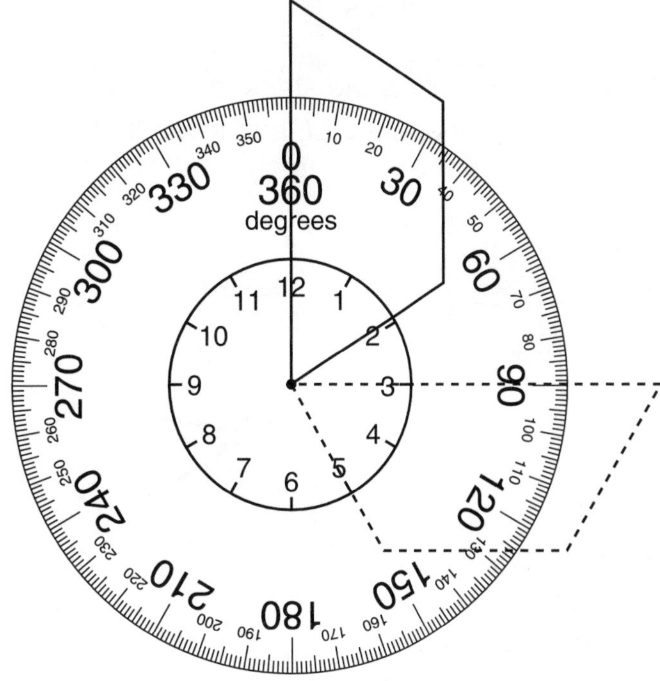

For each problem below, rotate and then trace the pattern block in its new position.

1. Rotate 90° counterclockwise.

2. Rotate 270° clockwise.

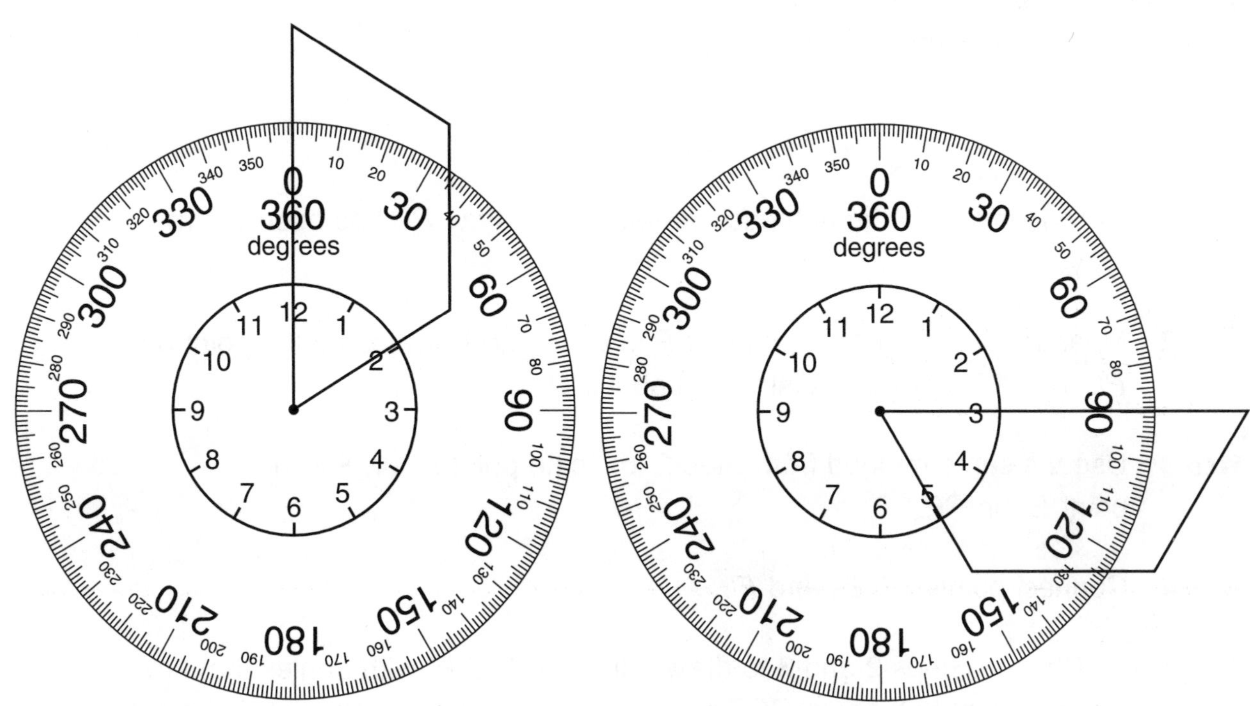

Name Date Time

Scaling Transformations

Some scaling transformations produce a figure that is the same shape as the original figure but not necessarily the same size. Enlargements and reductions are types of scaling transformations.

Enlargement: Follow the steps to draw a triangle *D′E′F′* with angles that are congruent to triangle *DEF* and sides that are twice as long as triangle *DEF*.

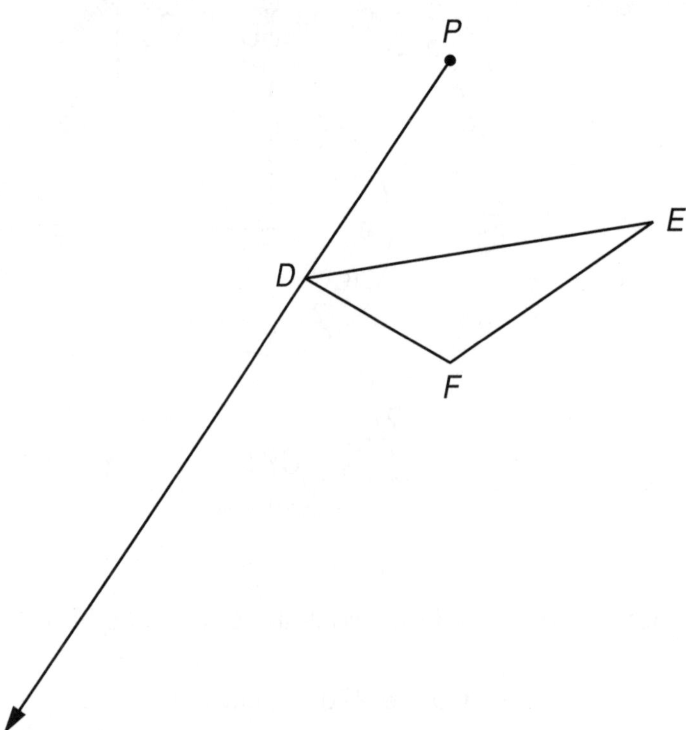

Step 1 Draw rays from *P* through each vertex. The first ray $\overrightarrow{PD}$ has been drawn for you.

Step 2 Measure the distance from point *P* to vertex *D*. Then locate the point on $\overrightarrow{PD}$ that is 2 times that distance. Label it *D′*.

Step 3 Use the same method from Step 2 to locate point *F′* on $\overrightarrow{PF}$ and point *E′* on $\overrightarrow{PE}$.

Step 4 Connect points *D′*, *E′*, and *F′*.

Reduction: Change Steps 2 and 3 to draw a triangle *D″E″F″* with angles that are congruent to triangle *DEF* and sides that are half as long as triangle *DEF*.

Name　　　　　　　　　　　　　　　　Date　　　　　　　　　　　　Time

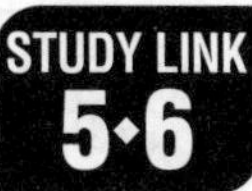

Congruent Figures and Copying

Column 1 below shows paths with the Start points marked. Complete each path in Column 2 so that it is congruent to the path in Column 1. Use the Start points marked in Column 2. In Problems 2 and 3, the copy will not be in the same position as the original path.

(*Hint:* If you have trouble, try tracing the path in Column 1 and then slide, flip, or rotate it so that its starting point matches the starting point in Column 2.)

Example: These two paths are congruent, but they are not in the same position.

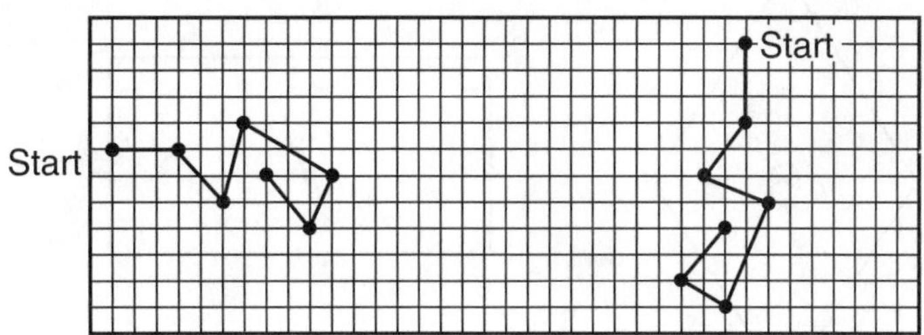

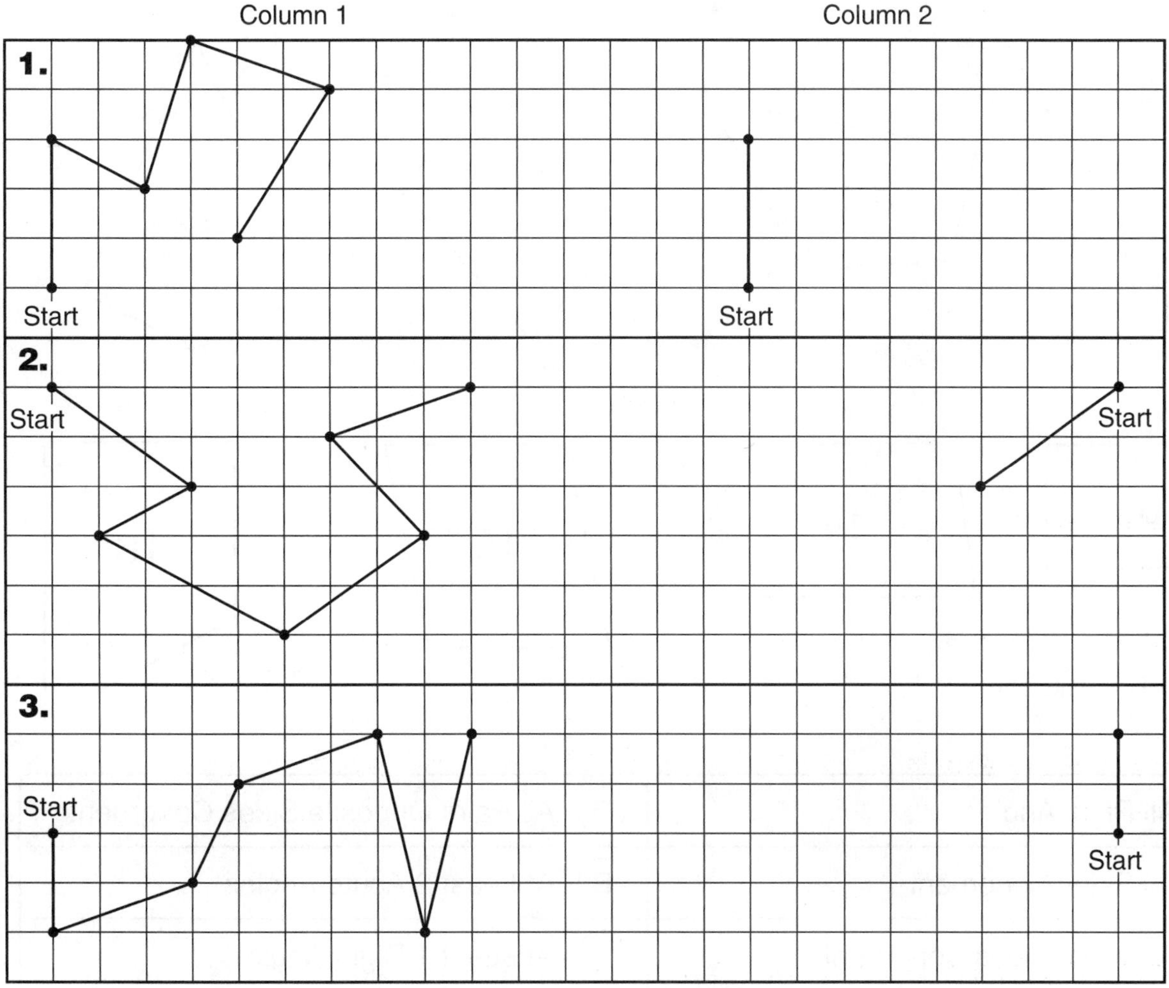

Column 1　　　　　　　　　　Column 2

1. Start　　　　Start

2. Start　　　　Start

3. Start　　　　Start

Name Date Time

Quadrangles and Congruence

Cut out the 16 quadrangles and the 6 set labels.

1 2 3 4

5 6 7 8

9 10 11 12

13 14 15 16

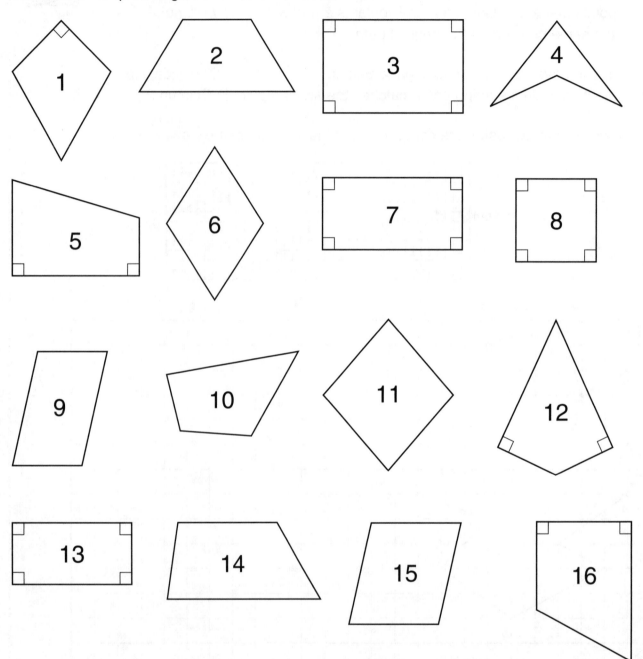

(A) All Right Angles	(B) All Pairs Opposite Sides Congruent
(A) All Sides Congruent	(B) At Least 2 Acute Angles
(C) Adjacent Sides Congruent	(C) At Least 1 Right Angle

Name Date Time

LESSON 5•6

Quadrangles and Congruence *continued*

Cut out the quadrangles and set labels from *Math Masters*, page 164. Place the two A, B, or C set labels in the placeholders above the rings and sort the quadrangles accordingly.

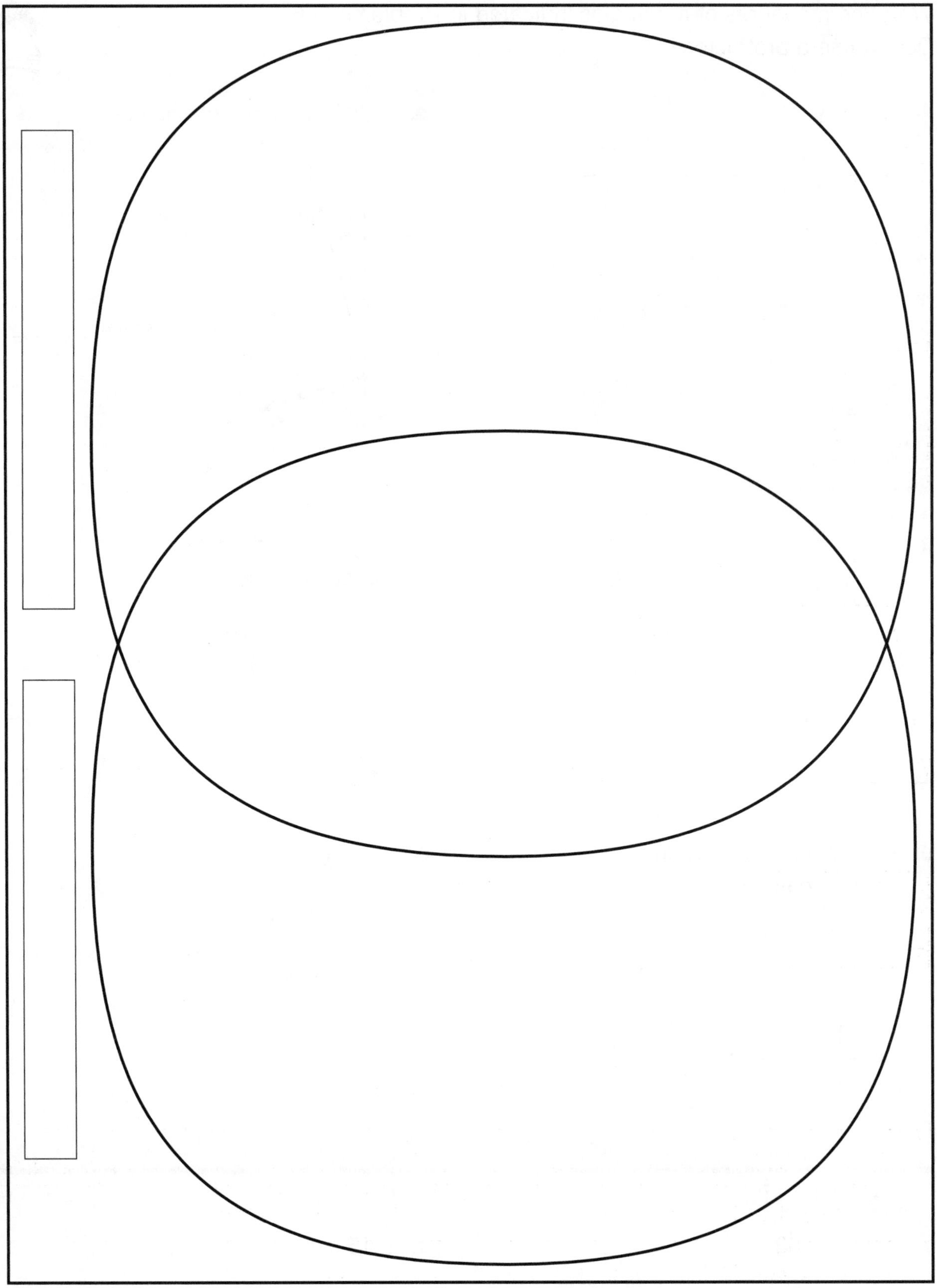

Name Date Time

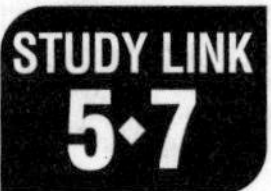

Angle Relationships

Write the measures of the angles indicated in Problems 1–6.
Do not use a protractor.

1.

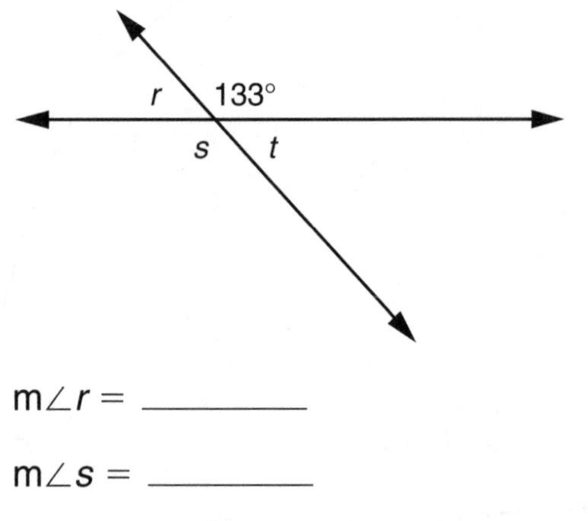

m∠*r* = ________

m∠*s* = ________

m∠*t* = ________

2. ∠*JKL* is a straight angle.

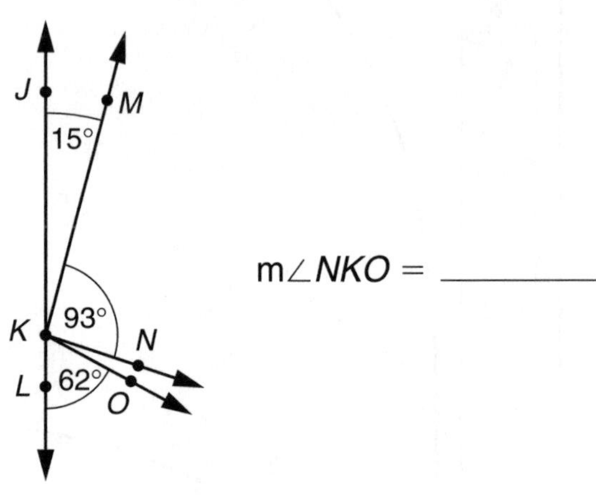

m∠*NKO* = ________

3.

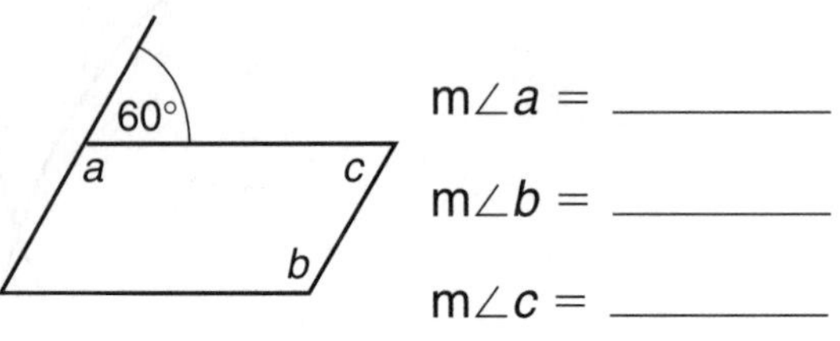

m∠*a* = ________

m∠*b* = ________

m∠*c* = ________

4. Angles *a* and *t* have the same measure.

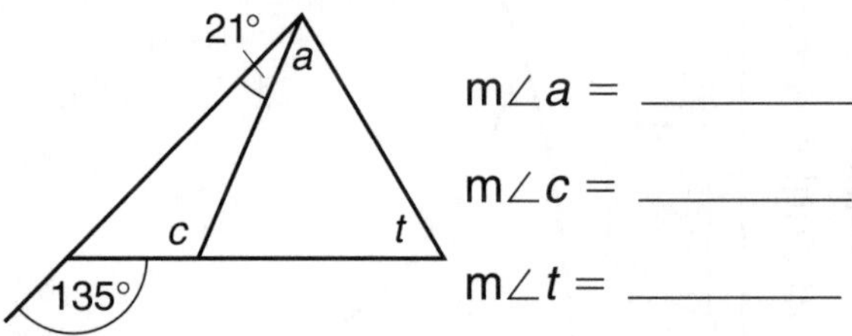

m∠*a* = ________

m∠*c* = ________

m∠*t* = ________

5. Angles *x* and *y* have the same measure.

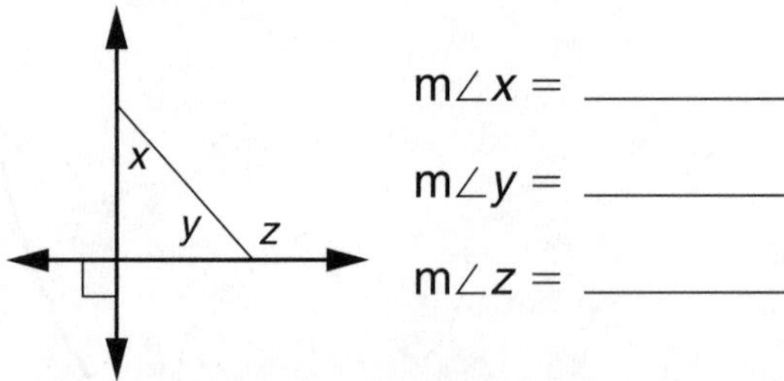

m∠*x* = ________

m∠*y* = ________

m∠*z* = ________

6.

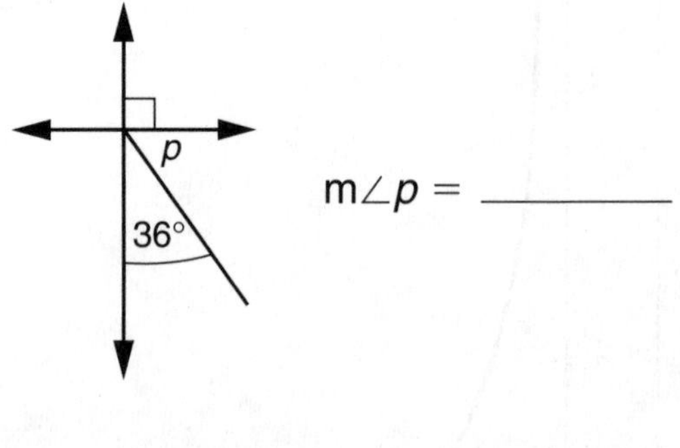

m∠*p* = ________

Practice

7. 0.09 ∗ 0.03 = ____________

8. 0.15 ∗ 0.8 = ____________

9. 0.07 ∗ 0.07 = ____________

10. 0.75 ∗ 0.3 = ____________

Name Date Time

Circle Constructions

Use the directions and the pictures below to make one or both of the constructions. You may need to make several versions of the construction before you are satisfied with your work. Cut out your best constructions and tape or glue them to another sheet of paper.

Construction #1

Step 1 Draw a small point that will be the center of the circle. Press the compass anchor firmly on the center of the circle.

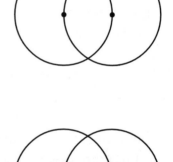

Step 2 Hold the compass at the top and rotate the pencil around the anchor. The pencil must go all the way around to make a circle. You may find it easier to firmly hold the compass in place and carefully turn the paper under the compass.

Step 3 Without changing the opening of the compass, draw another circle that passes through the center of the first circle. Mark the center of the second circle.

Step 4 Repeat Step 3 to draw a third circle that passes through the center of each of the first two circles.

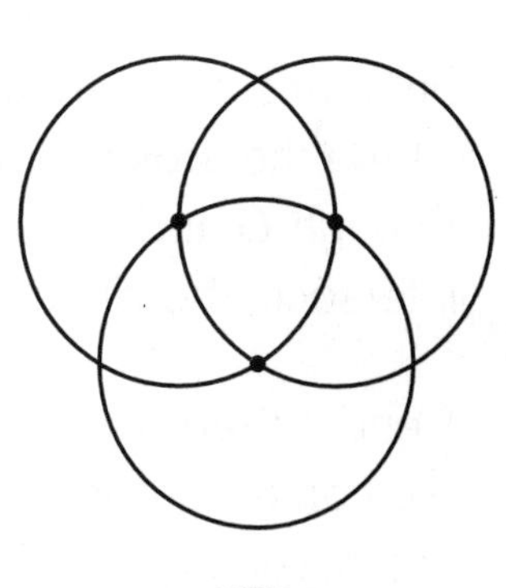

Construction #2

Follow the steps to make the three circles from Construction #1. Then draw more circles to create the construction shown at the right.

Name Date Time

Octagon Construction

Use the directions and the pictures to construct an octagon.

Step 1 Draw a circle with a compass. Label the center of the circle *A*. Then draw a diameter through *A*. Label the two points where the diameter intersects the circle *S* and *T*.

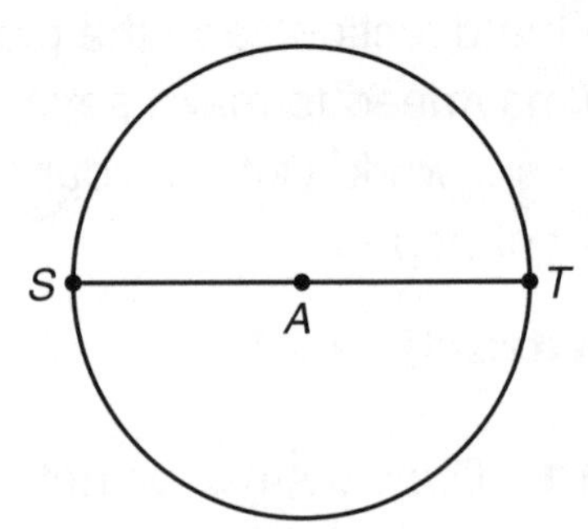

Step 2 Use the length of $\overline{ST}$ to set the compass opening. Then place the anchor of your compass on *S* and draw an arc below the circle and another arc above the circle. Without changing the compass opening, place the compass anchor on *T* and draw another set of arcs above and below the circle. Label the points where the arcs intersect as *D* and *E*. Draw a line through *D* and *E*. Label the points where $\overleftrightarrow{DE}$ intersects the circle as *M* and *N*.

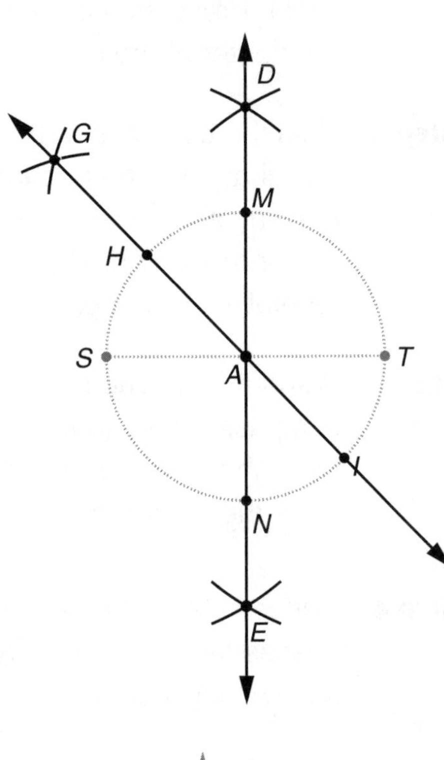

Step 3 Set the compass opening so that it is equal to the length of $\overline{SM}$. Then place the compass anchor on *S* and draw an arc; reposition the anchor on *M* and draw another arc. Label the point where the arcs intersect as *G*. Draw a line through *G* and *A*. Label the points where $\overleftrightarrow{GA}$ intersects the circle as *H* and *I*.

Step 4 Repeat Step 3, using the length of $\overline{MT}$ to set the compass opening. Label the points of intersection as *X, Y,* and *Z*.

Step 5 Connect the points on the circle to form an octagon.

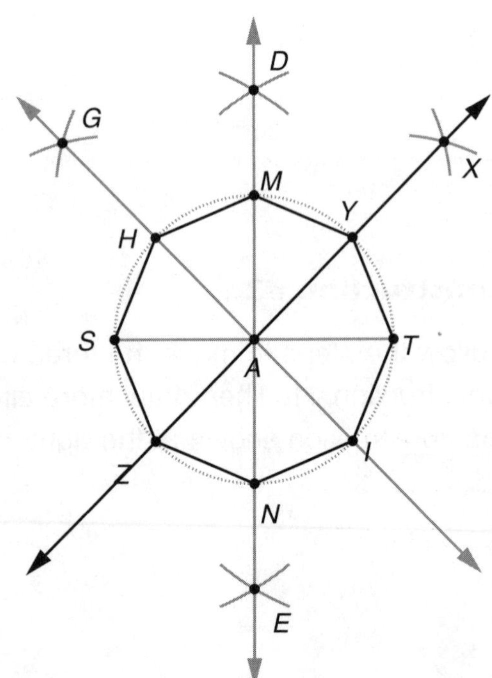

Name Date Time

STUDY LINK 5•8

Isometry Transformations on a Grid

1. Graph and label the following points on the coordinate grid. Connect the points to form quadrangle *ABCD*.

A: (−2,1) *B:* (−6,2)
C: (−8,4) *D:* (−5,7)

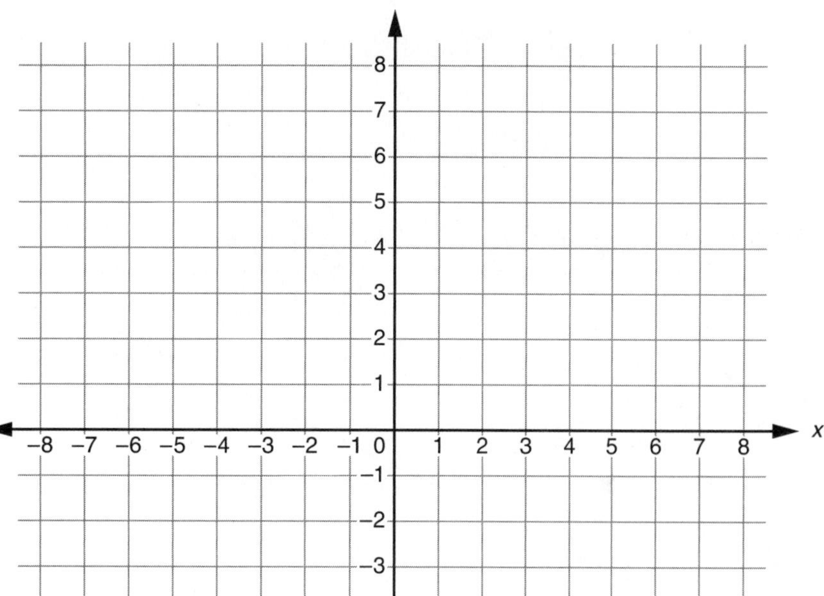

2. Translate each vertex of *ABCD* (in Problem 1) 0 units to the left or right and 8 units down. Plot and connect the new points. Label them *A′*, *B′*, *C′*, and *D′*.

Record the coordinates of the image.

____

____

____

____

3. Reflect quadrangle *ABCD* across the *y*-axis. Plot and connect the new points. Label them *A″*, *B″*, *C″*, and *D″*. Record the coordinates of the image.

__________ __________ __________ __________

Try This

4. Rotate quadrangle *A″B″C″D″* 90° clockwise around point (0,0). Plot and connect the new points. Label them *A‴*, *B‴*, *C‴*, and *D‴*. Record the coordinates of the rotated image.

__________ __________ __________ __________

Practice

5. $300 * 0.001 =$ ________ **6.** $143 * 10^{-3} =$ ________ **7.** $35.9 * \frac{1}{1,000} =$ ________

Name Date Time

Inscribing a Circle in a Triangle

Follow the steps to inscribe a circle in triangle *ABC*.

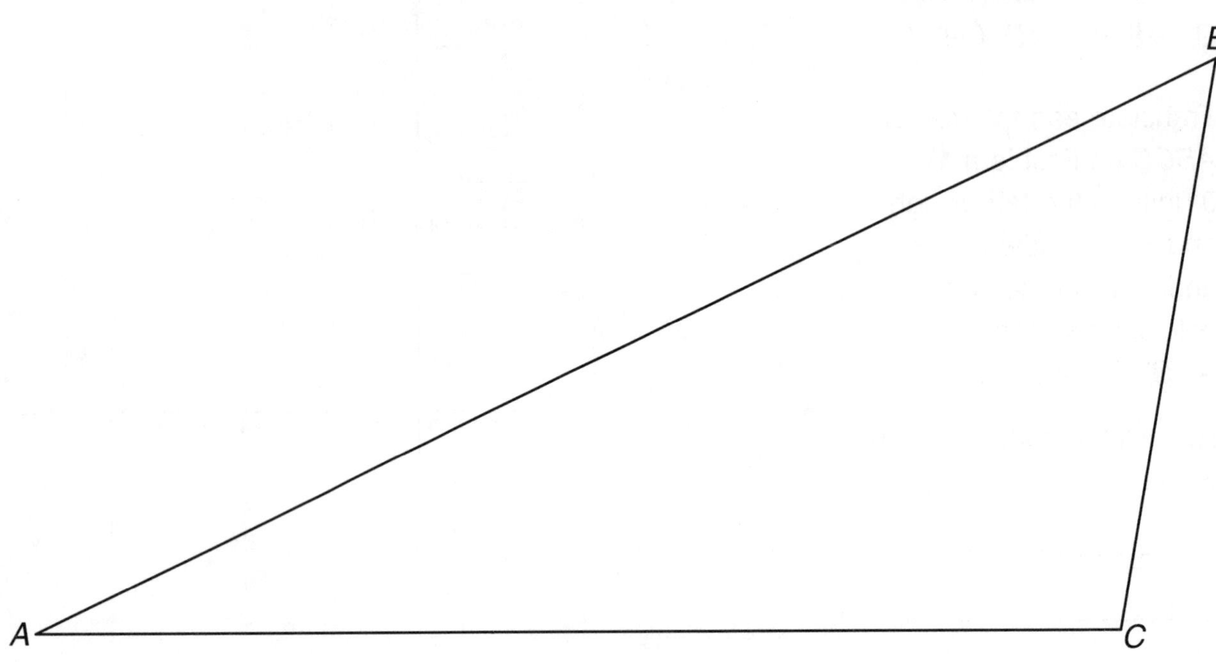

Step 1 Construct the bisectors of $\angle A$ and $\angle B$. Then label the intersection of the angle bisectors as *P*.

Step 2 Construct a line segment through point *P*, perpendicular to $\overline{AB}$. Label the point at which the line segment intersects $\overline{AB}$ as *Q*.

Step 3 Center the compass anchor on *P* and the pencil point on *Q*. Draw a circle through *Q*. The circle will be tangent to all three sides of the triangle.

Name Date Time

Constructing Perpendicular Bisectors

1. Draw a large triangle. Construct perpendicular bisectors for each side of the triangle. What observations can you make?

____

____

____

____

2. Use a protractor and a ruler to draw a large square. Draw a diagonal. Then construct the perpendicular bisector of the diagonal. What observations can you make?

____

____

____

Name Date Time

STUDY LINK 5·9

Parallel Lines and a Transversal

1. Use a ruler and a straightedge to draw 2 parallel lines. Then draw another line that crosses both parallel lines.

2. Measure the 8 angles in your figure.
Write each measure inside the angle.

3. What patterns do you notice in your angle measures?

____

____

____

____

____

____

Practice

Remember: 1,000 milliliters (mL) = 1 liter (L)

4. 500 mL = __________ L

5. 2.5 L = __________ mL

6. 1,300 mL = __________ L

7. 0.95 L = __________ mL

8. 3,250 mL = __________ L

9. 0.045 L = __________ mL

Name Date Time

Angle Relationships and Algebra

Apply your knowledge of angle relationships to find the missing values and angle measures. Do not use a protractor.

1.

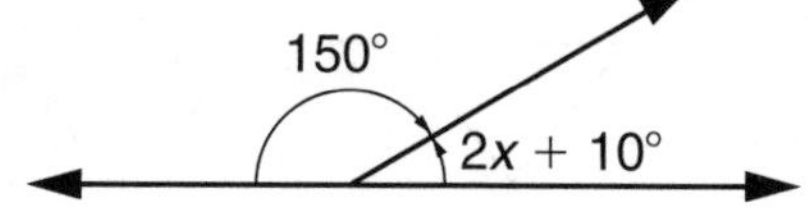

$x =$ ______ °

2.

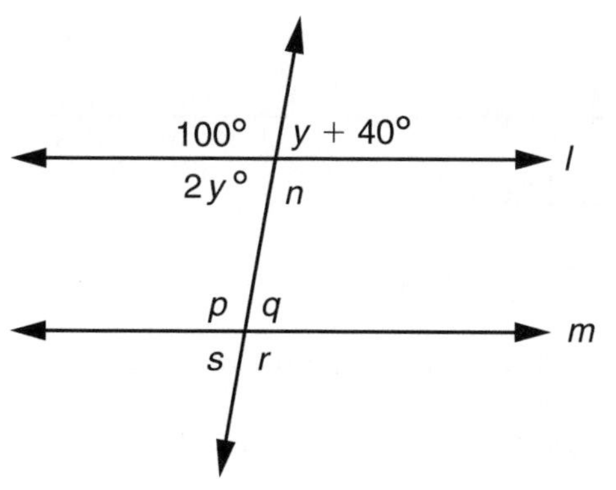

Lines *l* and *m* are parallel.

$y =$ ______ °

$m\angle p =$ ______ ° $m\angle r =$ ______ °

$m\angle q =$ ______ ° $m\angle s =$ ______ °

3.

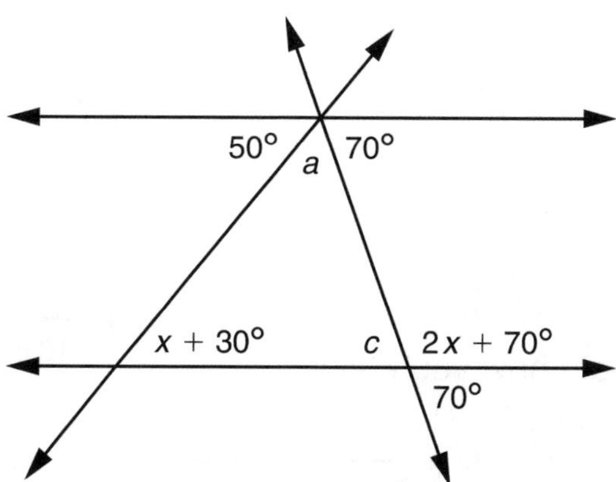

$x =$ ______ °

$m\angle a =$ ______ ° $m\angle c =$ ______ °

4. Turn this page over. Using only a straightedge and a compass, design a problem that uses angle relationships. Create an answer key for your problem. Then ask a classmate to solve your problem.

Name Date Time

STUDY LINK 5•10

Parallelogram Problems

All of the figures on this page are parallelograms.
Do not use a ruler or a protractor to solve Problems 1, 2, or 3.

1. a. The measure of $\angle X$ = ________°. Explain how you know.

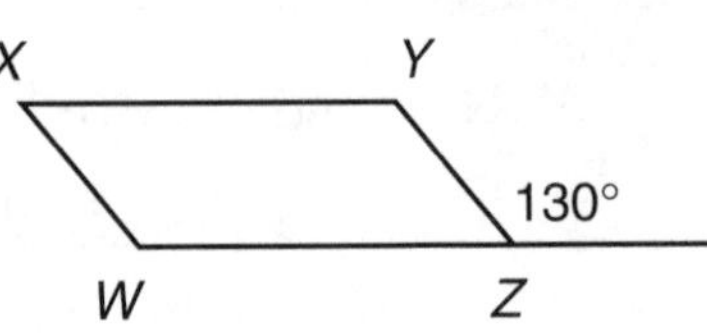

____

____

____

____

b. The measure of $\angle Y$ = ________°. Explain how you know.

____

____

____

2. Alexi said that the only way to find the length of sides *CO* and *OA* is to measure them with a ruler. Explain why he is incorrect.

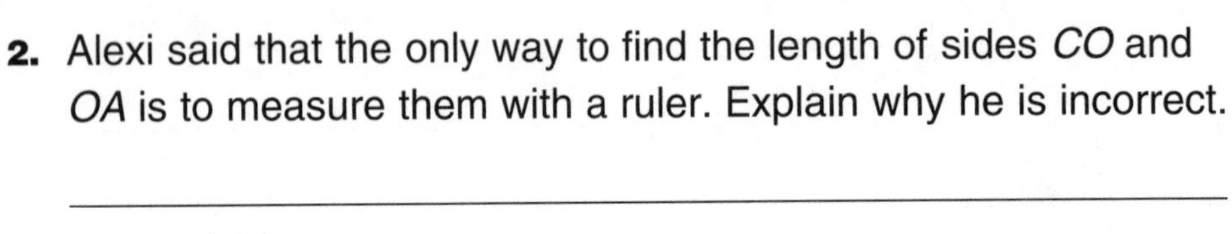

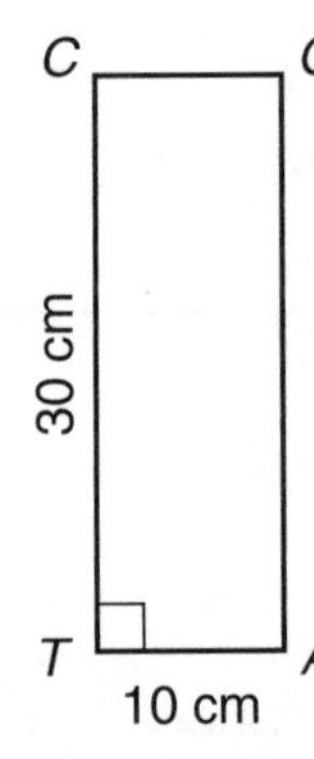

____

____

3. What is the measure of $\angle MAR$? ________. Explain how you know.

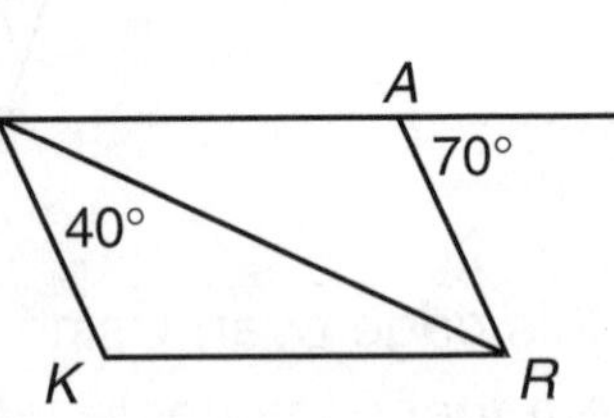

____

____

4. Draw a parallelogram in which all sides have the same length and all angles have the same measure.

What is another name for this parallelogram? ________________

5. Draw a parallelogram in which all sides have the same length and no angle measures 90°.

What is another name for this parallelogram? ________________

Name ______________________ Date ______________ Time ______________

LESSON 5•10 Using Quadrangles to Classify Quadrangles

Read each statement. Then decide if the statement is *always, sometimes,* or *never* true. If you write *sometimes,* identify a case for which the statement is true.

Example: A rectangle is a square. <u>sometimes</u>

A rectangle is a square when its 4 sides are the same length.

1. A square is a rectangle. ______________________

2. A rhombus is a trapezoid. ______________________

3. A square is a parallelogram. ______________________

4. A rhombus is a parallelogram. ______________________

5. A kite is a parallelogram. ______________________

6. A rhombus is a rectangle. ______________________

7. A square is a rhombus. ______________________

8. A trapezoid is a parallelogram. ______________________

Fill in the blank using *always, sometimes,* or *never.* If you write *sometimes,* identify a case for which the statement is true.

9. A rectangle ______________ has consecutive sides that are congruent.

____

____

10. The diagonals of a rhombus are ______________ congruent.

____

____

Name Date Time

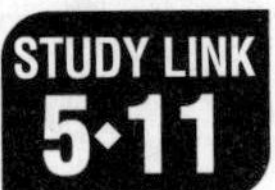

Unit 6: Family Letter

Number Systems and Algebra Concepts

In *Fourth* and *Fifth Grade Everyday Mathematics,* your child worked with addition and subtraction of positive and negative numbers. In this unit, students use multiplication patterns to help them establish the rules for multiplying and dividing with positive and negative numbers. They also develop and use an algorithm for the division of fractions.

In the rest of the unit, your child will explore beginning algebra concepts. First, the class reviews how to determine whether a number sentence is true or false. This involves understanding what to do with numbers that are grouped within parentheses and knowing in what order to calculate if the groupings of numbers are not made explicit by parentheses.

Students then solve simple equations by trial and error to reinforce what it means to solve an equation—to replace a variable with a number that will make the number sentence true.

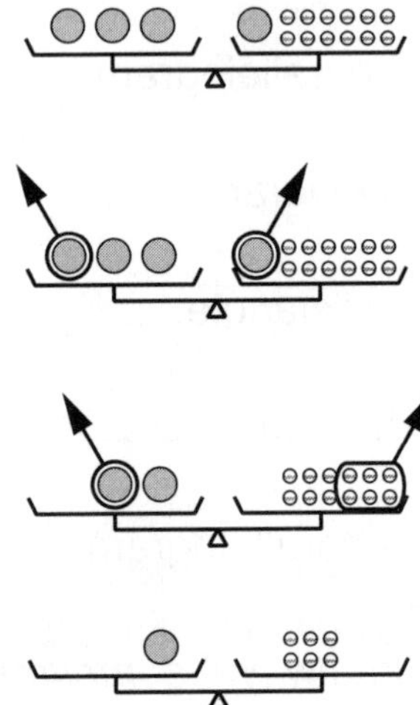

Next, they solve pan-balance problems, first introduced in *Fifth Grade Everyday Mathematics,* to develop a more systematic approach to solving equations. For example, to find out how many marbles weigh as much as 1 orange in the top balance at the right, you can first remove 1 orange from each pan and then remove half the remaining oranges from the left side and half the marbles from the right side. The pans will still balance.

Students learn that each step in the solution of a pan-balance problem can be represented by an equation, thus leading to the solution of the original equation. You might ask your child to demonstrate how pan-balance problems work.

Finally, your child will learn how to solve inequalities—number sentences comparing two quantities that are not equal.

Please keep this Family Letter for reference as your child works through Unit 6.

Vocabulary

Important terms in Unit 6:

cover-up method An informal method for finding the solution of an open sentence by covering up a part of the sentence containing a variable.

Division of Fractions Property A property of dividing that says division by a fraction is the same as multiplication by the *reciprocal* of the fraction. Another name for this property is the "invert and multiply rule." For example:

$$5 \div 8 = 5 * \frac{1}{8} = \frac{5}{8}$$
$$15 \div \frac{3}{5} = 15 * \frac{5}{3} = \frac{75}{3} = 25$$
$$\frac{1}{2} \div \frac{3}{5} = \frac{1}{2} * \frac{5}{3} = \frac{5}{6}$$

In symbols: For a and nonzero b, c, and d,

$$\frac{a}{b} \div \frac{c}{d} = \frac{a}{b} * \frac{d}{c}$$

If $b = 1$, then $\frac{a}{b} = a$ and the property is applied as in the first two examples above.

equivalent equations Equations with the same solution. For example, $2 + x = 4$ and $6 + x = 8$ are equivalent equations with solution 2.

inequality A number sentence with a *relation symbol* other than =, such as $>$, $<$, $\geq$, $\leq$, $\neq$, or $\approx$.

integer A number in the set {..., −4, −3, −2, −1, 0, 1, 2, 3, 4, ...}. A whole number or its *opposite*, where 0 is its own opposite.

Multiplication Property of −1 A property of multiplication that says multiplying any number by −1 gives the opposite of the number. For example, $-1 * 5 = -5$ and $-1 * -3 = -(-3) = 3$. Some calculators apply this property with a [+/−] key that toggles between a positive and negative value in the display.

open sentence A number sentence with one or more variables. An open sentence is neither true nor false. For example, 9 + __ = 15, ? −24 < 10, and $7 = x + y$ are open sentences.

opposite of a number *n* A number that is the same distance from zero on the number line as n, but on the opposite side of zero. In symbols, the opposite of a number n is $-n$, and, in *Everyday Mathematics,* OPP(n). If n is a negative number, $-n$ is a positive number. For example, the opposite of $-5 = 5$. The sum of a number n and its opposite is zero; $n + -n = 0$.

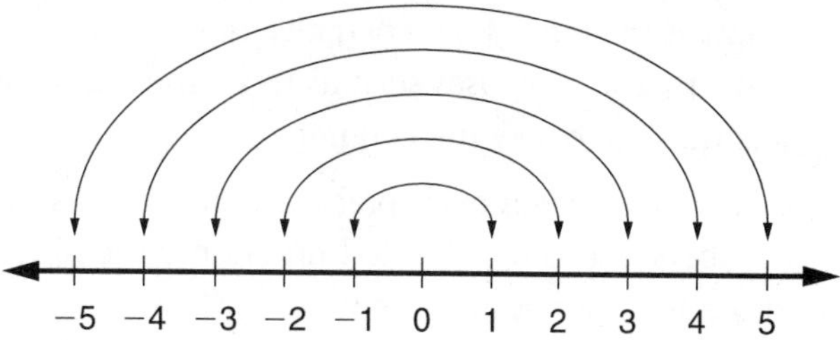

order of operations Rules that tell the order in which operations in an expression should be carried out. The conventional order of operations is:

1. Do the operations inside grouping symbols. Work from the innermost set of grouping symbols outward. Inside grouping symbols, follow Rules 2–4.
2. Calculate all the expressions with exponents.
3. Multiply and divide in order from left to right.
4. Add and subtract in order from left to right.

For example:
$$\begin{aligned} 5^2 + (3 * 4-2)/5 &= 5^2 + (12-2)/5 \\ &= 5^2 + 10/5 \\ &= 25 + 10/5 \\ &= 25 + 2 \\ &= 27 \end{aligned}$$

reciprocals Two numbers whose product is 1. For example, 5 and $\frac{1}{5}$, $\frac{3}{5}$ and $\frac{5}{3}$, and 0. 2 and 5 are all pairs of multiplicative inverses.

trial-and-error method A method for finding the solution of an equation by trying a sequence of test numbers.

Do-Anytime Activities

To work with your child on concepts taught in this unit, try these interesting and engaging activities:

1. If your child helps with dinner, ask him or her to identify uses of positive and negative numbers in the kitchen. For example, negative numbers might be used to describe the temperature in the freezer. Positive numbers are used to measure liquid and dry ingredients. For a quick game, you might imagine a vertical number line with the countertop as 0; everything above is referenced by a positive number, and everything below is referenced by a negative number. Give your child directions for getting out items by using phrases such as this: "the −2 mixing bowl"; that is, the bowl on the second shelf below the counter.
2. If your child needs extra practice adding and subtracting positive and negative numbers, ask him or her to bring home the directions for the *Credits/Debits Game.* Play a few rounds for review.
3. After your child has completed Lesson 6, ask him or her to explain to you what the following memory device means: *Please Excuse My Dear Aunt Sally.* It represents the rule for the order of operations: parentheses, exponents, multiplication, division, addition, subtraction. Your family might enjoy inventing another memory device that uses the same initial letters; for example, *Please Excuse My Devious Annoying Sibling; Perhaps Everything Might Drop Again Soon,* and so on.

Building Skills Through Games

In Unit 6, your child will work on his or her understanding of algebra concepts by playing games like the ones described below.

Algebra Election See *Student Reference Book*, pages 304 and 305.
Two teams of two players will need 32 *Algebra Election* cards, an Electoral Vote map, 1 six-sided die, 4 pennies or other small counters, and a calculator. This game provides practice with solving equations.

Credits/Debits Game (Advanced Version) See *Student Reference Book*, page 308.
Two players use a complete deck of number cards and a recording sheet to play the advanced version of the *Credits/Debits Game.* This game provides practice with adding and subtracting positive and negative integers.

Top-It See *Student Reference Book*, pages 337 and 338.
Top-It with Positive and Negative Numbers provides practice finding sums and differences of positive and negative numbers. One or more players need 4 each of number cards 0–9 and a calculator to play this *Top-It* game.

As You Help Your Child with Homework

As your child brings assignments home, you might want to go over the instructions together, clarifying them as necessary. The answers listed below will guide you through some of the Unit 6 Study Links.

Study Link 6•1

2. ✓ **3.** ✓ **5.** ✓ **7.** $\frac{1}{19}$

9. $\frac{7}{26}$ **11.** $\frac{3}{4}$ **13.** $12\frac{1}{2}$ lb **14.** $38\frac{1}{4}$ in.

15. $67\frac{1}{2}$ in.^{3} **16.** 81 **17.** −2 **18.** −67

Study Link 6•2

1. $\frac{4}{5}$ **3.** 1 **5.** 1 **7.** $\frac{5}{98}$

9. 10 **10.** 14 **11.** 17 **12.** 13.56

13. 589.36 **14.** 13

Study Link 6•3

1. a. $46 + (-19) = 27$ **c.** $-5 + 6.8 = 1.8$

2. a. −29 **c.** $-2\frac{1}{5}$ **e.** $-3\frac{1}{4}$ **g.** −18.2

3. a. (−2) **c.** $2\frac{1}{4}$ **e.** −3.7 **g.** $-\frac{7}{16}$

4. 2 **5.** 11 **6.** 8 **7.** −6

Study Link 6•4

1. −60 **3.** −6 **5.** −5 **7.** −6

9. −1,150 **11.** −54 **13.** −2 **15.** $-\frac{5}{9}$

17. −2 **19. a.** 36 **b.** 77

Study Link 6•6

1. 21 **3.** $\frac{21}{32}$ **5.** 72 **7.** 1

9. 28 **11.** 3 **12.** 23 **13.** 6, 1

14. 2, 1 **15.** 4, 4

Study Link 6•7

1. a. $17 < 27$; $3 * 15 < 100$; $(5 - 4) * 20 = 20$; $12 \neq 12$

b. Sample answer: A number sentence must contain a relation symbol. 56/8 does not include one.

2. a. true **b.** false **c.** false **d.** true

3. a. $(28 - 6) + 9 = 31$ **b.** $20 < (40 - 9) + 11$

c. $(36/6) / 2 < 12$ **d.** $4 * (8 - 4) = 16$

4. a. $60 - 14 = 50$; false **b.** $90 = 3 * 30$; true

c. $21 + 7 < 40$; true **d.** $\sqrt{36} > \frac{1}{2} * 10$; true

5. 0.92 **6.** 3.51 **7.** 251.515

Study Link 6•8

1. a. $b = 19$ **b.** $n = 24$ **c.** $y = 3$ **d.** $m = \frac{1}{5}$

2. a. $\frac{x}{6} = 10$; $x = 60$ **b.** $200 - 7 = n$; $n = 193$

c. $b * 48 = 2{,}928$; $b = 61$

3. Sample answers:

a. $(3 * 11) + (12 - 9)$ **b.** $2 * 18 + 14$

4. 54 **5.** 3.6 **6.** 121

Study Link 6•9

1. 1 **2.** $1\frac{1}{2}$ **3.** 5 **4.** 1

6. Answers vary. **7.** 10 **8.** $\frac{1}{4}$ **9.** $\frac{2}{3}$

10. $\frac{1}{2}$

Study Link 6•10

1. $k - 4 = 5$; $3k - 12 = 15$; $20k - 12 = 15 + 17k$

2. Multiply by 2; M 2
Subtract $3q$; S $3q$
Add 5; A 5

3. Add $5m$; A $5m$
Divide by 2; D 2
Subtract 6; S 6

Study Link 6•11

1. $k = 12$ **3.** $x = 1$ **5.** $r = 2$

Study Link 6•12

1. a. $15 \neq 3 * 7$ **b.** $x + 5 = 75$

c. $\frac{9}{9} + 13 \leq 14$

2. a. $200 \div (4 * 5) = 10$

b. $16 + 2^2 - (5 + 3) = 12$

3. a. 46 **b.** 18 **c.** 0 **d.** 8

4. a. $x = -1$ **b.** $y = 6.5$

5. a. Sample answers: -3, $-2\frac{1}{2}$, -2

6. \$0.25; \$0.21 **7.** 1; 1.28 **8.** 800; 781

Name Date Time

Practice with Fractions

Put a check mark next to each pair of equivalent fractions.

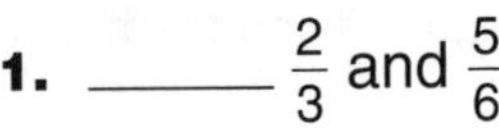

1. ______ $\frac{2}{3}$ and $\frac{5}{6}$

2. ______ $1\frac{3}{4}$ and $\frac{28}{16}$

3. ______ $\frac{24}{30}$ and $\frac{4}{5}$

4. ______ $\frac{7}{3}$ and $\frac{3}{7}$

5. ______ $\frac{56}{8}$ and $\frac{49}{7}$

6. ______ $2\frac{3}{8}$ and $\frac{19}{4}$

Find the reciprocal of each number. Multiply to check your answers.

7. 19 ______

8. $\frac{2}{5}$ ______

9. $3\frac{5}{7}$ ______

10. $\frac{1}{6}$ ______

Multiply. Write your answers in simplest form. Show your work.

11. $\frac{2}{3} * 1\frac{1}{8} =$ ______

12. $3\frac{1}{7} * \frac{7}{22} =$ ______

Solve the number stories.

13. How much does a box containing 5 horseshoes weigh if each horseshoe weighs about $2\frac{1}{2}$ pounds? ______

14. One and one-half dozen golf tees are laid in a straight line, end to end. If each tee is $2\frac{1}{8}$ inches long, how long is the line of tees? ______

15. A standard-size brick is 8 inches long and $2\frac{1}{4}$ inches high and has a depth of $3\frac{3}{4}$ inches. What is the volume of a standard-size brick? ______

Practice

16. $107 + (-82) + 56 =$ ______

17. $4 + (12 + -18) =$ ______

18. $-85 + 66 + (-48) =$ ______

19. $7 + (-11 + -22) =$ ______

Name Date Time

Products and Sums of Reciprocals

1. Read Statement 1. Then find each reciprocal or product to help you decide whether the statement is true or false.

Statement 1 The product of the reciprocals of two positive numbers is equal to the reciprocal of their product.

a. The reciprocal of 4 is ______. **b.** The reciprocal of 6 is ______.

c. The product of the reciprocals from 1a and 1b is ______.

d. The product of 4 and 6 is ______.

e. The reciprocal of the product of 4 and 6 is ______.

f. Repeat Problems 1a–1e using a different pair of positive numbers.

g. Do you think Statement 1 is true or false for all positive numbers? Explain.

____

____

2. Read Statement 2. Then find each reciprocal or sum to help you decide whether the statement is true or false.

Statement 2 The sum of the reciprocals of two positive numbers is equal to the reciprocal of their sum.

a. The reciprocal of 5 is ______. **b.** The reciprocal of 10 is ______.

c. The sum of the reciprocals from 2a and 2b is ______.

d. The sum of 5 and 10 is ______.

e. The reciprocal of the sum of 5 and 10 is ______.

f. Repeat Problems 2a–2e using a different pair of positive numbers.

g. Do you think Statement 2 is true or false for all numbers having reciprocals? Explain.

____

____

Name Date Time

LESSON 6•1

Finding Reciprocals

Solve.

1. ________ $* 5 = 1$

2. ________ $* \frac{1}{2} = 1$

3. ________ $* 17 = 1$

4. ________ $* 0.25 = 1$

5. ________ $* 0.6 = 1$

6. ________ $* n = 1$

7. Explain how you solved Problem 5.

____

____

____

____

For each number, fill in the circle next to the reciprocal.
(There may be more than one correct answer.)

8. $\frac{5}{6}$	**9.** $1\frac{2}{7}$	**10.** 3	**11.** 1.25
O 56	O $\frac{7}{3}$	O $\frac{9}{3}$	O 5.21
O $1\frac{1}{5}$	O $\frac{7}{12}$	O $\frac{3}{9}$	O $\frac{5}{4}$
O 1.2	O $\frac{7}{9}$	O $\frac{1}{3}$	O 0.8
O $\frac{6}{5}$	O 2.7	O 1.3	O $\frac{12}{5}$

12. Explain how you solved Problem 10.

____

____

____

____

Name Date Time

Fraction Division

Division of Fractions Algorithm

$$\frac{a}{b} \div \frac{c}{d} = \frac{a}{b} * \frac{d}{c}$$

Divide. Show your work.

1. $\frac{2}{3} \div \frac{5}{6} =$ ______

2. $1\frac{3}{4} \div \frac{28}{16} =$ ______

3. $\frac{24}{30} \div \frac{4}{5} =$ ______

4. $\frac{7}{3} \div \frac{3}{7} =$ ______

5. $\frac{5}{8} \div \frac{5}{8} =$ ______

6. $2 \div \frac{1}{4} =$ ______

7. $\frac{1}{7} \div 2\frac{4}{5} =$ ______

8. $5\frac{5}{6} \div 6 =$ ______

Try This

9. How many $\frac{3}{10}$-centimeter segments are in 3 centimeters? ______ segments

10. How many $\frac{3}{10}$-centimeter segments are in $4\frac{1}{5}$ centimeters? ______ segments

11. How many $\frac{4}{10}$-centimeter segments are in $6\frac{4}{5}$ centimeters? ______ segments

0 1 2 3 4 5 6 7 8 9 10

cm

Practice

Round each number to the underlined place.

12. $13.5\underline{6}1$ ______

13. $589.3\underline{5}52$ ______

14. $12.\underline{9}694$ ______

Name Date Time

LESSON 6•2

Complex Fractions

A *complex fraction* is a fraction whose numerator and/or denominator is also a fraction or a mixed number. Fractions such as $\frac{10}{\frac{2}{3}}$, $\frac{\frac{1}{6}}{\frac{4}{9}}$, and $\frac{22\frac{1}{5}}{\frac{15}{4}}$ are complex fractions.

To simplify a complex fraction, rewrite it as a division problem and divide.

Example 1:	**Example 2:**
Simplify $\frac{10}{\frac{2}{3}}$	Simplify $\frac{\frac{1}{6}}{\frac{4}{9}}$
$\frac{10}{\frac{2}{3}} = 10 \div \frac{2}{3}$	$\frac{\frac{1}{6}}{\frac{4}{9}} = \frac{1}{6} \div \frac{4}{9}$
$= 10 * \frac{3}{2}$	$= \frac{1}{6} * \frac{9}{4}$
$= \frac{30}{2}$	$= \frac{9}{24}$
$= 15$	$= \frac{3}{8}$

Simplify each complex fraction. Show your work.

1. $\frac{3}{\frac{1}{2}}$ ______

2. $\frac{\frac{3}{7}}{6}$ ______

3. $\frac{\frac{3}{4}}{\frac{5}{6}}$ ______

4. $\frac{6\frac{1}{5}}{\frac{2}{3}}$ ______

Try This

Find each missing divisor.

5. $\frac{1}{4} \div$ ______ $= 1\frac{3}{4}$

6. $2\frac{1}{2} \div$ ______ $= 1\frac{1}{4}$

Name Date Time

Dividing Fractions and Mixed Numbers

Division of Fractions Algorithm

$\frac{a}{b} \div \frac{c}{d} = \frac{a}{b} * \frac{d}{c}$

Divide. Show your work.

1. $\frac{7}{8} \div \frac{3}{6} =$ ______

2. $\frac{11}{15} \div \frac{1}{3} =$ ______

3. $\frac{7}{6} \div \frac{5}{12} =$ ______

4. $6 \div \frac{2}{3} =$ ______

5. $\frac{4}{5} \div 2 =$ ______

6. $\frac{8}{14} \div \frac{8}{14} =$ ______

7. $1\frac{2}{5} \div \frac{3}{10} =$ ______

8. $\frac{16}{3} \div 2\frac{1}{4} =$ ______

9. $2\frac{3}{4} \div \frac{6}{8} =$ ______

Try This

10. $\frac{5}{7} \div 1\frac{3}{5} =$ ______

11. $7 \div 5\frac{1}{3} =$ ______

12. $3\frac{4}{5} \div 8\frac{1}{2} =$ ______

Name Date Time

STUDY LINK 6•3

Subtraction of Signed Numbers

For any numbers a and b, $a - b = a + \text{OPP}(b)$, or $a - b = a + (-b)$.

1. Rewrite each subtraction problem as an addition problem. Then solve the problem.

a. $46 - 19 =$ ______________________

b. $-43 - 17 =$ ______________________

c. $-5 - (-6.8) =$ ______________________

d. $21 - (-21) =$ ______________________

2. Subtract.

a. $-72 - (-43) =$ ______

b. ______ $= 4 - (-39)$

c. $-\left(\frac{7}{10}\right) - 1\frac{1}{2} =$ ______

d. $4.8 - (-3.6) =$ ______

e. ______ $= -2\frac{1}{2} - \frac{3}{4}$

f. $-\left(\frac{5}{6}\right) - \left(-\frac{1}{3}\right) =$ ______

g. $-12.3 - 5.9 =$ ______

h. $-8.5 - (-2.7) =$ ______

3. Fill in the missing numbers.

a. $19 = 17 -$ ______

b. $-43 = -26 -$ ______

c. $\frac{1}{2} -$ ______ $= -1\frac{3}{4}$

d. ______ $- \left(-2\frac{4}{5}\right) = 3\frac{7}{10}$

e. $-17.6 =$ ______ $- 13.9$

f. $83.5 = -62.7 -$ ______

g. ______ $= 5\frac{3}{4} - 6\frac{3}{16}$

h. $9.6 -$ ______ $= 10$

Practice

4. $100 = 10^x$; $x =$ ______

5. $10^x = 100$ billion; $x =$ ______

6. 100 million $= 10^x$; $x =$ ______

7. $10^x = 0.00001$; $x =$ ______

Name Date Time

Modeling Subtraction with Signed Numbers

Cut out the + and − tiles on *Math Masters,* page 188.
Use your tiles to work through each example.

Example 1: +2 − (−4)

Step 1 Use + tiles to represent 2.

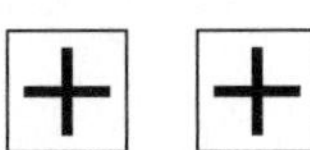

Step 2 Because there are no negative tiles to subtract, add 4 zero pairs.

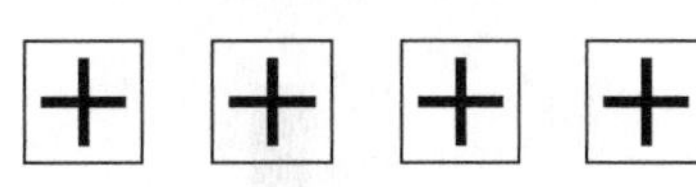

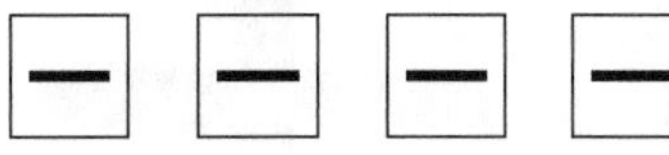

Step 3 Subtract −4.

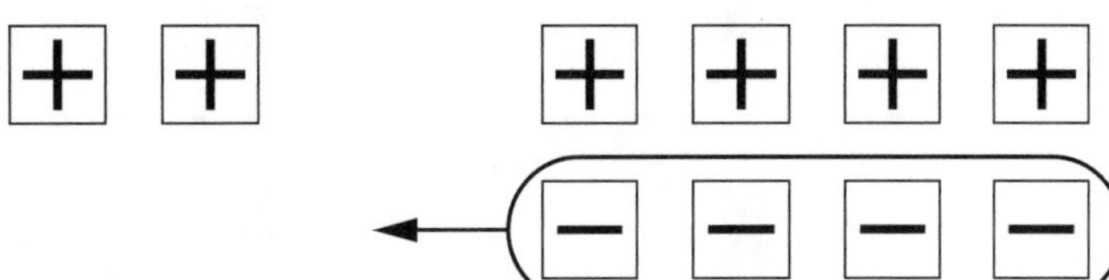

Step 4 Count the remaining tiles.

6 (+) tiles are left, so 2 − (−4) = +6.

Example 2: −2 − (−3)

Step 1 Use − tiles to represent −2.

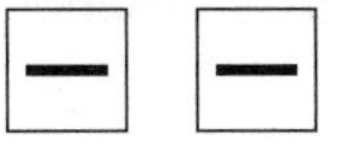

Step 2 Because there are not enough negative tiles to subtract, add 1 more zero pair.

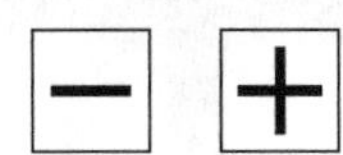

Step 3 Subtract −3.

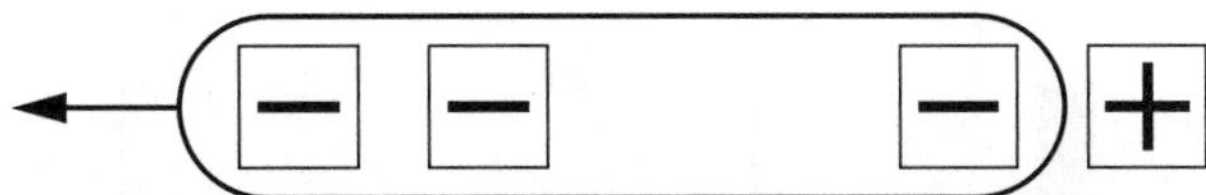

Step 4 Count the remaining tiles.

1 (+) tile is left, so −2 − (−3) = +1.

Use your tiles to solve each problem. Record the model you used on the back of this page.

1. 6 − (−2) = ________

2. −3 − (+2) = ________

3. −7 − (+4) = ________

4. −4 − (−5) = ________

Name Date Time

LESSON 6•3

Positive and Negative Tiles

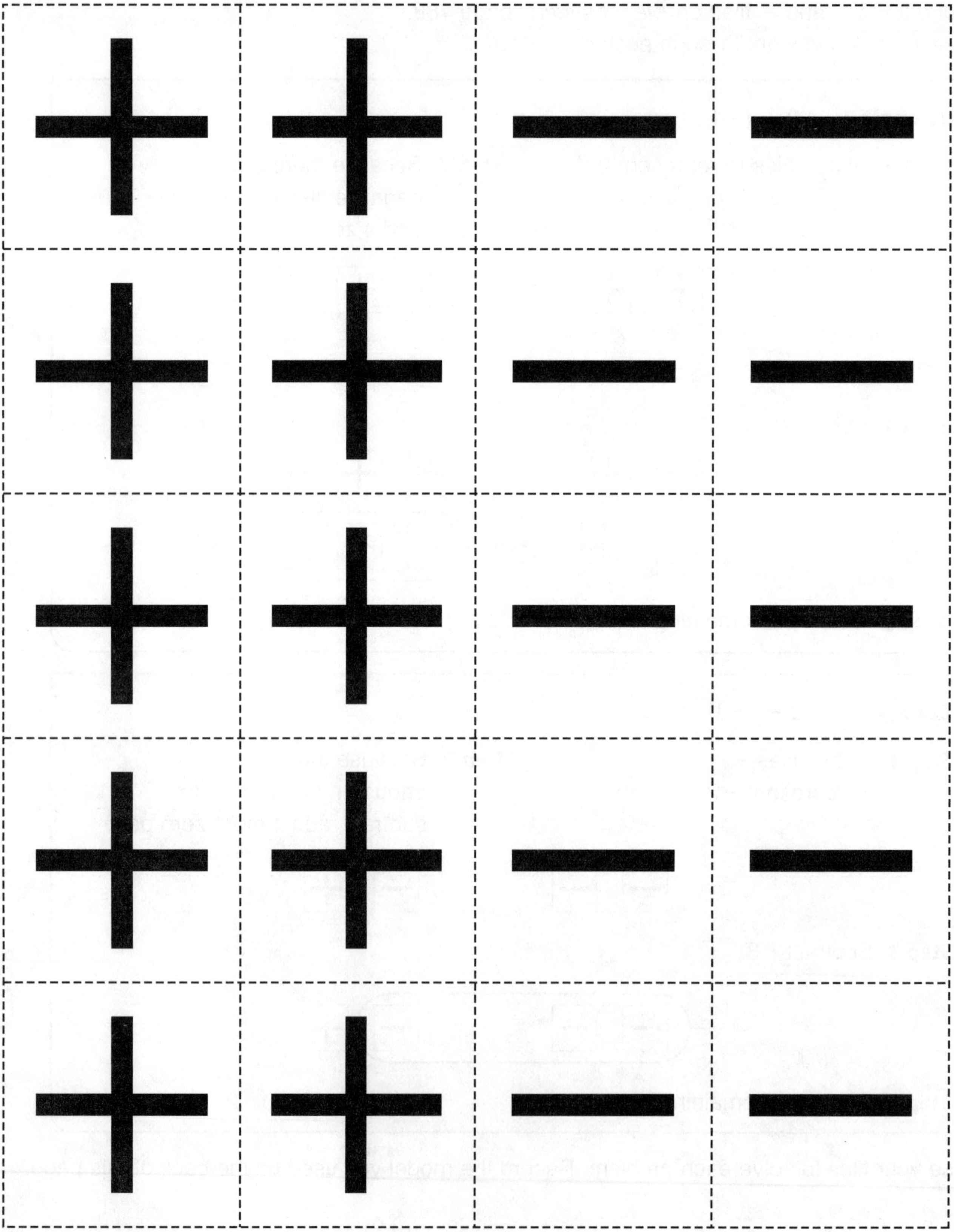

+	+	−	−
+	+	−	−
+	+	−	−
+	+	−	−
+	+	−	−

Name Date Time

LESSON 6•3 The Absolute Value of a Number

|← 3 units →|← 3 units →|

−4 −3 −2 −1 0 1 2 3 4

The absolute value of a number is its distance from 0 on the number line. Use the symbol | | to indicate absolute value. For example, the absolute value of 3 is written $|3|$. On the number line above, both 3 and −3 are 3 units from 0. So, $|3| = 3$ and $|-3| = 3$.

Because absolute value tells the distance and not the direction from 0, the absolute value of any number (except 0) is positive. The absolute value of 0 is 0.

You can use absolute value to find sums of positive and negative numbers.

- The sum of two positive numbers is the sum of their absolute values.
  Example: $3 + 5 = |3| + |5| = 8$.
- The sum of two negative numbers is the opposite of the sum of their absolute values.
  Example: $-3 + -5 = OPP(|-3| + |-5|) = OPP(3 + 5) = OPP(8) = -8$
- To add two numbers with different signs, first find their absolute values. Then subtract the lesser absolute value from the greater absolute value. Give the result the sign of the number with the greater absolute value.

Example 1: $4 + -7$	**Example 2:** $-2 + 8$
$|4| = 4$ $\quad |-7| = 7$	$|-2| = 2$ $\quad |8| = 8$
Subtract: $7 - 4 = 3$	Subtract: $8 - 2 = 6$
Because the negative number has the greater absolute value, the sum is negative. $4 + -7 = -3$	Because the positive number has the greater absolute value, the sum is positive. $-2 + 8 = 6$

1. Describe how Example 1 would be different if you found the sum $-4 + 7$.

____

____

2. Describe how to find the sum $4 + (-4)$ using absolute values.

____

____

____

Name Date Time

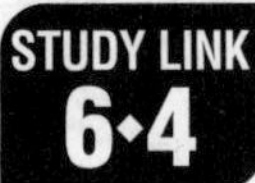
STUDY LINK 6·4

*, / of Signed Numbers

A Multiplication Property	A Division Property
◆ The product of two numbers with the same sign is positive. ◆ The product of two numbers with different signs is negative.	◆ The quotient of two numbers with the same sign is positive. ◆ The quotient of two numbers with different signs is negative.

Solve.

1. $-12 * 5 =$ ________

2. $-63 / 7 =$ ________

3. $24 \div (-4) =$ ________

4. $-9 *$ ________ $= 54$

5. $-50 /$ ________ $= 10$

6. $-6 * 5 * 8 =$ ________

7. $48 / (-6 - 2) =$ ________

8. $(-8 * 5) + 12 =$ ________

9. $50 * (-23) =$ ________

10. $6 * (12 + 15) =$ ________

11. $(-90 \div 10) + (-45) =$ ________

12. $56 / (-7) / (-4) =$ ________

13. ________ $* (-7) * (-4) = -56$

14. ________ $\div 40 = -9$

Try This

15. $\frac{2}{3} * \left(-\frac{5}{6}\right) =$ ________

16. $(8 * (-3)) - (8 * (-9)) =$ ________

17. $0.25 * (-8) =$ ________

18. $\left(-\frac{3}{4}\right) \div \left(-\frac{1}{2}\right) =$ ________

19. Evaluate each expression for $b = -7$.

a. $(-9 * b) - 27 =$ ________

b. $11 * (-b) =$ ________

c. $-b / (-14) =$ ________

d. $b - (b + 16) =$ ________

Name Date Time

A Multiplication Story

In many fairy tales and children's stories, there are good characters and bad characters. For example, in the story "Little Red Riding Hood," the grandmother is a good character; the wolf is a bad character.

You can use these character situations to remember a multiplication property for positive and negative numbers.

- When something good (+) happens to a good (+) character, we think it is good (+).

- When something bad (−) happens to a good (+) character, we think it is bad (−).

- When something good (+) happens to a bad (−) character, we think it is bad (−).

- When something bad (−) happens to a bad (−) character, we think it is good (+).

Example: Solve $-4 * 5 = ?$ Think, "When something bad (−4) happens to a good (+5) character, we think it is bad (−)." So, $-4 * 5 = -20$.

Name Date Time

Patterns with Signed Numbers

1. Multiply each number in the far left column by each number in the top row. Look for patterns. Use your calculator as few times as possible to complete the table.

*	−11	111	−1,111
−11			
111			
−1,111			
11,111			

2. Use the patterns from the table above to predict the products below. Then check each prediction with your calculator.

	*	−11	111
Prediction	111,111		
Actual	111,111		

3. Divide each number in the far left column by each number in the top row. Look for patterns. Use your calculator as few times as possible to complete the table. Write your own number pattern in last row.

	Divisor		
/	−99	999	−9,999
−12			
34			
−45			
67			

Name Date Time

Turn-Around Patterns

Fill in the missing numbers in the tables. Look for patterns in the results.

SRB 105

1.

x	y	OPP(x)	OPP(y)	$x + y$	$y + x$	$x - y$	$y - x$
7	9	−7	−9	−16			
−2	12						
−3	−9						
$\frac{2}{3}$	$\frac{5}{6}$						
2.7	−1.9						
2^2	2^3						

Which patterns did you find in your completed table?

____

____

____

2.

x	y	$\frac{1}{x}$	$\frac{1}{y}$	$x * y$	$y * x$	$x \div y$	$y \div x$
7	9	$\frac{1}{7}$	$\frac{1}{9}$	63			
−2	12						
−3	−9						
$\frac{2}{3}$	$\frac{5}{6}$						
2.7	−1.9						
2^2	2^3						

Which patterns did you find in your completed table?

____

____

____

Name Date Time

LESSON 6•5

Properties of Numbers

For each statement below, indicate whether it is always true or can be false. If the statement can be false, give an example.

	True or false?	Example
1. $\frac{a}{b} + \frac{c}{d} = \frac{a + c}{b + d}$	________	________
2. $\frac{a}{b} * \frac{c}{d} = \frac{a * c}{b * d}$	________	________
3. $\frac{a}{b} - \frac{c}{d} = \frac{a - c}{b - d}$	________	________
4. $\frac{a}{b} \div \frac{c}{d} = \frac{a \div c}{b \div d}$	________	________

5. Explain why giving only one example for a true statement is not enough to prove that it is true.

____

____

____

Try This

6. Correct each false statement in Problems 1–4 so the statement is true for all special cases. Give one example for each statement.

____

____

____

Name Date Time

LESSON 6•5

Renaming Repeating Decimals

You can use a power-of-10 strategy when renaming a repeating decimal as a fraction. Work through each of the examples shown below.

Example 1: Rename $0.\overline{3}$ as a fraction.

Let $1x = 0.3333\ldots$ Because one digit repeats, multiply both sides by 10 to eliminate the repeating digits to the right of the decimal point.	If $1x = 0.333\ldots$, then $10x = 3.33\ldots$.
Subtract	$10x = 3.333$ $-1x = 0.333$ $9x = 3$
Divide to solve for x.	$\frac{9x}{9} = \frac{3}{9}$
Simplify.	$x = \frac{3}{9} = \frac{1}{3}$
$0.\overline{3}$ renamed as a fraction is $\frac{1}{3}$.	

Example 2: Rename $0.\overline{45}$ as a fraction.

Let $1x = 0.4545\ldots$ Because two digits repeat, multiply both sides by 100 to eliminate the repeating digits to the right of the decimal point.	If $1x = 0.454545\ldots$, then $100x = 45.45\ldots$.
Subtract.	$100x = 45.4545$ $-\ 1x = \ \ 0.4545$ $99x = 45$
Divide to solve for x.	$\frac{99x}{99} = \frac{45}{99}$
Simplify.	$x = \frac{45}{99} = \frac{5}{11}$
$0.\overline{45}$ renamed as a fraction is $\frac{5}{11}$.	

Rename each repeating decimal as a fraction.

1. $0.\overline{7}$ = ________

2. $0.\overline{25}$ = ________

3. Compare the denominators in the examples to the denominators of your answers for Problems 1 and 2. Use any patterns you notice to mentally rename $0.\overline{5}$ and $0.\overline{32}$. Check your answers with a calculator.

a. $0.\overline{5}$ = ________

b. $0.\overline{32}$ = ________

Name Date Time

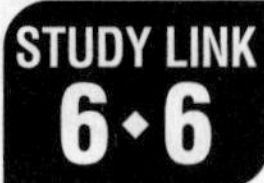

Using Order of Operations

Please Excuse My Dear Aunt Sally

Parentheses Exponents Multiplication Division Addition Subtraction

Evaluate each expression.

1. $5 + 6 * 3 - 2 =$ ________

2. $4 * 9 / 2 + (-4 + 6) =$ ________

3. $\frac{1}{2} + \frac{5}{8} * \frac{1}{2} \div 2 =$ ________

4. $(2.3 + 7.8) * 4 + 3 =$ ________

5. $4^2 + 7(3 - (-5)) =$ ________

6. $((2 * 4) + 3) * 6 / 2 =$ ________

Evaluate the following expressions for $m = -3$.

7. $-\frac{m}{m} + 6 - 4 =$ ________

8. $((4 + 11) * -3) / 9 * (-m) =$

9. $m^2 + (-(m^3)) - 8 =$ ________

10. $\frac{1}{2} * m \div \frac{5}{4} + \frac{3}{5} - \frac{1}{10} =$ ________

Practice

Find each missing number.

Units of Capacity

2 cups (c) = 1 pint (pt)

2 pints = 1 quart (qt)

4 quarts = 1 gallon (gal)

11. 3 gal 7 qt = 4 gal ______ qt

12. 5 gal 3 qt = ______ qt

13. 13 pt = ______ qt ______ pt

14. 10 c = ______ qt ______ pt

15. 18 qt = ______ gal ______ pt

Name Date Time

Another Grouping Symbol

A fraction bar (sometimes referred to as the *vinculum*) indicates division.

An expression such as (8 + 4) ÷ (5 − 2) can be written as $\frac{(8+4)}{(5-2)}$.

A fraction bar also acts as a grouping symbol. Both the numerator and the denominator can be treated as if there were parentheses around them. Any operations in the numerator or the denominator must be performed before the division.

Example: Evaluate $72 \div \left(\frac{29+7}{4*3}\right)$.

$$72 \div \left(\frac{29+7}{4*3}\right) = 72 \div \frac{(29+7)}{(4*3)} = 72 \div \frac{36}{12} = 72 \div 3 = 24$$

Evaluate each expression.

1. $20 - \frac{4+5}{3} =$ ________

2. $\frac{4(5+7)}{6(6-4)} =$ ________

3. $\frac{7(8-1)+(42 \div 3)}{(10-7)3} =$ ________

4. $\frac{6[24-2(7-3)]}{27 \div 9} =$ ________

Name Date Time

Another Grouping Symbol

A fraction bar (sometimes referred to as the *vinculum*) indicates division.

An expression such as (8 + 4) ÷ (5 − 2) can be written as $\frac{(8+4)}{(5-2)}$.

A fraction bar also acts as a grouping symbol. Both the numerator and the denominator can be treated as if there were parentheses around them. Any operations in the numerator or the denominator must be performed before the division.

Example: Evaluate $72 \div \left(\frac{29+7}{4*3}\right)$.

$$72 \div \left(\frac{29+7}{4*3}\right) = 72 \div \frac{(29+7)}{(4*3)} = 72 \div \frac{36}{12} = 72 \div 3 = 24$$

Evaluate each expression.

1. $20 - \frac{4+5}{3} =$ ________

2. $\frac{4(5+7)}{6(6-4)} =$ ________

3. $\frac{7(8-1)+(42 \div 3)}{(10-7)3} =$ ________

4. $\frac{6[24-2(7-3)]}{27 \div 9} =$ ________

Name Date Time

Order of Operations

Please Excuse My Dear Aunt Sally

Parentheses Exponents Multiplication Division Addition Subtraction

Evaluate each expression. Compare your result to a partner's. If you don't agree, discuss how you evaluated the expression to decide which result is correct.

1. $26 + 15 * 2 - 6 =$ ________

2. $18 - 5 + 10^2 =$ ________

3. $50 + 70 / 2 =$ ________

4. $39 + 1 - 24 / 6 =$ ________

5. $18 / 3 + (37 + 13) =$ ________

6. $10 + 28 \div 14 - 5 =$ ________

7. $42 + 6 / 6 - 8 =$ ________

8. $5 + 3^2 * 4 / 2 =$ ________

Name Date Time

Number Sentences

1. a. Draw a circle around each number sentence.

$17 < 27$ $\quad$ $3 * 15 < 100$ $\quad$ $56 / 8$

$(5 - 4) * 20 = 20$ $\quad$ $(4 + 23) / 9$ $\quad$ $12 \neq 12$

b. Choose one item that you did not circle. Explain why it is not a number sentence.

____

____

2. Tell whether each number sentence is true or false.

a. $9 - (6 + 2) > 0.5$ ________ **b.** $94 = 49 - 2 * 2$ ________

c. $\frac{24}{6} < 33 / 11$ ________ **d.** $70 - 25 = 45$ ________

3. Insert parentheses to make each number sentence true.

a. $28 - 6 + 9 = 31$ **b.** $20 < 40 - 9 + 11$

c. $36 / 6 / 2 < 12$ **d.** $4 * 8 - 4 = 16$

4. Write a number sentence for each word sentence. Tell whether the number sentence is true or false.

Word sentence	Number sentence	True or false?
a. If 14 is subtracted from 60, the result is 50.	________	________
b. 90 is 3 times as much as 30.	________	________
c. 21 increased by 7 is less than 40.	________	________
d. The square root of 36 is greater than half of 10.	________	________

Practice

5. $1.867 - 0.947 =$ ________ **6.** $6 - 2.49 =$ ________ **7.** $256.3 - 4.785 =$ ________

Name Date Time

Ordering Operations

The order of operations is shown in the diagram below.

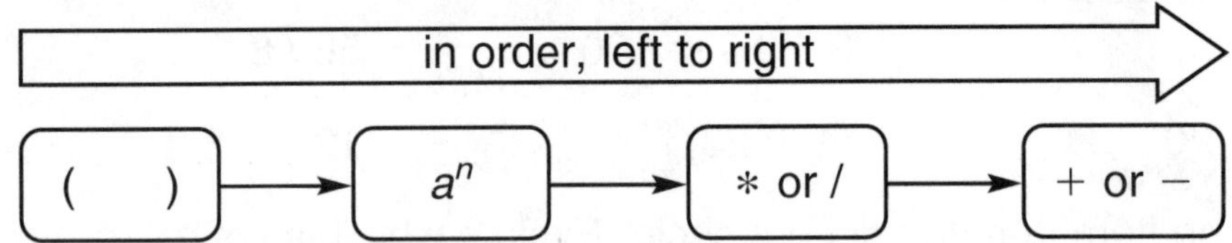

Use the diagram to help you label which operation you should perform first, second, third, and so on when evaluating an expression.

Example: Label the order in which you should perform the operations to evaluate the expression 9 / (8 − 5). Then evaluate the expression.

② ① ④ ③ ⑤
9 / (8 − 5) + 12 ∗ 4 − 11

(1)	Do the operation inside the parentheses.	(8 − 5) = 3
(2–3)	Divide and multiply in order from left to right.	9 / 3 = 3 12 ∗ 4 = 48
(4–5)	Add and subtract in order from left to right.	3 + 48 = 51 51 − 11 = 40

9 / (8 − 5) + 12 ∗ 4 − 11 = 40

For each expression, label the operation you would perform first, second, third, and so on. Then evaluate the expression.

1. $7 * 2^3$ = ________

2. 6 + 0.3 ∗ 10 = ________

3. $6 + 4 * 4^2$ = ________

4. $(9 + 1) / 2 * 3^2$ = ________

5. 14 − 28 / 7 ∗ 2 = ________

6. 1 ∗ 7 + 5 / 1 = ________

Name-Collection Boxes

Name ______________________

Date ______________________

Name ______________________

Date ______________________

Name ______________________

Date ______________________

Name ______________________

Date ______________________

Name Date Time

Solving Simple Equations

1. Find the solution to each equation.

a. $b - 7 = 12$ __________ **b.** $53 = n + 29$ __________

c. $45 / y^2 = 5$ __________ **d.** $m * \frac{2}{3} = 1 - \frac{13}{15}$ __________

2. Translate the word sentences below into equations. Then solve each equation.

Word sentence	Equation	Solution
a. If you divide a number by 6, the result is 10.	__________	__________
b. Which number is 7 less than 200?	__________	__________
c. A number multiplied by 48 is equal to 2,928.	__________	__________
d. 27 is equal to 13 increased by which number?	__________	__________

3. For each problem, use parentheses and as many numbers and operations as you can to write an expression equal to the target number. You may use each number only once in an expression. Write expressions with more than two numbers.

a. Numbers: 3, 9, 11, 12, 19 Target number: 36 __________

b. Numbers: 1, 2, 6, 14, 18 Target number: 50 __________

c. Numbers: 4, 5, 8, 14, 17 Target number: 22 __________

d. Numbers: 6, 7, 12, 14, 20 Target number: 41 __________

Practice

Complete.

4. $540 \div 90 =$ ______ $\div 9$ **5.** $36 \div 6 =$ ______ $\div 0.6$ **6.** ______ $\div 11 = 1.21 \div 0.11$

Name Date Time

LESSON 6•8

Solving Challenging Equations

1. $x - x = 0$ $n + 5 = 1$ $a + 8 < 3$ $y \neq y$ $\frac{0}{g} \geq 1$

Which of the above sentences have

a. no solution? ______________________

b. more than one solution? ______________________

c. a solution that is a negative number? ______________________

2. Find the solution to each equation below.

a. $x + (x + 1) + (x + 2) = 90$ ______________

(*Hint:* Think of this equation as a sum of three numbers.)

b. $a + (a + 1) + (a + 2) + (a + 3) + (a + 4) = 90$ ______________

3. Whole numbers are said to be **consecutive** if they follow one another in an uninterrupted pattern. For example, 5, 6, 7, 8, 9, and 10 are six consecutive whole numbers.

a. Find three consecutive whole numbers whose sum is 90.

(*Hint:* Replace each variable *x* in Problem 2a with the solution of the equation.)

_______ + _______ + _______ = 90

b. Find five consecutive whole numbers whose sum is 90.

_______ + _______ + _______ + _______ + _______ = 90

c. Find four consecutive whole numbers whose sum is 90.

_______ + _______ + _______ + _______ = 90

4. Each letter in the subtraction problem below represents a different digit from 0 through 9. The digits 3 and 5 do not appear. Replace each letter so the answer to the subtraction problem is correct.

```
 GRAPE
−PLUM
 APPLE
```

G = _______ R = _______ A = _______ P = _______

E = _______ L = _______ U = _______ M = _______

Name Date Time

STUDY LINK 6•9

Solving Pan-Balance Problems

Solve these pan-balance problems. In each figure, the two pans are balanced.

1. One ball weighs

as much as ________ coin(s).

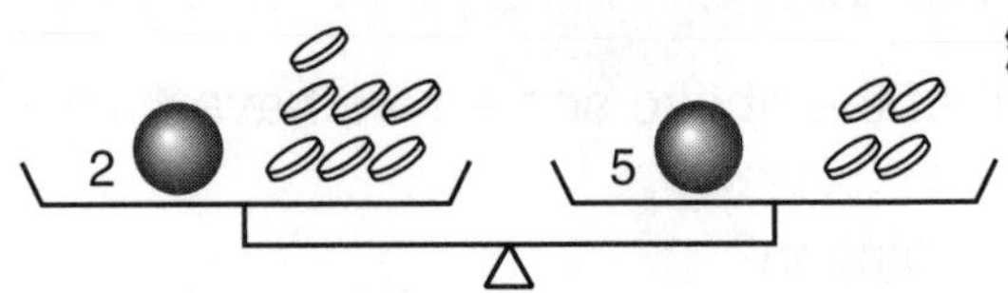

2. One cube weighs

as much as ________ marble(s).

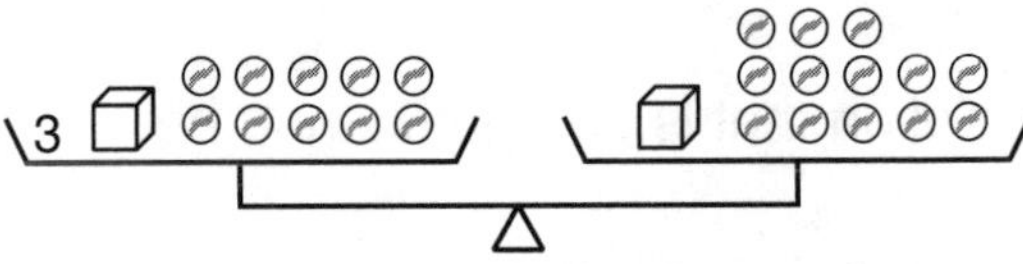

3. One x weighs

as much as ________ y(s).

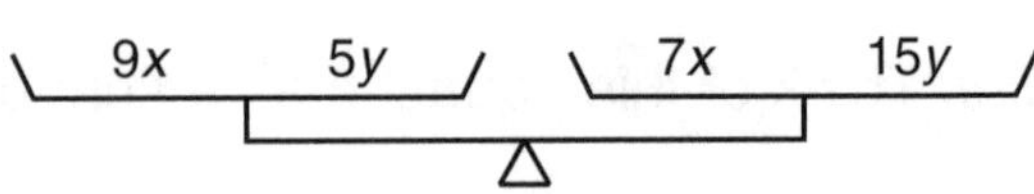

4. One a weighs

as much as ________ b(s).

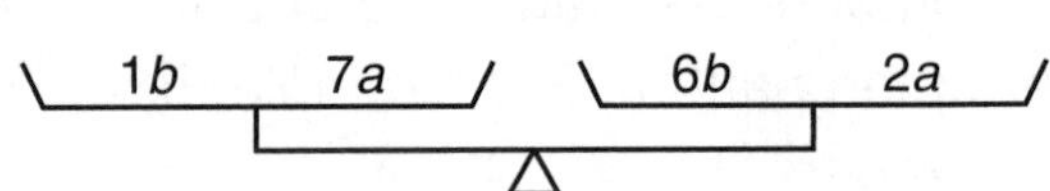

Make up two pan-balance problems for a classmate to solve.

5. ________________

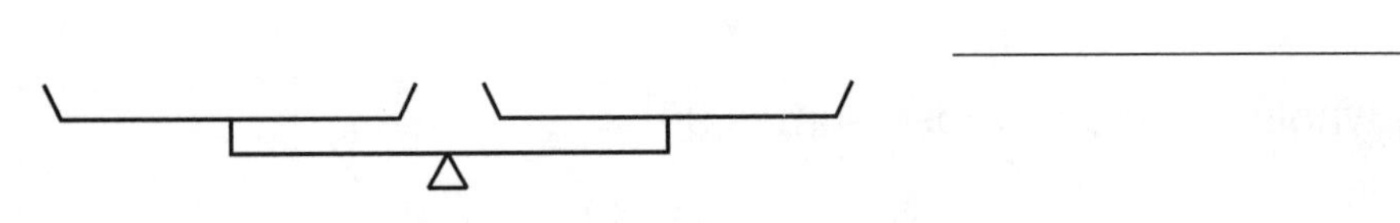

6. ________________

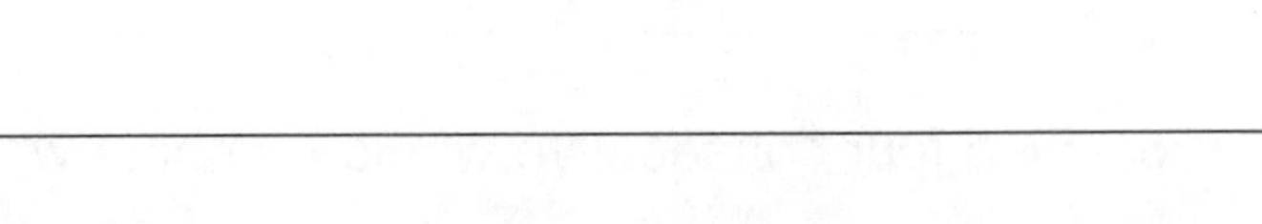

Practice

7. $605 * \frac{1}{10} = 605 \div$ ______

8. $72 *$ ______ $= 72 \div 4$

9. ______ $* 30 = (2 * 30) \div 3$

10. ______ $* (x + 5) = \frac{x + 5}{2}$

Name Date Time

Pan-Balance Problems

Problems 1 and 2 each consist of two parts. You need to solve one part before you have enough information to solve the other part. You must figure out which statement to complete first—it may be either the first or the second statement.

In each of the figures for Problems 1–3, the two pans are balanced.

1. 

One cube weighs as much as

_________ marbles.

One coin weighs as much as

_________ marbles.

2. 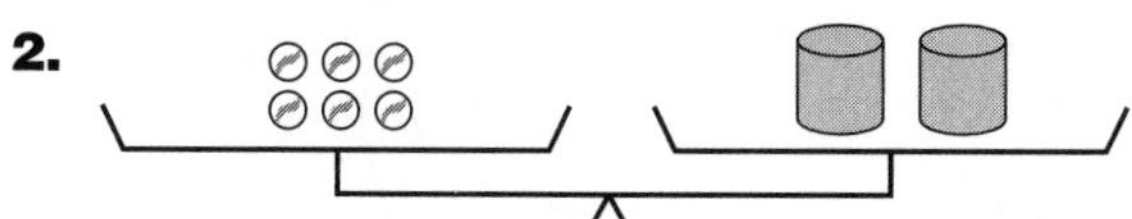

One marble weighs as much as

_________ paper clips.

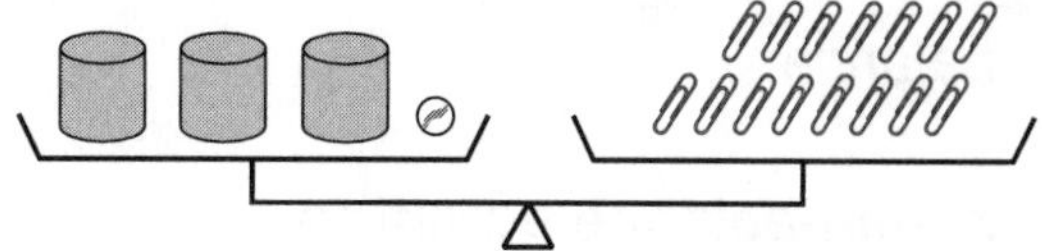

One can weighs as much as

_________ paper clips.

3. 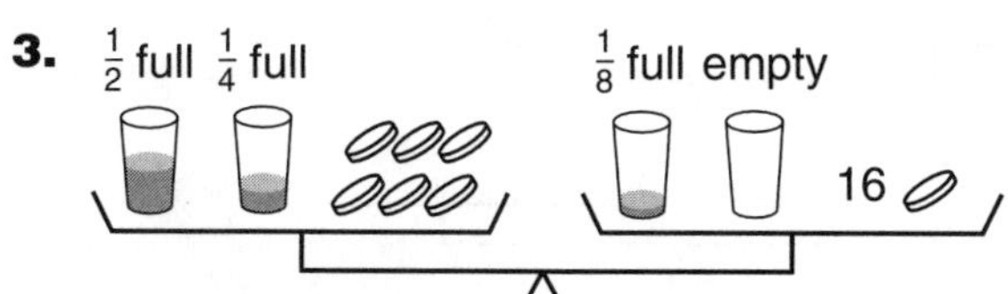

An empty juice glass weighs as much as 5 coins.

If the juice glass is full, the juice in the glass weighs as much as _________ coins.

If the juice glass is full, the juice and the glass weigh as much as _________ coins.

Name Date Time

Balancing Equations

SRB 250–252

For Problem 1, record the result of each operation on each pan.

1. Original pan-balance equation $k = 9$

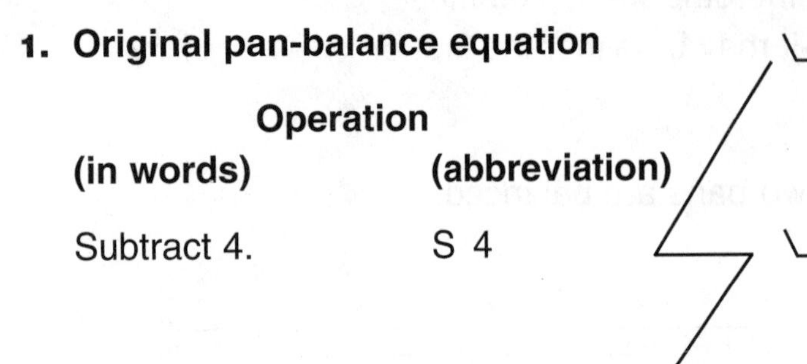

Operation (in words)	(abbreviation)	
Subtract 4.	S 4	______ = ______
Multiply by 3.	M 3	______ = ______
Add 17*k*.	A 17*k*	______ = ______

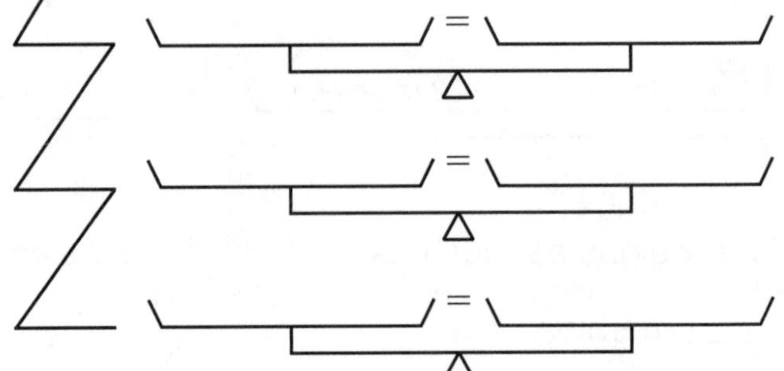

For Problems 2 and 3, record the operation that was used to obtain the result on each pan balance.

2. Original pan-balance equation $1 + 1.5q = 2q - 2.5$

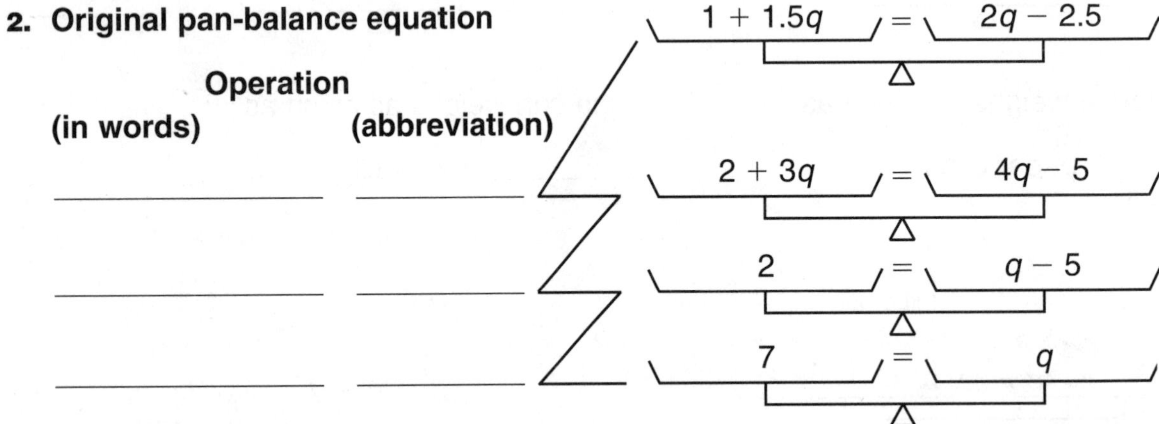

Operation (in words)	(abbreviation)	
______	______	$2 + 3q = 4q - 5$
______	______	$2 = q - 5$
______	______	$7 = q$

3. Original pan-balance equation $-3m + 12 = 13 - 5m$

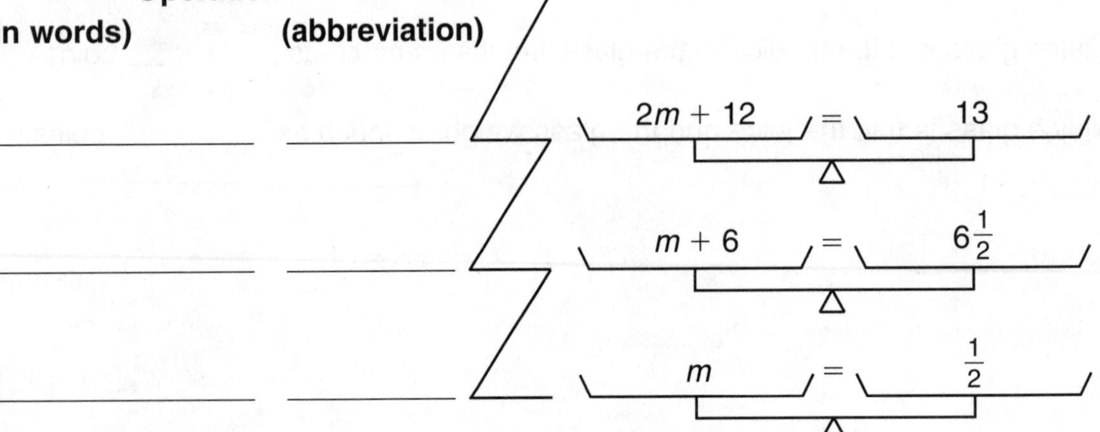

Operation (in words)	(abbreviation)	
______	______	$2m + 12 = 13$
______	______	$m + 6 = 6\frac{1}{2}$
______	______	$m = \frac{1}{2}$

Name Date Time

Equations

A pan balance is a good model for an equation. To keep the pans balanced, do the same thing to both pans.

Example:

$n + 17 = 98$

You can find the value of the variable *n* by removing, or subtracting, 17 from the left pan and the right pan.

$$n + 17 - 17 = 98 - 17$$

$$n = 81$$

To check the solution, replace *n* with 81.

$81 + 17 = 98$ true

Fill in the missing numbers that will keep the pans balanced. Check each solution.

1. $76 = y + 33$

   $76 - \square = y + 33 - \square$

   $43 = y$

2. $m - 45 = -10$

   $m - 45 + \square = -10 + \square$

   $m = 35$

3. $k * 5 = 130$

   $k * 5 \div \square = 130 \div \square$

   $k = 26$

4. $b \div 4 = 31$

   $b \div 4 * \square = 31 * \square$

   $b = 124$

5. You can use one operation to undo another. Name the operation that will undo each of the following:

   a. addition ________________

   b. multiplication ________________

Name Date Time

Pan-Balance Equations

Solve each equation. Record the operations you use and the equation that results. Check your solution by substituting it for the variable in the original equation.

1. Equation: $-2m + 4 = 29 - 7m$

Operation | Resulting equation

2. Equation: $2.5 - t = 2 + 1.5t$

Operation | Resulting equation

3. Equation: $7 + y = 3^2 + 5$

Operation | Resulting equation

Try This

4. Equation: $5x + 5 = \frac{2}{10}x + 29$

Operation | Resulting equation

Name Date Time

Solving Equations

Solve each equation. Then check the solution.

1. $9 + 5k = 45 + 2k$

Original equation

$9 + 5k = 45 + 2k$

Operation

S 9 $5k = 36 + 2k$

$k = 12$

Check

2. $\frac{9}{2}m - 8 = -5.5 + 4m$

Original equation

Operation

Check

3. $24x - 10 = 18x - 4$

Original equation

Operation

Check

4. $12d - 9 = 15d + 9$

Original equation

Operation

Check

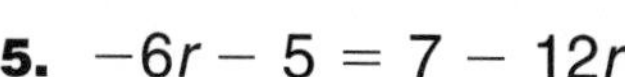

5. $-6r - 5 = 7 - 12r$

Original equation

Operation

Check

6. $\frac{1}{3}p + 7 = 12 - \frac{2}{3}p$

Original equation

Operation

Check

Name Date Time

Review

1. Write a number sentence for each word sentence.

Word sentence	Number sentence
a. 15 is not equal to 3 times 7.	______
b. 5 more than a number is 75.	______
c. 13 more than 9 divided by 9 is less than or equal to 14.	______

2. Insert parentheses to make each equation true.

a. $200 \div 4 * 5 = 10$

b. $16 + 2^2 - 5 + 3 = 12$

3. Use the order of operations to evaluate each expression.

a. $5 * 6 + 8 * 2 =$ ______

b. $20 - \frac{8}{2^2} =$ ______

c. $40 + 8 - 24 * 2 =$ ______

d. $4^2 \div (4 * 2) + 3 * 2 =$ ______

4. Solve each equation.

a. $3x - 5 = 5x - 3$

Solution ______

b. $\frac{(4y + 5)}{2} = y + 9$

Solution ______

5. Name three solutions of the inequality. Then graph the solution set.

a. $f < -\frac{3}{2}$ ______

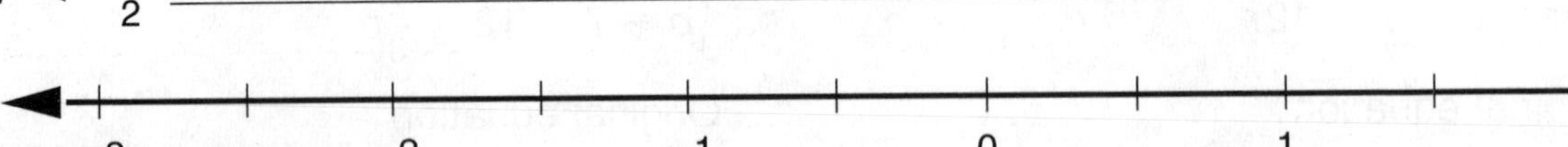

Practice

6. $2.52 ÷ 12 Estimate ______ Quotient ______

7. $45\overline{)57.60}$ Estimate ______ Quotient ______

8. $120\overline{)93{,}720}$ Estimate ______ Quotient ______

Name ______________________ Date ______________ Time ______________

LESSON 6•12

Reviewing Relation Symbols and Inequalities

1. Translate between word and number sentences.

	Word sentence	Number sentence
a.	$\frac{7}{9}$ is greater than $\frac{2}{3}$.	______________
b.	______________________________	$19 \neq 54 \div 3$
c.	20 is greater than or equal to 5 less than 5 squared.	______________
d.	The product of 4 and 19 is less than 80.	______________
e.	62 plus a number *y* is greater than −28.	______________
f.	______________________________	$2 \leq \frac{x}{17}$

2. Indicate whether each inequality is true or false.

a. $5 * 4 < 20$ ______________

b. $(7 + 3) * 6 \neq 60$ ______________

c. $54 / 9 > 7$ ______________

d. $45 \geq 9 * 5$ ______________

e. $29 - 12 \leq \frac{51}{3}$ ______________

f. $18 < 2 * 7 + 6$ ______________

3. Are the inequalities $17 - 6 \geq 9$ and $9 \leq 17 - 6$ equivalent? Explain.

____

____

Name Date Time

LESSON 6•12

Graphing Compound Inequalities

Graph all solutions of each inequality.

1. $-1 \leq x < 8$

(*Hint:* $-1 \leq x < 8$ means $x \geq -1$ and $x < 8$. For a number to be a solution, it must make both number sentences true.)

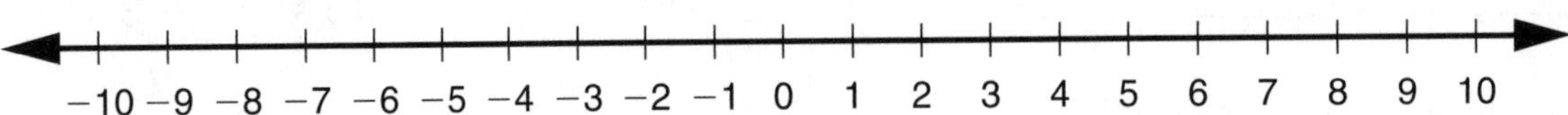

2. $3 < y + 2 \leq 7$

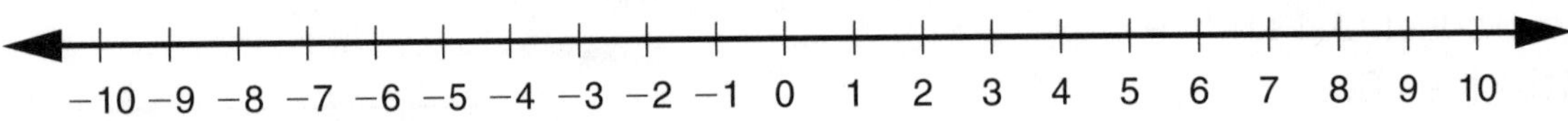

3. $m \neq -2$

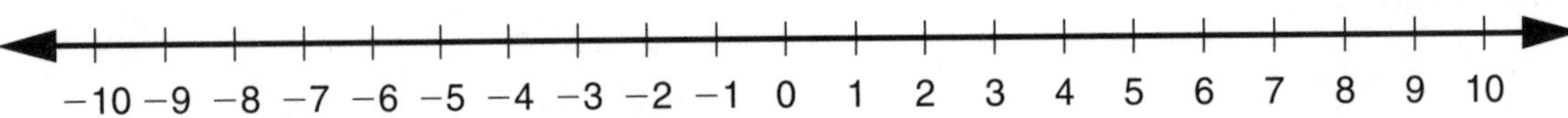

4. $x^2 \geq 9$

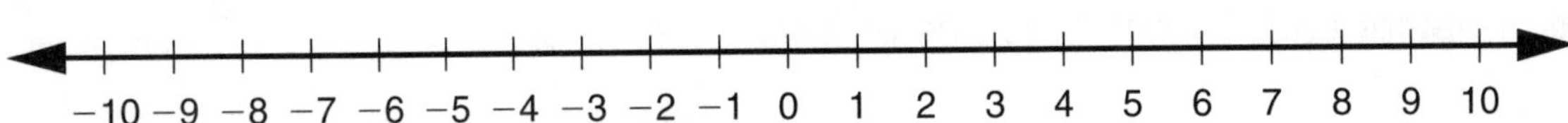

Write an inequality for each graph.

5. ______________________

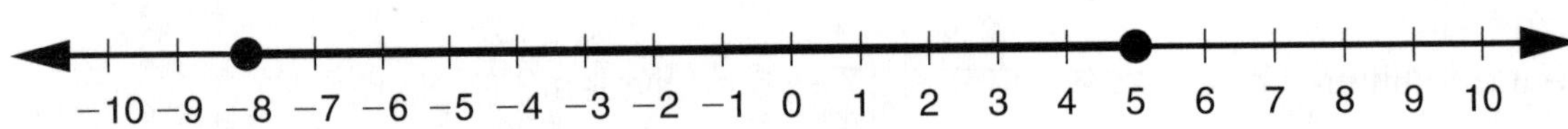

6. ______________________

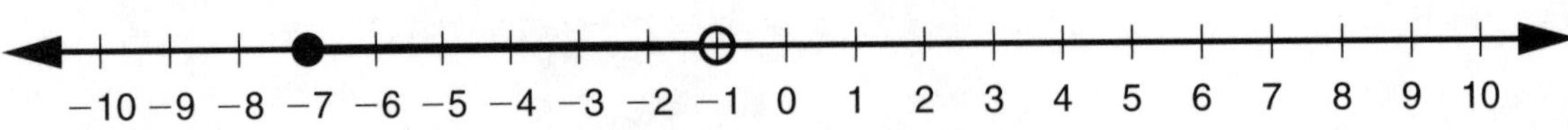

7. ______________________

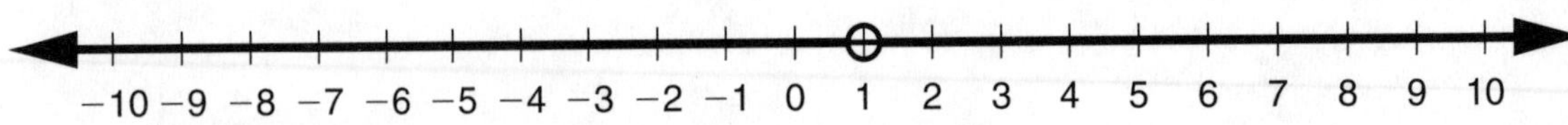

Name Date Time

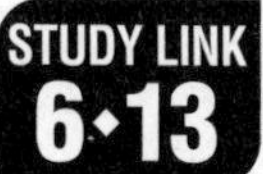

Unit 7: Family Letter

Probability and Discrete Mathematics

All of us are aware that the world is filled with uncertainties. As Ben Franklin wrote, "Nothing is certain except death and taxes!" Of course, there are some things we can be sure of: The sun will rise tomorrow, for example. We also know that there are degrees of uncertainty—some things are more likely to happen than others. There are occurrences that, although uncertain, can be predicted with reasonable accuracy.

While predictions are usually most reliable when they deal with general trends, it is possible and often helpful to predict the outcomes of specific situations. In Unit 7, your child will learn how to simulate a situation with random outcomes and how to determine the likelihood of various outcomes. Additionally, the class will analyze games of chance to determine whether or not they are fair; that is, whether or not all players have the same chance of winning.

We will be looking at two tools for analyzing probability situations: tree diagrams (familiar from single-elimination sports tournaments) and Venn diagrams (circle diagrams that show relationships between overlapping groups).

One lesson concerns strategies for taking multiple-choice tests based on probability. Should test-takers guess at answers they don't know? Your child will learn some of the advantages and disadvantages of guessing on this type of test.

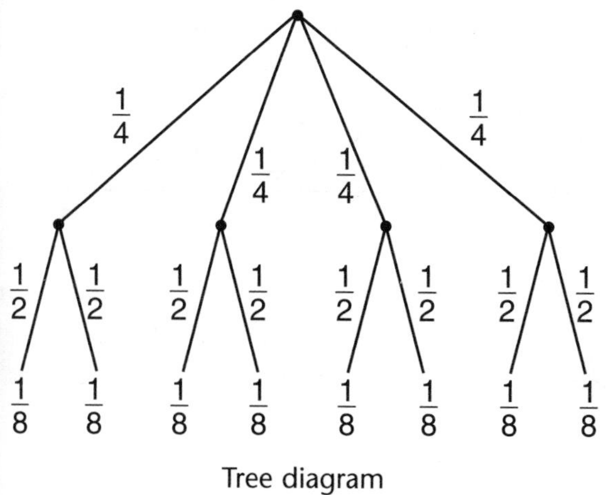

Tree diagram

Venn diagram

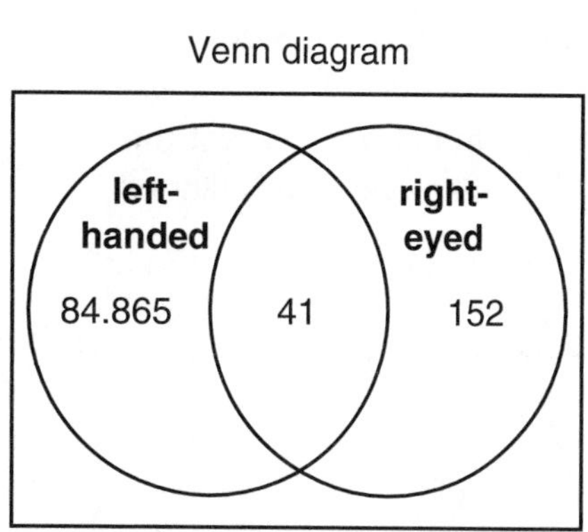

Please keep this Family Letter for reference as your child works through Unit 7.

Vocabulary

Important terms in Unit 7:

equally likely outcomes *Outcomes* of a chance experiment or situation that have the same probability of happening. If all the possible outcomes are equally likely, then the probability of an event is equal to:

$$\frac{\text{number of favorable outcomes}}{\text{number of possible outcomes}}$$

expected outcome The average outcome over a large number of repetitions of a random experiment. For example, the expected outcome of rolling one die is the average number of dots showing over a large number of rolls.

outcome A possible result of a chance experiment or situation. For example, heads and tails are the two possible outcomes of tossing a coin.

probability A number from 0 through 1, giving the likelihood that an event will happen. The closer a probability is to 1, the more likely the event is to happen.

probability tree diagram A drawing used to analyze a *probability* situation that consists of two or more choices or stages. For example, the branches of the probability tree diagram below represent the four *equally likely outcomes* when one coin is flipped two times.

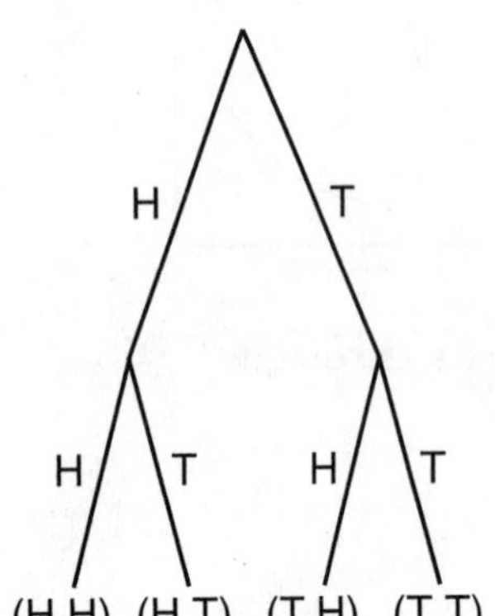

random number A number produced by a random experiment, such as rolling a die or spinning a spinner. For example, rolling a fair die produces random numbers because each of the six possible numbers 1, 2, 3, 4, 5, and 6 has the same chance of coming up.

simulation A model of a real situation. For example, a fair coin can be used to simulate a series of games between two equally matched teams.

Venn diagram A picture that uses circles or rings to show relationships among sets. The Venn diagram below shows the number of students who have a dog, a cat, or both.

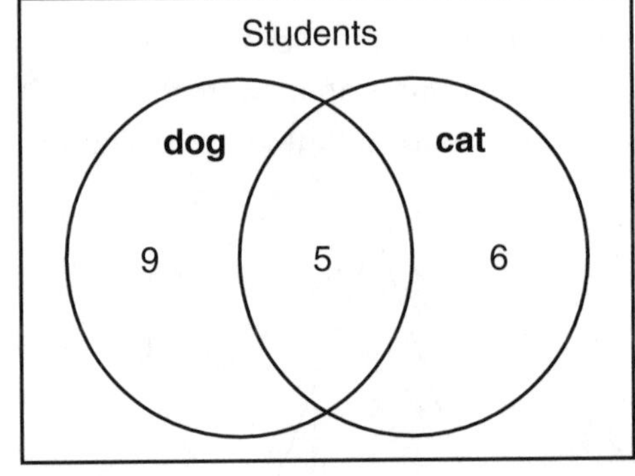

Do-Anytime Activities

To work with your child on the concepts taught in this unit and in previous units, try these interesting and rewarding activities:

1. While playing a game that uses a die, keep a tally sheet of how many times a certain number lands. For example, try to find out how many times during the game the number 5 comes up. Have your child write the probability for the chosen number. ($\frac{1}{6}$ is the probability that any given number on a six-sided die will land.) The tally sheet should show how many times the die was rolled during the game and how many times the chosen number came up.
2. Have your child listen to the weather forecast on television and pick out the language of probability. Have him or her listen for such terms as *likely, probability, (percent) chance, unlikely,* and so on.
3. Watch with your child for events that occur without dependence on any other event. In human relationships, truly independent events may be difficult to isolate, but this observation alone helps to define the randomness of events. Guide your child to see the difference between dependent events and independent events. For example, "Will Uncle Mike come for dinner?" depends on whether or not he got his car fixed. However, "Will I get heads or tails when I flip this coin?" depends on no other event.

Building Skills through Games

In Unit 7, your child will continue to review concepts from previous units and prepare for topics in upcoming units by playing games such as:

***2-4-8 and 3-6-9 Frac-Tac-Toe* (Percent Versions)** See *Student Reference Book*, pages 314–316
The two versions, *2-4-8 Frac-Tac-Toe* and *3-6-9 Frac-Tac-Toe,* help students practice conversions between fractions and percents. Two players need a deck of number cards with four each of the numbers 0–10; a gameboard, a 5 × 5 grid that resembles a bingo card; a *Frac-Tac-Toe* Number-Card Board; markers or counters in two different colors, and a calculator.

Angle Tangle See *Student Reference Book,* page 306
Two players need a protractor, straightedge, and blank sheets of paper to play this game. Mastering the estimation and measurement of angles is the goal of *Angle Tangle.*

Name That Number See *Student Reference Book,* page 329
This game provides practice in using order of operations to write number sentences. Two or three players need a complete deck of number cards.

Solution Search See *Student Reference Book,* page 332
This game provides practice solving open number sentences. Players use a complete deck of number cards as well as *Solution Search* cards to solve inequalities.

As You Help Your Child with Homework

As your child brings assignments home, you may want to go over the instructions together, clarifying them as necessary. The answers listed below will guide you through some of the Unit 7 Study Links.

Study Link 7•1

1. Quarter, nickel, dime; No. There is an unequal number of each type of coin.

2. 1, 2, 4, 5, 10, and 20

Yes. Each number card is a factor of 20.

3. 37.5% **4.** 100% **5.** 25%, 50%, 75%

6. 27.12

Study Link 7•2

1. No. Sample answer: Teams should be evenly matched. A team selected at random might not have a balance of skilled and unskilled players.

2. Yes and no. Sample answer: In an elementary school, preference for the better seats should go to the youngest children so they can see the game. However, in Grades 3–6, the principal should choose seat assignments randomly.

3. Disagree. Sample answer: There is always an even chance of this spinner landing on black or white. Previous spins do not affect the outcome.

4. Agree. Sample answer: There is always a better chance that this spinner will land on white because the white area is larger. The outcome does not depend on previous spins.

Study Link 7•3

1. 6 ways **2.** 30, 26, 23, 22, 19, 18, 16, 15, 12, 9

3a. 25% **3b.** 33.33%

Study Link 7•4

3. 12 **4.** 15 **5.** 15

Study Link 7•5

1. Tree diagram probabilities (from top, left to right)

$\frac{1}{2}, \frac{1}{2}$

Box 1: $\frac{1}{3}, \frac{1}{3}, \frac{1}{3}, \frac{1}{3}, \frac{1}{3}, \frac{1}{3}$

Box 2: $\frac{1}{2}, \frac{1}{2}, \frac{1}{2}, \frac{1}{2}, \frac{1}{2}, \frac{1}{2}, \frac{1}{2}, \frac{1}{2}, \frac{1}{2}, \frac{1}{2}, \frac{1}{2}, \frac{1}{2}$

Box 3: $\frac{1}{12}, \frac{1}{12}, \frac{1}{12}, \frac{1}{12}, \frac{1}{12}, \frac{1}{12}, \frac{1}{12}, \frac{1}{12}, \frac{1}{12}, \frac{1}{12}, \frac{1}{12}, \frac{1}{12}$

2. 12

3. a. $\frac{1}{6}$ **b.** $\frac{3}{3}$, or 100% **c.** $\frac{1}{3}$ **d.** 0%

4. 36.5 **5.** 22.6 **6.** 12.6

Study Link 7•6

1. a. Track **b.** Basketball **c.** 22 **d.** 8

e. 30 **f.** 52 **g.** 22

3. $\frac{17}{40}$ **4.** $2\frac{11}{12}$ **5.** $8\frac{3}{20}$

Study Link 7•7

1. Tree diagram probabilities (from top, left to right)

$\frac{1}{4}, \frac{1}{4}, \frac{1}{4}, \frac{1}{4}$

R1: $\frac{1}{3}, \frac{1}{3}, \frac{1}{3}$; **R2:** $\frac{1}{3}, \frac{1}{3}, \frac{1}{3}$; **R3:** $\frac{1}{3}, \frac{1}{3}, \frac{1}{3}$; **G:** $\frac{1}{3}, \frac{1}{3}, \frac{1}{3}$

Bottom row probabilities:

$\frac{1}{12}, \frac{1}{12}, \frac{1}{12}, \frac{1}{12}, \frac{1}{12}, \frac{1}{12}, \frac{1}{12}, \frac{1}{12}, \frac{1}{12}, \frac{1}{12}, \frac{1}{12}, \frac{1}{12}$

a. 50 **b.** 25

2. a. HHT; HTH; HTT; THH; THT; TTH

b. 37.5 **c.** 87.5

Study Link 7•8

1. C, D, A, B

2. Tree diagram with branches labeled as follows (from left to right):

Swimsuits: red, white, blue

Sandals: red, white; red, white; red, white

a. 6 **b.** $\frac{2}{6}$, or $\frac{1}{3}$

3. a.

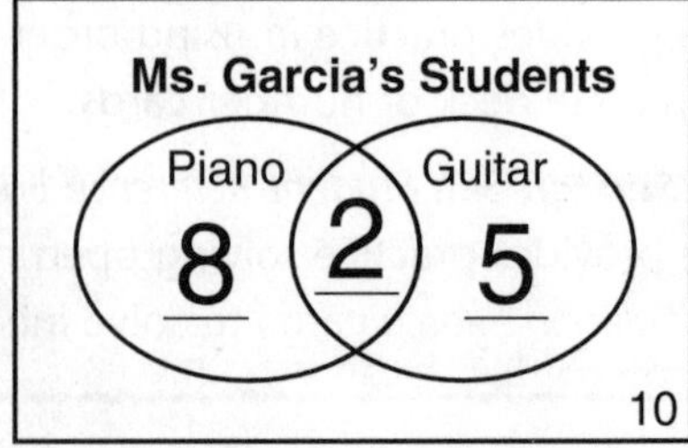

b. 25

Sample answer: 8 students play the piano, 5 students play the guitar, 2 students play both instruments, and 10 students play neither instrument. 8 + 2 + 5 + 10 = 25

Name Date Time

Outcomes and Probabilities

SRB 150–153

Complete the table.

Experiment	Possible Outcomes	Outcomes Equally Likely?
Example: Spin the spinner.	A, B, C	No. The area for C is twice as large as each of the other 2 areas.
1. Choose a coin.		
2. Choose a factor of 20.		

Use the problems from the table to answer the following questions. Express each probability as a percent.

3. What is the probability of selecting a quarter from the coins in Problem 1? ________

4. What is the probability of choosing a factor of 20 from the cards in Problem 2? ________

5. Suppose you spin the spinner from the Example in the table. Complete the number sentence below to determine the probability of the spinner landing on A or C.

________ + ________ = ________

Probability of A Probability of C Probability of A or C

Practice

Simplify the expression using the order of operations.

6. $3.8 + 6.4 \div 0.2 - 1.8 * 2.6 - 3.2 \div 0.8$ ________

Name Date Time

Carnival Games

At the carnival, you will play 10 games and will try to win as many prize coupons as possible. You must visit at least three different booths.

Booth 1 **Two in a Row** Flip a coin twice. If the coin lands on the same side both times, you win a prize coupon.	**Booth 2** **Odd Tail Toss** Flip a coin once and roll a die once. If you get TAILS and an odd number, you win a prize coupon.
Booth 3 **Roll It Up** Roll a die twice. If the second roll is a greater number than the first, you win a prize coupon.	**Booth 4** **10 or More** Roll a die twice. If you get 5 or greater both times, you win a prize coupon.
Booth 5 **Make the Call** Predict the roll of a die. If that number comes up, you win a prize coupon.	**Booth 6** **7 or More** Roll a die twice. If the total of the rolls is 7 or greater, you win a prize coupon.

Name Date Time

Carnival Games Records

Below, record the number of each booth you visit. Make a tally mark for each prize coupon you win during your 10 games.

Booth Number	Number of Prize Coupons Won
Total Number of Prize Coupons Won	

1. Describe a strategy for winning the greatest number of prize coupons in 10 games if you must visit at least 3 different booths.

____

____

2. At which booths does it seem easy to win?

____

____

3. Describe how you would change the rules of one game to make it easier to win.

____

____

____

Name Date Time

Random-Number Results

Outcome	Group 1	Group 2	Group 3	Group 4	Group 5	Group 6	Group 7	Group 8	All Groups	% of Total
1										
2										
3										
4										
5										
								Total		**100%**

Name Date Time

Using Random Numbers

1. A gym teacher is dividing her class into two teams to play soccer. Do you think she should choose the teams at random? ______

   Explain. ______________________________

2. The entire school is going to a baseball game. Some seats are better than others. Should the principal select the section where each class will sit at random? ______________

   Explain. ______________________________

3. The spinner at the right has landed on black 5 times in a row. Renee says, "On the next spin, the spinner is more likely to land on white than on black."

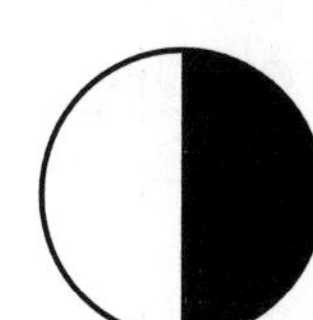

   Do you agree or disagree with Renee? ______________

   Explain. ______________________________

4. The spinner at the right has landed on black 5 times in row. Matthew says, "On the next spin, the spinner has a better chance of landing on white than on black."

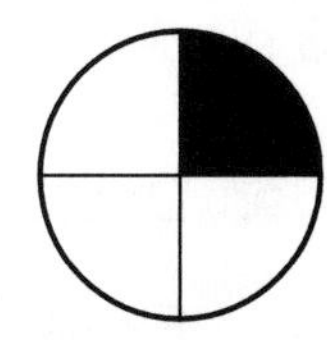

   Do you agree or disagree with Matthew? ______________

   Explain. ______________________________

Name Date Time

Predict Which Blocks Are in a Bag

1. Pick one person in your group to be the Director.

2. The Director selects 5 blocks and hides them in a bag. The blocks should NOT all be the same color. The group members should NOT see the blocks.

3. Group members take turns drawing one block out of the bag without looking. Each time a block is drawn, group members tally the color.

   Example (for first 5 draws):

red	////
blue	/

4. The person who drew the block puts it back into the bag, shakes the bag, and gives it to the next person to draw.

5. After 5 draws, each person writes a prediction for how many blocks of each color are in the bag.

6. Discuss the group's predictions. If everyone has the same prediction, the Director shows the contents of the bag and checks the prediction.

7. If your group does not agree on a prediction, take turns making 5 more draws (for a total of 10). Everyone predicts again and compares predictions.

8. Continue until the group agrees on a prediction. Then the Director shows the contents of the bag.

Repeat this experiment with a different number of blocks in the bag. Try it with 3 blocks. Try it with 7 blocks.

9. Does the number of blocks in the bag make a difference? ______

   Explain. ______________________________

   ____

10. Do you think there must be a minimum number of draws to make an informed decision about the contents of the bag? ______

   Explain. ______________________________

   ____

   ____

Name Date Time

A Table of Random Digits

This is a table of 500 random digits, which includes the digits 0 through 9. Sometimes statisticians generate random numbers for projects or studies they are conducting by using a random digits table.

9 4 0 1 5 4 6 8 7 4 3 2 4 4 4 4 8 2 7 7 5 9 8 2 0

9 6 1 6 3 6 4 6 5 4 2 5 8 4 3 4 1 1 4 5 4 2 8 2 0

7 4 1 0 8 8 8 2 2 2 8 8 5 7 0 7 4 0 1 5 2 5 7 0 4

9 1 0 3 5 0 1 7 5 5 1 4 7 5 0 4 8 9 6 8 3 8 6 0 3

6 2 8 8 0 8 7 8 7 3 9 5 1 6 0 5 9 2 2 1 2 2 3 0 4

9 0 3 1 4 7 2 8 7 7 1 7 3 3 4 3 9 2 8 3 0 4 1 4 9

1 1 7 4 8 1 2 1 0 2 8 0 5 8 0 4 1 8 6 7 1 7 7 1 0

5 9 6 2 1 0 6 5 5 4 0 7 8 5 0 7 3 9 5 0 7 9 5 5 2

1 7 9 4 4 0 5 6 0 0 6 0 4 7 8 0 3 3 4 3 2 5 8 5 2

5 8 9 0 5 5 7 2 1 6 3 9 6 1 8 4 9 8 5 6 9 9 3 2 6

6 6 0 6 7 4 2 7 9 2 9 5 0 4 3 5 2 6 8 0 4 6 7 8 0

5 6 4 8 7 0 9 9 7 1 5 9 4 8 1 3 7 0 0 6 2 2 1 8 6

5 4 2 4 4 9 1 0 3 0 4 5 5 4 7 7 0 8 1 8 5 9 8 4 9

9 6 1 6 9 6 1 4 5 9 2 1 6 4 7 8 7 4 1 7 1 7 1 9 8

3 0 9 4 5 5 7 5 8 9 3 1 7 3 2 5 7 2 6 0 4 7 6 7 0

0 7 6 5 4 4 6 3 7 6 2 5 3 6 6 9 4 7 4 6 4 9 5 8 0

6 9 1 7 0 3 7 4 0 3 8 6 9 9 5 9 0 3 0 7 9 4 3 0 4

7 1 8 0 3 2 6 8 2 5 0 5 5 1 1 1 2 4 5 9 9 1 3 1 4

0 8 3 4 5 8 8 9 7 5 3 5 8 4 1 8 5 7 7 1 0 8 1 0 5

5 9 9 8 7 8 7 1 1 2 2 1 4 7 6 1 4 7 1 3 7 1 1 8 1

1. About what percent of the time would you expect each digit to appear? About ______________

2. Use the table at the right to make a tally of the digits. Use a calculator to find what percent of the total each digit appears.

3. Are the digits random in the table of 500 digits?

____

Digit	Tally of Appearances	Number of Appearances	Percent of Total
0			
1			
2			
3			
4			
5			
6			
7			
8			
9			
Total	**500**	**500**	**100%**

Name Date Time

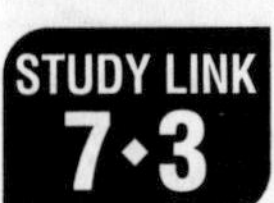

Making Organized Lists

Solve each problem by making an organized list. The list in Problem 1 has been started for you.

1. In how many ways can you make $0.60 using at least 1 quarter? You can only use quarters, dimes, and nickels.

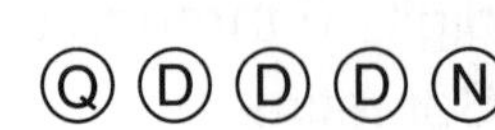

____

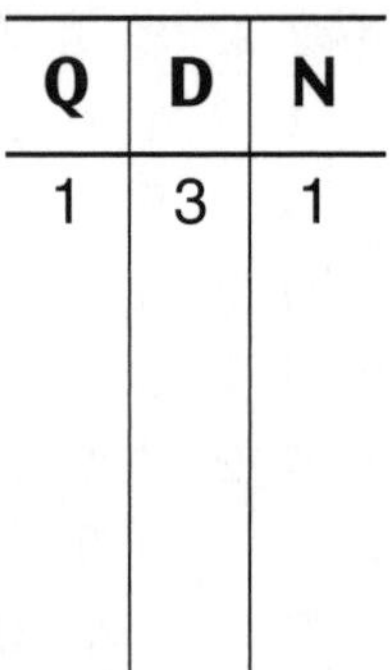

Q	D	N
1	3	1

2. You throw three darts and hit the target at the right. List the different total points that are possible.

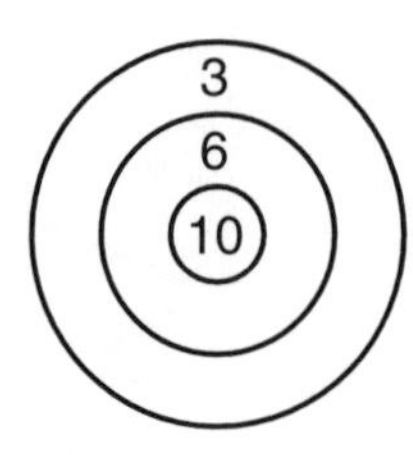

10 pts	6 pts	3 pts	Total pts

Use what you know about angle measures of sectors to find the probabilities in Problem 3.

Example:

Probability of landing on striped sector $= \frac{150^\circ}{360^\circ} = \frac{5}{12} = 41.67\%$

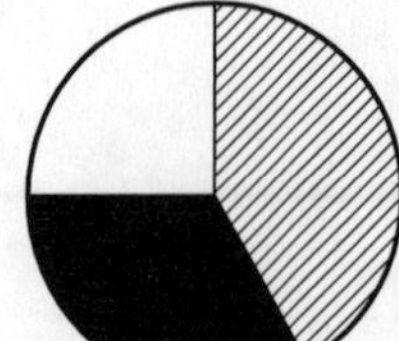

3. Find the probability of the spinner landing on

a. white. _______________ **b.** black. _______________

Name Date Time

Coin-Toss Experiment

Step 1 Working alone, toss a coin 10 times for Round 1.
Enter a tally mark for each time a HEAD or a TAIL occurs in Round 1.

Coin-Toss Data		
Round	**HEADS**	**TAILS**
1		
2		
3		
4		
5		
Totals		

Step 2 Repeat Step 1 for Rounds 2–5, for a total of 50 tosses.

Step 3 **a.** Record the total number of HEADS and TAILS for your 50 tosses from the frequency table above.

My Totals HEADS $\frac{\quad}{50}$ TAILS $\frac{\quad}{50}$

b. Record your partner's HEADS and TAILS totals for all 5 rounds.

My Partner's Totals HEADS $\frac{\quad}{50}$ TAILS $\frac{\quad}{50}$

c. Combine your totals with those of your partner.

Partnership Totals HEADS $\frac{\quad}{100}$ TAILS $\frac{\quad}{100}$
(Step 3a + Step 3b)

d. Now combine your partnership totals with those of the others in your group.

Group Totals HEADS $\frac{\square}{\square}$ TAILS $\frac{\square}{\square}$
(Step 3c + Step 3d)

Name Date Time

LESSON 7•4

Tree Diagrams

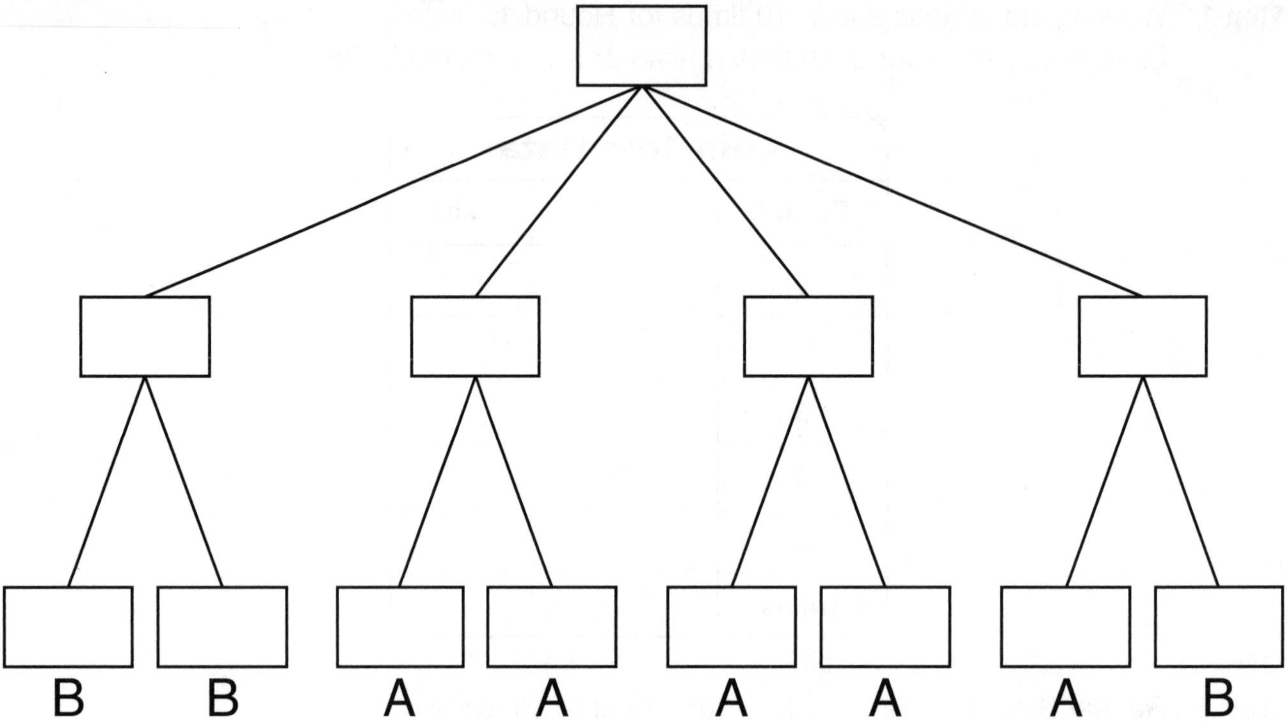

B B A A A A A B

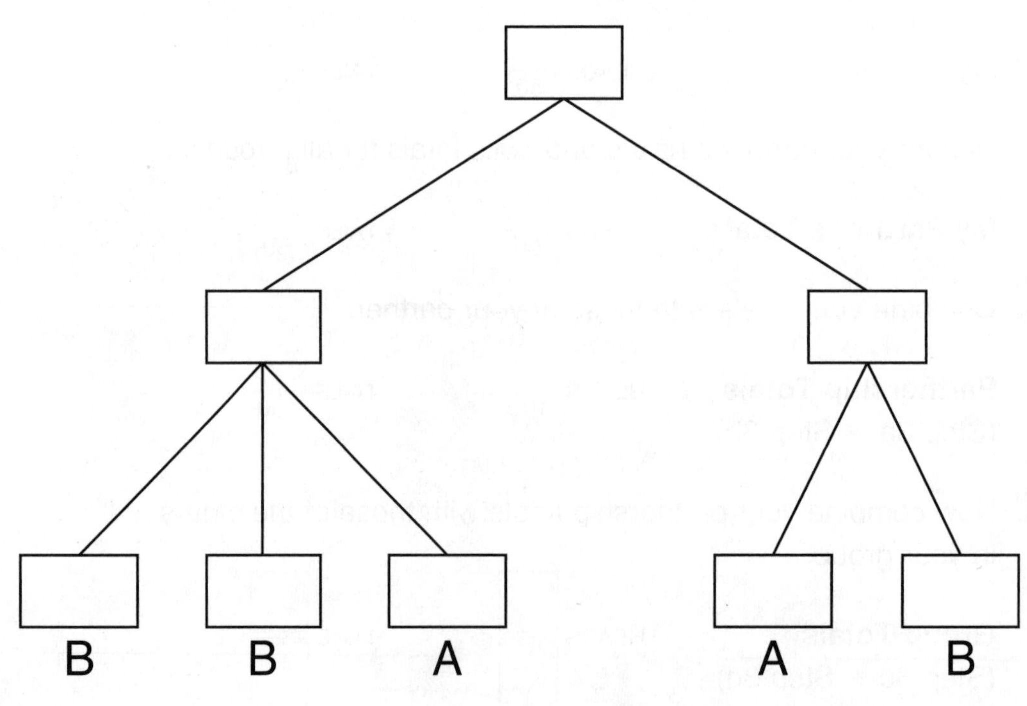

Name Date Time

Maze

Enter

① ② ③ ④

① ② ① ② ① ② ① ②

Room A

Room B

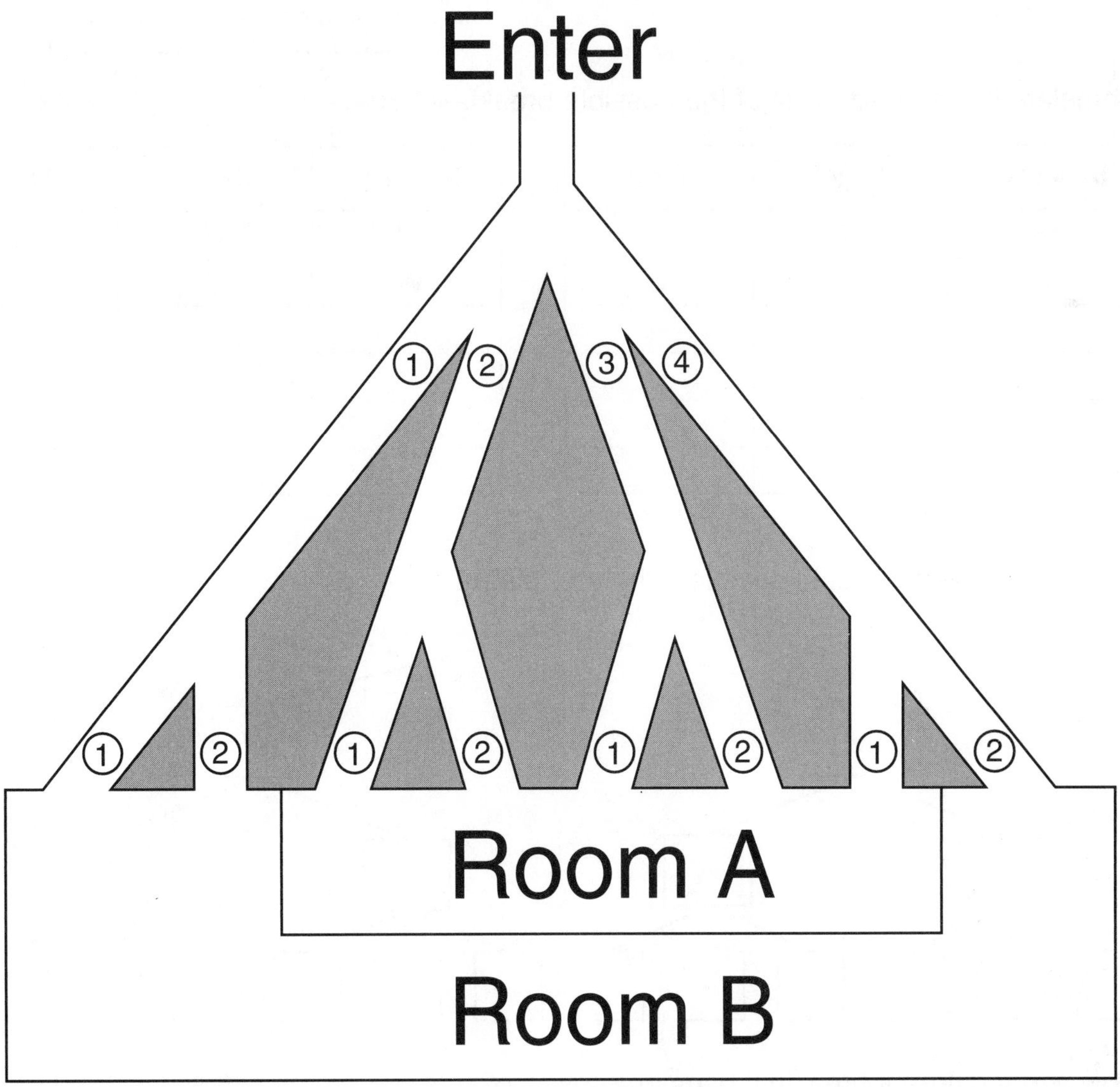

Name Date Time

Lists and Tree Diagrams

Suppose members of the hiking club are served a breakfast bag whenever they have a Saturday morning meeting. Members use the form at the right to place their orders.

Breakfast Order Form
Beverage ☐ Milk ☐ Water **Bagel** ☐ Plain ☐ Raisin **Fruit** ☐ Apple ☐ Banana ☐ Orange

1. Complete the organized list of the possible breakfast bags.

Beverage	Bagel	Fruit
M	P	A
M	P	B

Beverage	Bagel	Fruit
W	P	A
W	P	B

2. Use your organized list to complete the tree diagram.

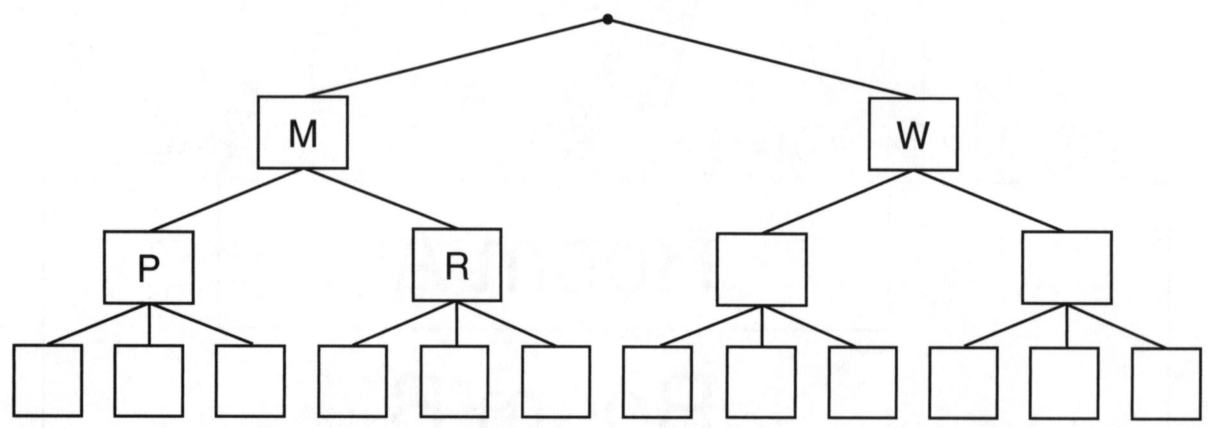

3. How many different breakfast bags are possible? ______

4. Suppose 60 members fill out an order form. About how many people would you expect to order milk and a plain bagel? ______ people

5. Suppose each of the 60 members brings 2 guests to the next Saturday meeting. About how many people would you expect to order water, a raisin bagel, and an orange? ______ people

Name Date Time

LESSON 7•4

An Amazing Contest

The sixth graders at Bailey School want to raise money to buy a microscope. Students have created the maze shown below, which they will use for a contest. Each contestant pays a fee and tries to go from Start to Exit without retracing any steps. Anyone not ending up at a dead end wins a prize.

The paths at each intersection are numbered. When a contestant reaches an intersection, the contestant chooses the next path at random, using number cards.

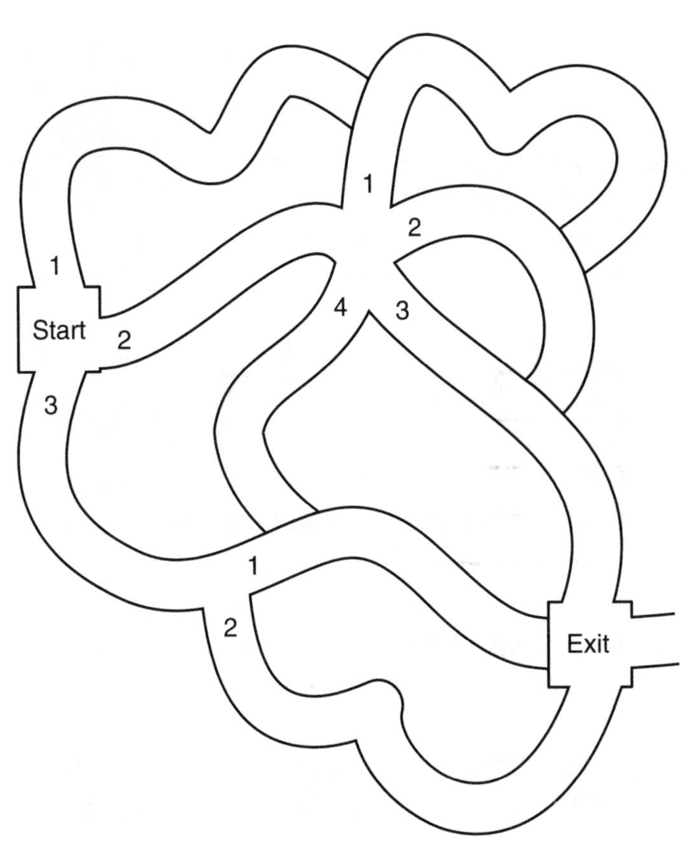

Suppose you are going to try the maze. There are 3 different paths at Start. To decide which path to follow, pick a card, without looking, from a set of cards having 1, 2, and 3. If the card you draw is 1, follow Path 1. This leads to a dead end, so you lose.

If the card you choose at Start is 2, follow Path 2. This leads to an intersection that divides into 4 different paths. Pick from a set of cards having 1, 2, 3, and 4 to see which path to follow next. You win if you follow Path 3.

If you choose the number 3 at Start, follow Path 3. This leads to an intersection that divides into 2 different paths. Pick from a set of cards having 1 and 2 to see which path to follow next. You win if you follow Path 2.

Work with a partner. Take turns trying to get through the maze. Each of you should try a total of 6 times.

What fraction of the time did you and your partner reach Exit?

I reached Exit ____________ of the time.

My partner reached Exit ____________ of the time.

Name Date Time

Analyzing the Amazing Contest

Make a tree diagram of the contest maze to help you solve the following problems.

1. If 60 people enter the maze, how many would you expect to reach the exit? ____________

2. Suppose the class charges $5 per person to enter the maze. How much money would the class collect from the contestants? ______

3. If the prize for winning the Amazing Contest is $12, how much can the class expect to make? ______

4. If the goal for the class is to make $150, how much should the prize be? ______

5. If the class wants to break even, how much should the prize be? ______

6. Explain how you found the answer to Problem 4.

____

____

____

____

____

Name Date Time

A Random Draw and a Tree Diagram

Boxes 1, 2, and 3 contain letter tiles.

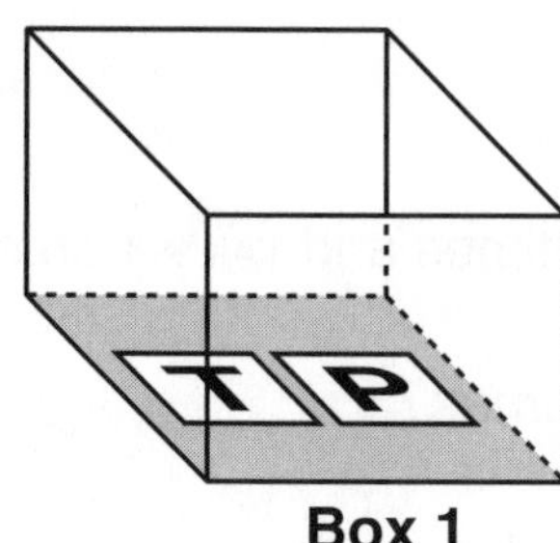

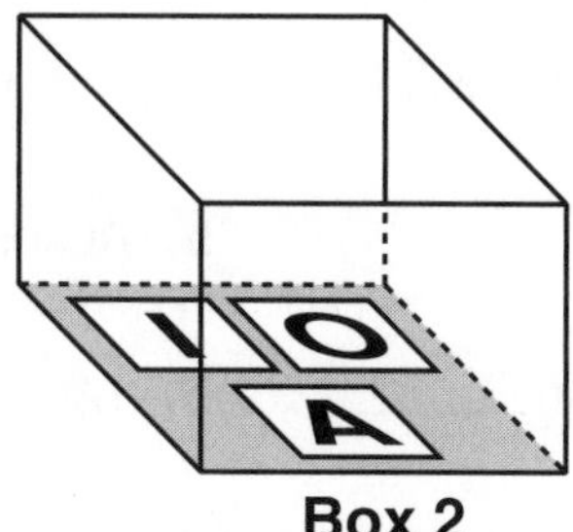

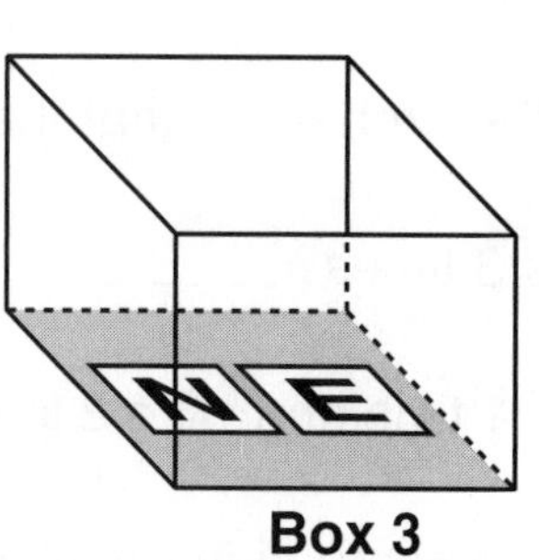

Suppose you draw one letter from each box without looking. You lay the letters in a row—the Box 1 letter first, the Box 2 letter second, and the Box 3 letter third.

1. Complete the tree diagram. Fill in the blanks to show the probability for each branch.

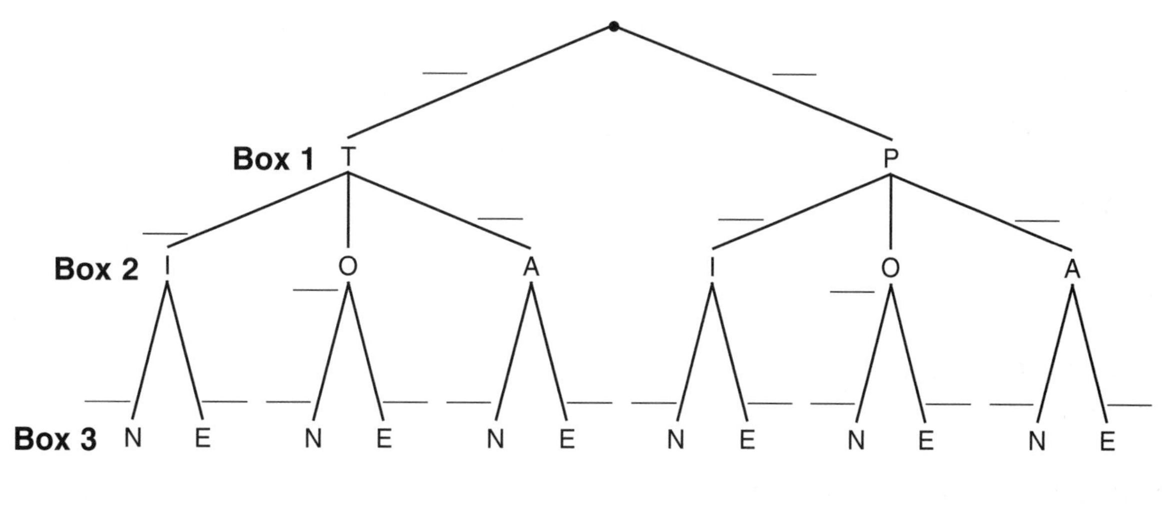

2. How many possible combinations of letter tiles are there? ________

3. What is the probability of selecting:

a. the letters P and I? ________

b. the letter I, O, or A? ________

c. the letter combinations TO or PO? ________

d. two consonants in a row? ________

Practice

4. $657 \div 18 =$ ________

5. $858.8 \div 38 =$ ________

6. $1,575 \div 125 =$ ________

Name Date Time

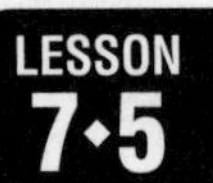

A Coin-Flipping Experiment

1. Suppose you flip a coin 3 times.

What is the probability that the coin will land

a. HEADS 3 times? ______

b. HEADS 2 times and TAILS 1 time? ______

c. HEADS 1 time and TAILS 2 times? ______

d. TAILS 3 times? ______

e. with the same side up all 3 times (that is, all HEADS or all TAILS)? ______

Make a tree diagram to help you solve the problems.

2. One trial of an experiment consists of flipping a coin 3 times. Suppose you perform 100 trials. For about how many trials would you expect to get HHH or TTT? ______________

What percent of the trials is that? ______________

Name Date Time

STUDY LINK 7•6

Venn Diagrams

SRB 263 264

There are 200 girls at Washington Middle School.

- 30 girls are on the track team.
- 38 girls are on the basketball team.
- 8 girls are on both teams.

1. Complete the Venn diagram below to show the number of girls on each team.

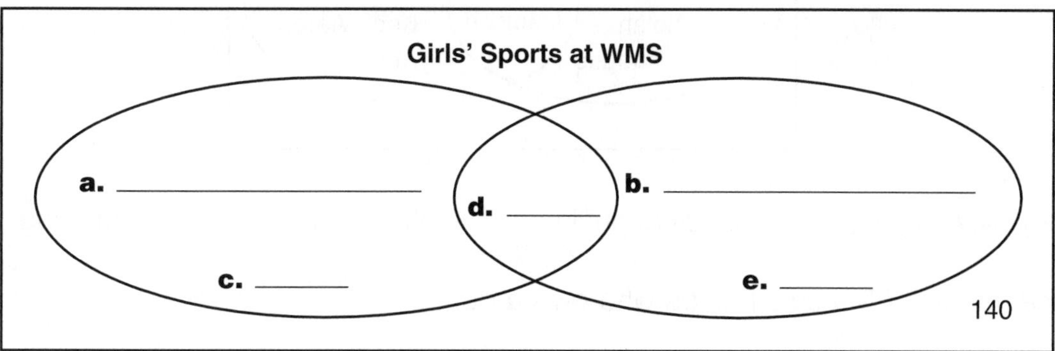

f. How many girls are on one team but not both? ______ girls

g. How many girls are on the track team but not the basketball team? ______ girls

2. Write a situation (2d) for the Venn diagram below. Complete the diagram by adding a title (2a) and labeling each ring (2b and 2c).

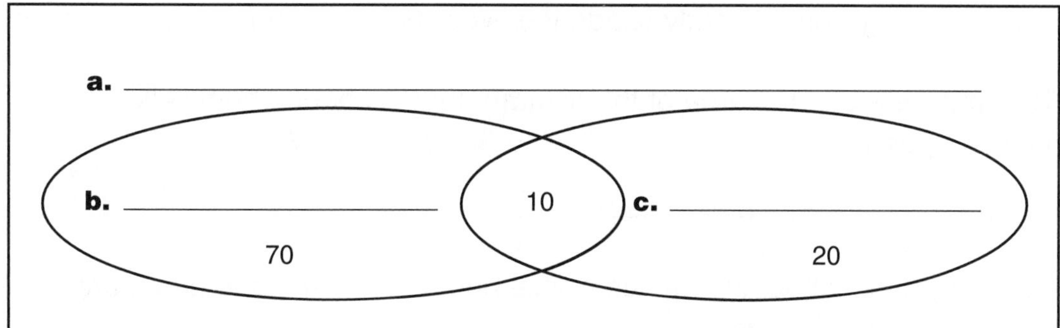

d. ______________________________

____

____

Practice

3. $\frac{7}{8} - \frac{9}{20} =$ ______

4. $7\frac{1}{3} - 4\frac{5}{12} =$ ______

5. $9\frac{2}{5} - 1\frac{1}{4} =$ ______

Name Date Time

LESSON 7•6

Reviewing Venn Diagrams

A Venn diagram shows how data can belong in more than one group. The diagram is made up of rings that sometimes overlap.

Study the Venn diagram below.

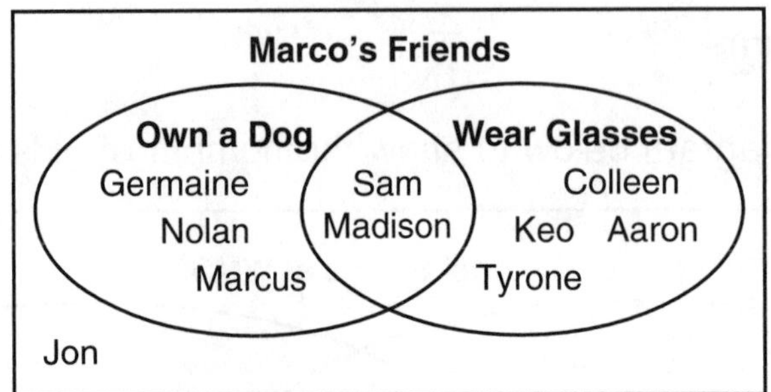

1. Use a yellow highlighter or pencil to outline and lightly shade the Own a Dog ring.

2. List the names of Marco's friends who own a dog.

____

3. Use a blue highlighter or pencil to outline the Wear Glasses ring.

4. List the names of Marco's friends who wear glasses.

____

5. Using your blue highlighter, lightly shade the Wear Glasses ring.

   a. Which names are in the area of the diagram that is shaded both yellow and blue (green)?

   ____

   b. What can you tell about the friends whose names appear in the green area of the diagram?

   ____

6. Explain why Jon's name is outside the rings of the diagram.

____

Name Date Time

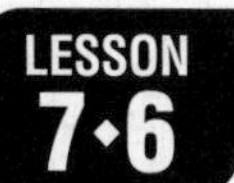

Frequency Tables and Venn Diagrams

Suppose researchers chose 1,000 adults at random and tested them to find out whether they were right- or left-handed. People who showed no preference were classified according to the hand they used more often when writing.

Each person was also tested to determine which eye was dominant.*

Possible results are shown in the table at the right. For example, the table shows that 30 people were left-handed and right-eyed.

		Dominant Hand	
		Left	**Right**
Dominant Eye	**Left**	70	200
	Right	30	700

Refer to the table to answer the following questions.

1. The sum of the numbers in the table is ______________.

2. a. How many people in the sample were right-handed and right-eyed? ______________ people

b. How many people were right-handed? ______________ people

3. a. How many people in the sample were left-handed and left-eyed? ______________ people

b. How many people were left-handed? ______________ people

c. How many people were left-eyed? ______________ people

4. Use your answers from Problem 3 to complete the Venn diagram. Fill in the missing numbers.

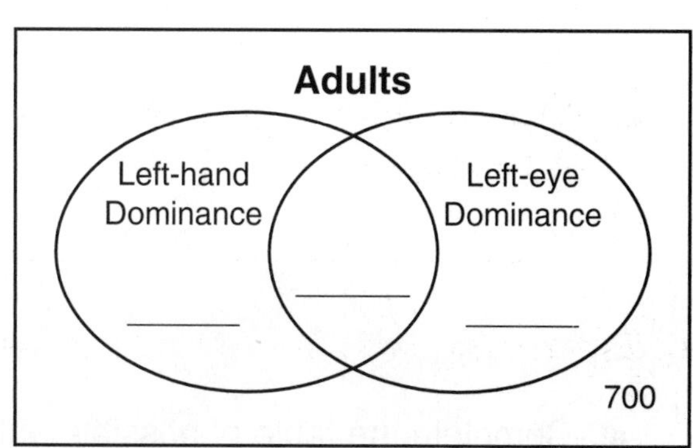

5. What percent of the people in the sample have their dominant hand and dominant eye on the same side?

____

*Eye dominance refers to the tendency to use one eye more than the other in certain tasks involving precise hand-eye coordination and a reasonably distant target. Your dominant eye is the eye you use to aim when you throw darts, for example.

Name Date Time

More Tree Diagrams

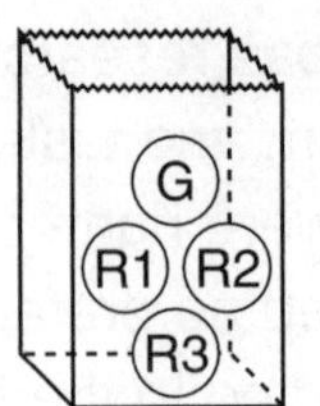

Denise has 3 red marbles and 1 green marble in a bag. She draws 1 marble at random. Then she draws a second marble without putting the first marble back in the bag.

1. Find the probabilities for each branch of the tree diagram below.

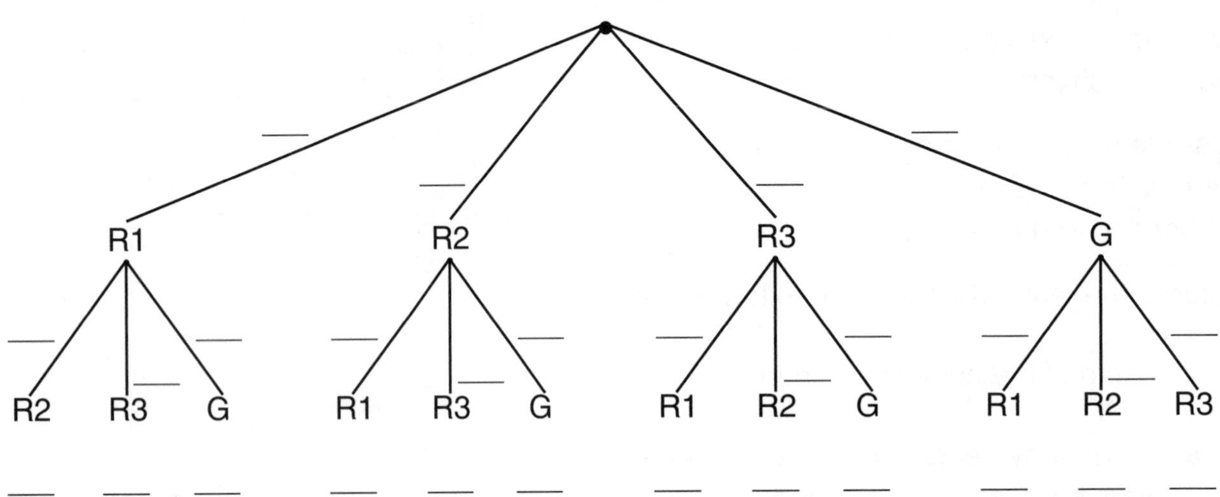

a. What is the probability that Denise will select 2 red marbles? ________%

b. What is the probability that Denise will first draw a green marble and then a red marble? ________%

2. Three coins are tossed.

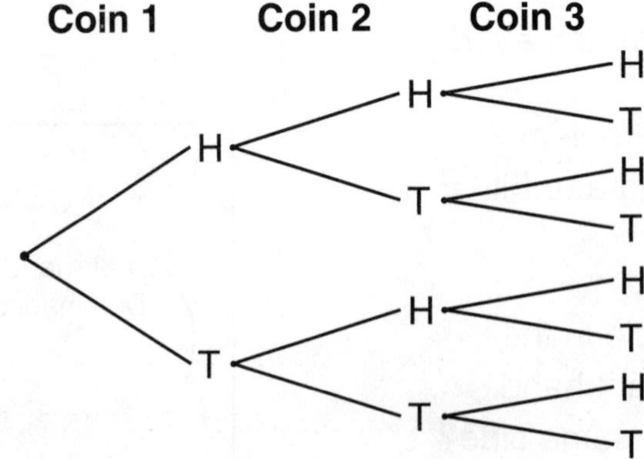

Outcomes
HHH
TTT

a. Complete the table of possible outcomes at the right.

b. What is the probability of tossing *exactly* 2 HEADS? ________%

c. What is the probability of tossing *at least* 1 TAIL? ________%

Name Date Time

A Coin-Flipping Experiment

1. Draw a tree diagram to show all possible outcomes when you flip a coin 4 times.

2. How many possible outcomes are there? ______

3. What is the probability that the coin will land TAILS once and HEADS 3 times? ______

4. What is the probability that the coin will land TAILS the same number of times it lands HEADS? ______

5. What is the probability that the coin will land on the same side all 4 times? ______

6. What is the probability that the coin will land TAILS more often than HEADS? ______

7. What is the probability that the coin will land TAILS 75 percent of the time? ______

8. What is the probability that the coin will land HEADS *at least* once? ______

Optional Experiment

9. Do the coin-flipping experiment several times and record the actual results. Combine your results with those of your classmates. Do the actual results come close to the predicted results?

Actual Results ______

Conclusions ______

______

Name Date Time

Making a Fair Game

Work with your group to figure out how to make the following game fair.

Sum Game

Materials ☐ one each of number cards 1, 3, 6, and 10 (from the Everything Math Deck, if available)

Players 1

Directions

1. Mix the cards and place them facedown on the playing surface.
2. Turn over two of the cards.
3. Add the numbers on the two cards. The 1-card (or ace) is worth 1, the 3-card is worth 3, and so on. The sum is your score for the game.
4. You win if you score at least a *certain number* of points. Otherwise, you lose.

Your group's job is to figure out the *certain number* so the game is fair. In other words, you must find the answer to the following question:

What is the least number of points you must score to win half of the time?

Answer: You win if you score at least ________ points.

Explain how you found the answer.

____

____

____

____

____

____

Name Date Time

Reviewing Probability

1. Each fraction in the left column below shows the probability of a chance event. Write the letter of the description next to the fraction that represents it.

___ $\frac{1}{3}$ **A.** Probability of getting HEADS if you flip a coin

___ $\frac{1}{4}$ **B.** Probability of rolling 3 on a 6-sided die

___ $\frac{1}{2}$ **C.** Probability of choosing a red ball from a bag containing 2 red balls, 3 white balls, and 1 green ball

___ $\frac{1}{6}$ **D.** Probability of drawing a heart card from a deck of playing cards

2. Sidone bought 3 new swimsuits—1 red suit, 1 blue suit, and 1 white suit. She also bought 2 pairs of beach sandals—1 red pair and 1 white pair. Make a tree diagram in the space at the right to show all possible combinations of swimsuits and sandals.

a. How many different combinations of suits and sandals are there? ______

b. If Sidone chooses a swimsuit and a pair of sandals at random, what is the probability that they will be the same color? ______

3. a. Ten students in Ms. Garcia's class play the piano. Seven students play the guitar. Two students play both the piano and the guitar. Complete the Venn diagram at the right.

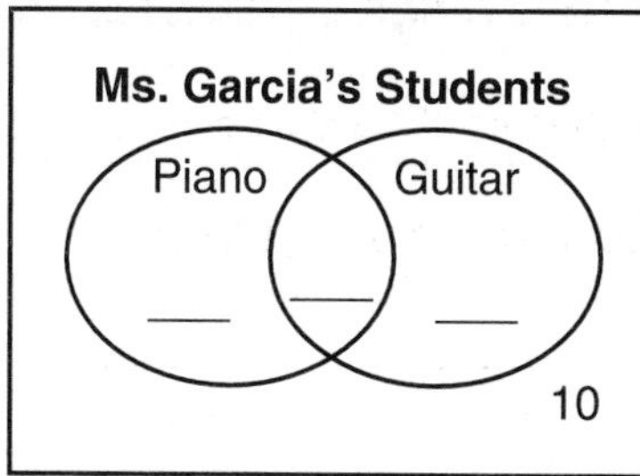

b. How many students are in Ms. Garcia's class? ______ students

Explain how you know.

____

____

____

Name Date Time

Pascal's Triangle

The triangular array of natural numbers shown below is called Pascal's triangle. This triangle is named after the French mathematician Blaise Pascal. A pattern is used to generate the numbers of the triangle. This pattern can be extended indefinitely.

Compare the numbers in each row of the triangle to the numbers in the row above and below it. Then complete Rows 6 and 7.

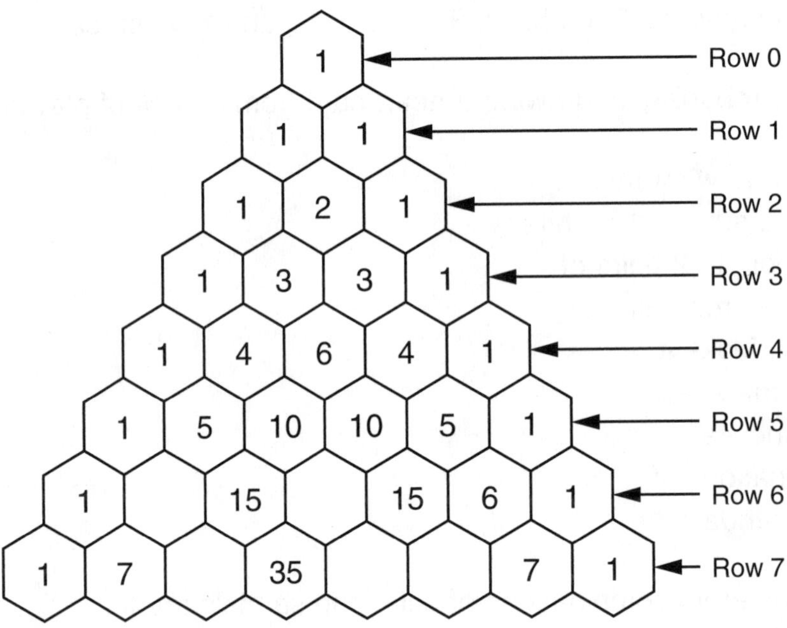

Study your completed triangle, looking along rows and diagonals for additional patterns. Describe any pattern(s) you find on the lines below. Then share your pattern(s) with a partner.

____

____

____

____

____

Name ______________________ Date ______________ Time ______________

Probability and Pascal's Triangle

1. Suppose you toss 2 coins.

a. Complete the table of possible outcomes at the right.

Coin 1	Coin 2
H	H

b. How many outcomes are possible? ________

c. Find the probability of tossing

both HEADS. ________

only one HEAD. ________

both TAILS. ________

2. Look at Row 2 of Pascal's triangle on *Math Masters,* page 240.

a. What is the sum of the numbers in Row 2? ________

b. Copy the numbers from Row 2 of the triangle in the spaces below.

________ ________ ________

c. Compare your answers for Problems 1b and 1c (above) with your answers for Problems 2a and 2b.

What do you notice? ____

____

3. Suppose you toss 3 coins. Use Row 3 of Pascal's triangle to complete the following.

a. How many outcomes are possible? ________

b. Find the probability of getting

3 HEADS. ________

2 HEADS and 1 TAIL. ________

1 HEAD and 2 TAILS. ________

3 TAILS. ________

4. Which row of Pascal's triangle would you use to find the possible outcomes and probabilities when 6 coins are tossed? Row ________

5. How many different ways could you answer 5 true/false questions? ________ ways

Name Date Time

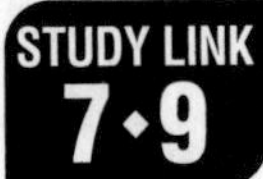

Unit 8: Family Letter

Rates and Ratios

The next unit is devoted to the study of rates and ratios. Fraction and decimal notation will be used to express rates and ratios and to solve problems.

Ratios compare quantities that have the same unit. These units cancel each other in the comparison, so the resulting ratio has no units. For example, the fraction $\frac{2}{20}$ could mean that 2 out of 20 people in a class got an A on a test or that 20,000 out of 200,000 people voted for a certain candidate in an election.

Another frequent use of ratios is to indicate relative size. For example, a picture in a dictionary drawn to $\frac{1}{10}$ scale means that every length in the picture is $\frac{1}{10}$ the corresponding length in the actual object. Students will use ratios to characterize relative size as they examine map scales and compare geometric figures.

Rates, on the other hand, compare quantities that have different units. For example, rate of travel, or speed, may be expressed in miles per hour (55 mph); food costs may be expressed in cents per ounce (17 cents per ounce) or dollars per pound ($2.49 per pound).

Easy ratio and rate problems can be solved intuitively by making tables, such as *What's My Rule?* tables. Problems requiring more complicated calculations are best solved by writing and solving proportions. Students will learn to solve proportions by cross multiplication. This method is based on the idea that two fractions are equivalent if the product of the denominator of the first fraction and the numerator of the second fraction is equal to the product of the numerator of the first fraction and the denominator of the second fraction. For example, the fractions $\frac{4}{6}$ and $\frac{6}{9}$ are equivalent because $6 * 6 = 4 * 9$. This method is especially useful because proportions can be used to solve any ratio and rate problem. It will be used extensively in algebra and trigonometry.

$9 * 4 = 36$ $6 * 6 = 36$

$$\frac{4}{6} = \frac{6}{9}$$

Students will apply these rate and ratio skills as they explore nutrition guidelines. The class will collect nutrition labels and design balanced meals based on recommended daily allowances of fat, protein, and carbohydrate. You might want to participate by planning a balanced dinner together and by examining food labels while shopping with your child. Your child will also collect and tabulate various kinds of information about your family and your home and then compare the data by converting them to ratios. In a final application lesson, your child will learn about the Golden Ratio—a ratio found in many works of art and architecture.

Vocabulary

Important terms in Unit 8:

Golden Ratio The *ratio* of the length of the long side to the length of the short side of a Golden Rectangle, approximately equal to 1.618 to 1. The Greek letter ϕ (phi) sometimes stands for the Golden Ratio. The Golden Ratio is an irrational number equal to $\frac{1 + \sqrt{5}}{2}$.

***n*-to-1 ratio** A *ratio* of a number to 1. Every ratio $a:b$ can be converted to an n-to-1 ratio by dividing a by b. For example, a ratio of 3 to 2 is a ratio of 3 / 2 = 1.5, or a 1.5-to-1 ratio.

part-to-part ratio A *ratio* that compares a part of a whole to another part of the same whole. For example, *There are 8 boys for every 12 girls* is a part-to-part ratio with a whole of 20 students. Compare to *part-to-whole ratio.*

part-to-whole ratio A *ratio* that compares a part of a whole to the whole. For example, *8 out of 20 students are boys* and *12 out of 20 students are girls* are part-to-whole ratios. Compare to *part-to-part ratio.*

per-unit rate A *rate* with 1 unit of something in the denominator. Per-unit rates tell how many of one thing there are for one unit of another thing. For example, *3 dollars per gallon, 12 miles per hour,* and *1.6 children per family* are per-unit rates.

proportion A number sentence equating two fractions. Often the fractions in a proportion represent *rates* or *ratios.*

rate A comparison by division of two quantities with different units. For example, traveling 100 miles in 2 hours is an average rate of $\frac{100 \text{ mi}}{2 \text{ hr}}$ or 50 miles per hour. Compare to *ratio.*

ratio A comparison by division of two quantities with the same units. Ratios can be fractions, decimals, percents, or stated in words. Ratios can also be written with a colon between the two numbers being compared. For example, if a team wins 3 games out of 5 games played, the ratio of wins to total games is $\frac{3}{5}$, 3 / 5, 0.6, 60%, 3 to 5, or 3:5 (read "three to five"). Compare to *rate.*

similar figures Figures that have the same shape, but not necessarily the same size. For example, all squares are similar to one another, and the preimage and image of a *size-change* are similar. The *ratio* of lengths of corresponding parts of similar figures is a *scale* or *size-change factor.* In the example below, the lengths of the sides of the larger polygon are 2 times the lengths of the corresponding sides of the smaller polygon. Compare to congruent.

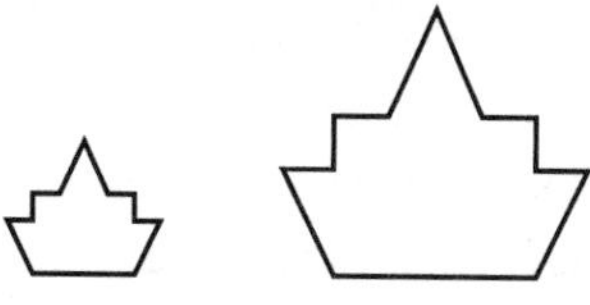

Similar polygons

size-change factor Same as *scale factor.*

scale factor (1) The *ratio* of lengths on an image and corresponding lengths on a preimage in a *size-change.* Same as *size-change factor.* (2) The *ratio* of lengths in a scale drawing or scale model to the corresponding lengths in the object being drawn or modeled.

Do-Anytime Activities

To work with your child on the concepts taught in this unit and in previous units, try these interesting and rewarding activities:

1. Look with your child through newspapers and magazines for photos, and check them to see if a size-change factor is mentioned in the caption: that is, 2X for an enlarged photo 2 times life-size; or $\frac{1}{2}$X for a photo reduced by half. You might find photos of insects, stars, bacteria, and so on. Have your child explain to you what the size-change factor means.
2. Encourage your child to read nutrition labels and calculate the percent of fat in the item.

   $$\frac{\text{fat calories}}{\text{total calories}} = \frac{?}{100} = ?\% \text{ of calories from fat}$$

   If your child enjoys this activity, extend it by figuring the percent of calories from protein and carbohydrate.
3. Help your child distinguish between part-to-part and part-to-whole ratios. When comparing a favorite sports team's record, decide which ratio is being used. For example, wins to losses (such as 5 to 15) or losses to wins (15 to 5) are part-to-part ratios. Part-to-whole ratios are used to compare wins to all games played (5 out of 20) or losses to all games played (15 out of 20).

Building Skills through Games

In Unit 8, your child will continue to review concepts from previous units and prepare for topics in upcoming units by playing games such as:

***Division Top-It* (Advanced Version)** See *Student Reference Book,* page 336
Two to four people can play this game using number cards 1–9. Players apply place-value concepts, division facts, and estimation strategies to generate whole-number division problems that will yield the largest quotient.

Spoon Scramble See *Student Reference Book,* page 333
Playing *Spoon Scramble* helps students practice finding fraction, decimal, and percent parts of a whole. Four players need a deck of 16 *Spoon Scramble* cards and 3 spoons to play this game.

As You Help Your Child with Homework

As your child brings assignments home, you may want to go over the instructions together, clarifying them as necessary. The answers listed below will guide you through some of the Study Links in this unit.

Study Link 8•1

2. a. 13 **b.** $6.50

3. a.

Words	1	2	4	5
Minutes	75	150	300	375

b. 375 words **c.** 14 minutes

4. 0.6 hours **5.** About 44

6. –1 **7.** –1.856

Study Link 8•2

1. $\frac{3}{15} = \frac{a}{125}$; 25

2. $\frac{30}{48} = \frac{w}{64}$; 40

3. $\frac{240}{10} = \frac{216}{g}$; 9

4. $\frac{60.96}{2} = \frac{c}{3}$; 91.44

Sample estimates are given.

5. 600; 674 **6.** 100; 91 **7.** 40; 35

Unit 8: Family Letter *cont.*

Study Link 8•3

1. a. \$0.13 per worm **b.** \$3.38

2. a. \$0.18 per oz **b.** \$2.88

3. 150,000 people **4.** 625 gallons

5. \$840; \$15,120 **6.** $\frac{1}{2}$ cent

7. 16 hours; Sample answer: 128 oz = 1 gal; 12 gal = 1,536 oz; $\frac{1{,}536 \text{ oz}}{1.6 \text{ oz per min}} = 960$ min; $\frac{960 \text{ min}}{60 \text{ min per hour}} = 16$ hr

Study Link 8•4

Answers vary.

Study Link 8•5

Answers vary.

Study Link 8•6

1. 25 **2.** 27 **3.** 24; 40

4. San Miguel Middle School; Sample answer: I wrote a ratio comparing the number of students to the number of teachers for each school. Richards Middle School, $\frac{14}{1}$; San Miguel, $\frac{13}{1}$.

5.

Shelf	Mystery Books	Adventure Books	Humor Books
1	4	10	18
2	6	15	27
3	8	20	36
4	10	25	45
5	12	30	54
6	14	35	63

6. 14.83 **7.** 88.43 **8.** 12.06

Study Link 8•7

1. 20 **2.** 57 **3.** 27 **4.** 6

5. 250 **6.** 42 **7.** $12\frac{1}{24}$ **8.** $2\frac{8}{9}$

9. $4\frac{11}{20}$ **10.** $3\frac{27}{40}$

Study Link 8•8

Answers vary for 5a and 5b.

5. a. $6\frac{1}{2}$ in.; $4\frac{3}{4}$ in. **b.** 5 in.; 3 in. **c.** $7\frac{1}{4}$ in.; $3\frac{3}{4}$ in. **d.** $9\frac{1}{2}$ in.; $4\frac{1}{4}$ in. **e.** 11 in.; $8\frac{1}{2}$ in.

6. Answers vary.

7. Sample answers: **a.** $6\frac{1}{2}$ **b.** 11

8. 2.3 **9.** 57.7 **10.** 10.2

Study Link 8•9

1. a. 64 mm **b.** 32 mm

2. a. 45 mm **b.** 180 mm; $\frac{1}{4}$

3. a. 45 mm **b.** 15 mm; 3

4. a. 55 mm **b.** 165 mm; $\frac{1}{3}$

Study Link 8•10

1. a. 2:1 **b.** 90° **c.** 9 **d.** 2:1

2. a. 15 **b.** $\frac{3}{2}$ **3.** 90

4. 0.007 **5.** 63.498 **6.** 4.892 **7.** 5.920

Study Link 8•11

1. 1.2; Answers vary.

2. 1.65; No. Sample answer: The ratio for a standard sheet of paper is about 1.3 to 1.

3. Lucille; Sample answer: Compare ratios of correct problems to total problems. Jeffrey's ratio is 0.93 to 1; Lucille's ratio is 0.94 to 1.

4. 12 **5.** 2.8; Answers vary. **6.** 888

7. 21,228 **8.** 15,456 **9.** 126,542

Study Link 8•12

1. a. 3.14 to 1 **b.** 1.16 to 1 **c.** 2 to 1 **d.** 1 to 1 **e.** 3 to 5

2. a. 40% **b.** 3:5, or $\frac{3}{5}$

3. b. \$7.50 **c.** 8 cans

4. a. 24 members **b.** $\frac{3}{5} = \frac{12}{n}$; 20 free throws

5. Answers vary. **6.** Answers vary.

Name Date Time

More Rates and Proportions

1. Bring nutrition labels from a variety of food packages and cans to class. A sample label is shown at the right.

Nutrition Facts
Serving Size 1 slice (23 g)
Servings Per Container 20

Amount Per Serving	
Calories 65	Calories from Fat 9
	% Daily Value
Total Fat 1 g	**2%**
Total Carbohydrate 12 g	**4%**
Protein 2 g	

2. Express each rate as a per-unit rate.

   a. 143 players per 11 teams ______ players/team

   b. $260 for 40 hours ______/hour

3. Kendis types 150 words in 2 minutes.

   a. Fill in the rate table.

minutes	1	2	4	5
words	____	150	____	____

   b. At this rate, how many words can Kendis type in 5 minutes? ______

   Complete the proportion to show your solution. $\frac{\square \text{ words}}{\square \text{ minute}} = \frac{\square \text{ words}}{\square \text{ minutes}}$

   c. How many minutes would it take Kendis to type 1,050 words? ______

   Complete the proportion to show your solution. $\frac{\square \text{ words}}{\square \text{ minute}} = \frac{\square \text{ words}}{\square \text{ minutes}}$

Try This

Use any method you wish to solve the following problems.

4. How long would it take to lay 8 rows of 18 bricks each at a rate of 4 bricks per minute? Express your answer in hours. ______

5. Apples are on sale for $0.90/pound. One pound is about 4 apples. Trisha purchased a crate of apples for $10. About how many apples should the crate contain? ______

Practice

6. $7 = 2 - 5m$; $m =$ ______

7. $x + 0.054 = -1.802$; $x =$ ______

Name Date Time

Patterns and Equations

While walking with her father, Stephanie noticed that for every 2 steps her father took, she needed to take 3 steps to cover the same distance.

1. Complete the rate table below.

Number of Father's Steps (*f*)	2	4	5	8	10	15		20	36
Number of Stephanie's Steps (*s*)	3						27		

2. Describe any pattern(s) you used to complete the table.

____

____

3. Suppose Stephanie's father takes 100 steps. Explain how you can calculate the number of steps Stephanie will take.

____

____

4. a. Write an equation to calculate the number of steps Stephanie takes (*s*) for any given number of her father's steps (*f*).

Equation: ______________________

b. Check your equation by substituting values from the completed rate table for *f* or *s*.

____

c. Use your equation to find the number of steps Stephanie will take if her father takes 1,500 steps. ______________________

Name Date Time

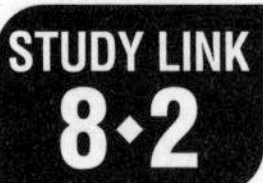
STUDY LINK 8·2

More Rate Problems and Proportions

For each of the following problems, first complete the rate table. Use the table to write an open proportion. Solve the proportion. Then write the answer to the problem.

1. A science museum requires 3 adult chaperones for every 15 students on a field trip. How many chaperones would be needed for a group of 125 students?

adults	3	*a*
students	15	

$\frac{\square}{\square} = \frac{\square}{\square}$

Answer: A group of 125 students would need ______ adult chaperones.

2. Crust and Crunch Deli sells 30 salads for every 48 sandwiches. At this rate, how many salads will they sell for every 64 sandwiches?

salads	30	*w*
sandwiches	48	

$\frac{\square}{\square} = \frac{\square}{\square}$

Answer: For every 64 sandwiches, they will sell ______ salads.

3. Tonya's car averages 240 miles for each 10 gallons of gasoline. How many gallons of gasoline will the car need to travel 216 miles?

miles	240	
gallons	10	

$\frac{\square}{\square} = \frac{\square}{\square}$

Answer: Tonya's car needs ______ gallons of gasoline to travel 216 miles.

4. There are 60.96 centimeters in 2 feet. How many centimeters are in 1 yard?

cm	60.96	
ft	2	

$\frac{\square}{\square} = \frac{\square}{\square}$

Answer: There are ______ centimeters in 1 yard.

Practice

Estimate each quotient and then divide. Round your answer to the nearest whole number. Show your work on the back of this sheet.

5. 38,419 ÷ 57 is about ______. 38,419 ÷ 57 = ______

6. 7,648 ÷ 84 is about ______. 7,648 ÷ 84 = ______

7. 86.5 ÷ 2.5 is about ______. 86.5 ÷ 2.5 = ______

Name Date Time

Calculating Rates

If necessary, draw a picture, find a per-unit rate, make a rate table, or use a proportion to help you solve these problems.

1. A can of worms for fishing costs $2.60. There are 20 worms in a can.
   a. What is the cost per worm? ____________________
   b. At this rate, how much would 26 worms cost? __________

2. An 11-ounce bag of chips costs $1.99.
   a. What is the cost per ounce, rounded to the nearest cent? __________
   b. What is the cost per pound, rounded to the nearest cent? __________

3. Just 1 gram of venom from a king cobra snake can kill 150 people. At this rate, about how many people would 1 kilogram kill? ____________________

4. A milking cow can produce nearly 6,000 quarts of milk each year. At this rate, about how many gallons of milk could a cow produce in 5 months? ____________________

5. A dog-walking service costs $2,520 for 6 months.

   What is the cost for 2 months? __________ For 3 years? __________

Try This

6. A 1-pound bag of candy containing 502 pieces costs 16.8 cents per ounce. What is the cost of 1 piece of candy? Circle the best answer.

   1.86 cents 2.99 cents 0.33 cent $\frac{1}{2}$ cent

7. Mr. Rainier's car uses about 1.6 fluid ounces of gas per minute when the engine is idling. One night, he parked his car but forgot to turn off the motor. He had just filled his tank. His tank holds 12 gallons.

   About how many hours will it take before his car runs out of gas? ____________________

   Explain what you did to find the answer.

   ____

   ____

Sources: 2201 Fascinating Facts; Everything Has Its Price

Name Date Time

LESSON 8•3 Ingredients for Peanut Butter Fudge

1. The list at the right shows the ingredients used to make peanut butter fudge but not how much of each ingredient is needed. Use the following clues to calculate the amount of each ingredient needed to make 1 pound of peanut butter fudge. Record each amount in the ingredient list.

Peanut Butter Fudge
(makes 1 pound)

_____ cups of sugar

_____ cup of milk

_____ tablespoons of peanut butter

_____ tablespoons of corn syrup

_____ teaspoons of vanilla

_____ teaspoon of salt

Clues

- Use 20 cups of sugar to make 10 pounds of fudge.
- You need $3\frac{3}{4}$ cups of milk to make 5 pounds of fudge.
- You need 15 cups of peanut butter to make 48 pounds of fudge. (*Hint:* 1 cup = 16 tablespoons)
- An 8-pound batch of fudge uses 1 cup of corn syrup.
- Use 6 teaspoons of vanilla for each 4 pounds of fudge.
- Use $\frac{1}{2}$ teaspoon of salt for each 4 pounds of fudge.

2. Suppose you wanted to make an 80-pound batch of fudge. Record how much of each ingredient you would need.

Ingredient List for 80 Pounds of Peanut Butter Fudge	
_____ cups of sugar	_____ tablespoons of corn syrup
_____ cups of milk	_____ teaspoons of vanilla
_____ tablespoons of peanut butter	_____ teaspoons of salt

Use the following equivalencies and your ingredient lists to complete each problem.

- 3 teaspoons = 1 tablespoon
- 16 tablespoons = 1 cup

3. _________ cups of peanut butter are needed for 80 pounds of fudge.

4. _________ cups of corn syrup are needed for 80 pounds of fudge.

5. _________ tablespoons of vanilla are needed for 80 pounds of fudge.

Name Date Time

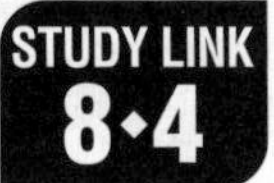

Food Costs as Unit Rates

Visit a grocery store with a parent or guardian. Select 10 different items and record the cost and weight of each item in Part A of the table below.

- Select items that include a wide range of weights.
- Select only items whose containers list weights in pounds and ounces or a combination of pounds and ounces, such as 2 lb 6 oz.
- Do not choose produce items (fruits and vegetables).
- Do not choose liquids that are sold by volume (gallons, quarts, pints, liters, milliliters, or fluid ounces).

1. Complete Part A of the table at the store.

2. Complete Parts B and C of the table by

- converting each weight to ounces and pounds.
- calculating the unit cost in cents per ounce and in dollars per pound.

Example: A jar of pickles weighs 1 lb 5 oz and costs $2.39.

Convert Weight	Calculate Unit Cost
to ounces: 1 lb 5 oz = 21 oz	in cents per ounce: $\frac{\$2.39}{21\text{ oz}} = \frac{11.4\text{ cents}}{1\text{ oz}}$
to pounds: 1 lb 5 oz = $1\frac{5}{16}$ lb = 1.31 lb	in dollars per pound: $\frac{\$2.39}{1.31\text{ lb}} = \frac{\$1.82}{1\text{ lb}}$

Part A			Part B		Part C	
Item	Cost	Weight Shown	Weight in Ounces	Cents per Ounce	Weight in Pounds	Dollars per Pound

Name Date Time

Calorie Use for a Triathlon

In a triathlon, athletes compete in swimming, cycling, and running races. In a short-course triathlon, athletes go the distances shown in the table below. Tevin is a fit sixth grader who plans to compete in the short-course triathlon. He estimates his rate of speed for each event to be as shown.

Event	Miles	Tevin's Estimated Times
Swimming	1	40 yards per minute
Cycling	25	20 miles per hour
Running	6.2	7.5 miles per hour

Refer to the information above and the table on journal page 292 to answer these questions.

1. **a.** About how long will it take Tevin to swim the mile? ______________________
(*Hint:* Find the number of yards in a mile.)

b. About how many calories will he use? ______________________

2. **a.** About how long will it take Tevin to cycle 25 miles? ______________________

b. About how many calories will he use? ______________________

3. **a.** About how long will it take Tevin to run 6.2 miles? ______________________

b. About how many calories will he use? ______________________

4. About how many calories will Tevin use to complete the triathlon?

____

5. Use the following equivalencies to express the distance of each event and Tevin's estimated times in kilometers.

- 1 mi is about 1.6 km.
- 1 m is about 39 in.
- 1 yd is about 0.9 m.

Event	Kilometers (approximate)	Tevin's Estimated Times
Swimming	1.6	____ meters per minute
Cycling		____ kilometers per hour
Running		____ kilometers per hour

Name Date Time

Calculating Calories from Fat

1. Choose 5 breakfast items from the menu at the right. Pay no attention to total calories, but try to limit the percent of calories from fat to 30% or less. Put a check mark next to each of your 5 items.

Food	Total Calories	Calories from Fat
Toast (1 slice)	70	10
Corn flakes (8 oz)	95	trace
Oatmeal (8 oz)	130	20
Butter (1 pat)	25	25
Doughnut	205	105
Jam (1 tbs)	55	trace
Pancakes (butter, syrup)	180	60
Bacon (2 slices)	85	65
Yogurt	240	25
Sugar (1 tsp)	15	0
Scrambled eggs (2)	140	90
Fried eggs (2)	175	125
Hash browns	130	65
Skim milk (8 fl oz)	85	0
2% milk (8 fl oz)	145	45
Blueberry muffin	110	30
Orange juice (8 fl oz)	110	0
Bagel	165	20
Bagel with cream cheese	265	105

2. Record the 5 items you chose in the table. Then find the total number of calories for each column.

Food	Total Calories	Calories from Fat
Total		

3. What percent of the total number of calories comes from fat? ______________

Name Date Time

Planning a Meal

Plan a menu of foods that you would enjoy for one meal of the day—breakfast, lunch, or dinner. In the table below, record nutrition label information for the foods you chose. Fill in the rest of the table and find the total number of calories for each column. Then find the total percent for each column. (*Note:* The percents from fat, carbohydrate, and protein should total about 100%.)

Meal ____________________

Food	Number of Calories	Calories from Fat	Calories from Carbohydrate	Calories from Protein
Total Number of Calories				
Percent of Calories	**100%**			

In the space at the right, make a circle graph to show the percentages of calories from fat, carbohydrate, and protein in the meal you planned. Be sure to label each section of the circle graph and write the percent of the total number of calories. Title your graph.

____
(title)

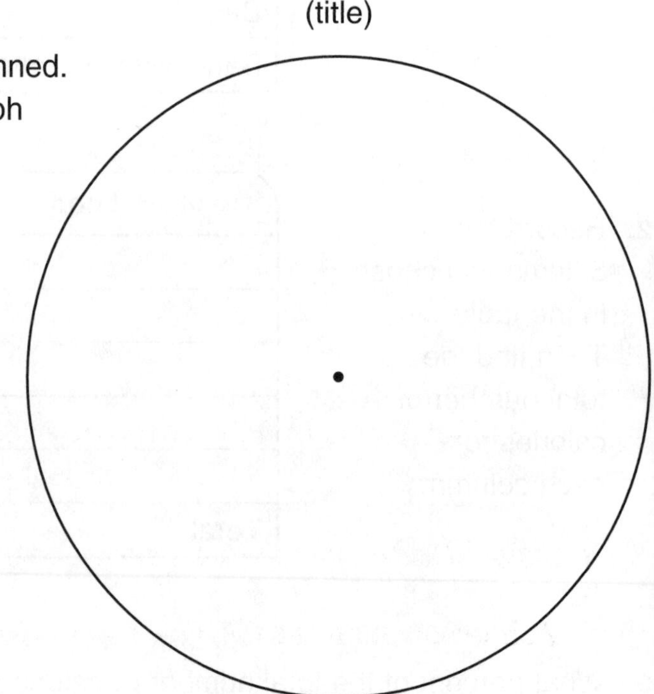

Name Date Time

Rate Problems

1. Find the average speed (in meters per second) for each running event.

Event	Time (minutes and seconds)	Time (seconds)	Average Speed (meters per second)
100 meters	0 min 10.94 sec	10.94 sec	m/sec
200 meters	0 min 22.12 sec	22.12 sec	m/sec
400 meters	0 min 48.25 sec	48.25 sec	m/sec
800 meters	1 min 57.73 sec	sec	m/sec
1,500 meters	4 min 0.83 sec	sec	m/sec

2. Why do you think the average speed is different for each event?

____

____

____

The picture at the right shows a stack of 50 pennies, drawn to actual size.

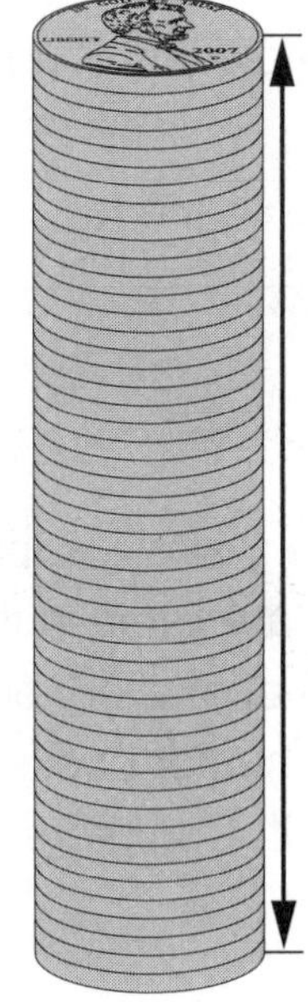

Stack of 50 pennies (actual size)

3. Carefully measure the height of the stack. Use your measurement to calculate about how many pennies would be in a stack 1 centimeter high.

About _______________ (unit)

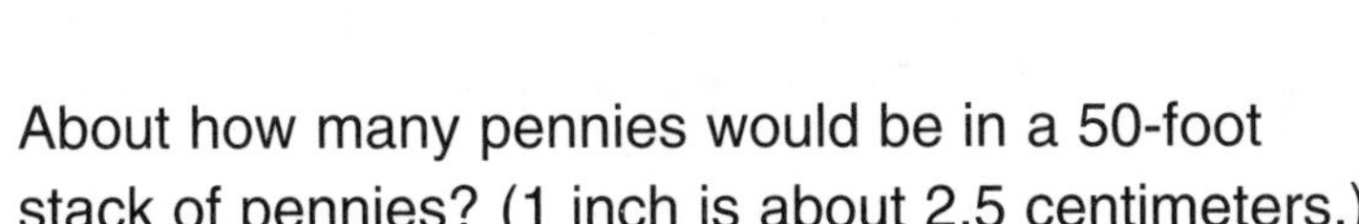

4. About how many pennies would be in a 50-foot stack of pennies? (1 inch is about 2.5 centimeters.)

About _______________ (unit)

5. Some people believe that to determine the temperature in degrees Fahrenheit, you can count the number of times a cricket chirps in 14 seconds and then add 40.

a. What is the temperature if a cricket chirps 3 times per second? _______________ (unit)

b. At a temperature of 61°F, how many times does a cricket chirp per second? _______________

Source: The Handy Science Answer Book

Name Date Time

Solving Ratio Problems

Solve the following problems. Use coins or 2-color counters to help you. If you need to draw pictures, use the back of this page.

1. You have 45 coins. Five out of every 9 are HEADS and the rest are TAILS. How many coins are HEADS? ______ coins

2. You have 36 coins. The ratio of HEADS to TAILS is 3 to 1. How many coins are HEADS? ______ coins

3. You have 16 coins that are HEADS up and 18 coins that are TAILS up. After you add some coins that are TAILS up, the ratio of HEADS up to TAILS up is 1 to 1.5.

How many coins are TAILS up? ______ coins How many coins in all? ______ coins

4. At Richards Middle School, there are 448 students and 32 teachers. The San Miguel Middle School has 234 students and 18 teachers. Which school has a better ratio of students to teachers; that is, fewer students per teacher? ______________________

Explain how you found your answer. ______________________

____

____

5. You have 6 shelves for books. Numbers of books are listed in the table at the right. The ratio of mystery books to adventure books to humor books is the same on each shelf. Complete the table.

Shelf	Mystery Books	Adventure Books	Humor Books
1	4	10	18
2	6		
3			
4		25	
5	12		
6			63

Practice

Write each quotient as a 2-place decimal.

6. $12\overline{)178}$ **7.** $84\overline{)7,428}$ **8.** $36\overline{)434}$

Name Date Time

STUDY LINK 8·7 Body Composition by Weight

SRB 51 52

Solve using any method of your choice.

1. About 1 out of every 5 pounds of an average adult's body weight is fat. What percent of body weight is fat? ________%

2. About 60% of the human body is water. At this rate, how many pounds of water are in the body of a 95-pound person? ________ lb

For Problems 3–6, use a variable to represent each part, whole, or percent that is known. Set up and solve each proportion.

3. The width of a singles tennis court is 75% the width of a doubles court. A doubles court is 36 ft wide. How wide is a singles court?

$\frac{\text{(width of singles court)}}{\text{(width of doubles court)}}$ $\frac{\square}{\square} = \frac{\square}{100}$ A singles court is ________ ft wide.

4. Nadia put $500 into a savings account. At the end of 1 year, she had earned $30 in interest. What interest rate was the bank paying?

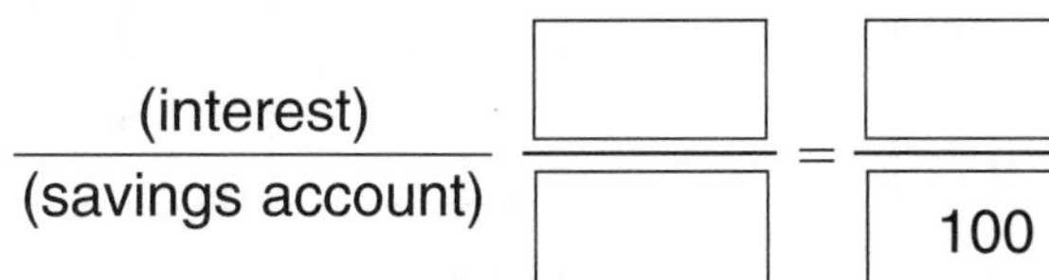
$\frac{\text{(interest)}}{\text{(savings account)}}$ $\frac{\square}{\square} = \frac{\square}{100}$

The bank was paying ________% interest.

5. 15 is 6% of what number?

$\frac{\text{(part)}}{\text{(whole)}}$ $\frac{\square}{\square} = \frac{\square}{100}$ 15 is 6% of ________.

6. 25% of what number is $10\frac{1}{2}$?

$\frac{\text{(part)}}{\text{(whole)}}$ $\frac{\square}{100} = \frac{\square}{\square}$ 25% of ________ is $10\frac{1}{2}$.

Practice

7. $5\frac{2}{3} + 6\frac{3}{8} =$ ________

8. $3\frac{2}{3} - \frac{7}{9} =$ ________

9. $2\frac{3}{5} * 1\frac{3}{4} =$ ________

10. $5\frac{1}{4} \div 1\frac{3}{7} =$ ________

Name Date Time

LESSON 8•7

Fractions, Decimals, and Percents

Shade the grid and fill in the numbers to represent the fractions your teacher assigns.

100%
large square

1. Ways of showing ____:

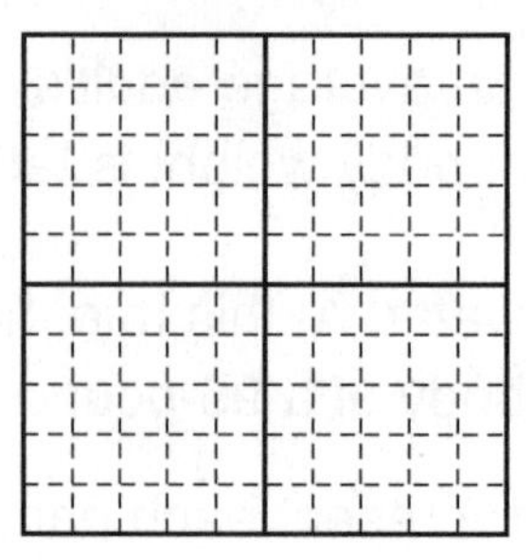

$\frac{\square}{4} = \frac{\square}{100}$

0.____ = ____%

2. Ways of showing ____:

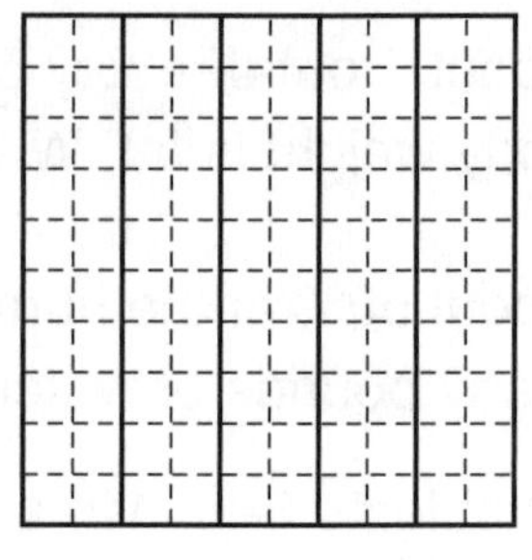

$\frac{\square}{5} = \frac{\square}{100}$

0.____ = ____%

3. Ways of showing ____:

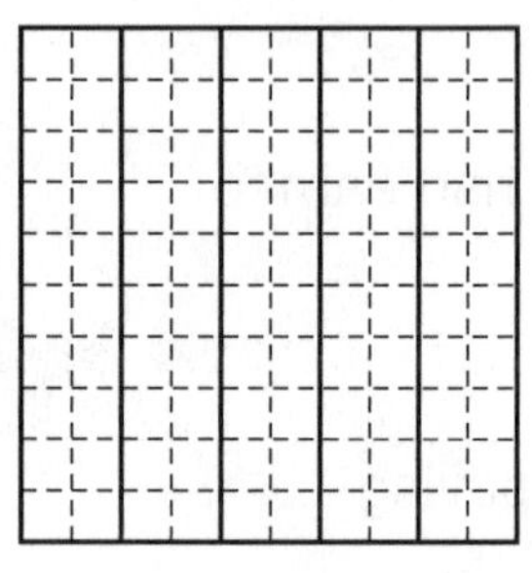

$\frac{\square}{5} = \frac{\square}{100}$

0.____ = ____%

4. Ways of showing ____:

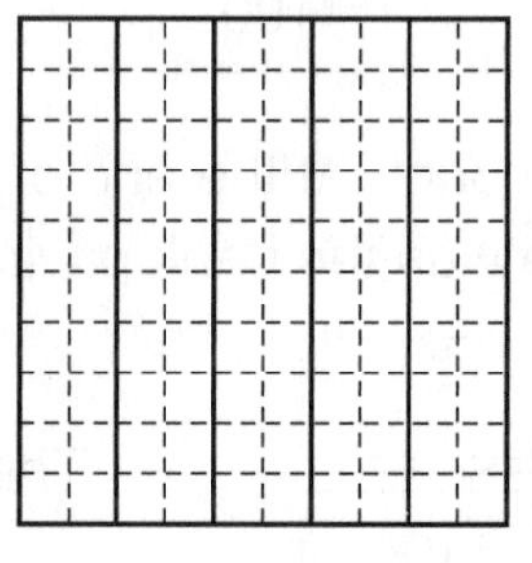

$\frac{\square}{5} = \frac{\square}{100}$

0.____ = ____%

5. Ways of showing ____:

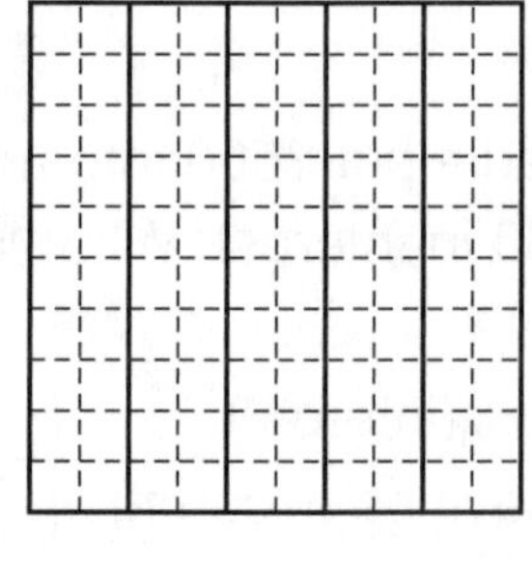

$\frac{\square}{5} = \frac{\square}{100}$

0.____ = ____%

6. Ways of showing ____:

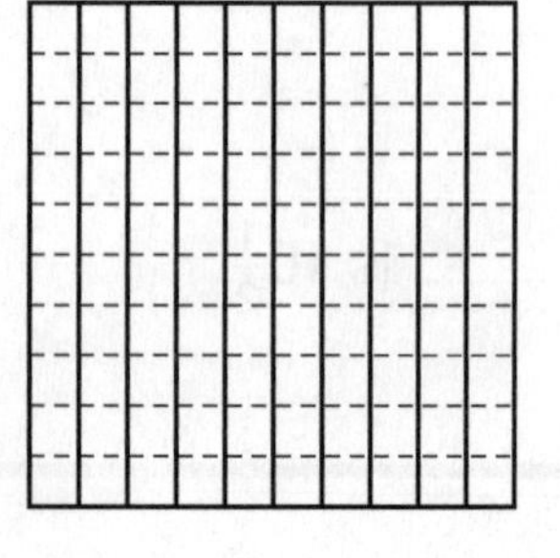

$\frac{\square}{10} = \frac{\square}{100}$

0.____ = ____%

7. Ways of showing ____:

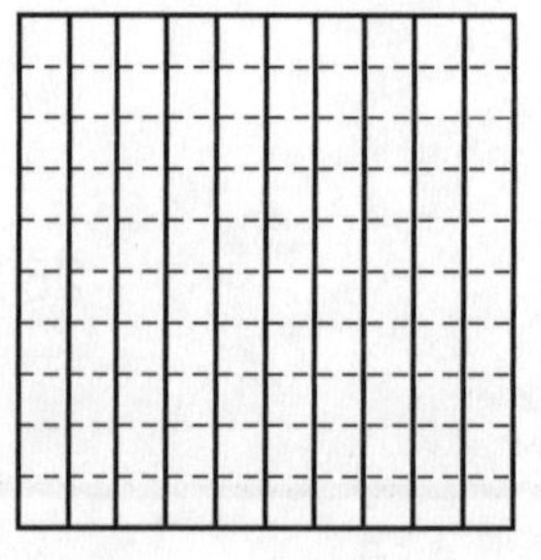

$\frac{\square}{10} = \frac{\square}{100}$

0.____ = ____%

8. Ways of showing ____:

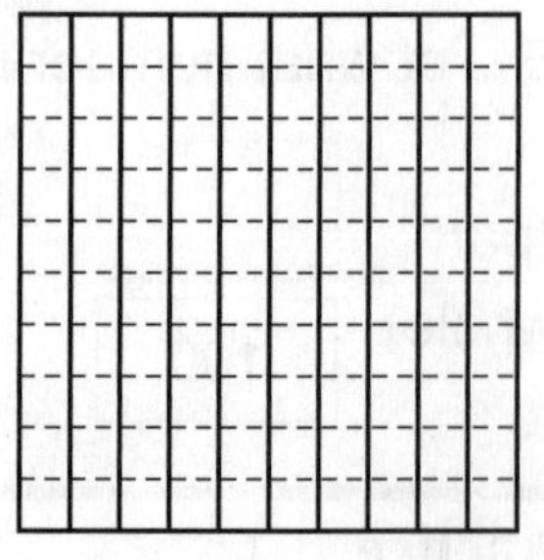

$\frac{\square}{10} = \frac{\square}{100}$

0.____ = ____%

Name Date Time

The World of Percents

Solve.

1. If reduced-fat hot dogs have 8 fewer grams of fat than regular hot dogs, how much fat do regular hot dogs have?

____

Reduced-Fat
Hot Dogs with
40% Less Fat!
Lean
Links
40% less fat!

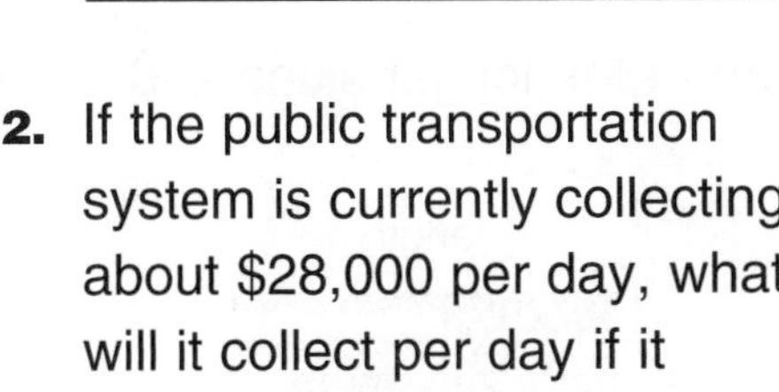

2. If the public transportation system is currently collecting about $28,000 per day, what will it collect per day if it reaches its goal?

____

Public Transportation Authority Aims to Increase Ridership by 25%

3. If 420 fewer people attended the concert series, what was the total attendance for the previous year?

____

Attendance at Music Hall Down 12% Over Previous Year for 10-Concert Series

4. Reginald read 168 pages of his book. He has 42 pages left. What percent of the book has he read? _______________

5. Last year, Maria's insect collection had 250 insects. She added 60 more to her collection this summer. By what percent did she increase her collection? _______________

6. Jackie had a batting average of .250 for the season. If she went to bat 52 times during the season, how many hits did she get? (*Hint:* 0.250 = 0.25 = ___%) _______________

7. Make up and solve a problem. Write it on the back of this page.

Name Date Time

Home Data

1. Record the following data about all the members of your household.

 a. Total number of people ________ b. Number of males ________

 c. Number of females ________ d. Number of left-handed people ________

 e. Number of right-handed people ________ (For people who are ambidextrous, record the hand most often used for writing.)

For the rectangles in this Study Link, use length as the measure of the longer sides and width as the measure of the shorter sides.

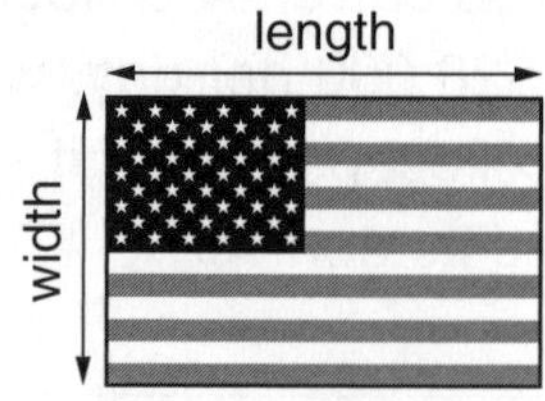

2. Find an American flag or a picture of one. Measure its length and width.

 a. length ________ (unit) b. width ________ (unit)

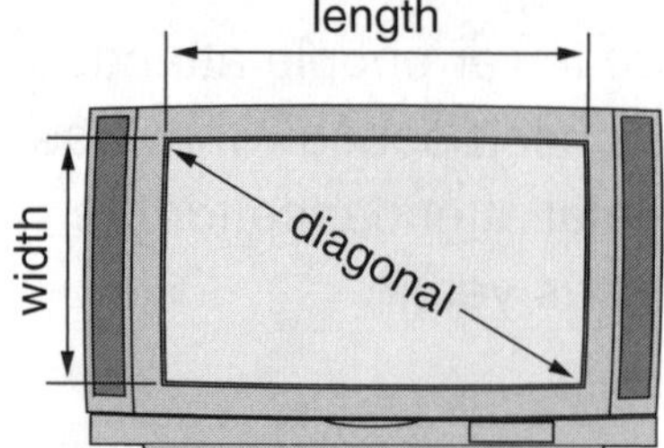

3. Measure the length and width of a television screen to the nearest $\frac{1}{2}$ inch.

 a. length ________ (unit) b. width ________ (unit)

4. Find 3 books of different sizes, such as a small paperback, your math journal, and a large reference book. Measure the length and width of each book to the nearest $\frac{1}{2}$ inch.

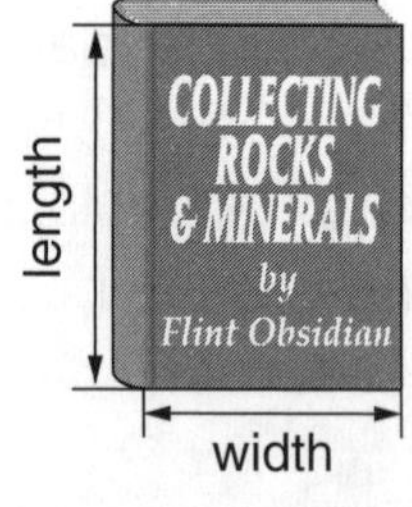

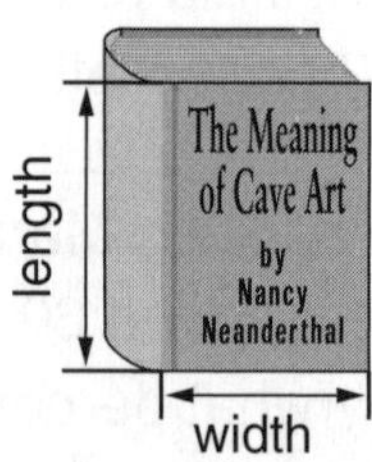

 a. Small book: length ________ (unit) width ________ (unit)

 b. Medium book: length ________ (unit) width ________ (unit)

 c. Large book: length ________ (unit) width ________ (unit)

Name Date Time

Home Data *continued*

5. Find samples of the following items. Measure the length and width of each to the nearest $\frac{1}{4}$ inch.

a. Postcard length ________ (unit) width ________ (unit)

b. Index card length ________ (unit) width ________ (unit)

c. Envelope (regular) length ________ (unit) width ________ (unit)

d. Envelope (business) length ________ (unit) width ________ (unit)

e. Notebook paper length ________ (unit) width ________ (unit)

6. Show the 4 rectangles below to each member of your household. Ask each person to select the rectangle that he or she likes best or thinks is the nicest looking. Tally the answers. Remember to include your own choice.

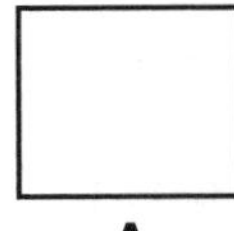

A

B

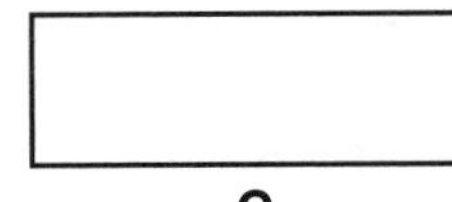

C

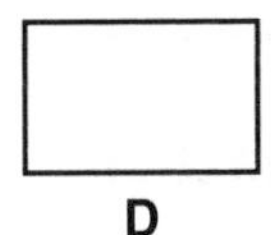

D

Voting Results	A	B	C	D
Tally of Votes				
Number of Votes				

7. Measure the rise and run of stairs in your home. The diagram shows what these dimensions are. (If there are no stairs in your home, measure stairs outdoors or in a friend's or neighbor's home.)

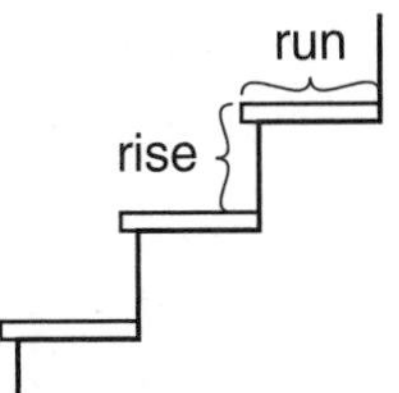

a. rise ________ in. **b.** run ________ in.

Practice

Round each quotient to the nearest tenth.

8. $32\overline{)74.9}$ = ________ **9.** $15\overline{)864.9}$ = ________ **10.** $68\overline{)696.1}$ = ________

Name Date Time

Converting and Rounding

One way to convert fractions to decimals and percents is to use a calculator.

Depending on your calculator, to convert $\frac{3}{7}$ to a percent, press:

3 [n] 7 [d] [▸%] [Enter]

Display: 42.85714286%

OR

3 [b/c] 7 [F↔D] [X] 100 [=]

Display: = 42.857143

You can round decimals and percents when you want to estimate an answer or when you don't need a precise measurement.

For example, 42.85714286% rounded to the nearest whole percent is 43%.

Use your calculator to convert each fraction in the table below to a decimal. Write all the digits shown in your calculator display. Then write the equivalent percent rounded to the nearest whole percent. The first row has been completed for you.

Fraction	Decimal	Percent (rounded to nearest whole percent)
$\frac{18}{35}$	51.42857143	51%
$\frac{12}{67}$		
$\frac{24}{93}$		
$\frac{13}{24}$		
$\frac{576}{1,339}$		

Name Date Time

LESSON 8•8

From Fractions to Percents

Write $<$, $>$, or $=$.

1. $\frac{3}{11}$ ______ 30%
2. $\frac{18}{49}$ ______ 35%
3. $\frac{28}{35}$ ______ 80%
4. $\frac{15}{24}$ ______ 60%
5. 30% ______ $\frac{9}{34}$
6. 45% ______ $\frac{4}{7}$
7. On the back of this page, explain how you got your answer to Problem 4.

Circle the percent that is the best estimate for each fraction.

8. $\frac{3}{17}$ 25% 50% 75% 100%
9. $\frac{9}{29}$ 25% 50% 75% 100%
10. $\frac{6}{7}$ 25% 50% 75% 100%
11. $\frac{5}{9}$ 25% 50% 75% 100%

Name Date Time

LESSON 8•8

From Fractions to Percents

Write $<$, $>$, or $=$.

1. $\frac{3}{11}$ ______ 30%
2. $\frac{18}{49}$ ______ 35%
3. $\frac{28}{35}$ ______ 80%
4. $\frac{15}{24}$ ______ 60%
5. 30% ______ $\frac{9}{34}$
6. 45% ______ $\frac{4}{7}$
7. On the back of this page, explain how you got your answer to Problem 4.

Circle the percent that is the best estimate for each fraction.

8. $\frac{3}{17}$ 25% 50% 75% 100%
9. $\frac{9}{29}$ 25% 50% 75% 100%
10. $\frac{6}{7}$ 25% 50% 75% 100%
11. $\frac{5}{9}$ 25% 50% 75% 100%

Name Date Time

A Pizza Problem

Math Message

Zach and Regina both wanted cheese pizza. An 8-inch pizza costs $2 and a 12-inch pizza costs $4.

Zach said that they should buy two 8-inch pizzas because the 12-inch pizza costs twice as much as the 8-inch pizza, and 2 times 8 is more than 12.

Regina disagreed. She said that the 12-inch pizza was a better deal.

Who was right? ____________ Explain your answer. ____________

____

____

____

____

Name Date Time

A Pizza Problem

Math Message

Zach and Regina both wanted cheese pizza. An 8-inch pizza costs $2 and a 12-inch pizza costs $4.

Zach said that they should buy two 8-inch pizzas because the 12-inch pizza costs twice as much as the 8-inch pizza, and 2 times 8 is more than 12.

Regina disagreed. She said that the 12-inch pizza was a better deal.

Who was right? ____________ Explain your answer. ____________

____

____

____

____

Name Date Time

Scale Drawings

Measure the object in each drawing to the nearest millimeter. Then use the size-change factor to determine the actual size of the object.

Size-change Factor: $\frac{\text{changed length}}{\text{actual length}}$

1. a. Diameter in drawing: __________

b. Actual diameter: __________

Size Change	Size-change Factor
Scale 2:1	

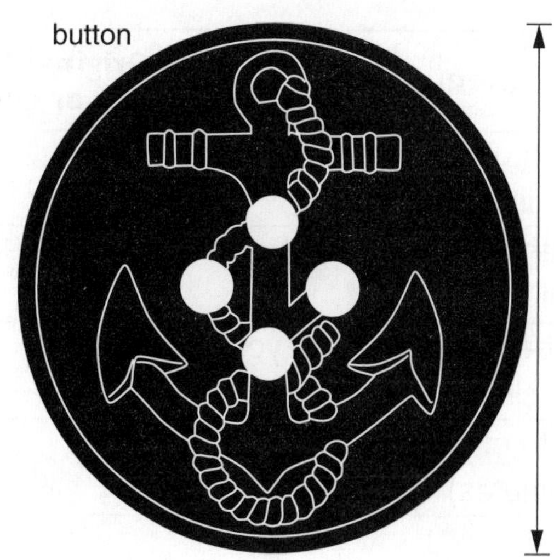

2. a. Height in drawing:

____

b. Actual height:

____

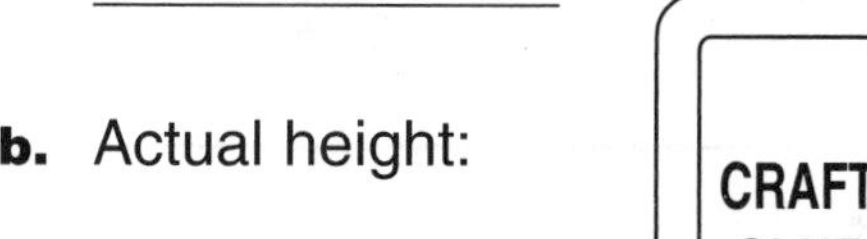

Size Change	Size-change Factor
$\frac{1}{4}$X	

3. a. Length in drawing:

____

b. Actual length:

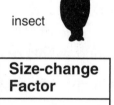

____

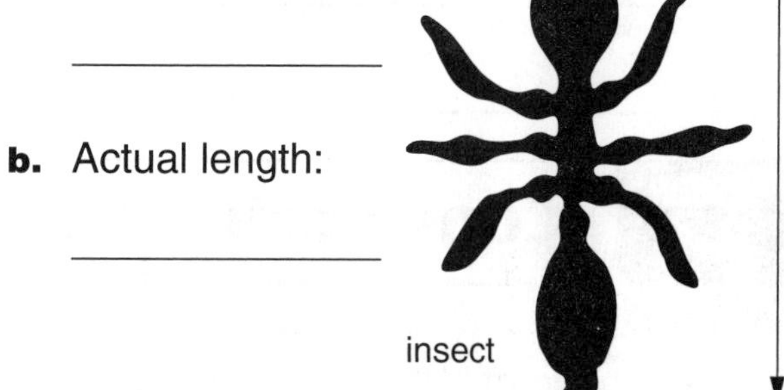

Size Change	Size-change Factor
Scale 3:1	

4. a. Height in drawing: __________

b. Actual height: __________

Size Change	Size-change Factor
Scale 1:3	

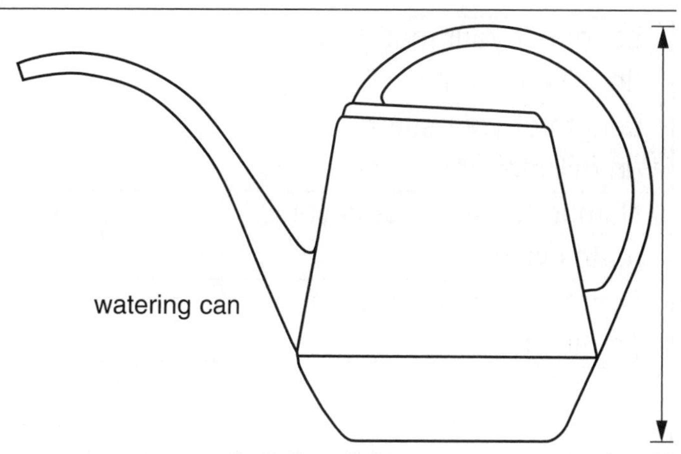

Name Date Time

Considering Size Changes

A size change of "10 times as many" or "$\frac{1}{10}$ as many" can mean a big difference when considering events or items.

Complete the table below. Use the last row to write your own event or item.

Event or Item	Original Measure or Count	10 Times as Much or Many	$\frac{1}{10}$ as Much or Many
Length of your math journal (in millimeters)			
Length of your stride (in millimeters)			
Number of students in your math class			
Length of school day (in minutes)			

Name Date Time

Considering Size Changes

A size change of "10 times as many" or "$\frac{1}{10}$ as many" can mean a big difference when considering events or items.

Complete the table below. Use the last row to write your own event or item.

Event or Item	Original Measure or Count	10 Times as Much or Many	$\frac{1}{10}$ as Much or Many
Length of your math journal (in millimeters)			
Length of your stride (in millimeters)			
Number of students in your math class			
Length of school day (in minutes)			

Name Date Time

LESSON 8•9

Reductions: Scale Models

The dimensions in the drawing below are for a scale model of an actual car. Every length measured on the scale model is $\frac{1}{30}$ of the same length on the actual car.

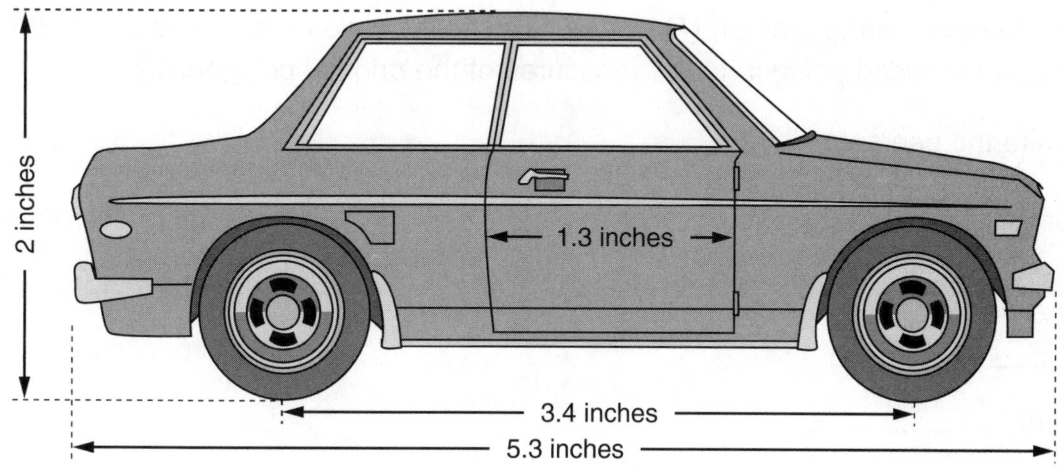

$\frac{1}{30}$ actual size Scale: 1:30 1 inch represents 30 inches.

1. Use the information in the drawing to find the dimensions of the actual car.

   a. length = _____ inches = _____ feet
   b. wheel base = _____ inches = _____ feet
   c. height = _____ inches = _____ feet
   d. door width = _____ inches = _____ feet

2. Aletta's dad built her a dollhouse that is a scale model of the house pictured at the right. The model was built to a scale of 1 to 12.

   $\frac{\text{model length}}{\text{actual length}} = \frac{1 \text{ ft}}{12 \text{ ft}}$

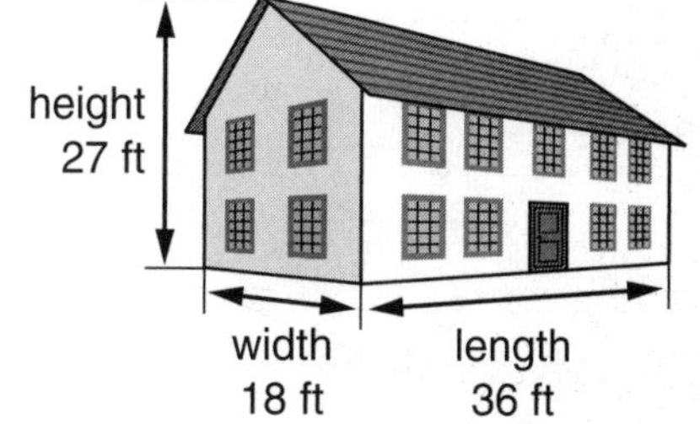

   a. Find the dimensions of the scale model.

      length = ________ feet width = ________ feet height = ________ feet

   b. Find the area of the first floor.

      Scale model = ________ ft^2 Actual house = ________ ft^2

   c. Find the following ratios.

      $\frac{\text{(length of actual house)}}{\text{(length of scale model)}}$ $\frac{\square \text{ ft}}{1 \text{ ft}}$ $\frac{\text{(first-floor area of actual house)}}{\text{(first-floor area of scale model)}}$ $\frac{\square \text{ ft}^2}{\square \text{ ft}^2} = \frac{\square \text{ ft}^2}{1 \text{ ft}^2}$

   d. Compare the ratio of the lengths to the ratio of the areas. Are they the same? ________________

   e. How many times greater is the ratio of the areas than the ratio of the lengths? ________________

Name Date Time

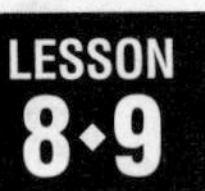

Perimeter of Figures

- Measure the sides of each polygon below to the nearest half-centimeter. Record your measurements next to the sides. Circle Enlargement or Reduction.
- Record the size-change factor. (*Reminder:* This is the ratio of the measures of the enlarged or reduced polygon to the measures of the original polygon.)
- Calculate the perimeter.

1.

Perimeter ____________

Enlargement Reduction

Size-change factor ____________

Perimeter ____________

2.

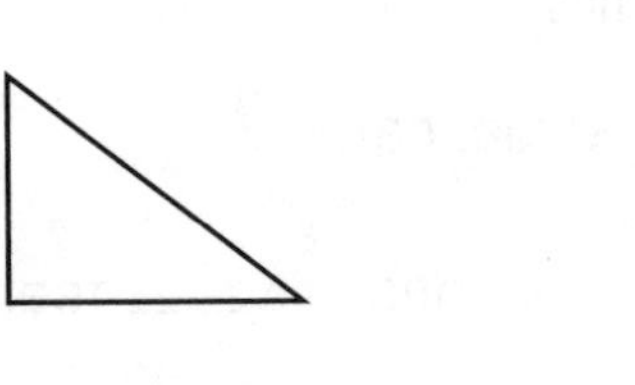

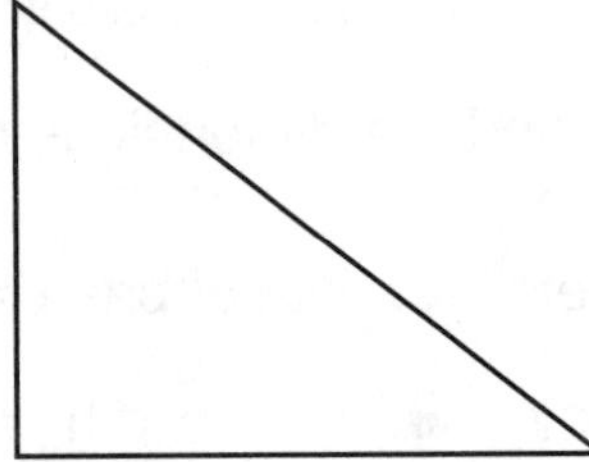

Perimeter ____________

Enlargement Reduction

Size-change factor ____________

Perimeter ____________

3.

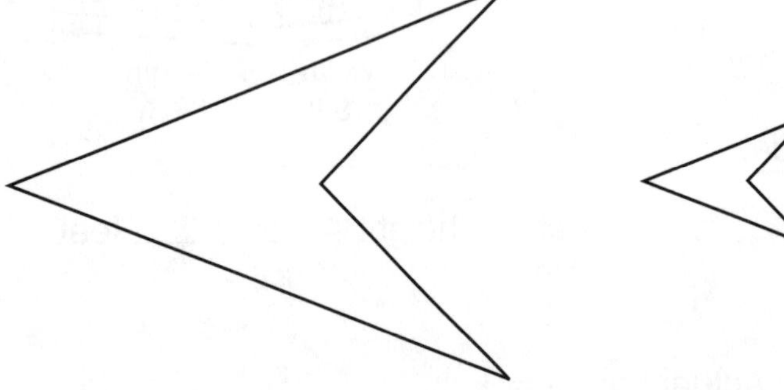

Perimeter ____________

Enlargement Reduction

Size-change factor ____________

Perimeter ____________

4. Explain how the perimeter and the size-change factor are related.

____

____

Name Date Time

STUDY LINK 8·10

Similar Polygons

1. Triangles *JKL* and *RST* are similar.

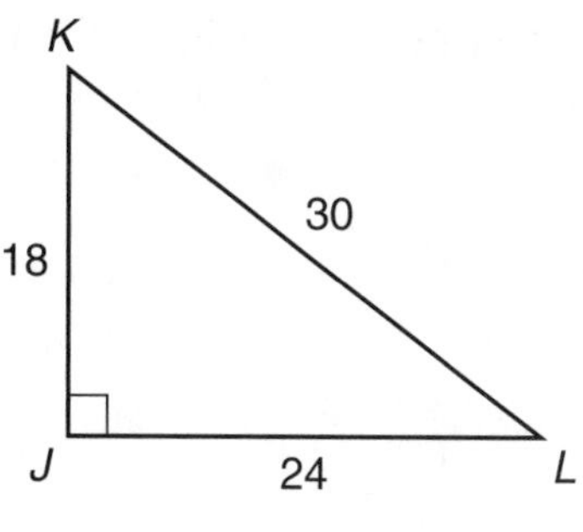

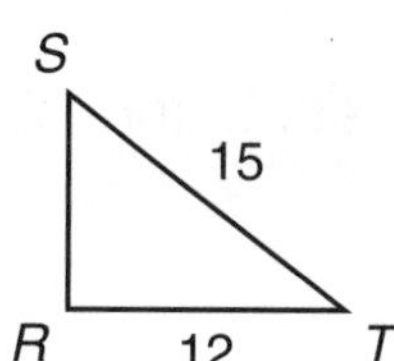

a. Find the ratio *KL*:*ST*. __________

b. m∠*R* = __________

c. The length of $\overline{RS}$ = __________

d. $\frac{\text{perimeter of } \triangle JKL}{\text{perimeter of } \triangle RST}$ = __________

2. Quadrangles *ABCD* and *MLON* are similar.

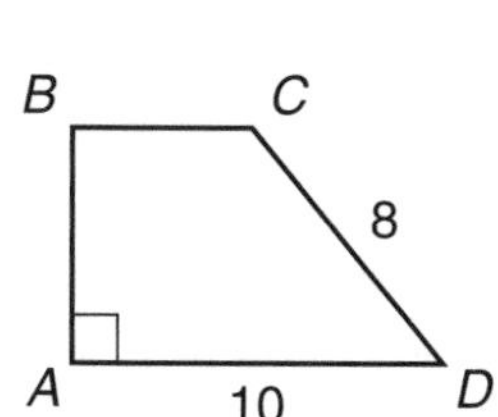

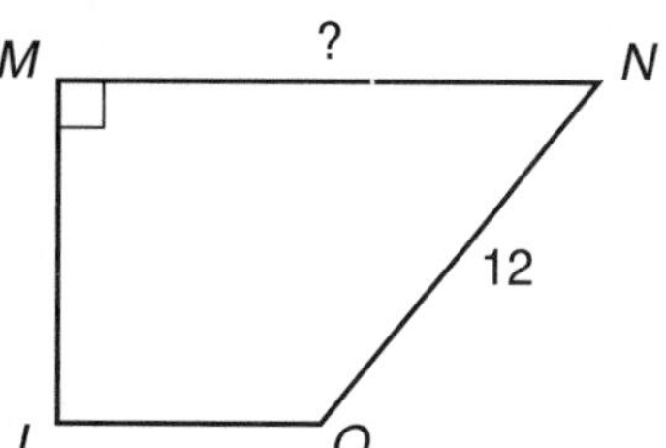

a. The length of $\overline{MN}$ = __________

b. The size-change factor: $\frac{\text{large trapezoid}}{\text{small trapezoid}}$ = __________X

3. Find the distance (*d*) across the pond if the small triangle is similar to the large triangle.

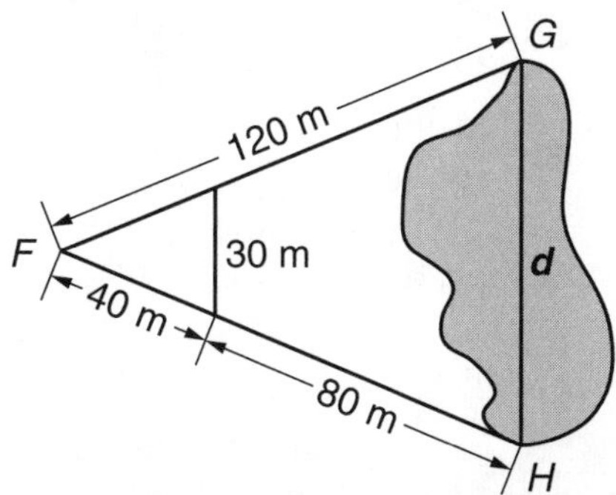

d = __________ m

Practice

Round each number to the nearest thousandth.

4. 0.00673 __________

5. 63.4982 __________

6. 4.8919 __________

7. 5.9198 __________

Name Date Time

LESSON 8·10

Identifying Proportions

Tell whether each pair of ratios forms a proportion.

1. $\frac{1}{5}, \frac{2}{10}$

2. $\frac{5}{7}, \frac{7}{9}$

3. $\frac{20}{25}, \frac{16}{20}$

4. $\frac{48}{9}, \frac{16}{3}$

5. $\frac{2}{3}, \frac{18}{21}$

6. $\frac{14}{10}, \frac{70}{50}$

7. $\frac{8}{3}, \frac{24}{9}$

8. $\frac{5}{4}, \frac{20}{12}$

9. $\frac{3}{11}, \frac{11}{3}$

Use each set of 4 numbers to form 2 proportions.

10. 3, 4, 24, 32

11. 5, 2, 20, 50

12. 7, 6, 30, 35

13. 220, 4, 1.5, 82.5

Name Date Time

LESSON 8·10

Identifying Proportions

Tell whether each pair of ratios forms a proportion.

1. $\frac{1}{5}, \frac{2}{10}$

2. $\frac{5}{7}, \frac{7}{9}$

3. $\frac{20}{25}, \frac{16}{20}$

4. $\frac{48}{9}, \frac{16}{3}$

5. $\frac{2}{3}, \frac{18}{21}$

6. $\frac{14}{10}, \frac{70}{50}$

7. $\frac{8}{3}, \frac{24}{9}$

8. $\frac{5}{4}, \frac{20}{12}$

9. $\frac{3}{11}, \frac{11}{3}$

Use each set of 4 numbers to form 2 proportions.

10. 3, 4, 24, 32

11. 5, 2, 20, 50

12. 7, 6, 30, 35

13. 220, 4, 1.5, 82.5

Name Date Time

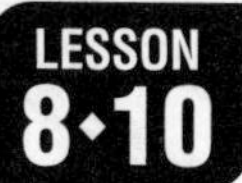

Cutting It Down to Size

Use the grids to make 2 similar copies of the original design below. Make the copies so that they fit exactly on the grids provided. Figure out the scale you used to make each drawing.

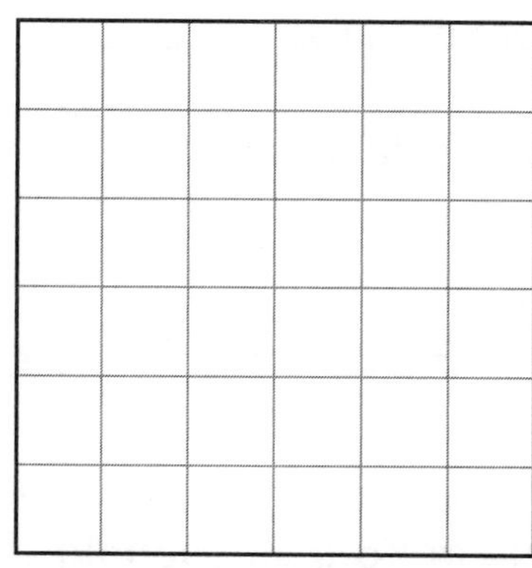

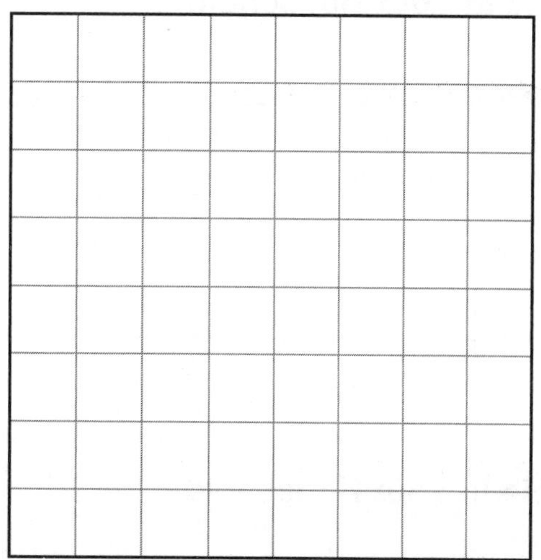

Scale ____________ Scale ____________

Name Date Time

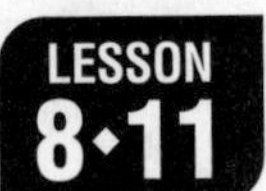

LESSON 8•11 Survey Slips

People in Your Household

Number of males ________

Number of females ________

People in Your Household

Number of males ________

Number of females ________

People in Your Household

Number of males ________

Number of females ________

People in Your Household

Number of males ________

Number of females ________

People in Your Household

Number of males ________

Number of females ________

People in Your Household

Number of males ________

Number of females ________

People in Your Household

Number of males ________

Number of females ________

People in Your Household

Number of males ________

Number of females ________

Name Date Time

Comparing Ratios

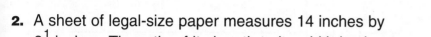

1. A dictionary measures 24 centimeters by 20 centimeters.

   The ratio of its length to its width is about ________ to 1.

   Explain. ________

2. A sheet of legal-size paper measures 14 inches by $8\frac{1}{2}$ inches. The ratio of its length to its width is about ________ to 1.

   Is this the same ratio as for a sheet of paper that measures 11 inches by $8\frac{1}{2}$ inches? ______

   Explain. ________

3. Jeffrey answered 28 out of 30 problems correctly on his math test. Lucille answered 47 out of 50 problems correctly on her math test. Who did better on the test? ________

   Explain. ________

4. A ruler is 30 centimeters long and 2.5 centimeters wide. The ratio of its length to its width is about ________ to 1.

Try This

5. If a ruler is 33.6 centimeters long, how wide would it have to be to have the same length-to-width ratio as the ruler in Problem 4? ________ centimeters

   Explain. ________

Practice

6. 74 * 12

7. 366 * 58

8. 483 * 32

9. 806 * 157

Name-Collection Boxes

Name ______________________

Date ______________________

Name ______________________

Date ______________________

Name ______________________

Date ______________________

Name ______________________

Date ______________________

Name Date Time

LESSON 8•11

Finding the Slope of a Line

Just like stairs, a line has steepness, or slope. As you move from one point to another on a line, the vertical movement is called the *rise* and the horizontal movement is called the *run*. The slope of a line is the ratio of the rise to the run.

$$\text{Slope} = \frac{\text{rise}}{\text{run}}$$

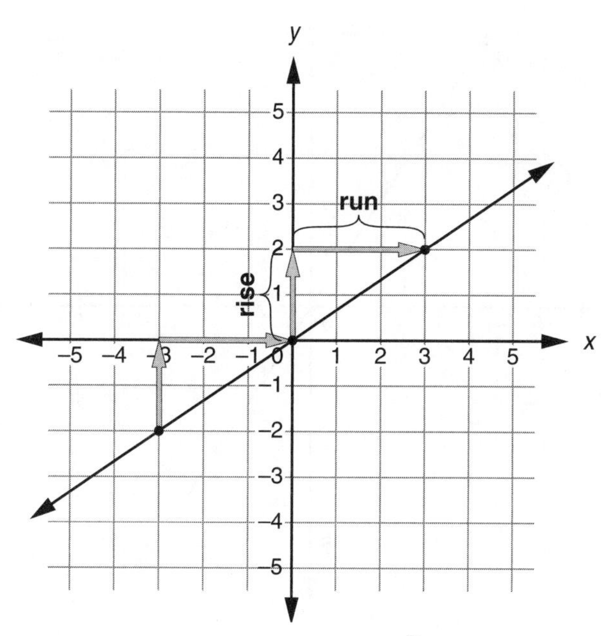

The slope of the line above is $\frac{2}{3}$.

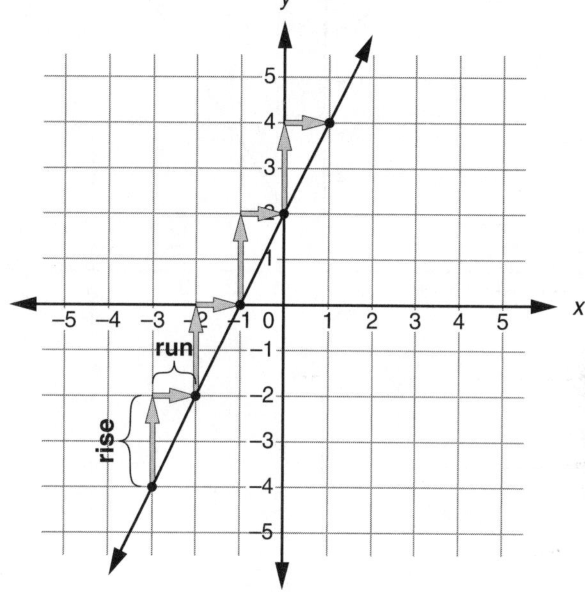

The slope of the line above is $\frac{2}{1}$.

Find the slope of each line.

1.

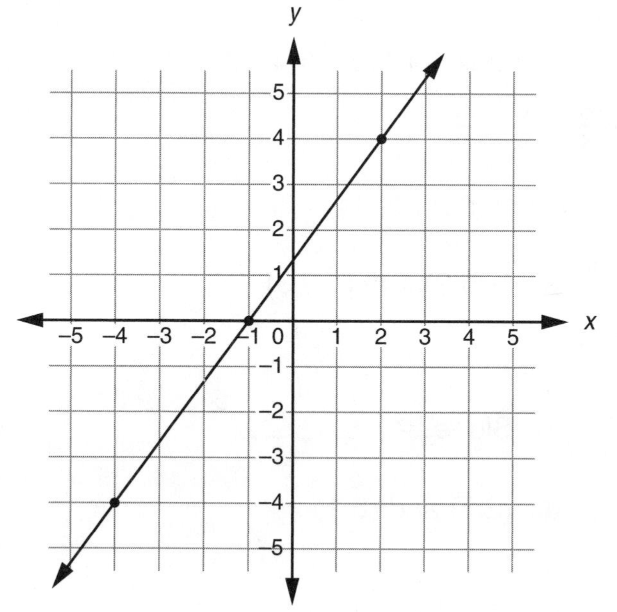

Slope = __________

2.

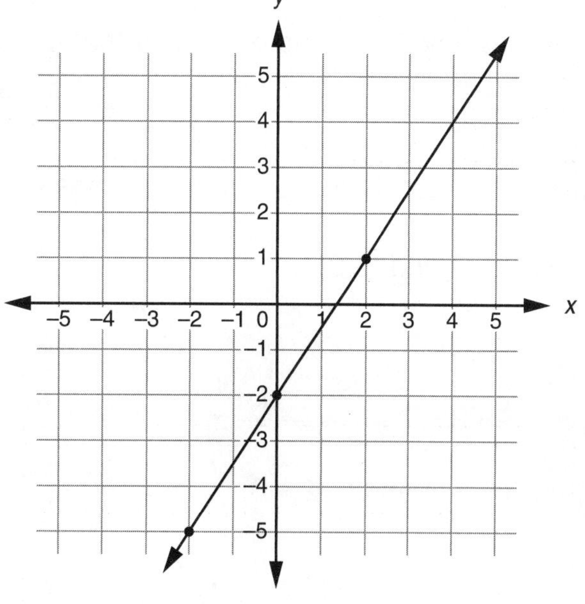

Slope = __________

Name Date Time

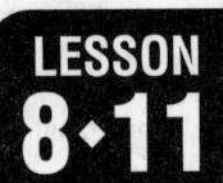

LESSON 8·11 Finding the Slope of a Line *continued*

A line that moves upward from left to right has positive slope.

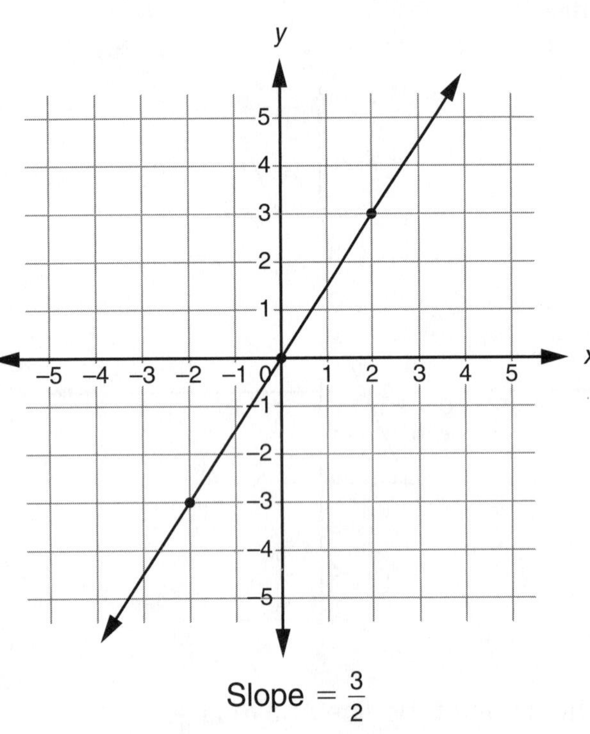

Slope = $\frac{3}{2}$

A line that moves downward from left to right has negative slope.

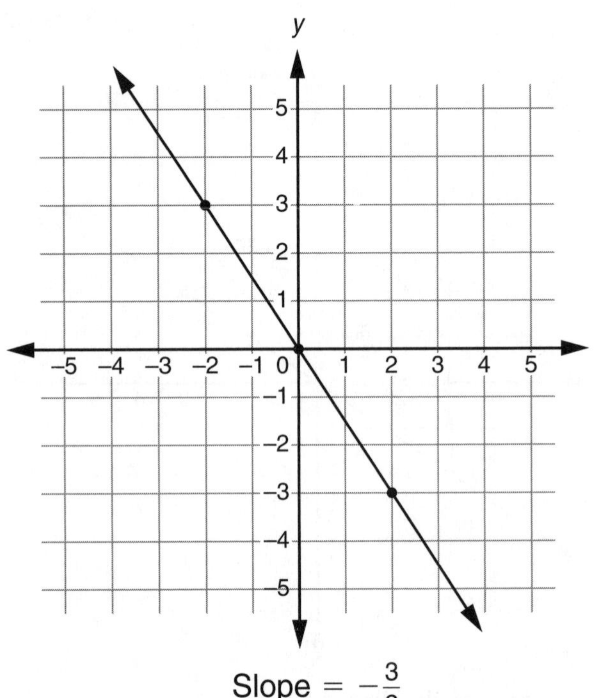

Slope = $-\frac{3}{2}$

The slope of a line tells how the value of *y* changes as the value of *x* changes. You can find the slope of a line by choosing 2 points on the line and using the following formula:

$$\text{Slope} = \frac{\text{second } y - \text{first } y}{\text{second } x - \text{first } x}, \text{ or } \frac{y_2 - y_1}{x_2 - x_1}$$

Example: Find the slope of the line that passes through points (2,3) and (−2,−3).

$$\text{Slope} = \frac{-3 - 3}{-2 - 2} = \frac{-6}{-4} = \frac{6}{4} = \frac{3}{2}$$

3. Find the slope of the line that passes through each pair of points.

a. (2,1) and (5,3)

Slope = __________

b. (−5,2) and (−3,3)

Slope = __________

c. (1,−1) and (−2,−6)

Slope = __________

d. (2,5) and (6,1)

Slope = __________

Name Date Time

Rate and Ratio Review

1. Match each ratio on the left with one of the ratios on the right.

   a. Circumference to diameter of a circle ________ 1.6 to 1

   b. Length to width of a Golden Rectangle ________ 3 to 5

   c. Diameter to radius of a circle ________ 2 to 1

   d. Length of one side of a square to another ________ 3.14 to 1

   e. 12 correct answers out of 20 problems ________ 1 to 1

2. Refer to the following numbers to answer the questions below.

   1 2 3 4 5 6 7 8 9 10

   a. What percent of the numbers are prime numbers? ________

   b. What is the ratio of numbers divisible by 3 to numbers divisible by 2? ________

3. A 12-pack of Chummy Cola costs \$3 at Stellar Supermart.

   a. Complete the rate table at the right to find the per-unit rates.

dollars		3.00	1.00
cans	1	12	

   b. At this price, how much would 30 cans of Chummy Cola cost? ________

   c. How many cans could you buy for \$2.00? ________

4. Complete or write a proportion for each problem. Then solve the problem.

   a. Only $\frac{4}{9}$ of the club members voted in the last election. There are 54 members in the club. How many members voted?

   Proportion $\frac{4}{9} = \frac{x}{54}$ Answer ________

   b. During basketball practice, Christina made 3 out of every 5 free throws she attempted. If she made 12 free throws, how many free throws did she attempt in all?

   Proportion ________ Answer ________

Name Date Time

Rate and Ratio Review *continued*

5. a. Draw circles and squares so the ratio of circles to squares is 3 to 2 and the total number of shapes is 10.

b. Draw circles and squares so the ratio of circles to total shapes is 2 to 3 and the total number of squares is 2.

c. Draw circles and squares so the ratio of circles to squares is 1 to 3 and the total number of shapes is 12.

6. The city is planning to build a new park. The park will be rectangular in shape, approximately 800 feet long and 625 feet wide. Make a scale drawing of the park on the $\frac{1}{2}$-inch grid paper below.

Scale: $\frac{1}{2}$ inch represents 100 feet.

Name Date Time

Leonardo's Rabbits

In January, Leonardo began with 1 pair of baby rabbits. He kept track of his rabbits in a table. The row for January shows 1 pair of baby rabbits. In February, the baby rabbits grew to be adolescents. Leonardo still had 1 pair of rabbits. He recorded this information for February. In March, Leonardo's pair of rabbits became parents—they had a pair of baby rabbits. He now had a total of 2 pairs of rabbits. In April, the baby rabbits born in March became adolescents. The parent pair also had another pair of baby rabbits. Leonardo now had 3 pairs of rabbits. The rabbits kept multiplying in this way.

Month	Parent Pairs	Adolescent Pairs	Baby Pairs	Total Number of Pairs
January	0	0	1	1
February	0	1	0	1
March	1	0	1	2
April	1	1	1	3
May	2	1	2	5
June	3	2	3	8
July	5	3	5	
August	8	5	8	21
September		8		
October		13		55
November				
December	55			

1. Use these rules to fill in the table.
   - Every month, the babies from the month before become adolescents.
   - Every month, the adolescents from the month before become parents. The rabbits that were already parents become parents again.
   - Every month, each pair of parents has a pair of baby rabbits.

2. Continue this number sequence. Each number is the sum of the two numbers before it.

   1 1 2 3 5 8 ______ ______ 34 ______ ______

3. The numbers in Problem 2 are called the Fibonacci numbers. Where are the Fibonacci numbers in the table above?

   ____

Name Date Time

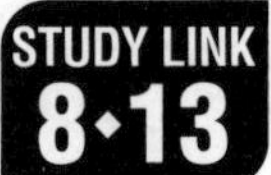

Unit 9: Family Letter

More about Variables, Formulas, and Graphs

You may be surprised at some of the topics that are covered in Unit 9. Several of them would be traditionally introduced in a first-year algebra course. If you are assisting your child, you might find it useful to refer to the *Student Reference Book* to refresh your memory.

Your child has been applying many mathematical properties, starting as early as first grade. In Unit 9, the class will explore and apply one of these properties, the distributive property, which can be stated as follows:

For any numbers a, b, and c, $a * (b + c) = (a * b) + (a * c)$.

Students will use this property to simplify algebraic expressions. They will use these procedures, together with the equation-solving methods that were presented in Unit 6, to solve more difficult equations that contain parentheses or like terms on at least one side of the equal sign. Here is an example:

To solve the equation $5(b + 3) - 3b + 5 = 4(b - 1)$,

1. Use the distributive property to remove the parentheses. $5b + 15 - 3b + 5 = 4b - 4$
2. Combine like terms. $2b + 20 = 4b - 4$
3. Solve the equation. $20 = 2b - 4$

$24 = 2b$

$b = 12$

Much of Unit 9 also focuses on applying formulas—in computer spreadsheets and in calculating the areas of circles, rectangles, triangles, and parallelograms, the perimeters of polygons, and the circumferences of circles. Students will also use formulas for calculating the volumes of rectangular prisms, cylinders, and spheres to solve a variety of interesting problems.

Finally, your child will be introduced to the Pythagorean theorem, which states that if a and b are the lengths of the legs of a right triangle and c is the length of the hypotenuse, then $a^2 + b^2 = c^2$. By applying this theorem, students will learn how to calculate long distances indirectly—that is, without actually measuring them.

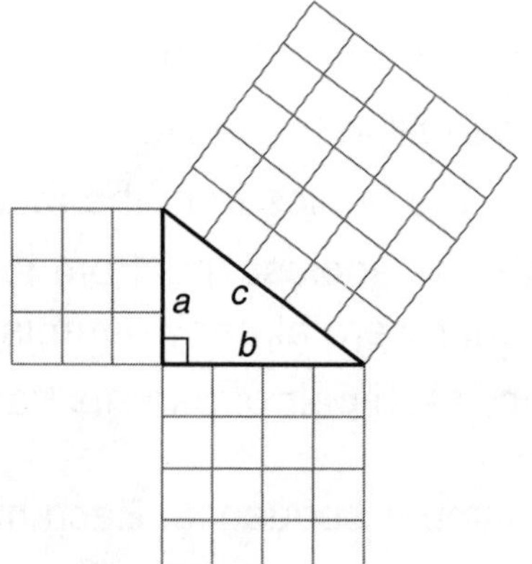

Please keep this Family Letter for reference as your child works through Unit 9.

Vocabulary

Important terms in Unit 9:

combine like terms To rewrite the sum or difference of *like terms* as a single term. For example, $5a + 6a$ can be rewritten as $11a$, because $5a + 6a = (5 + 6)a = 11a$. Similarly, $16t - 3t = 13t$.

Distributive Property of Multiplication over Addition A property relating multiplication to a sum of numbers by distributing a factor over the terms in the sum.
For example, $2 * (5 + 3) = (2 * 5) + (2 * 3) = 10 + 6 = 16$.
In symbols: For any numbers *a, b,* and *c:*
$a * (b + c) = (a * b) + (a * c)$,
or $a(b + c) = ab + ac$

Distributive Property of Multiplication over Subtraction A property relating multiplication to a difference of numbers by distributing a factor over the terms in the difference.
For example, $2 * (5 - 3) = (2 * 5) - (2 * 3) = 10 - 6 = 4$.
In symbols: For any numbers *a, b,* and *c:*
$a * (b - c) = (a * b) - (a * c)$,
or $a(b - c) = ab - ac$

equivalent fractions Fractions with different denominators that name the same number.

hypotenuse In a right triangle, the side opposite the right angle.

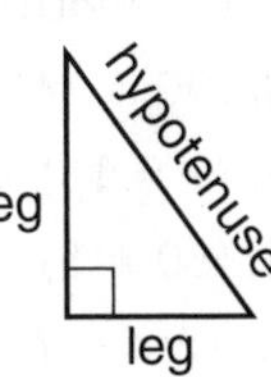

indirect measurement The determination of heights, distances, and other quantities that cannot be directly measured.

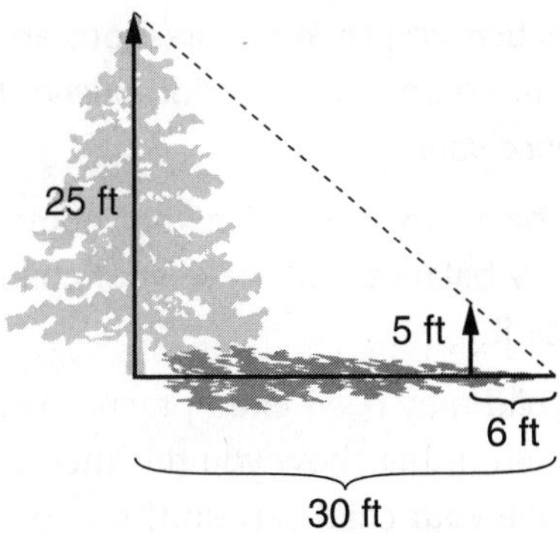

Indirect measurement lets you calculate the height of the tree from the other measure.

leg of a right triangle Either side of the right angle in a right triangle; a side that is not the *hypotenuse.*

like terms In an algebraic expression, either the constant terms or any terms that contain the same variable(s) raised to the same power(s). For example, $4y$ and $7y$ are like terms in the expression $4y + 7y - z$.

Pythagorean theorem If the *legs of a right triangle* have lengths *a* and *b* and the *hypotenuse* has length *c*, then $a^2 + b^2 = c^2$.

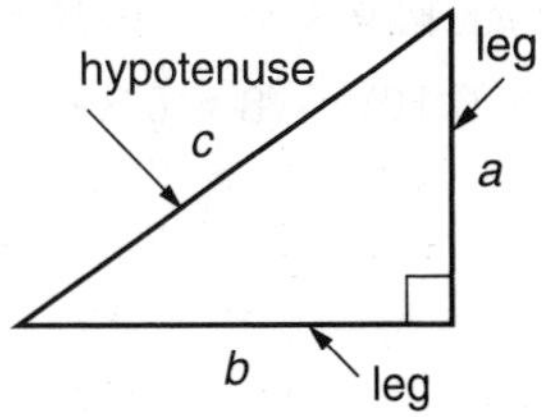

simplify an expression To rewrite an expression by clearing grouping symbols and combining *like terms* and constants.

Do-Anytime Activities

To work with your child on the concepts taught in this unit and previous units, try these interesting and rewarding activities:

1. To practice simplifying expressions and solving equations, ask your child to bring home the game materials for *Algebra Election.* Game directions are in the *Student Reference Book.*
2. If you have any mobiles in your home, ask your child to explain to you how to perfectly balance one. Have your child show you the equations he or she used to balance it.
3. Your child may need extra practice with the partial-quotients division algorithm. Have him or her show you this method. Provide a few problems to practice at home, and have your child explain the steps to you while working through them.

As You Help Your Child with Homework

As your child brings assignments home, you may want to go over the instructions together, clarifying them as necessary. The answers listed below will guide you through some of the Unit 9 Study Links.

Study Link 9•1

1. a. $(8 * 4) + (7 * 4)$; $4 * (7 + 8)$ **b.** $(8 * 6) + (5 * 6)$; $6 * (5 + 8)$

c. $(4 + 9) * 3$; $(9 * 3) + (4 * 3)$; $(8 + 5) * 6$

2. a. 6

b. $(9 - 3) * 5 = 30$ $(9 * 5) - (3 * 5) = 30$

3. a. N **b.** O **c.** O

d. N **e.** P **f.** O

4. 3.92 $(8 * 0.10) + (8 * 0.39) = 3.92$

Study Link 9•2

1. a. $(7 * 3) + (7 * 4)$

b. $(7 * 3) + (7 * \pi)$

c. $(7 * 3) + (7 * y)$

d. $(7 * 3) + (7 * (2 * 4))$

e. $(7 * 3) + (7 * (2 * \pi))$

f. $(7 * 3) + (7 * (2 * y))$

2. b. $(20 * 42) - (20 * 19) = 840 - 380 = 460$

c. $(32 * 40) + (50 * 40) = 1{,}280 + 2{,}000 = 3{,}280$

d. $(90 * 11) - (8 * 11) = 990 - 88 = 902$

e. $(9 * 15) + (9 * 25) = 135 + 225 = 360$

3. a. $(80 * 5) + (120 * 5) = (80 + 120) * 5$

c. $12(d - t) = 12d - 12t$

d. $(a + c) * n = (a * n) + (c * n)$

f. $(9 * \frac{1}{2}) - (\frac{1}{3} * \frac{1}{2}) = (9 - \frac{1}{3}) * \frac{1}{2}$

4. 3 **5.** $\frac{11}{14}$ **6.** $\frac{8}{57}$

Unit 9: Family Letter *cont.*

Study Link 9•3

1. $15x$ **2.** $\frac{3}{10}y$ **3.** $-11t$ **4.** d

5. -6 **6.** $3p$ **7.** -3 **8.** 8.3

9. $7b + 14$ **10.** $1\frac{1}{6}a + \frac{1}{4}t$

11. -53 **12.** 23 **13.** 132 **14.** -19

Study Link 9•4

1. $45f + 109$ **2.** $12m$ **3.** $32k + 44$

4. $-y + 2b + 24$

5. 65,800 **6.** 0.2348 **7.** 0.5163 **8.** 0.0796

Study Link 9•5

Column 1	Column 2
A. $4x - 2 = 6$	C $6j + 8 = 8 + 6j$
Solution: $x = 2$	A $2c - 1 = 3$
	B $6w = -12$
	C $\frac{2h}{2h} = 1$
	A $\frac{3q}{3} - 6 = -4$
	A $3(r + 4) = 18$
B. $3s = -6$	C $2(5x + 1) = 10x + 2$
Solution: $s = -2$	A $-5x - 5(2 - x) = 2(x - 7)$
	D $s = 0$
	B $5b - 3 - 2b = 6b + 3$
C. $3y - 2y = y$	B $\frac{t}{4} + 3 = 2\frac{1}{2}$
Solution: $y =$	A $6z = 12$
any number	D $2a = (4 + 7)a$
D. $5a = 7a$	
Solution: $a = 0$	

1. 2^5 **2.** 10^2 **3.** 5^4 **4.** 4^1

Study Link 9•6

1. 7 **2.** 38 **3.** 4 **4.** 2

5. $23 + 14y$ **6.** $-2b + 32$

7. $3f - 55 - 10k$ **8.** $225 + 35g$

9. $r + 23$ **10.** $4b + 72$; $72 - (-4b)$

11. $W = 5b$; $D = 4$; $w = 30$; $d = 12$

Equation: $5b * 4 = 30 * 12$; Solution: $b = 18$

Weight of the object on the left: 90

12. $5\frac{11}{24}$ **13.** 92 **14.** $5\frac{5}{7}$

Study Link 9•7

3. 2.7 feet

Study Link 9•8

1. 112 in.^{2} **2.** 2.5 ft^2 **3.** 108 cm^2

4. 45.5 mm^2 **5.** 55 ft^2 **6.** 696 m^2

7. $a * b$ **8.** $(n + m) * y$

9. 63.6 **10.** 0.1

Study Link 9•9

1. 120 in.^{3} **2.** 904.32 in.^{3} **3.** 11.97 in.^{2}

4. 10.4 m^3 **5.** 3,391 yd^2 **6.** 3.22 ft^3

7. 95 **8.** 37.8 **9.** 1,400

Study Link 9•10

1. Answers vary. **2.** Answers vary.

3. 13.48 **4.** 17.62

Unit 9: Family Letter *cont.*

Study Link 9•11

1. a. $C = \frac{5}{9} * (77 - 32)$; 25°C

   b. $50 = \frac{5}{9} * (F - 32)$; 122°F

2. a. $A = \frac{1}{2} * 17 * 5$; 42.5 cm^2

   b. $90 = \frac{1}{2} * 12 * h$; 15 in.

3. a. $V = \frac{1}{3} * \pi * 4 * 9$; 37.68 $in.^3$

   b. $94.2 = \frac{1}{3} * \pi * 9 * h$; 10 cm

Study Link 9•12

1. 12 **2.** 200 **3.** 30 **4.** 0.4

5. $\frac{5}{11}$ **6.** 100 **7.** 3.46 **8.** 7.14

9. 7.94 **10.** 25 m **11.** 9.8 ft **12.** 22 yd

13. 127.3 ft

14. 18 **15.** 23

Study Link 9•13

1. a. $7x$ b. $4x + 7$ c. $6x + 2$ d. 6
2. Sample answer: Liani did not multiply 10 by 8. The simplified expression should be $8x + 80$.
3. a. $x = -10$ b. $g = -5$

   c. $y = 4$ d. $x = 14$
4. Length of $\overline{AB}$: 5 in.; Length of $\overline{BC}$: 8 in.; Length of $\overline{AC}$: 5 in.
5. 6 cm^2
6. 4 blocks
7. 1.5 **8.** 1.75 **9.** 0.6

Name Date Time

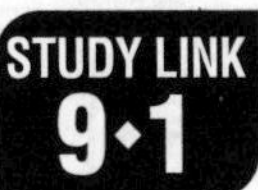

Multiplying Sums

1. For each expression in the top row, find one or more equivalent expressions below it. Fill in the oval next to each equivalent expression.

a. (8 + 7) ∗ 4

O (8 ∗ 4) + (7 ∗ 4)

O 4 ∗ (7 + 8)

O (8 + 4) ∗ 7

O (8 + 4) ∗ (7 + 4)

b. (6 ∗ 5) + (6 ∗ 8)

O (8 ∗ 6) + (5 ∗ 6)

O 6 ∗ (5 + 8)

O (8 + 5) ∗ 6

O (6 + 5) ∗ (6 + 8)

c. 3 ∗ (9 + 4)

O (9 + 4) ∗ (3 + 4)

O 9 ∗ (3 + 4)

O (4 + 9) ∗ 3

O (9 ∗ 3) + (4 ∗ 3)

2. The area of Rectangle M is 45 square units.

Rectangle M

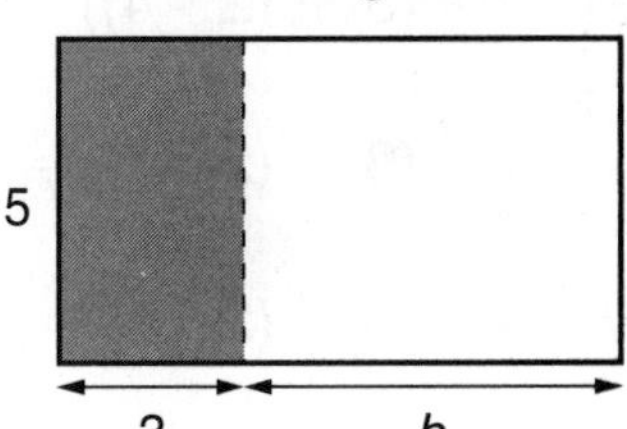

a. What is the value of *b*? ________

b. Write 2 different number sentences to describe the area of the unshaded part of Rectangle M.

(____ − ____) ∗ ____ = _____ (____ ∗ ____) − (____ ∗ ____) = _____

3. Each of the following expressions describes the area of one of the rectangles below. Write the letter of the rectangle next to its expression.

Rectangle N

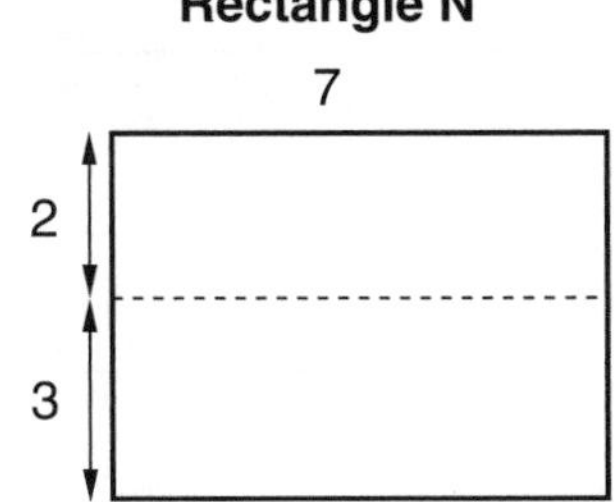

Rectangle O

3

2 7

Rectangle P

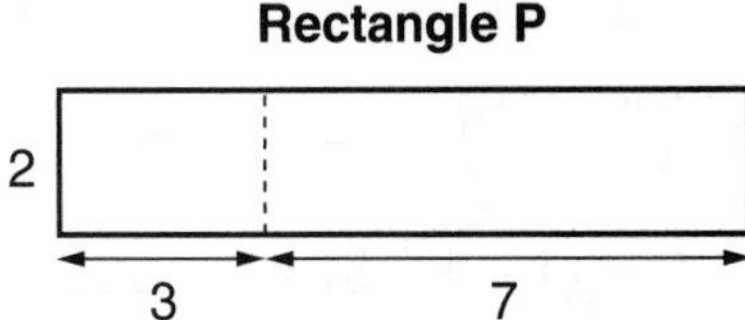

a. (3 + 2) ∗ 7 ________

b. (2 ∗ 3) + (7 ∗ 3) ________

c. (7 + 2) ∗ 3 ________

d. (3 ∗ 7) + (2 ∗ 7) ________

e. 2 ∗ (7 + 3) ________

f. 3 ∗ (2 + 7) ________

4. Sandra wants to buy envelopes and stamps to send cards to 8 friends. Envelopes cost $0.10 and stamps cost $0.39. How much will she spend? ________

Write a number model to show how you solved the problem.

____

Name Date Time

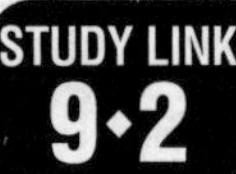

Using the Distributive Property

Reminder: $a * (x + y) = (a * x) + (a * y)$
$a * (x - y) = (a * x) - (a * y)$

1. Use the distributive property to rewrite each expression.

a. $7 * (3 + 4) = (\_\_\_\_ * \_\_\_\_) + (\_\_\_\_ * \_\_\_\_)$

b. $7 * (3 + \pi) = (\_\_\_\_ * \_\_\_\_) + (\_\_\_\_ * \_\_\_\_)$

c. $7 * (3 + y) = (\_\_\_\_ * \_\_\_\_) + (\_\_\_\_ * \_\_\_\_)$

d. $7 * (3 + (2 * 4)) = (\_\_\_\_ * \_\_\_\_) + (\_\_\_\_ * (2 * 4))$

e. $7 * (3 + (2 * \pi)) = (\_\_\_\_ * \_\_\_\_) + (\_\_\_\_ * (2 * \_\_\_\_))$

f. $7 * (3 + (2 * y)) = (\_\_\_\_ * \_\_\_\_) + (\_\_\_\_ * (\_\_\_\_ * \_\_\_\_))$

2. Use the distributive property to solve each problem. Study the first one.

a. $7 * (110 + 25) =$ $(7 * 110) + (7 * 25) = 770 + 175 = 945$

b. $20 * (42 - 19) =$ ____________

c. $(32 + 50) * 40 =$ ____________

d. $(90 - 8) * 11 =$ ____________

e. $9 * (15 + 25) =$ ____________

3. Circle the statements that are examples of the distributive property.

a. $(80 * 5) + (120 * 5) = (80 + 120) * 5$

b. $6 * (3 - 0.5) = (6 * 3) - 0.5$

c. $12(d - t) = 12d - 12t$

d. $(a + c) * n = a * n + c * n$

e. $(16 + 4m) + 9.7 = 16 + (4m + 9.7)$

f. $(9 * \frac{1}{2}) - (\frac{1}{3} * \frac{1}{2}) = (9 - \frac{1}{3}) * \frac{1}{2}$

Practice

Write each quotient in lowest terms.

4. $\frac{1}{5} \div \frac{1}{15}$ ______

5. $\frac{3}{7} \div \frac{6}{11}$ ______

6. $1\frac{1}{19} \div 7\frac{1}{2}$ ______

Name Date Time

LESSON 9·2

Applying the Distributive Property

1. Cheng and 5 of his friends are buying lunch. Each person gets a hamburger and a soda. How much money will they spend in all?

   Write a number model to show how you solved the problem. ______________________

   Answer ______________________

   Explain how the distributive property can help you solve Problem 1.

   ____

   ____

   ____

2. Minowa signed her new book at a local bookstore. In the morning she signed 36 books, and in the afternoon she signed 51 books. It took her 5 minutes to sign each. How much time did she spend signing books?

   Write a number model to show how you solved the problem. ______________________

   Answer ______________________

3. Ms. Hays bought fabric for the school musical chorus. She bought 4 yards each of one kind for 30 group costumes and 4 yards each of another kind for 6 soloists. How many yards did she buy in all?

   Write a number model to show how you solved the problem. ______________________

   Answer ______________________

4. Mr. Katz gave a party because all the students got 100% on their math test. He had budgeted $1.15 per student. It turned out that he saved $0.25 per student. If there are 30 students, how much did he spend?

   Write a number model to show how you solved the problem. ______________________

   Answer ______________________

Fill in the missing numbers according to the distributive property.

5. $28 * 6 = (\_\_\_\_ + \_\_\_\_) * 6$

6. $(\_\_\_\_ * 6) + (\_\_\_\_ * 6) = (20 + 8) * 6$

Name Date Time

STUDY LINK 9•3

Combining Like Terms

Simplify each expression by rewriting it as a single term.

1. $3x + 12x =$ ________

2. $(1\frac{3}{5})y - (1\frac{3}{10})y =$ ________

3. $-(5t) - 6t =$ ________

4. $4d + (-3d) =$ ________

Complete each equation.

5. $15k = (9 -$ ________ $)k$

6. $3.6p - p =$ ________ $- 0.4p$

7. $(8 +$ ________ $) * m = 5m$

8. ________ $j - 4.5j = 3.8j$

Simplify each expression by combining like terms. Check your answers by substituting the given values for the variables. Show your work on the back of this sheet.

Example: $18 + 6m + 2m + 26$

Combine the m terms. $6m + 2m = 8m$

Combine the number, or constant, terms. $18 + 26 = 44$

So, $18 + 6m + 2m + 26 = 8m + 44$.

Check: Substitute 5 for m.

$$18 + (6 * 5) + (2 * 5) + 26 = (8 * 5) + 44$$
$$18 + 30 + 10 + 26 = 40 + 44$$
$$84 = 84$$

9. $8b + 9 + 4b - 3b + (-2b) - (-5) =$ ________________

Check for: $b = -6$

10. $\frac{1}{2}a + \frac{3}{4}t + \frac{2}{3}a + (-\frac{1}{2}t) =$ ________________

Check for: $a = 2$ and $t = -2$

Practice

11. $-117 + 64 =$ ________

12. $-9 - (-32) =$ ________

13. $-12 * (-11) =$ ________

14. $\frac{57}{-3} =$ ________

Name ____________ Date ____________ Time ____________

LESSON 9•3

Simplifying and Evaluating Expressions

Each expression on the left of the equal sign can be simplified to the expression on the right. Fill in the missing variable or constant terms.

1. $9x +$ ________ $+$ ________ $+ 10 = 7x + 13$

2. $4m - 8n +$ ________ $+$ ________ $- 6 +$ ________ $= -4m + 32n + 6$

3. $-2t - (-2v) + 2w +$ ________ $+$ ________ $-$ ________ $= -4t - 2v + 4w$

4. $3c + 2c + 6d - 4d + 10 -$ ________ $+$ ______ $= 2d + 2$

5. $8f -$ ________ $+ 4g -$ ________ $+ 13 +$ ______ $= -f + g + 10$

Simplify each expression below. Then evaluate the expression for $x = -2$, $y = 3$, and $z = -4$.

6. $2y - 6z + 4x - 2z - 8y - 12x$ ______________________________

7. $3x - 10 - 4x - 9y + 6x - 4z$ ______________________________

8. $2x + 9 - 6z + 3y - 6z - 15$ ______________________________

9. $3z - 5x + 9y + x - y + 5z$ ______________________________

10. $\frac{1}{2}x - \frac{2}{3}y + \frac{3}{4}z - \frac{3}{2}x$ ______________________________

Name Date Time

Area and Variables

Math Message

Write an expression to show how you could find the area of each rectangle.
Then find the area by substituting the given value for the variable.

Rectangle A

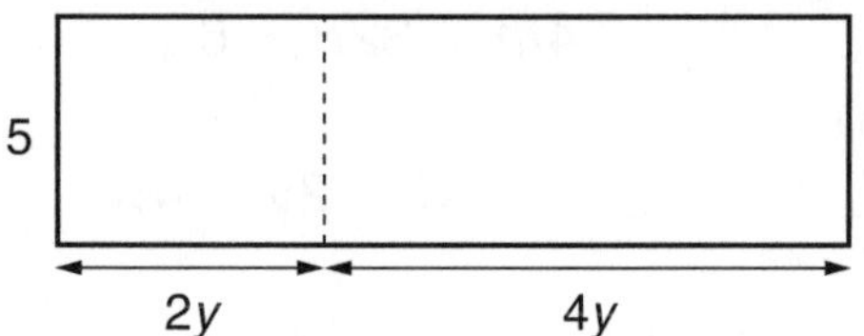

Rectangle B

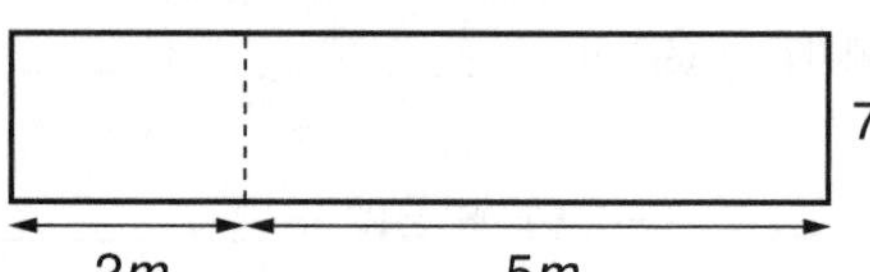

Expression ______________________

Evaluate for $y = 3$. ________

If $y = 3$, then the area of

Rectangle A is ________ units^2.

Expression ______________________

Evaluate for $m = 5$. ________

If $m = 5$, then the area of

Rectangle B is ________ units^2.

Name Date Time

Area and Variables

Math Message

Write an expression to show how you could find the area of each rectangle.
Then find the area by substituting the given value for the variable.

Rectangle A

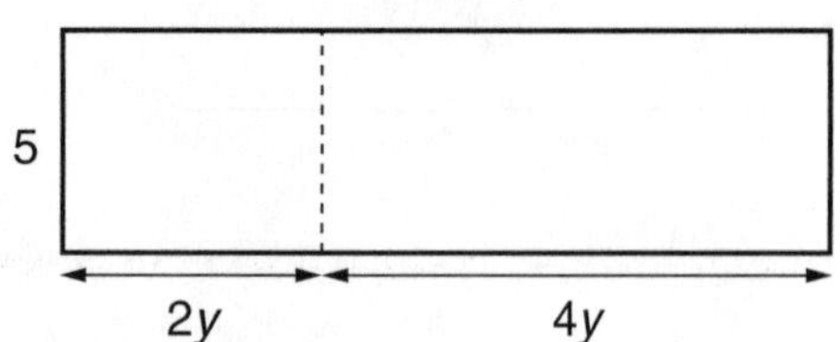

Rectangle B

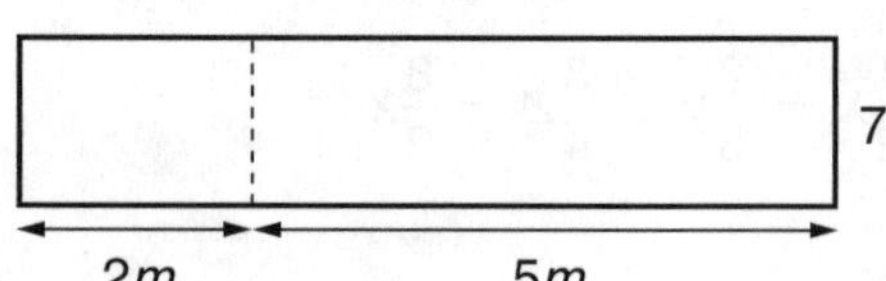

Expression ______________________

Evaluate for $y = 3$. ________

If $y = 3$, then the area of

Rectangle A is ________ units^2.

Expression ______________________

Evaluate for $m = 5$. ________

If $m = 5$, then the area of

Rectangle B is ________ units^2.

Name Date Time

Simplifying Expressions

Simplify each expression by removing parentheses and combining like terms. Check by substituting the given values for the variables. Show your work.

1. $7(7 + 5f) + (f + 6)10$ ____________________

Check: Substitute $-\frac{1}{5}$ for f.

2. $3(4 + 5m) - 12 + (-3m)$ ____________________

Check: Substitute $\frac{1}{3}$ for m.

3. $(12 - 3 + 5k)6 + 4k - 2(k + 5)$ ____________________

Check: Substitute 0.5 for k.

4. $5(y - b) + 3b - 6y + 4(6 + b)$ ____________________

Check: Substitute 1 for y and $\frac{2}{3}$ for b.

Practice

Find each product or quotient.

5. $0.658 * 10^5$ ____________

6. $234.8 \div 10^3$ ____________

7. $5{,}163 * 10^{-4}$ ____________

8. $7.96 \div 10^2$ ____________

Name Date Time

Variable-Term Tiles

Name Date Time

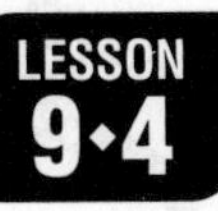

Constant-Term Tiles

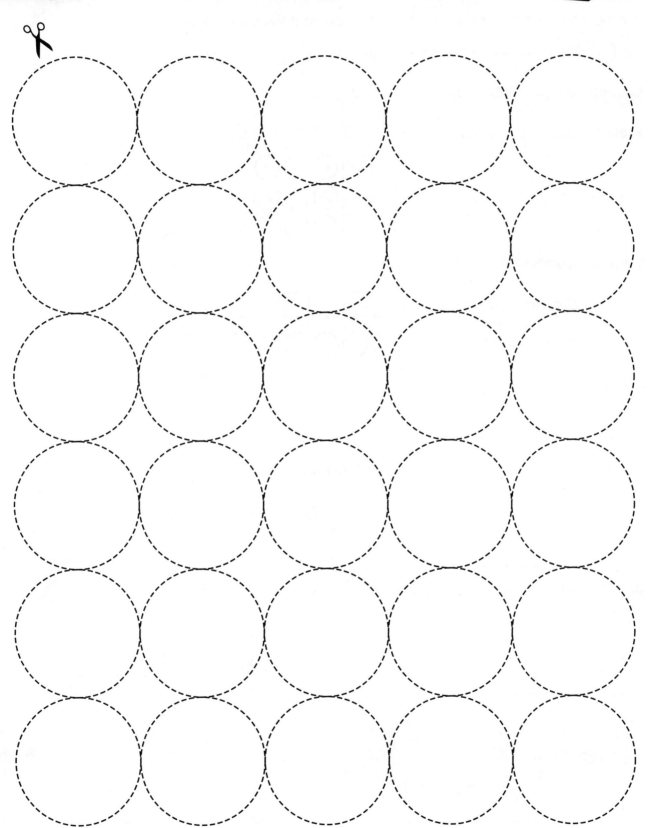

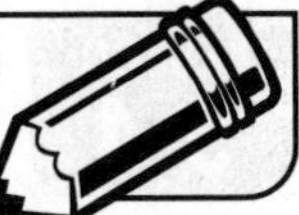

Name Date Time

Modeling and Simplifying Algebraic Expressions

For each expression, use the ☐ tiles to represent the variable terms and the ◯ tiles to represent the constant terms.

Example: Simplify $3(2x + 3)$.

Step 1 $3(2x + 3)$ means 3 *of* $(2x + 3)$. Model $(2x + 3)$ three times.

Step 2 Combine like terms.

Combine variable terms. ☐☐☐☐☐☐

Combine constant terms. ◯◯◯◯◯◯◯◯◯

Step 3 Simplify.

$3(2x + 3) = 6x + 9$

Use tiles or pictures to model each expression. Combine like terms and simplify.

1. $2(y + 4) =$ ________________

2. $4(2k + 3) =$ ________________

3. $5(w + 2) + 5 =$ ________________

4. $6(1 + x) + 3x =$ ________________

5. $p + 2(p + 3) + 2p =$ ________________

6. $2(n + 3n) + n + 1 =$ ________________

Name Date Time

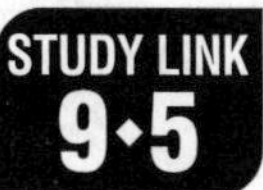

Equivalent Equations

Each equation in Column 2 is equivalent to an equation in Column 1. Solve each equation in Column 1. Write *Any number* if all numbers are solutions of the equation.

Match each equation in Column 1 with an equivalent equation in Column 2. Write the letter label of the equation in Column 1 next to the equivalent equation in Column 2.

Column 1

A $4x - 2 = 6$

Solution ______

B $3s = -6$

Solution ______

C $3y - 2y = y$

Solution ______

D $5a = 7a$

Solution ______

Column 2

______ $6j + 8 = 8 + 6j$

______ $2c - 1 = 3$

______ $6w = -12$

______ $\frac{2h}{2h} = 1$

______ $\frac{3q}{3} - 6 = -4$

__A__ $3(r + 4) = 18$

______ $2(5x + 1) = 10x + 2$

______ $-5x - 5(2 - x) = 2(x - 7)$

______ $s = 0$

______ $5b - 3 - 2b = 6b + 3$

______ $\frac{t}{4} + 3 = 2\frac{1}{2}$

______ $6z = 12$

______ $2a = (4 + 7)a$

Practice

Write each product or quotient in exponential notation.

1. $2^2 * 2^3$ ______ **2.** $\frac{10^4}{10^2}$ ______ **3.** $5^2 * 5^2$ ______ **4.** $\frac{4^3}{4^2}$ ______

Name Date Time

LESSON 9•5

Revisiting Pan Balances

Solve the equations. For each step, record the operation you use and the equation that results.

Check your solution by substituting it for the variable in the original equation.

1. Original equation ______ = ______

Operation

______ ______ = ______

______ ______ = ______

______ ______ = ______

2. Original equation ______ = ______

Operation

______ ______ = ______

______ ______ = ______

______ ______ = ______

3. Original equation ______ = ______

Operation

______ ______ = ______

______ ______ = ______

______ ______ = ______

4. Original equation ______ = ______

Operation

______ ______ = ______

______ ______ = ______

______ ______ = ______

Name Date Time

Writing and Solving Equations

Sometimes you need to translate words into algebraic expressions to solve problems.

Example: The second of two numbers is 4 times the first. Their sum is 50. Find the numbers.

If n = the first number, then

$4n$ = the second number, and $n + 4n = 50$.

Because $5n = 50$, $n = 10$.

The first number is 10 and the second number is 4(10), or 40.

For each problem, translate the words into algebraic expressions. Then write an equation and solve it.

1. The larger of two numbers is 12 more than the smaller. Their sum is 84. Find the numbers.

Equation ______________________

Smaller number ________ Larger number ________

2. Mr. Zock's sixth-grade class of 29 students has 9 more boys than girls. How many girls are in the class?

Equation ______________________ Number of girls ________

Sometimes it helps to label a diagram when you are translating words into algebraic expressions.

3. The base (b) of a parallelogram is 3 times as long as an adjacent side (s). The perimeter of the parallelogram is 64 m. What is the length of the base?

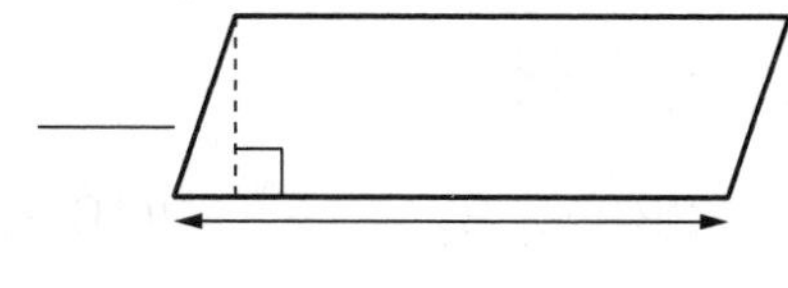

$b =$ ____

Label the diagram at the right. Then write an equation and solve it.

Equation ______________________

Length of the base ________ units

Name Date Time

LESSON 9•5

More Simplifying and Solving of Equations

Simplify each equation. Then solve it. Show your work.

1. $4(5t - 7) = 10t + 2$

Solution __________

2. $18(m + 6) = 15m - 6$

Solution __________

3. $4(12 - 8w) = w - 18$

Solution __________

4. $3g + 8(2g - 6) = 2 + 14g$

Solution __________

5. $-7(1 - 4y) = 13(2y - 3)$

Solution __________

6. $4n + 5(7n - 3) = 9(n - 5)$

Solution __________

7. $2(6v + 3) = 18 - 3(16 - 3v)$

Solution __________

8. $-5 + (-15d + 1) = 2(7d - 16) - d$

Solution __________

Name Date Time

Expressions and Equations

Solve.

1. $3x + 9 = 30$ $x =$ ______

2. $73 = \frac{1}{2}(108 + f)$ $f =$ ______

3. $55 = (9 - d) * 11$ $d =$ ______

4. $(m * 15) + (m * 6) = 42$ $m =$ ______

Simplify these expressions by combining like terms.

5. $8y + 27 + 6y + (-4)$ ______

6. $7b + 17 - 9b + 15$ ______

7. $3f - 80 + 25 - 10k$ ______

8. $240 + 5g + 3(10g - 5)$ ______

Circle all expressions that are equivalent to the original. There may be more than one. Check your answer by substituting values for the variable.

9. Original: $3r + 17 - 2r + 6$

$5r + 23$ $23 - r$ $r + 23$ $13 + r$

10. Original: $8(9 + b) - 4b$

$89 - 3b$ $72 - 3b$ $4b + 72$ $72 - (-4b)$

Try This

11. The top mobile is in balance. The fulcrum is at the center of the rod. A mobile will balance when $W * D = w * d$.

fulcrum (at center of rod)

D d

W w

Look at the bottom mobile. What is the weight of the object on the left?

15 15

4 12

5b 30

Write and solve an equation to answer the question.

$W =$ ______ $D =$ ______ $w =$ ______ $d =$ ______

Equation ______ Solution ______

The weight of the object on the left is ______ units.

Practice

12. $8\frac{1}{3} - 2\frac{7}{8}$ ______

13. $3\frac{5}{6} * 24$ ______

14. $25 \div 4\frac{3}{8}$ ______

Name Date Time

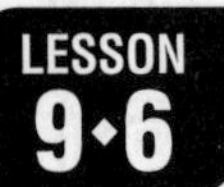

Challenge: Balancing a Mobile

In the mobile shown below, each rod is suspended at its center.

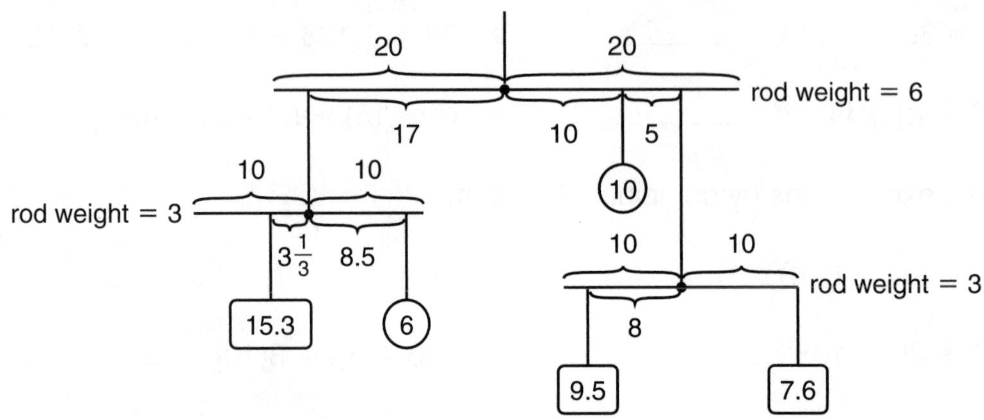

1. Is each rod in perfect balance? ____________

If not, which of the rods is not balanced? ____________

Explain how you found the answer. ____________

____

____

____

____

____

____

2. If you found a rod in the mobile that was not balanced, how would you move exactly one of the suspending wires so the rod would balance?

____

____

____

____

Name ____________ Date ____________ Time ____________

LESSON 9·7

Evaluating Expressions

Name ____________

Math Message

Evaluate the expression $(b^2 * 4) + k$ for the following values:

1. $b = 3$ and $k = 5$ ____________
2. $b = \frac{1}{2}$ and $k = \frac{3}{4}$ ____________
3. $b = -2$ and $k = -10$ ____________
4. $b = 5$ and $k = 115$ ____________

Name ____________

Math Message

Evaluate the expression $(b^2 * 4) + k$ for the following values:

1. $b = 3$ and $k = 5$ ____________
2. $b = \frac{1}{2}$ and $k = \frac{3}{4}$ ____________
3. $b = -2$ and $k = -10$ ____________
4. $b = 5$ and $k = 115$ ____________

Name ____________

Math Message

Evaluate the expression $(b^2 * 4) + k$ for the following values:

1. $b = 3$ and $k = 5$ ____________
2. $b = \frac{1}{2}$ and $k = \frac{3}{4}$ ____________
3. $b = -2$ and $k = -10$ ____________
4. $b = 5$ and $k = 115$ ____________

Name ____________

Math Message

Evaluate the expression $(b^2 * 4) + k$ for the following values:

1. $b = 3$ and $k = 5$ ____________
2. $b = \frac{1}{2}$ and $k = \frac{3}{4}$ ____________
3. $b = -2$ and $k = -10$ ____________
4. $b = 5$ and $k = 115$ ____________

Name Date Time

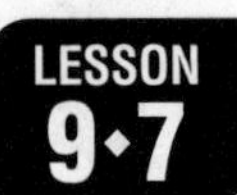

Sample Spreadsheet

address box | cancel | accept | display bar

Supplies ($)

D3 | x ✓ | = B3 * C3

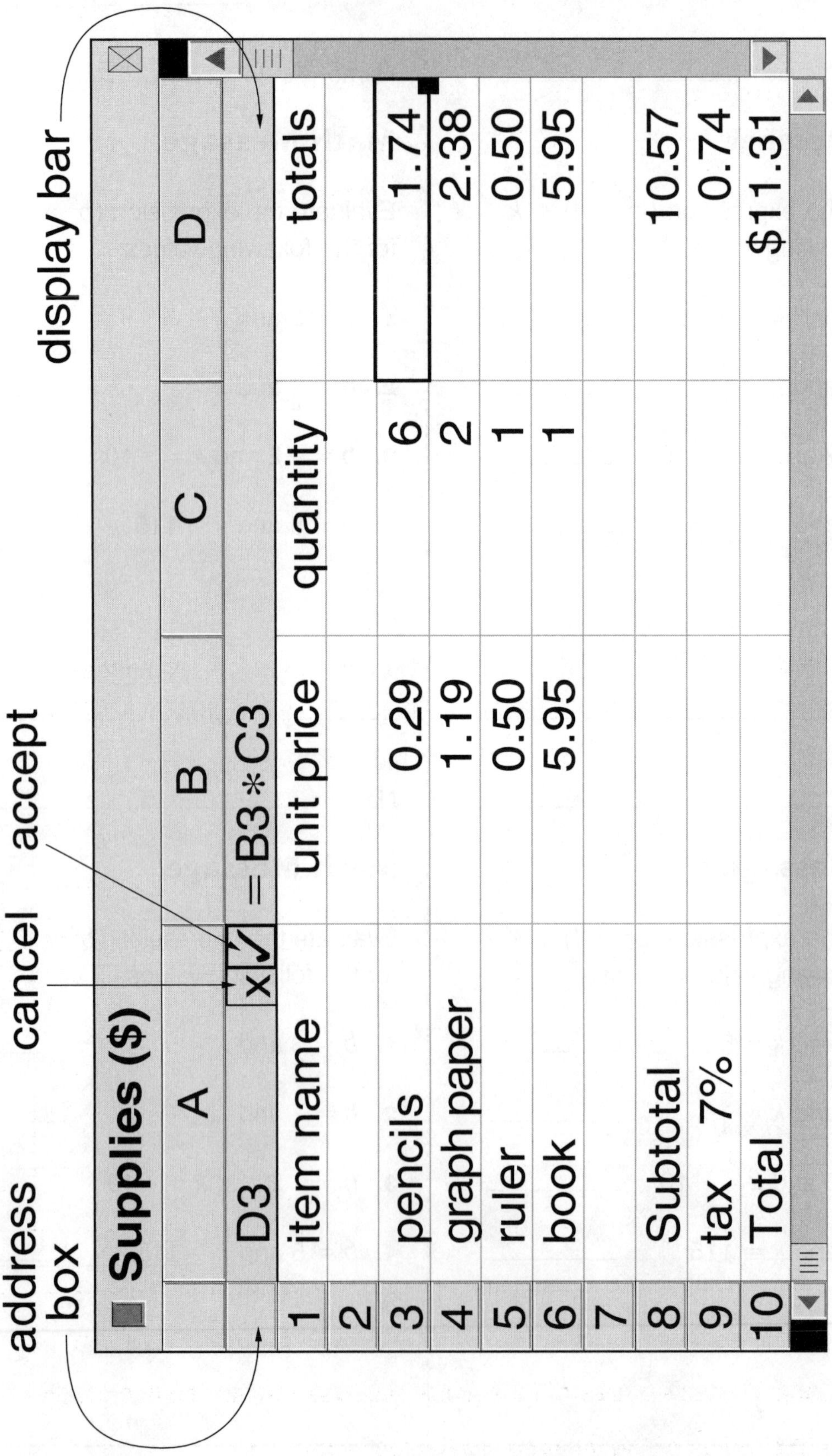

	A	B	C	D
1	item name	unit price	quantity	totals
2				
3	pencils	0.29	6	1.74
4	graph paper	1.19	2	2.38
5	ruler	0.50	1	0.50
6	book	5.95	1	5.95
7				
8	Subtotal			10.57
9	tax 7%			0.74
10	Total			$11.31

Name Date Time

STUDY LINK 9·7 Circumferences and Areas of Circles

Circles

	A	B	C
1	circumferences and areas of circles		
2	radius (ft)	circumference (ft)	area (ft^2)
3	r	$2\pi r$	πr^2
4	0.5		
5	1.0		
6	1.5	9.4	7.1
7	2.0	12.6	12.6
8	2.5		
9	3.0		

1. Complete the spreadsheet at the left. For each radius, calculate the circumference and area of a circle having that radius. Round your answers to tenths.

2. Use the data in the spreadsheet to graph the number pairs for radius and circumference on the first grid below. Then graph the number pairs for radius and area on the second grid below. Connect the plotted points.

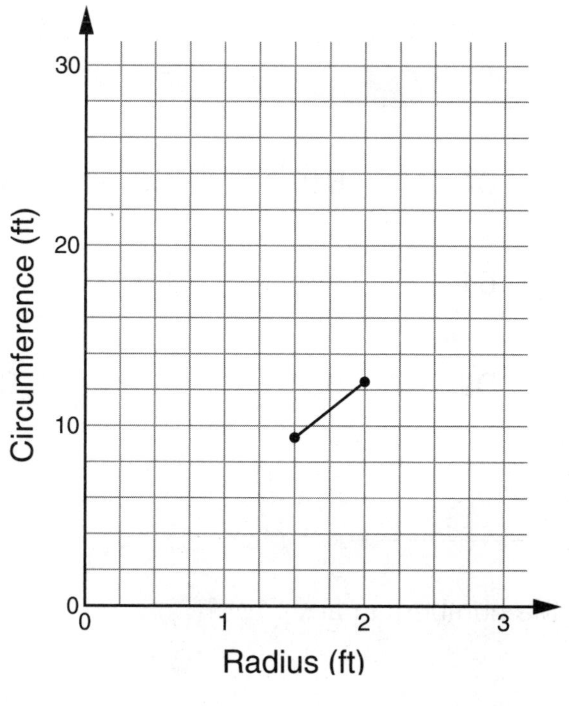

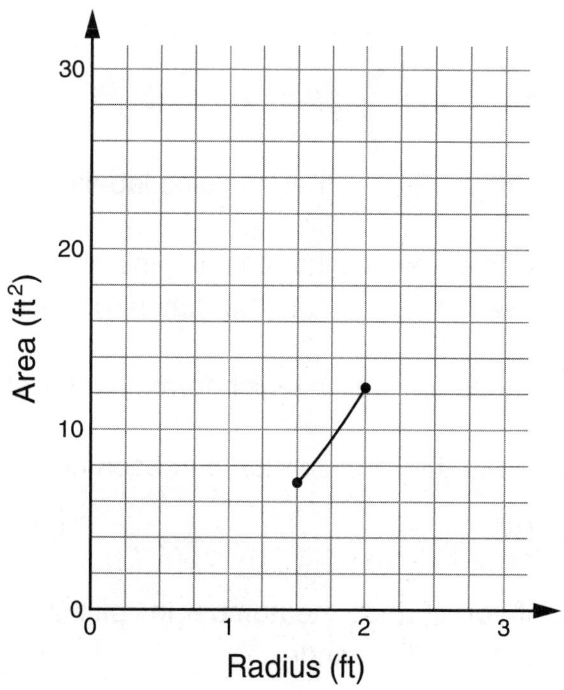

3. A circular tabletop has an area of 23 square feet. Use the second line graph to estimate the radius of the tabletop. Radius: About ________ (unit)

Name Date Time

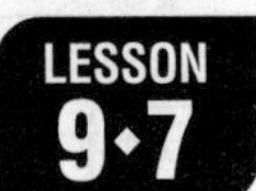

Stopping Distance for an Automobile

Drivers sometimes need to stop quickly. The time it takes to stop depends on the car's speed. A driver takes about $\frac{3}{4}$ second to react before actually stepping on the brake pedal. After the brake has been depressed, additional time passes before the car comes to a complete stop.

The spreadsheet below shows the minimum stopping distances for various speeds.

1. The spreadsheet is not completely filled in. Calculate and record the numbers for the cells in rows 9, 10, and 11. (*Hint:* Use the formulas in cells B4, C4, and D4.)

Stopping Distances

	A	B	C	D
1	minimum stopping distance on a dry, level, concrete surface			
2				
3	speed (mph)	reaction-time distance (ft)	braking distance (ft)	total stopping distance (ft)
4		distance = 1.1 * speed	distance = 0.06 * speed^2	distance = 1.1 * speed + 0.06 * speed^2
5	10	11	6	17
6	20	22	24	46
7	30	33	54	87
8	40	44	96	140
9	50			
10	60			
11	70			

2. Circle any cell that contains labels. D4 B10 C6 A3

3. Circle any cell that contains numbers used in calculations but not in formulas. B4 A5 D5 C10

4. Circle any cell in which formulas are stored. D9 B5 A11 C4

5. Write the formula stored in each cell.

B7 ____________ D11 ____________

6. If you change the number in cell A7 to 35, will the numbers in any other cells change?

____________ If so, which cells? ____________

Name Date Time

Stopping Distance for an Automobile *cont.*

7. Use the data in the spreadsheet on *Math Masters,* page 304.

a. Graph the number pairs for speed and reaction-time distance on the first grid below. Make a line graph by connecting the plotted points.

b. Graph the number pairs for speed and braking distance on the second grid below. Use a curved line to connect the plotted points.

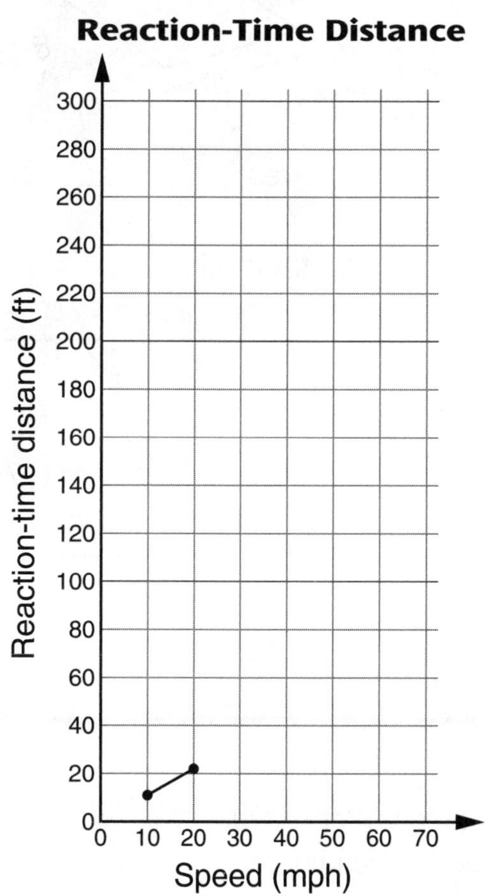

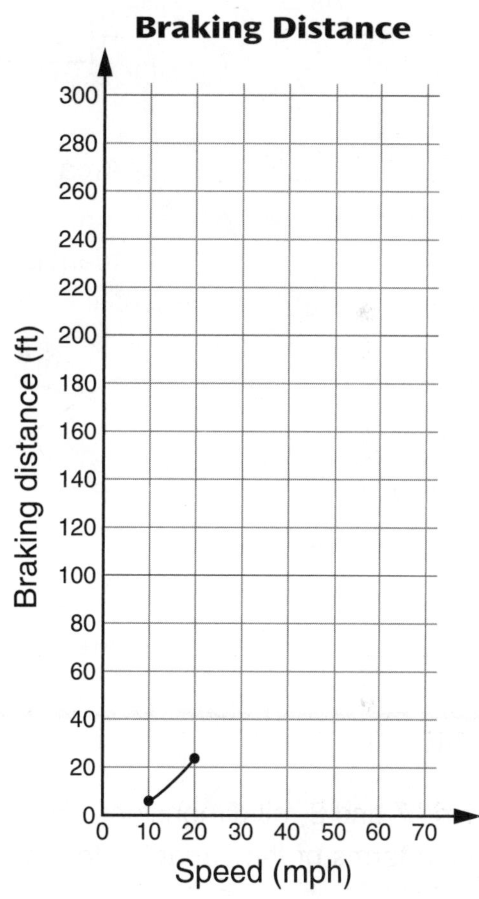

8. How are the two graphs different?

____

____

9. Complete the statement. At speeds of 50 miles per hour or more,

____

____

Name Date Time

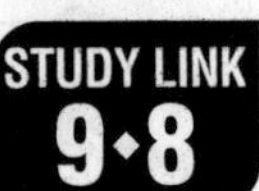

Area Problems

Calculate the area of each figure in Problems 1–6. Remember to include the unit in each answer.

1. parallelogram

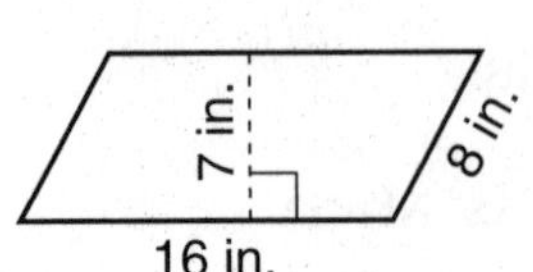

Area ______________

2. rectangle

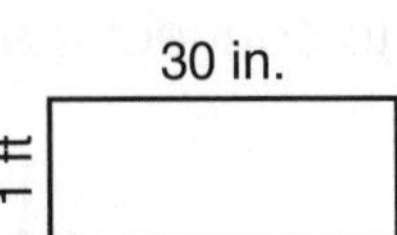

Area ______________

3. parallelogram

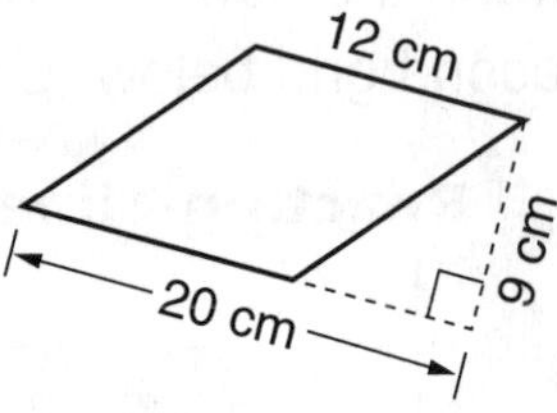

Area ______________

4. triangle

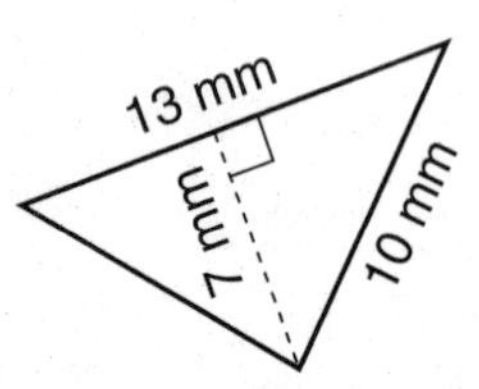

Area ______________

5. triangle

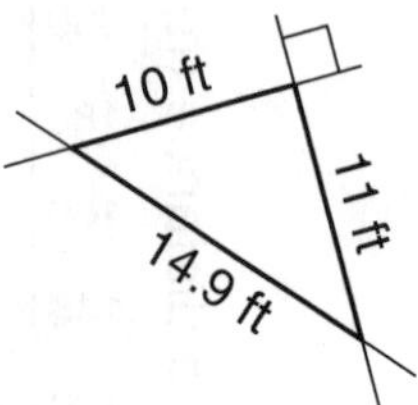

Area ______________

6. trapezoid

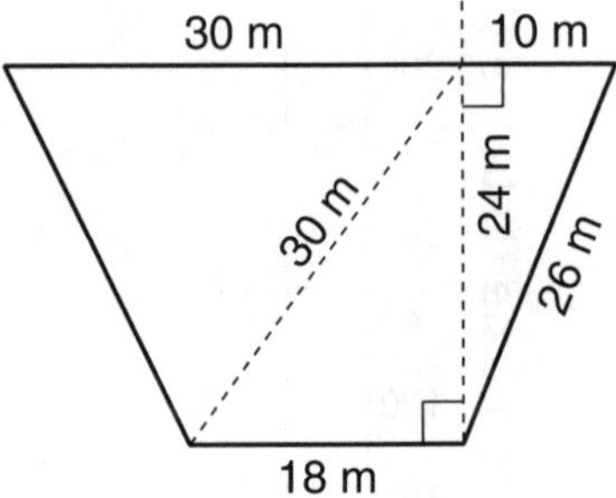

Area ______________

Try This

In Problems 7 and 8, all dimensions are given as variables. Write a true statement in terms of the variables to express the area of each figure.

Example:

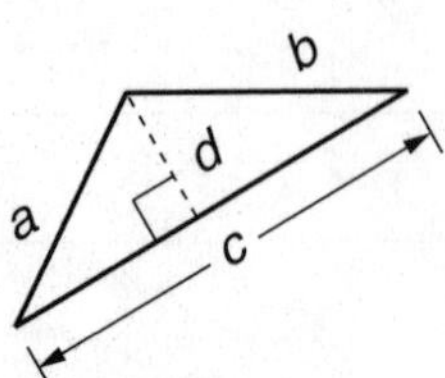

Area $\frac{1}{2} * c * d$

7.

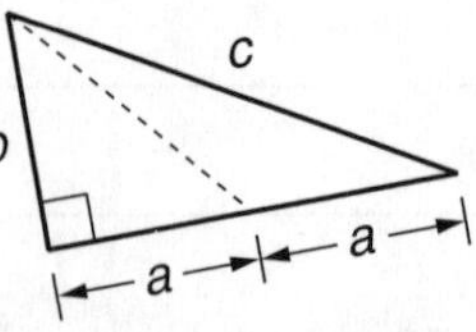

Area ______________

8.

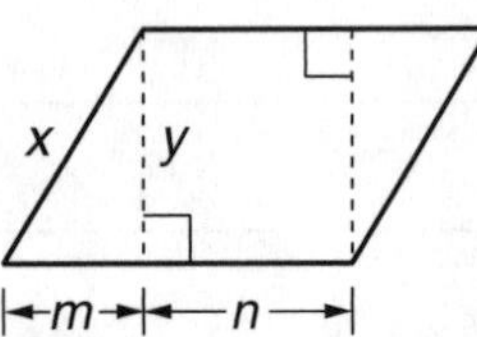

Area ______________

Practice

9. $x \div 5.3 = 12$ $x =$ ______________

10. $-3.1 = -31w$ $w =$ ______________

Name Date Time

LESSON 9•8

Areas of Parallelograms

1. Do not cut out the shapes on this page. Instead cut out Parallelogram A on *Math Masters,* page 309 and follow the directions there.

Parallelogram A

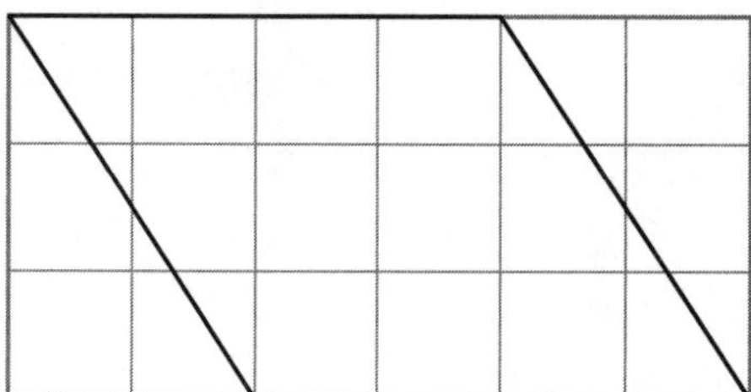

Tape your rectangle in the space below.

base = ________ cm

height = ________ cm

Area of parallelogram = ________ cm^2

length = ________ cm

width = ________ cm

Area of rectangle = ________ cm^2

2. Do the same with Parallelogram B on *Math Masters,* page 309.

Parallelogram B

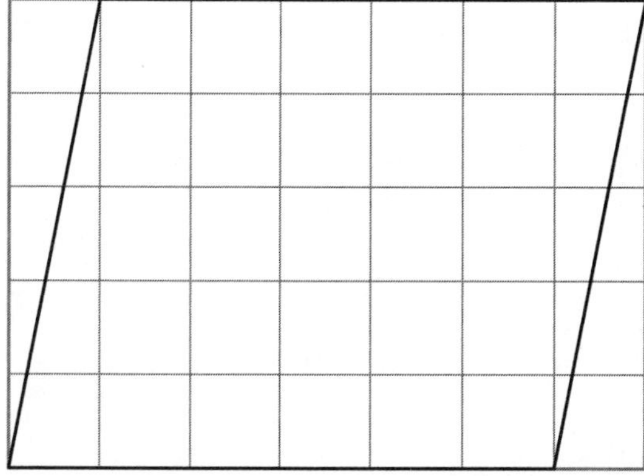

Tape your rectangle in the space below.

base = ________ cm

height = ________ cm

Area of parallelogram = ________ cm^2

length = ________ cm

width = ________ cm

Area of rectangle = ________ cm^2

3. Write a formula for the area of a parallelogram.

____

Name Date Time

LESSON 9·8

Areas of Triangles

1. Do not cut out the triangle below. Instead cut out Triangles C and D from *Math Masters,* page 309 and follow the directions there.

Triangle C

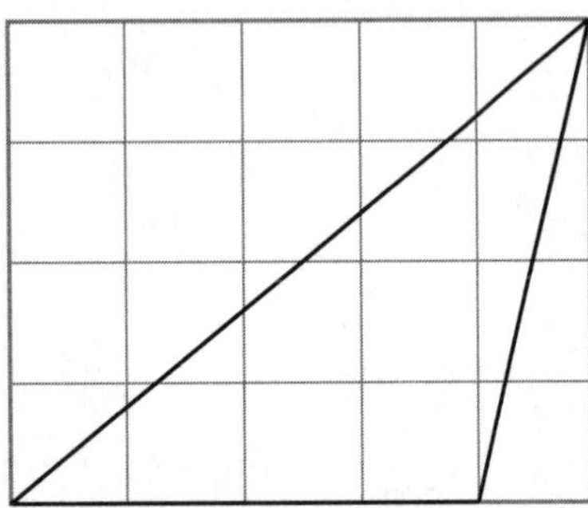

base = ________ cm

height = ________ cm

Area of triangle = ________ cm^2

Tape your parallelogram in the space below.

length = ________ cm

width = ________ cm

Area of parallelogram = ________ cm^2

2. Do the same with Triangles E and F.

Triangle E

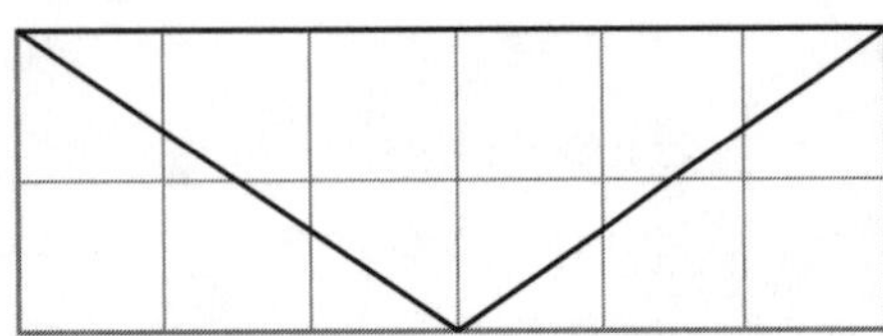

base = ________ cm

height = ________ cm

Area of triangle = ________ cm^2

Tape your parallelogram in the space below.

length = ________ cm

width = ________ cm

Area of parallelogram = ________ cm^2

3. Write a formula for the area of a triangle.

____

Name Date Time

Parallelograms

Cut out Parallelogram A. (Use the second Parallelogram A if you make a mistake.) Cut it into 2 pieces and tape the pieces together to make a rectangle. Tape the rectangle onto *Math Masters,* page 307.

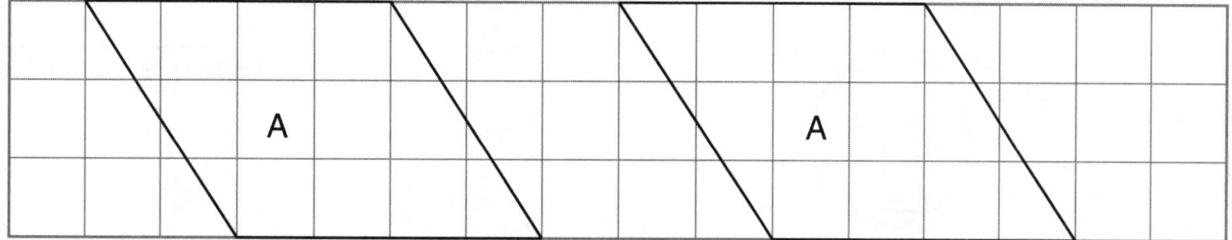

Do the same with Parallelogram B.

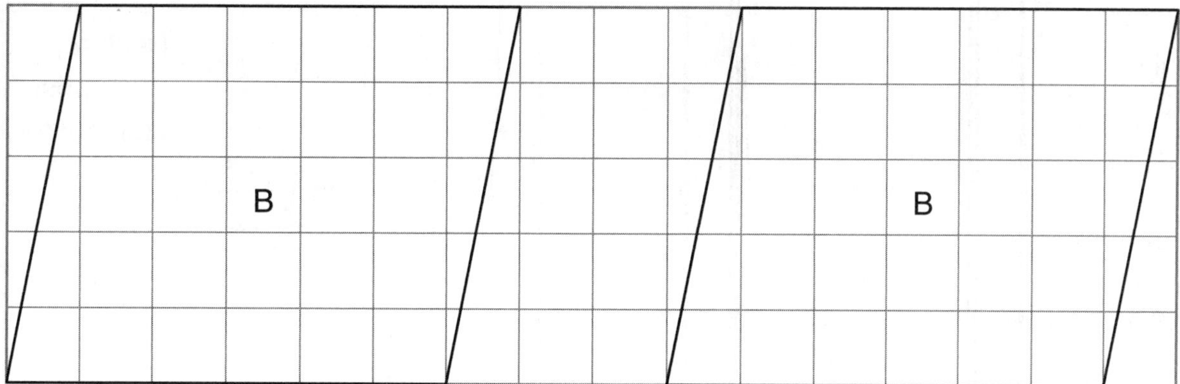

Triangles

Cut out Triangles C and D. Tape them together at the shaded corners to form a parallelogram. Tape the parallelogram onto the space next to Triangle C on *Math Masters,* page 308.

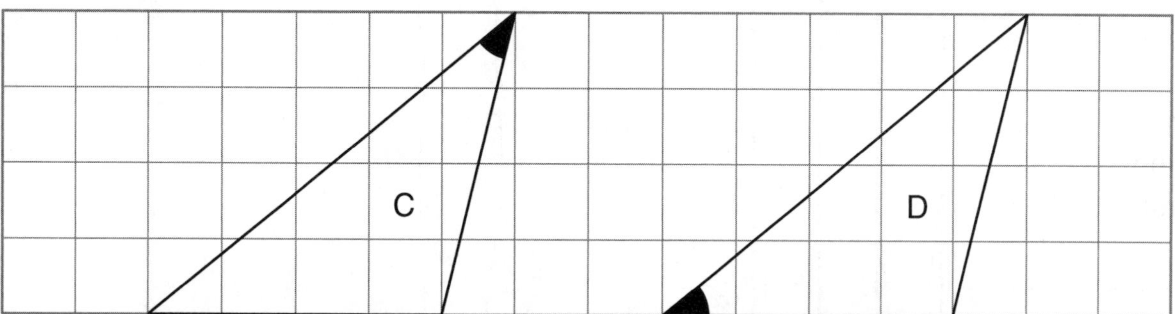

Do the same with Triangles E and F.

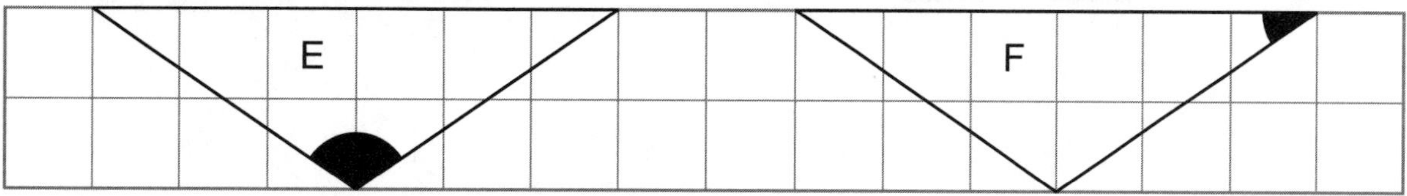

Name Date Time

Calculating the Volume of the Human Body

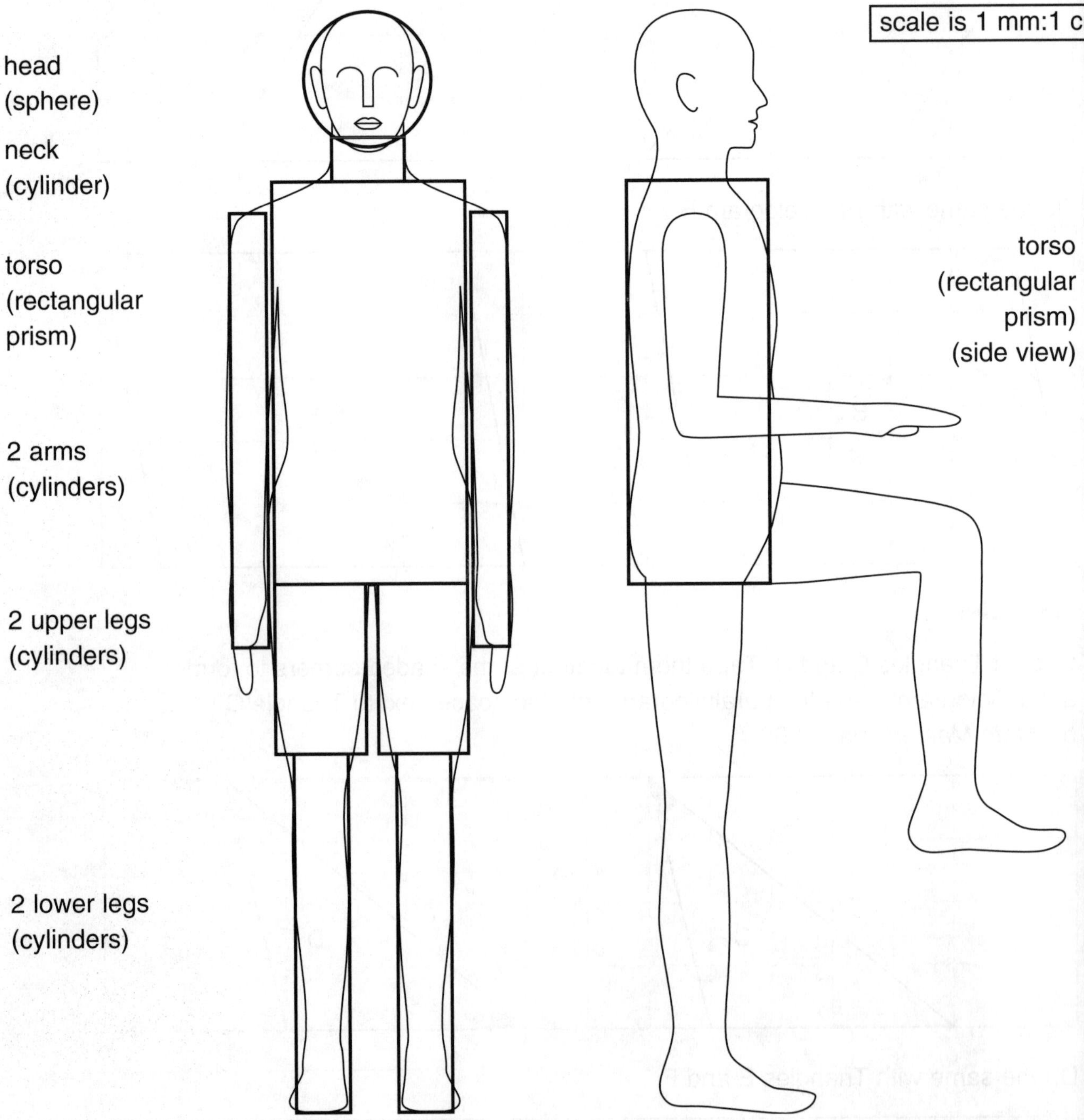

scale is 1 mm:1 c

head
(sphere)

neck
(cylinder)

torso
(rectangular
prism)

2 arms
(cylinders)

2 upper legs
(cylinders)

2 lower legs
(cylinders)

torso
(rectangular
prism)
(side view)

Name Date Time

Area and Volume Problems

Area formulas

Rectangle: $A = b * h$

Parallelogram: $A = b * h$

Triangle: $A = \frac{1}{2} * b * h$

Volume formulas

Cylinder: $V = B * h = \pi * r^2 * h$

Rectangular prism: $V = B * h = l * w * h$

Sphere: $V = \frac{4}{3} * \pi * r^3$

Circumference formula $C = 2\pi r$

A = area
V = volume
B = area of base
C = circumference
b = length of base
h = height
l = length
w = width
r = radius

Calculate the area or volume of each figure. Pay close attention to the units.

1.

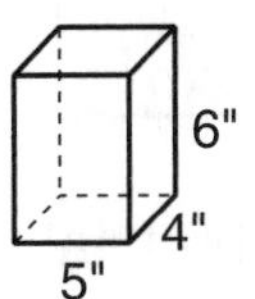

Volume ________________ (unit)

2.

diameter = 12"
Use 3.14 for π.

Volume ________________ (unit)

3.

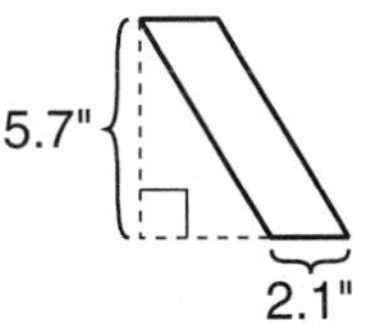

Area ________________ (unit)

4.

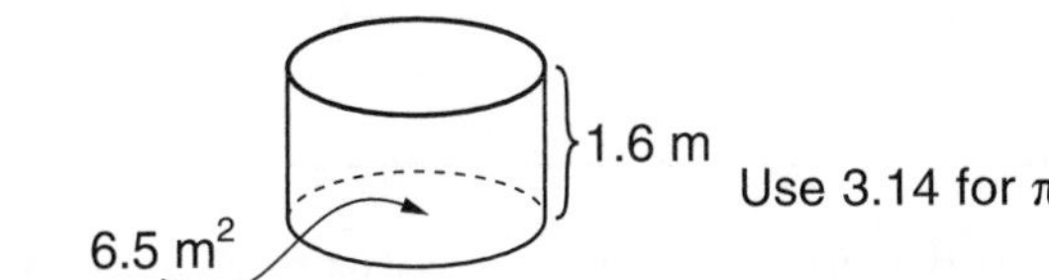

Volume ________________ (unit)

5.

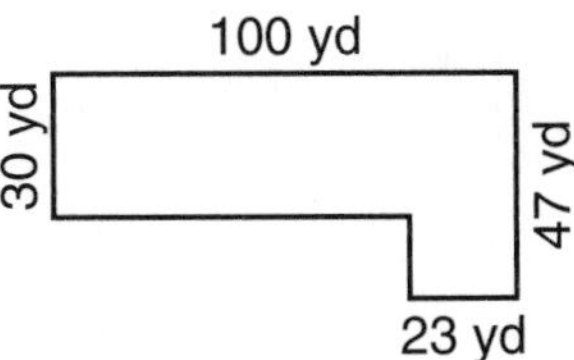

Area ________________ (unit)

Try This

6.

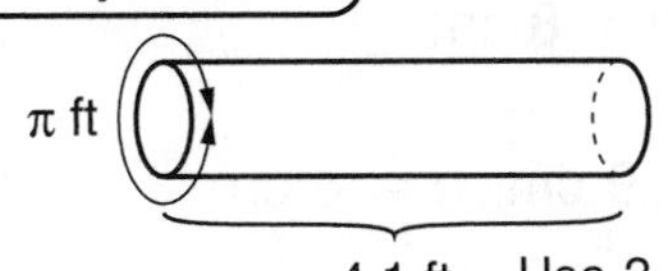

Use 3.14 for π.

Volume ________________ (unit)

Practice

7. 0.95 m = ________ cm **8.** 378 mm = ________ cm **9.** 1.4 m = ________ mm

Name Date Time

LESSON 9•9 Exploring Volume of Rectangular Prisms

Use what you know about area to help you find the volume of solid figures.

1. Find the area of each base (B) for the partial nets on *Math Masters,* page 313. Record each base's area in the space provided on each net.

2. Cut out the nets. Fold along the lines and tape the sides together to make an open box from each net.

3. Fill each box by carefully layering centimeter cubes. Count the number of layers and total number of cubes needed to fill each box. Record the results in the table below.

Box	Area of base (B)	Number of layers (h)	Total number of cubes (V)
Cube	____ cm^2	____ cm	____ cm^3
Rectangular prism	____ cm^2	____ cm	____ cm^3

4. Compare the area of the base (B) and the number of layers (h) with the total number of cubes (V). Explain any patterns you notice.

____

____

____

5. Use the pattern(s) from Problem 4 to find the volume of the rectangular prisms described below.

   a. $B = 40\ cm^2$; $h = 4$ cm $V =$ ________ cm^3

   b. $B = 50\ cm^2$; $h = 8$ cm $V =$ ________ cm^3

   c. $l = 5$ cm; $w = 9$ cm; $h = 6$ cm $V =$ ________ cm^3

6. Suppose you know the volume of a rectangular prism is 135 cm^3 and its square base has a side measuring 3 cm. Explain how to find the height of this prism.

____

____

Name Date Time

LESSON 9•9

Partial Nets

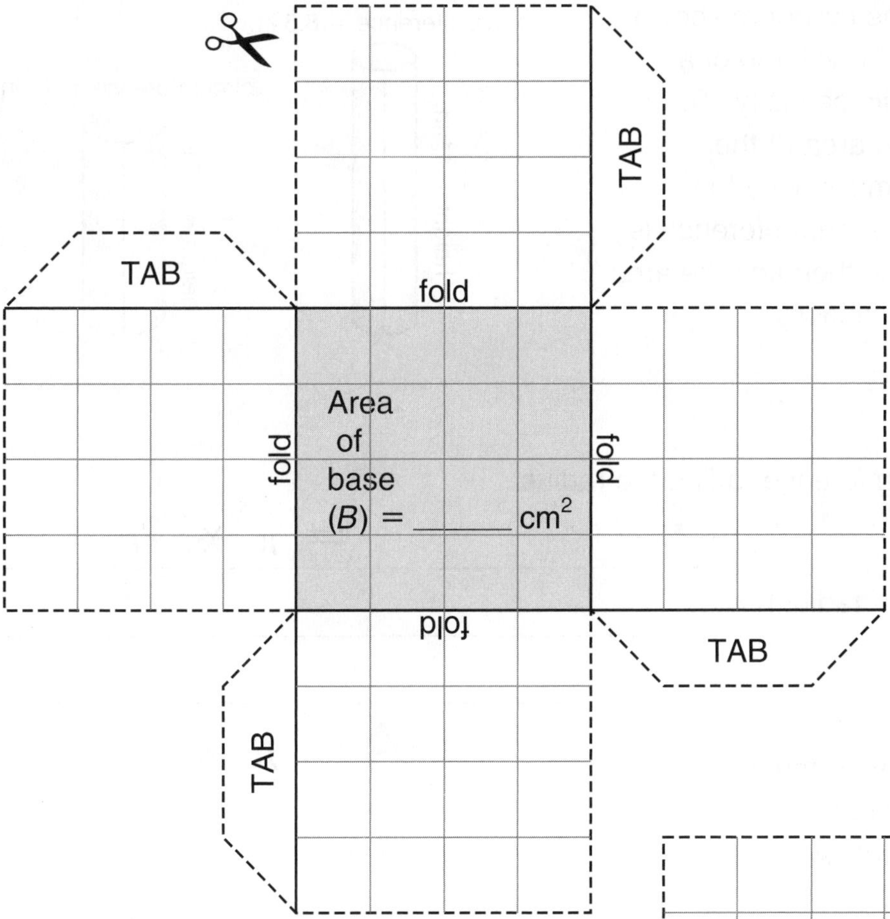

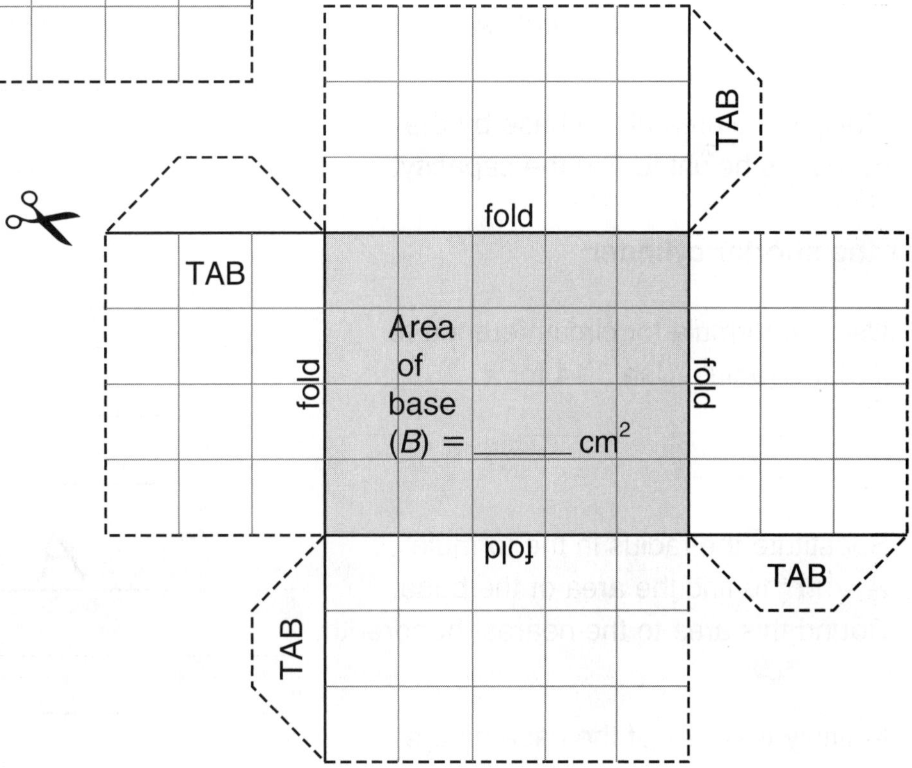

TAB

TAB

fold

fold

Area of base $(B) =$ ______ cm^2

fold

fold

TAB

TAB

TAB

TAB

fold

fold

Area of base $(B) =$ ______ cm^2

fold

fold

TAB

TAB

Name Date Time

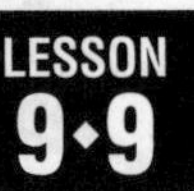

Comparing Capacities Using Formulas

Compare the capacities of the cylinders shown at the right. The formula for the volume of a cylinder can be used to find its capacity. To find the capacity, first find the area of the circular base ($A = \pi r^2$) and multiply by the cylinder's height. Because the circumference is given, use it to find the radius; then find the area of the base. Finally, find the capacity.

circumference = 8.5 in.
height = 11 in.

circumference = 11 in.
height = 8.5 in.

For the taller cylinder:

1. Use the formula for circumference to find the radius.

   $C = \pi * 2r$
   (Circumference = $\pi * 2 *$ radius)
   Use 3.14 for π.

   ______ $= \pi * 2r$
   ______
   ______

2. Substitute the radius in the formula $A = \pi r^2$ to find the area of the base. Round this area to the nearest hundredth.

   $A = \pi *$ ______
   ______
   ______

3. Multiply the area of the base by the cylinder's height to find the capacity. ______

For the shorter cylinder:

4. Use the formula for circumference to find the radius. Use 3.14 for π.

   ______ $\pi * 2r$
   ______
   ______

5. Substitute the radius in the formula $A = \pi r^2$ to find the area of the base. Round this area to the nearest hundredth.

   $A = \pi *$ ______
   ______
   ______

6. Multiply the area of the base by the cylinder's height to find the capacity. ______

7. Which cylinder holds more? ______

Name Date Time

Solving Equations by Trial and Error

Find numbers that are close to the solution of each equation.
Use the suggested test numbers to get started.

1. Equation: $r^2 + r = 15$

r	r^2	$r^2 + r$	Compare $r^2 + r$ to 15.
3	9	12	< 15
4	16	20	> 15
3.5	12.25	15.75	> 15

My closest solution ______________

2. Equation: $x^2 - 2x = 23$

x	x^2	$2x$	$x^2 - 2x$	Compare $x^2 - 2x$ to 23.
6	36	12	24	> 23
5	25	10	15	< 23
5.5	30.25	11	19.25	< 23

My closest solution ______________

Practice

3. $56 - 42.52 =$ ________

4. $23.5 - 5.88 =$ ________

Name Date Time

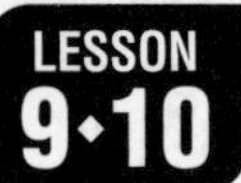

A Box Problem

Suppose you have a square piece of cardboard that measures 8 inches along each side. To construct an open box out of the cardboard, you can cut same-size squares from the 4 corners of the cardboard and then turn up and tape the sides.

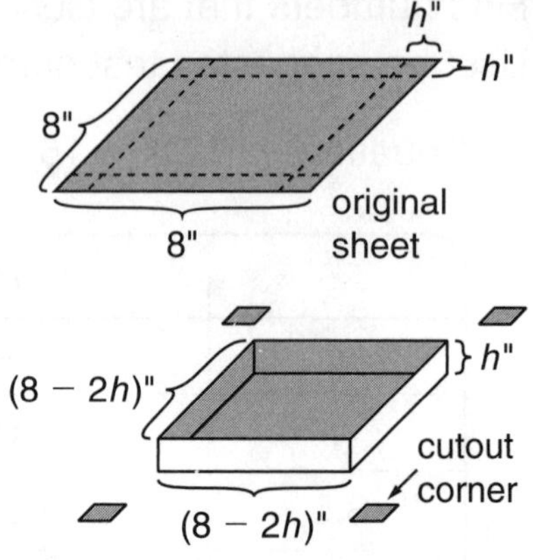

Box made by cutting out square corners and folding up sides

1. José cut out small square corners to make his box. Amy cut out large square corners to make her box.

   a. Whose box was taller? ______________________

   b. Whose box had a greater area of the base? ______________________

The volume of the box depends on the size of the squares cut from the corners.

2. Find the dimensions of the box with the greatest possible volume. Use trial and error to solve the problem. Keep a record of your results in the spreadsheet below.

   a. Three test values for h (the height of the box) are listed in Column A. Complete rows 4, 5, and 6.

Boxes

	A	B	C	D
1	Problem: Find the length that maximizes the box volume.			
2	box height (in.)	box length, width (in.)	base area of box (in.^{2})	volume of box (in.^{3})
3	h	$8 - 2h$	$(8 - 2h)^2$	$(8 - 2h)^2 * h$
4	1	6	36	
5	2			
6	3			
7				
8				
9				

   b. Use the spreadsheet results to select new test values for h that are likely to give a box of greater volume. Complete the statement below.

   The box that I found with the greatest volume has a height of

   __________ inches and a volume of __________ cubic inches.

Name Date Time

Using Formulas

Each problem below states a formula and gives the values of all but one of the variables in the formula. Substitute the known values for the variables in the formula and then solve the equation.

1. The formula $C = \frac{5}{9} * (F - 32)$ may be used to convert between Fahrenheit and Celsius temperatures.

a. Convert 77°F to degrees C.

Equation ______________________
Solve.

77°F = __________°C

b. Convert 50°C to degrees F.

Equation ______________________
Solve.

50°C = __________°F

2. The formula for the area of a trapezoid is $A = \frac{1}{2} * (a + b) * h$.

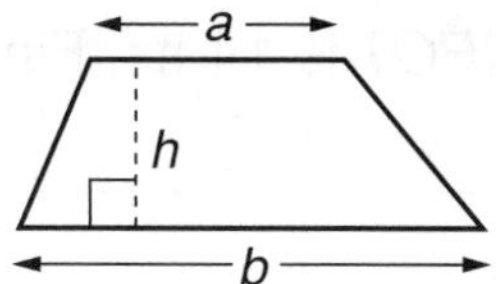

a. Find the area (A) of a trapezoid if $a = 7$ cm, $b = 10$ cm, and $h = 5$ cm.

Equation ______________________
Solve.

Area ____________ (unit)

b. Find the height (h) of a trapezoid if $a = 6.5$ inches, $b = 5.5$ inches, and $A = 90$ inches^2.

Equation ______________________
Solve.

Height ____________ (unit)

3. The formula for the volume of a cone is $V = \frac{1}{3} * \pi * r^2 * h$. Use 3.14 for π.

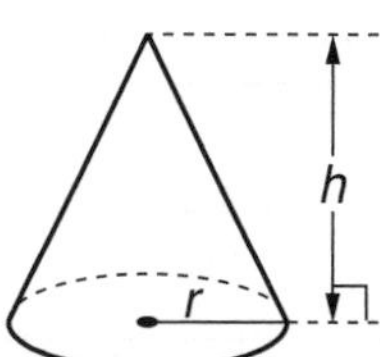

a. Find the volume (V) of a cone if $r = 2$ inches and $h = 9$ inches.

Equation ______________________
Solve.

Volume ____________ (unit)

b. Find the height (h) of a cone if $r = 3$ cm and $V = 94.2$ cm^3.

Equation ______________________
Solve.

Height ____________ (unit)

Name Date Time

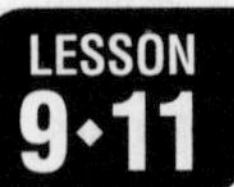

Perimeter and Area Problems

Study the example. Then solve the problems.

Example: The area of triangle *CBA* is 21 square inches. What is the length of side *BA*?

Solution

1. Write the formula for the area of a triangle. $A = \frac{1}{2} * b * h$
2. Substitute the dimensions in the formula. $21 = \frac{1}{2} * 6 * (3x + 1)$
3. Solve the equation. $21 = 3 * (3x + 1)$
   $21 = 9x + 3$
   $18 = 9x$, so $2 = x$.
4. Answer the question. $3x + 1 = (3 * 2) + 1$, or 7
   Side *AB* is 7 inches long.
5. Check the answer: Area $= \frac{1}{2} * 6 * 7 = \frac{1}{2} * 42 = 21$ in.^{2}

1. The area of rectangle *RPQT* is 14 ft^2. Find the length of side *RP*.

Formula: Area = ______________________

Substitute __________ = ______________________

Solve ______________________

Length of $\overline{RP}$ ______________________

Check ______________________

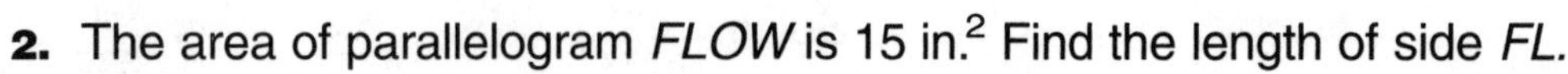

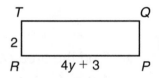

2. The area of parallelogram *FLOW* is 15 in.^{2} Find the length of side *FL*.

Formula: Area = ______________________

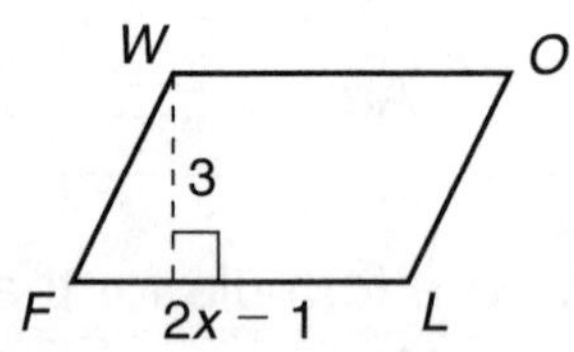

Substitute __________ = ______________________

Solve ______________________

Length of $\overline{FL}$ ______________________

Check ______________________

3. The perimeter of triangle *MON* is 29 cm. Find the length of each side.

Formula: Perimeter = ______________________

Substitute __________ = ______________________

Solve ______________________

Length of $\overline{NM}$ __________ $\overline{ON}$ __________ $\overline{MO}$ __________

Check ______________________

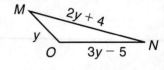

Name Date Time

STUDY LINK 9·12

Pythagorean Theorem

Mentally find the positive square root of each number.

1. $\sqrt{144}$ = ________ **2.** $\sqrt{200^2}$ = ________ **3.** $\sqrt{900}$ = ________

4. $\sqrt{0.16}$ = ________ **5.** $\sqrt{\frac{25}{121}}$ = ________ **6.** $\sqrt{10,000}$ = ________

Use a calculator to find each square root. Round to the nearest hundredth.

7. $\sqrt{12}$ = ________ **8.** $\sqrt{51}$ = ________ **9.** $\sqrt{63}$ = ________

Use the Pythagorean theorem to find each missing length. Round your answer to the nearest tenth.

10.

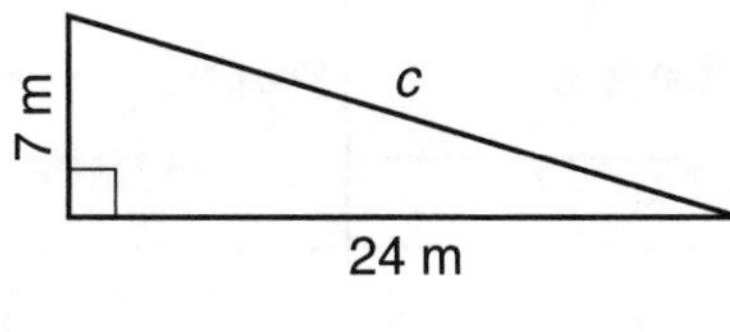

c = ________ (unit)

11.

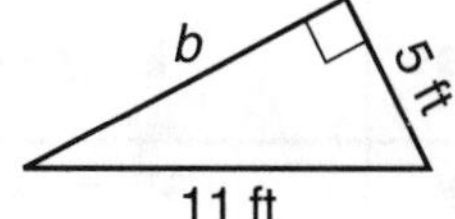

b = ________ (unit)

12.

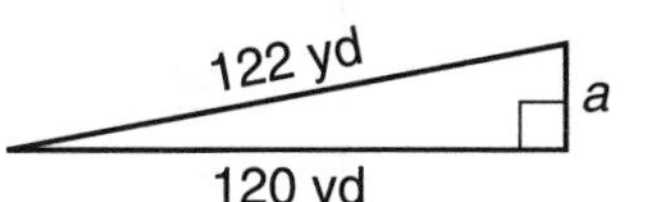

a = ________ (unit)

13. Find the distance (d) from home plate to second base.

d = ________ ft

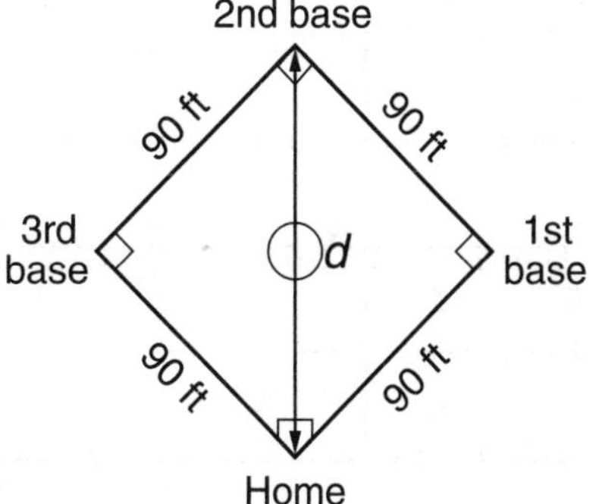

Practice

Simplify.

14. $2[9(6 - 5)]$ = ________

15. $5 + 3 * 4 - 8 + 2 * 7$ = ________

Name Date Time

Pythagorean Triples

Sets of positive integers that are solutions of the equation $a^2 + b^2 = c^2$ are Pythagorean triples. The smallest Pythagorean triple is 3, 4, 5.

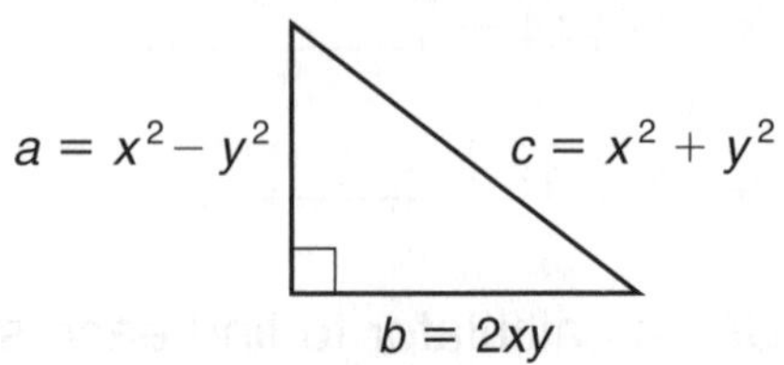

You can find Pythagorean triples by choosing any 2 positive integers, x and y, where $x > y$, and using the formulas $a = x^2 - y^2$, $b = 2xy$, and $c = x^2 + y^2$.

1. Study the example in the table below. Then use the formulas to complete the table. Use the Pythagorean theorem to make sure each triple works.

Formulas		Leg *a*	Leg *b*	Leg *c*	Pythagorean triple
x	*y*	$x^2 - y^2$	$2xy$	$x^2 + y^2$	
2	1	$2^2 - 1^2 = 3$	$2(2)(1) = 4$	$2^2 + 1^2 = 5$	3, 4, 5
3	1				
3	2				
4	1				
4	3				
5	4				
6	5				

2. Use any patterns you notice in the table above and a trial-and-error strategy to help you find the values of x and y that generate each triple.

a. 21, 20, 29 $x =$ ______ $y =$ ______

b. 27, 36, 45 $x =$ ______ $y =$ ______

Name Date Time

STUDY LINK 9•13

Unit 9 Review

1. Simplify the following expressions by combining like terms.

   a. $4x + 3x =$ ______ b. $3x + 7 + x =$ ______

   c. $4 * (x + 2) + 2x - 6 =$ ______ d. $(x + 3) * 2 - 2x =$ ______

2. Liani simplified the expression $8(x + 10)$ as $(8 * x) + 10$. What did she do wrong? Explain her mistake and show the correct way to solve the problem.

   ______

   ______

3. Solve each equation. Show your work on the back of this sheet.

   a. $3x - 4 = 4x + 6$ ______ b. $5 * (2 - 6) = 4g$ ______

   c. $3(2y - 3) = 15$ ______ d. $\frac{(2x - 1)}{3} = 9$ ______

4. The perimeter of triangle *ABC* is 18 inches. What is the length of each side?

   AB ______ *BC* ______ *AC* ______

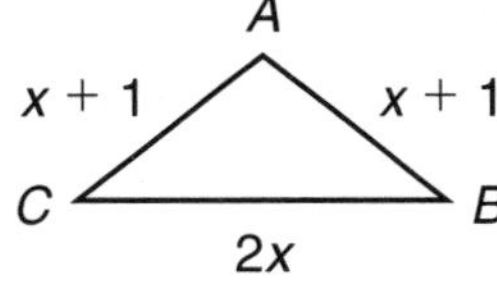

5. The perimeter of right triangle *GLD* is 12 centimeters.

   What is the area of the triangle? ______

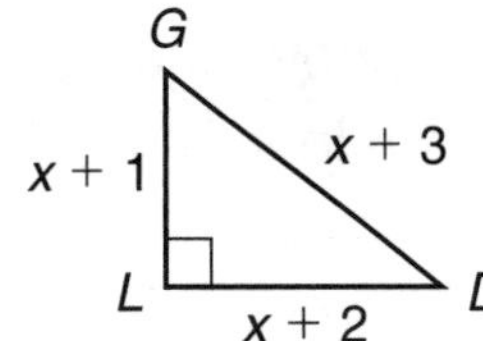

6. Toshi often walks to school along Main Street and Elm Street. If he were to take Pythagoras Avenue instead, how many fewer blocks would he walk? ______

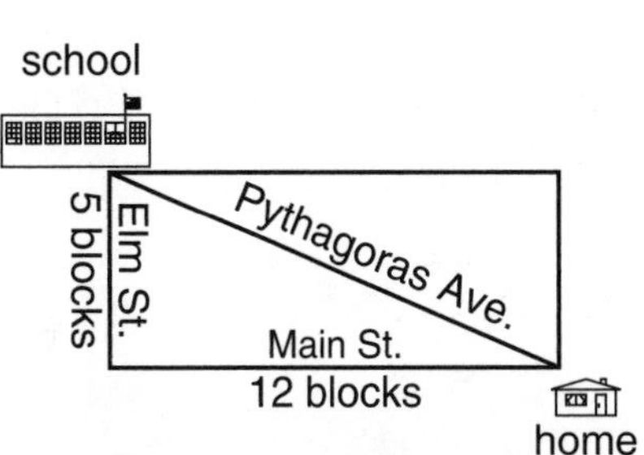

Practice

7. $28\overline{)42} =$ ______ 8. $161 \div 92 =$ ______ 9. $200\overline{)120} =$ ______

Name Date Time

An Indirect Measurement Problem

Work with 3 other students. Your teacher has taped a target on the wall. You will use an indirect method to determine the height of the target above the floor.

Study the diagram shown below. Each student has a special job.

Observer: Sit on the floor and face the target. Sit about 4.5 to 6 meters from the target.

Supporter: You and the observer hold a meterstick so it is at the observer's eye level. Make sure the meterstick is parallel to the floor.

Pointer: Take a second meterstick and place the 0 end on top of the end of the meterstick that the supporter is holding. The supporter holds the ends of the sticks together. Make sure to hold the meterstick vertically so angle *ACB* is approximately a right angle (90°).

Observer: Hold the end of the meterstick (point *A*) near your eye and look at the target (point *D*). Instruct the pointer to slide a finger up or down the vertical meterstick until the finger appears to point to the target (point *D*). Record the length of $\overline{BC}$.

Measurer: Measure the height above the floor of the observer's meterstick (the height of $\overline{AC}$ above the floor). Also measure the distance from the observer's eye to the wall (the length of $\overline{AE}$).

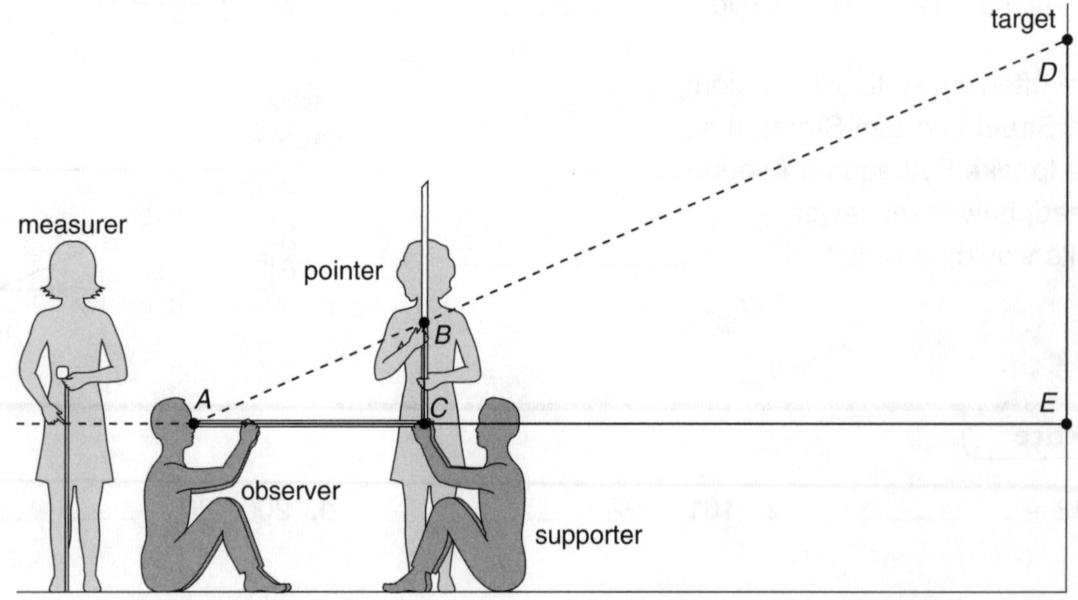

Name Date Time

LESSON 9•13

An Indirect Measurement Problem *cont.*

1. Record your measurements.

AC = 100 cm

AE = ____________ cm (distance from observer's eye to wall)

BC = ____________ cm

Distance from observer's eye to floor = ____________ cm

2. Draw sketches of triangles *ACB* and *AED* that include your measurement information.

3. Triangles *ACB* and *AED* are similar figures.
What is the size-change factor for these figures? ____________

Use the size-change factor to calculate the length of $\overline{DE}$.

DE = ____________ cm

4. What is the height of the target above the floor? ____________

Name Date Time

Proportions and Indirect Measurement

One way to solve an indirect measurement problem is to write a proportion. Study the example below.

Example:

A road sign casts a shadow that is 4.6 meters long. A stop sign near the road sign casts a shadow that is 3 meters long. The road sign and its shadow form 2 legs of a right triangle that are similar to the 2 legs of a right triangle formed by the stop sign and its shadow.

Find the height of the road sign.

Use the diagram to write a proportion involving the corresponding sides of the triangles.

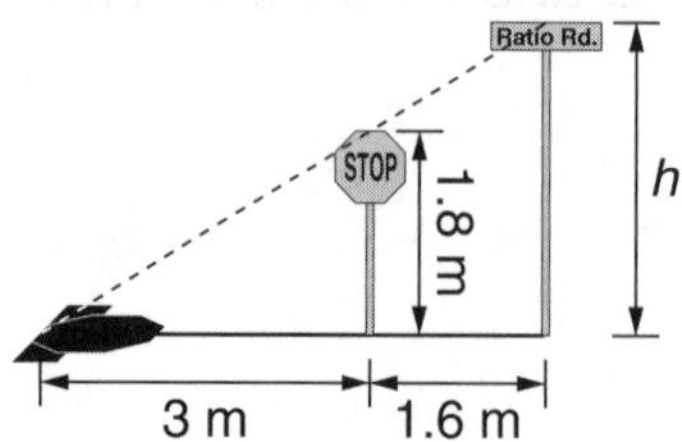

$$\frac{\text{stop sign's height}}{\text{road sign's height}} \rightarrow \frac{1.8}{h} = \frac{3}{4.6} \leftarrow \frac{\text{length of stop sign's shadow}}{\text{length of road sign's shadow}}$$

Use cross products to write an equation. $3h = (1.8)(4.6)$

Solve. $\frac{3h}{3} = \frac{8.28}{3}$

$h = 2.76$

The height of the road sign is 2.76 meters.

The triangles in Problems 1 and 2 are similar. Solve each problem by writing and solving a proportion.

1.

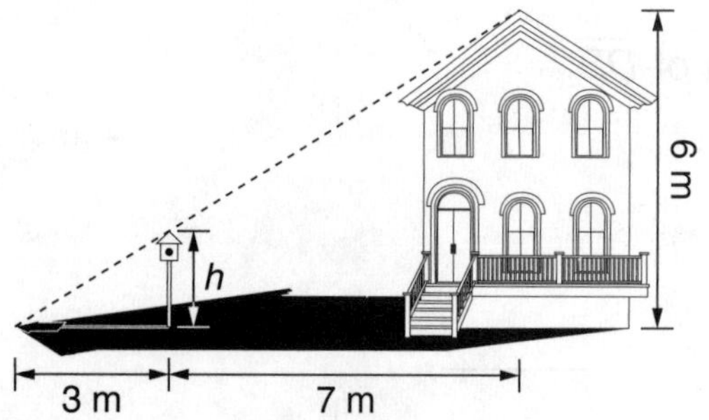

Height of birdhouse = ____________
(unit)

2.

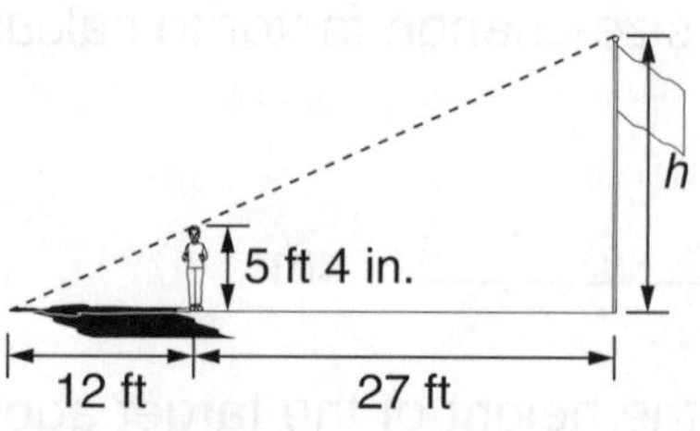

Height of flagpole = ____________
(unit)

Name Date Time

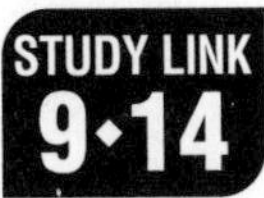

Unit 10: Family Letter

Geometry Topics

Unit 10 includes a variety of activities involving some of the more recreational, artistic, and lesser-known aspects of geometry. In *Fifth Grade Everyday Mathematics,* students explored same-tile **tessellations.** A tessellation is an arrangement of closed shapes that covers a surface completely, without gaps or overlaps. Your kitchen or bathroom floor may be an example of a tessellation. A regular tessellation involves only one kind of regular polygon. Three examples are shown at the right.

In Unit 10 of *Sixth Grade Everyday Mathematics,* your child will explore semiregular tessellations. A **semiregular tessellation** is made from two or more kinds of regular polygons. For example, a semiregular tessellation can be made from equilateral triangles and squares as shown below.

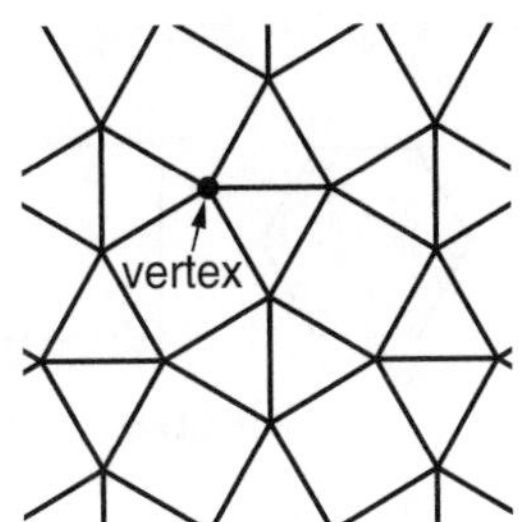

The angles around every vertex point in a semiregular tessellation must be congruent to the angles around every other vertex point. Notice that at each vertex point in the tessellation above, there are the vertices of three equilateral triangles and two squares, always in the same order.

The artist M. C. Escher used **transformation geometry**—translations, reflections, and rotations of geometric figures—to create intriguing tessellation art. Ask your child to show you the translation tessellation that students created in the style of Escher.

Your child will also explore topology. **Topology**, sometimes called *rubber-sheet geometry,* is a modern branch of geometry that deals with, among other topics, properties of geometric objects that do not change when the objects' shapes are changed. Ask your child to share with you some ideas from topology, such as Möbius strips.

Please keep this Family Letter for reference as your child works through Unit 10.

Unit 10: Family Letter *cont.*

Math Tools

Your child will use the **Geometry Template** to explore and design tessellations. This tool includes a greater variety of shapes than the pattern-block template from previous grades. It might more specifically be called a geometry-and-measurement template. The measuring devices include inch and centimeter scales, a Percent Circle useful for making circle graphs, and a full-circle and a half-circle protractor.

Vocabulary

Important terms in Unit 10:

genus In *topology,* the number of holes in a geometric shape. Shapes with the same genus are topologically equivalent. For example, a doughnut and a coffee cup are equivalent because both are genus 1.

Genus 0

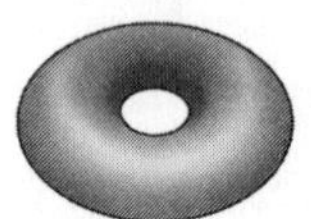

Genus 1

Möbius strip (Möbius band) A 3-dimensional figure with only one side and one edge, named for the German mathematician August Ferdinand Möbius (1790–1868).

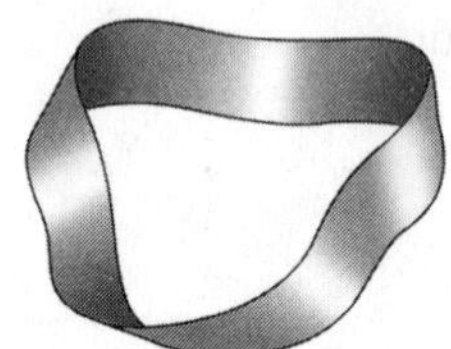

Möbius strip

order of rotation symmetry The number of times a rotation image of a figure coincides with the figure before completing a 360° rotation.

A figure with order 5 rotation symmetry

regular polygon A polygon in which all sides are the same length and all angles have the same measure.

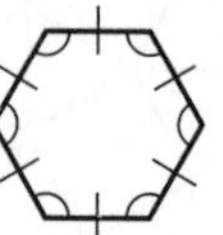
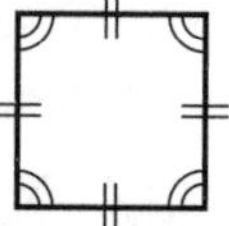

Regular polygons

regular tessellation A tessellation of one *regular polygon.* The three regular tessellations are shown below.

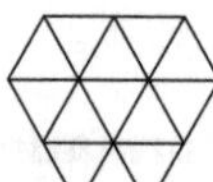
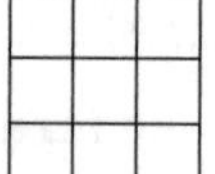
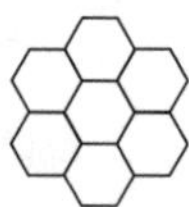

The three regular tessellations

rotation symmetry A figure has rotation symmetry if it is the rotation image of itself after less than a full turn around a center or axis of rotation.

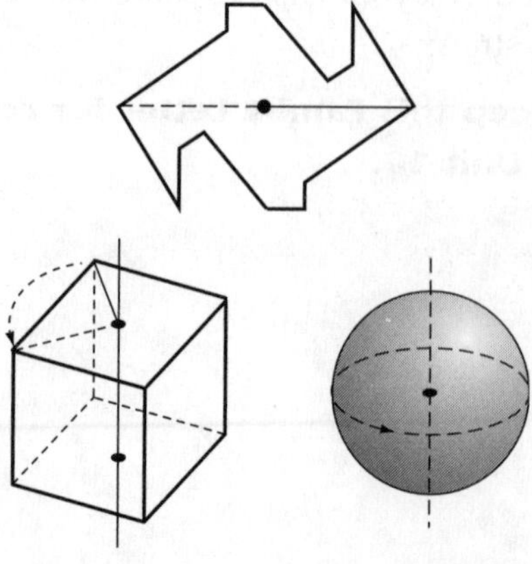

Shapes with rotation symmetry

topological transformation A transformation that pairs a figure with its image after shrinking, stretching, twisting, bending, or turning inside out. Tearing, breaking, and sticking together are not allowed. Shapes that can be changed into one another by a topological transformation are called "topologically equivalent shapes." For example, a doughnut is topologically equivalent to a coffee cup.

translation tessellation A *tessellation* made of a tile in which one or more sides is a translation image of the opposite side(s). Dutch artist M. C. Escher (1898–1972) created many beautiful and elaborate translation tessellations.

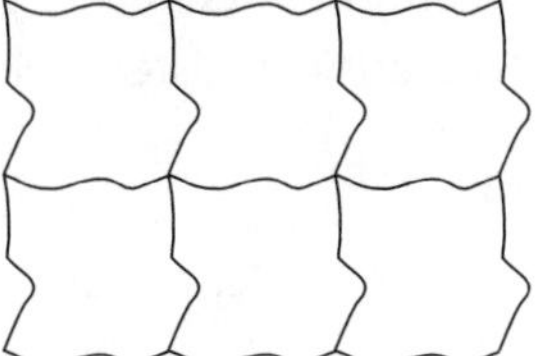

A translation tessellation

vertex point A point where the corners of tessellation tiles meet.

Do-Anytime Activities

To work with your child on the concepts taught in this unit, try these interesting and rewarding activities:

1. Familiarize yourself with the definition of *regular tessellation* (p. 326). Encourage your child to find tessellations in your home, such as floor tile patterns, wallpaper patterns, and wall tile patterns. Have your child identify the shapes that make up the pattern.
2. Encourage your child to use the local library or the Internet to find examples of M. C. Escher's artwork.
3. If you have art software for your home computer, allow your child time to experiment with computer graphic tessellations. Encourage him or her to share the creations with the class.

Building Skills through Games

In Unit 10, your child will reinforce skills and concepts learned throughout the year by playing the following games:

Angle Tangle See *Student Reference Book,* page 306
Two players will need a protractor, straightedge, and blank paper to play *Angle Tangle.* Skills practiced include estimating angle measures as well as measuring angles.

Name That Number See *Student Reference Book,* page 329
This game provides your child with practice in writing number sentences using order of operations. Two or three players need 1 complete deck of number cards to play *Name That Number.*

As You Help Your Child with Homework

As your child brings assignments home, you may want to go over the instructions together, clarifying them as necessary. The answers listed below will guide you through some of the Unit 10 Study Links.

Study Link 10•1

1. rotation
2. translation
3. Answers vary.
4. Answers vary.
5. 114.534
6. 35.488
7. 0.0338
8. 31.7025

Study Link 10•2

1.

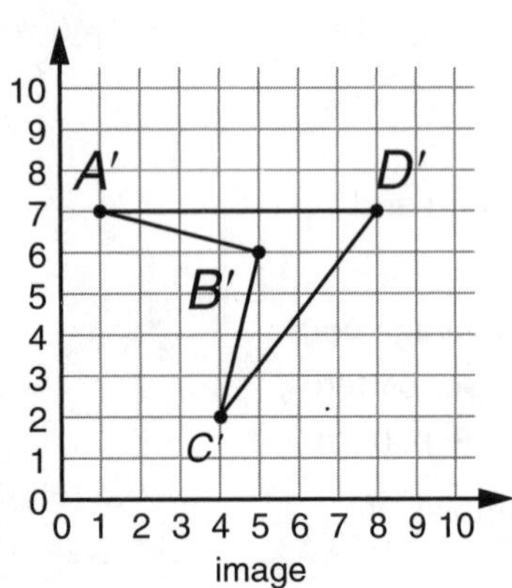

2.

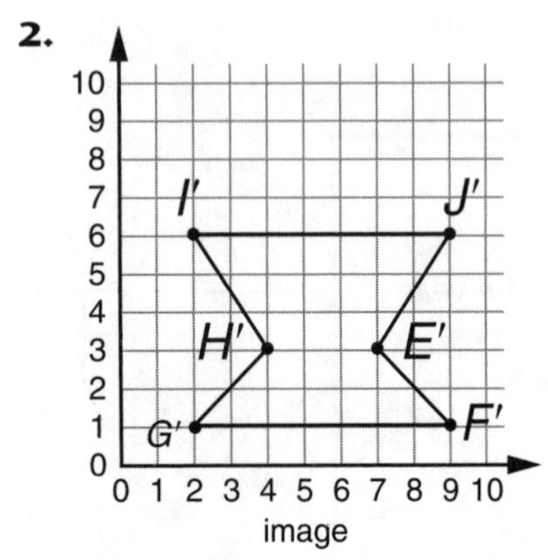

3.

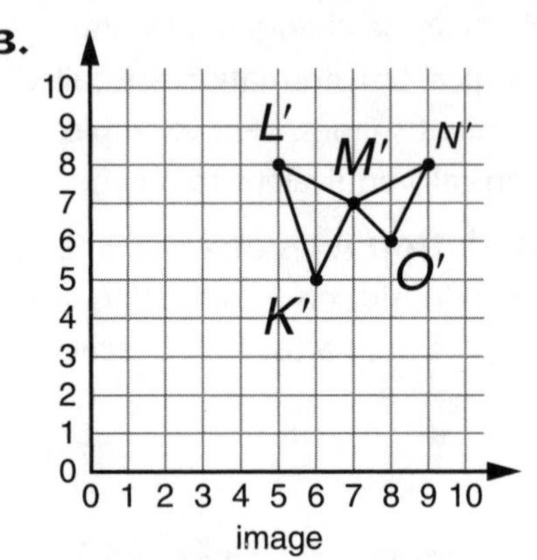

4. 0.8 **5.** 1.6 **6.** 8.9 **7.** 5.1

Study Link 10•3

1. 2
2. 1
3. 4
4. 6
5. 2
6. infinite
7. 2, 3, 5, 6, 9, 10
8. 2, 3, 6,

Study Link 10•5

Sample answers:

1. The paper clips are linked to one another.
2. The paper clips and the rubberband are linked.
3. All the paper clips are linked.
4. 60 **5.** 50 **6.** 63 **7.** 493

Name Date Time

Regular Dodecagon Templates

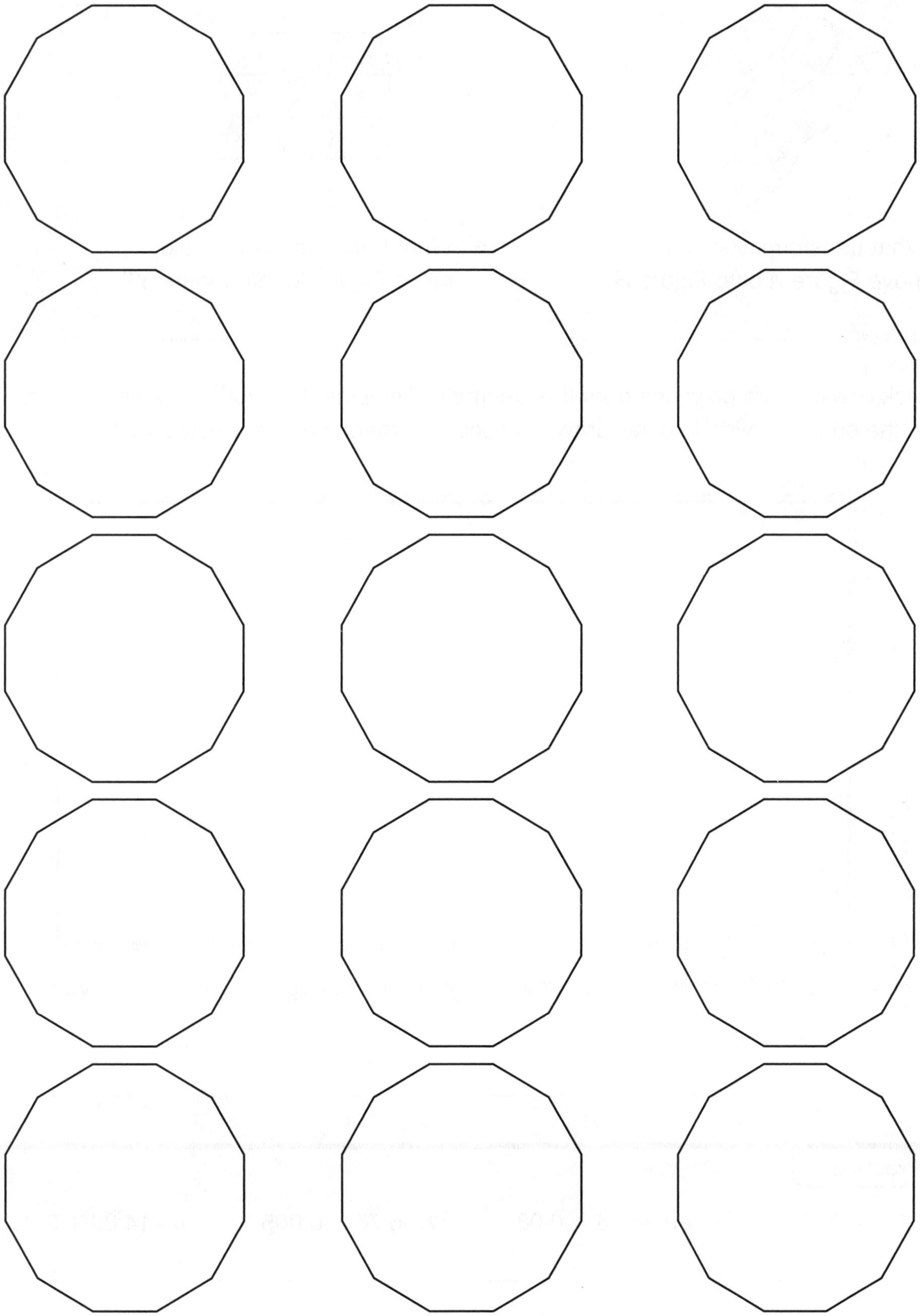

Name Date Time

Tessellation Exploration

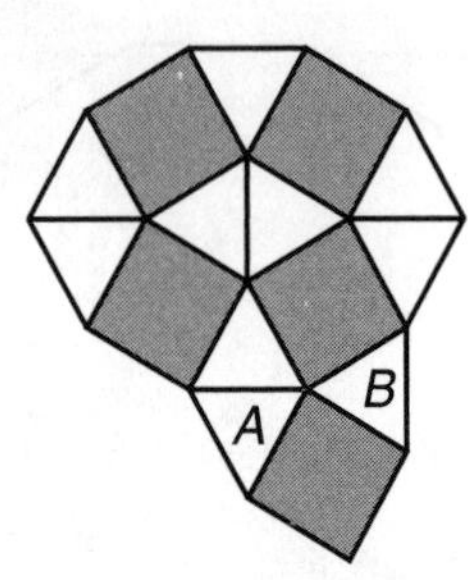

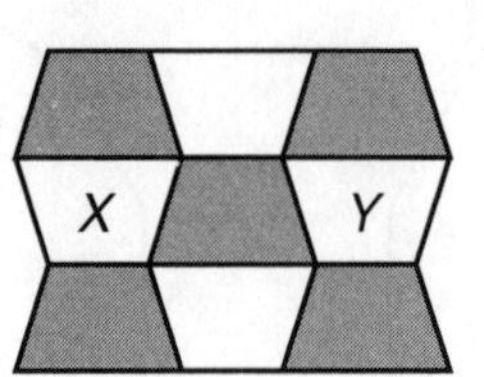

1. What transformation would move Figure *A* onto Figure *B?*

____

2. What transformation would move Figure *X* onto Figure *Y?*

____

3. Pick one or more polygons from the Geometry Template that you know will tessellate. In the space provided below, draw a tessellation made up of the polygon(s).

4. Tell whether the tessellation you drew is regular or semiregular. Explain how you know.

____

____

Practice

5. 5.67 ∗ 20.2 _______________

6. 443.6 ∗ 0.08 _______________

7. 6.76 ∗ 0.005 _______________

8. 14.09 ∗ 2.25 _______________

Name Date Time

Regular Polygons

Fold the page like this and then cut out four shapes at a time.

Cut on the lines.

Name Date Time

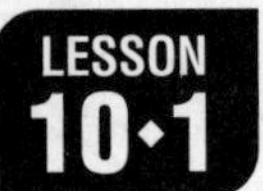

Same-Tile Tessellations

Decide whether each polygon can be used to create a same-tile tessellation. Write the name of the polygon. Then record your answers in Column A. In Column B, use your Geometry Template to draw examples illustrating your answers in Column A.

Polygon	A. Tessellation? (Yes or No)	B. Draw an example.
△ ______		
□ ______		
⬠ ______		
⬡ ______		
octagon ______		

Name Date Time

Investigating Same-Tile Tessellations

1. After you complete *Math Masters,* page 332, fill in the table below. Use your results from Column D to complete Column E.

Regular Polygon	Number of Sides (n)	C. Sum of interior angle measures $180 * (n - 2)$	D. Measure of one angle	E. Factor of 360°? (from Column D)
Example: Equilateral triangle	3	$180° * (3 - 2) =$ $180° * 1 = 180°$	$\frac{180°}{3} = 60°$	Yes. 60° is a factor of 360°.
Square				
Regular pentagon				
Regular hexagon				
Regular octagon				

2. Compare your results from Column A of the table on *Math Masters,* page 332 to Column E of the table above. What can you conclude about the relationship between a regular polygon's interior angle measurements and its ability to tessellate?

____

____

3. A regular dodecagon has 12 sides. Can you use a regular dodecagon to create a same-tile tessellation? Explain.

____

____

STUDY LINK 10•2

Translations

Plot and label the vertices of the image that would result from each translation. One vertex of each image has already been plotted and labeled.

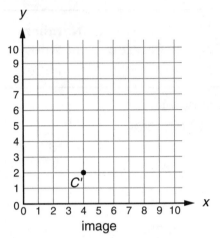

1.

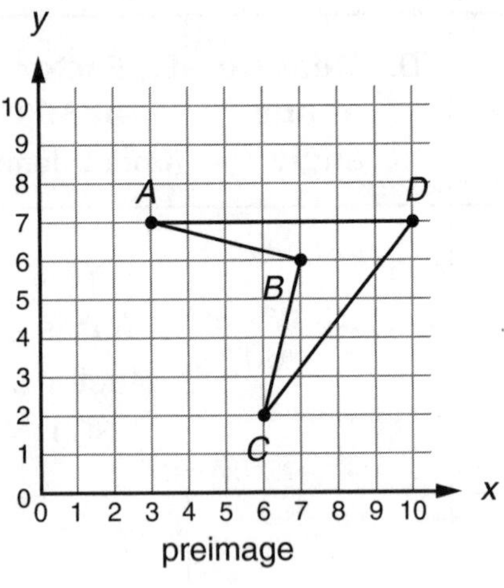

horizontal translation

C'

image

2.

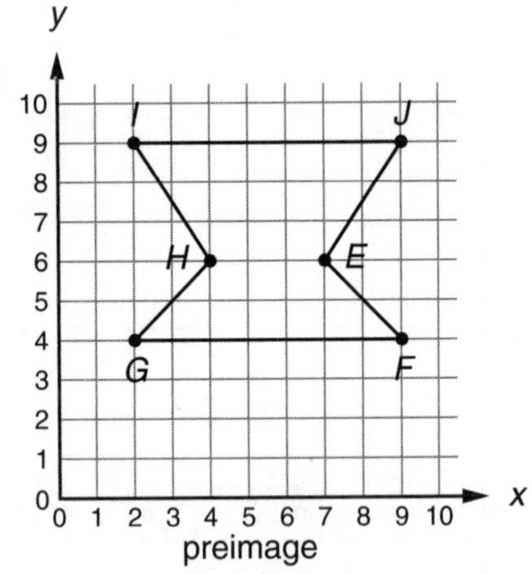

vertical translation

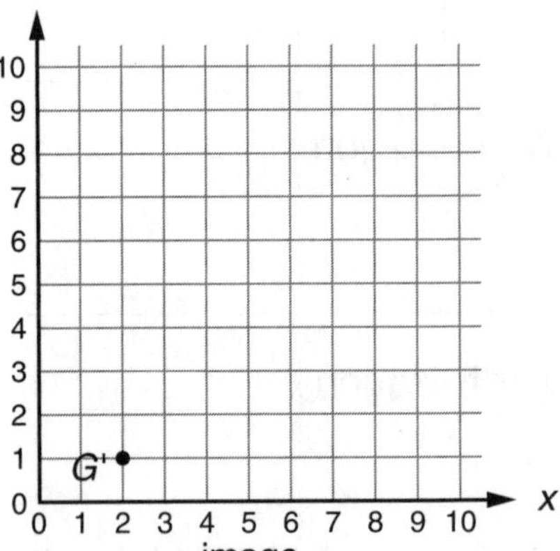

3.

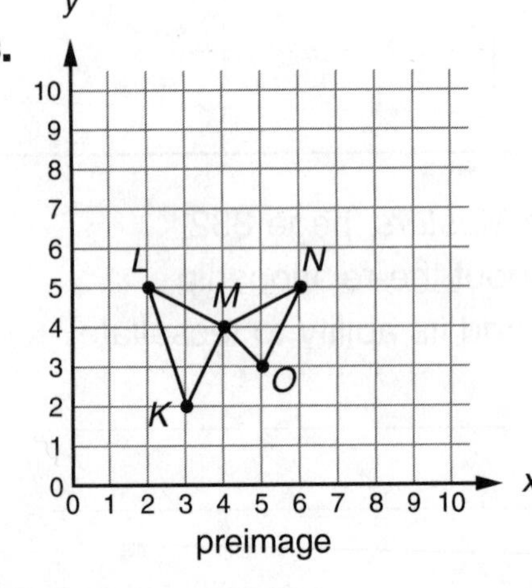

diagonal translation

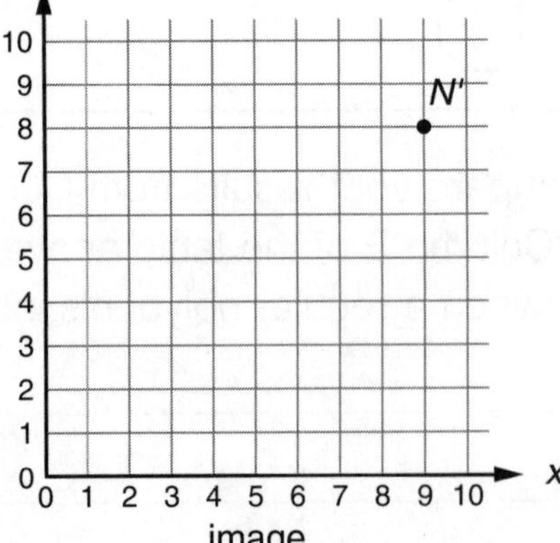

Practice

4. $\frac{25.6}{32}$ ________

5. $\frac{102.4}{64}$ ________

6. $\frac{41.83}{4.7}$ ________

7. $\frac{67.32}{13.2}$ ________

Name Date Time

An Angle Investigation

Do all convex quadrangles tessellate? (A convex quadrangle is one in which all vertices are pushed outward.) To find out, do the following:

1. Draw a convex quadrangle on a piece of cardstock paper.

2. Measure the angles of your quadrangle. Write the measure of each angle on the angle.

3. Find the sum of the angles. Write the sum of the angles on your quadrangle.

4. Cut out your quadrangle and try to make a tessellation by tracing your quadrangle repeatedly. Draw your tessellation in the space provided below or on the back of this page.
   (*Hint:* Label your angles *A, B, C,* and *D* so you can be sure that all four angles meet at each vertex.)

5. Repeat Steps 1–4 for a different convex quadrangle. Try to tessellate your second quadrangle. Draw your tessellation on the back of this page.

6. Do both of your quadrangles tessellate? ______

7. Do you think that all convex quadrangles will tessellate? ______

   Why or why not? ____________________

   ____

   ____

   ____

   ____

   ____

   ____

Name Date Time

Rotation Symmetry

Use the square below to show the original position of Square *ABCD*.

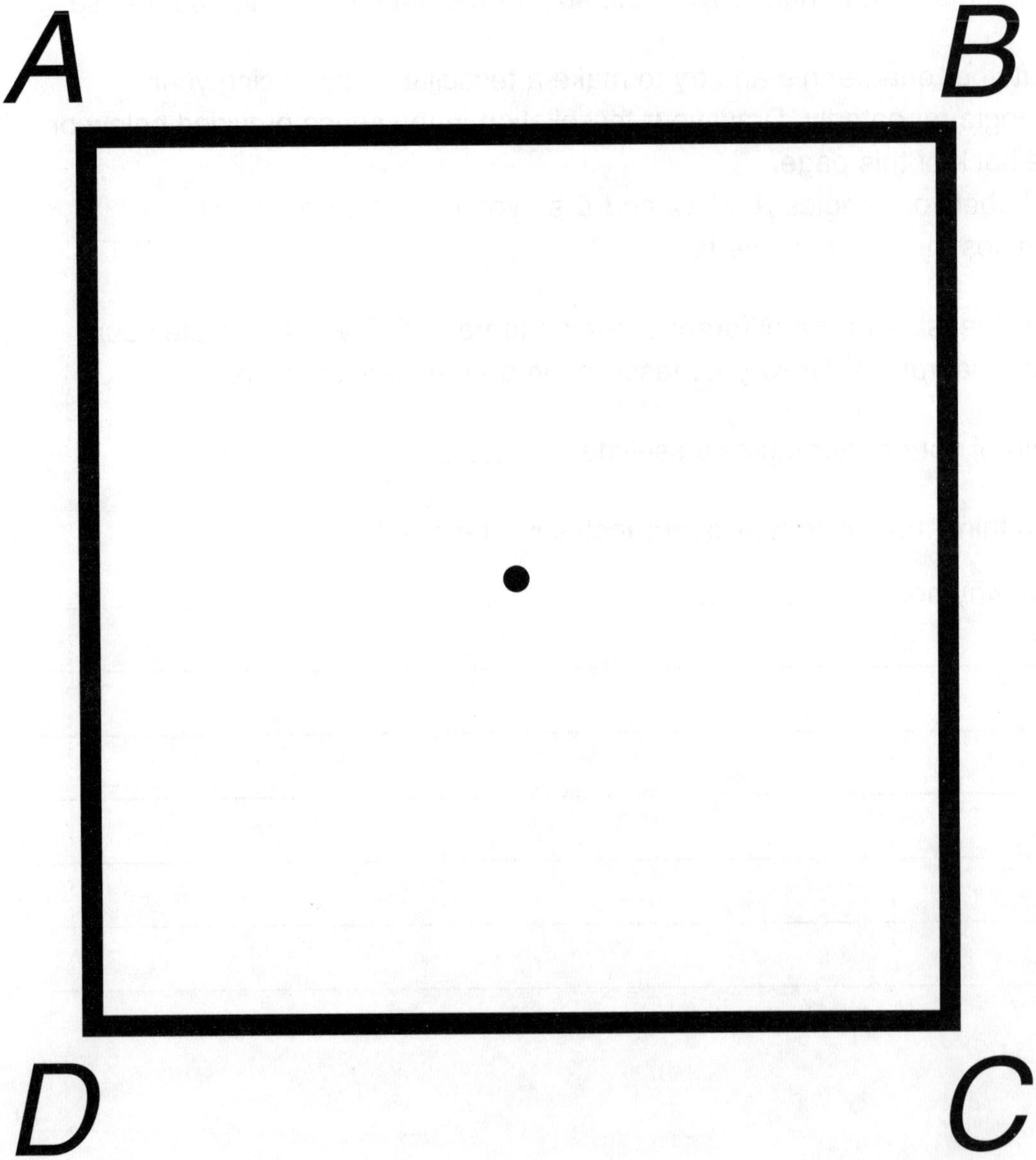

A B

D C

Name Date Time

Rotation Symmetry *continued*

Use the square below to demonstrate the rotation of Square *ABCD*.

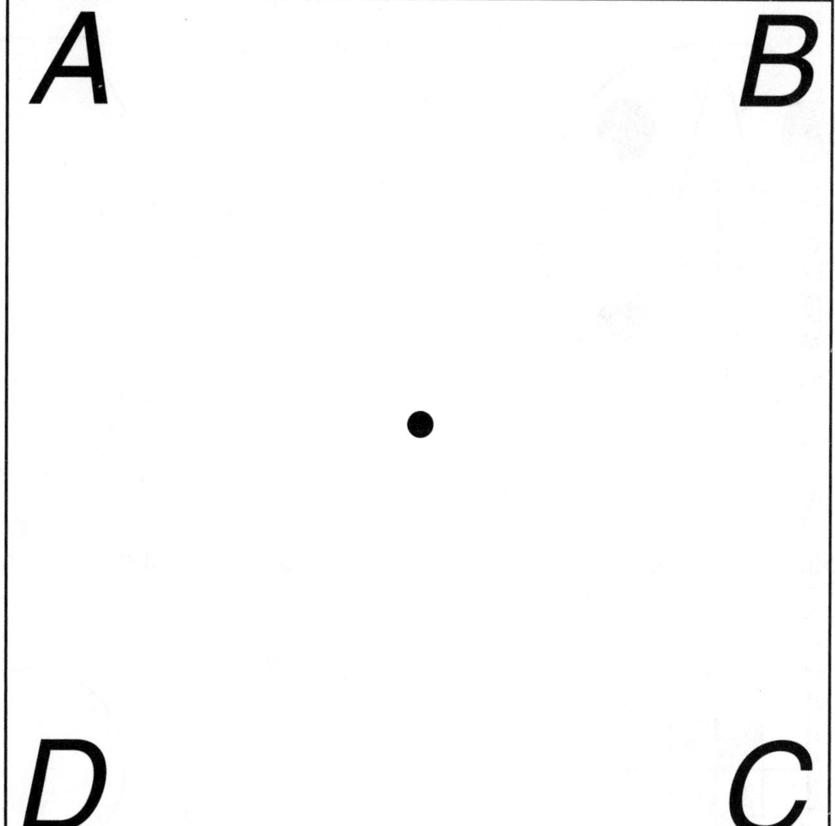

Name Date Time

Rotation Symmetry

For each figure, draw the line(s) of reflection symmetry, if any.
Then determine the order of rotation symmetry for the figure.

1.

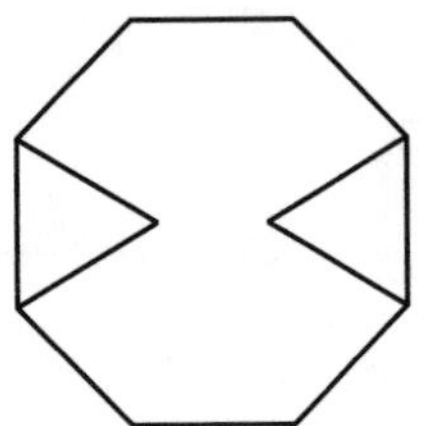

Order of rotation symmetry ________

2.

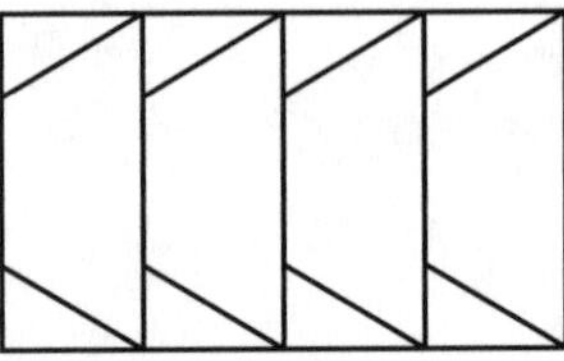

Order of rotation symmetry ________

3.

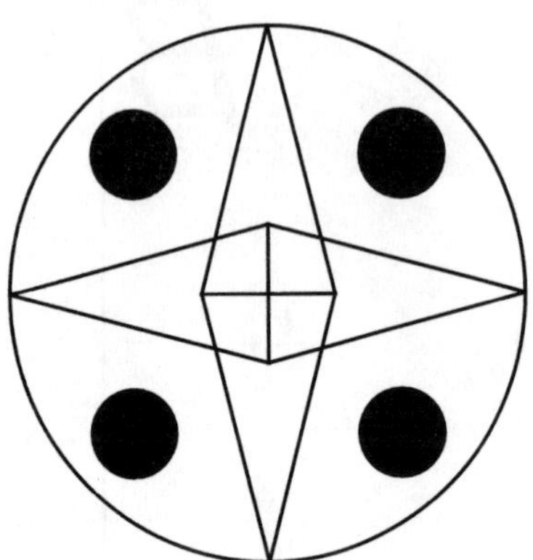

Order of rotation symmetry ________

4.

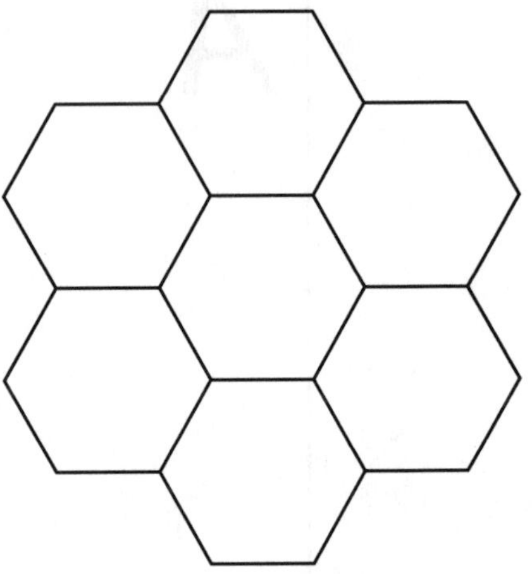

Order of rotation symmetry ________

5.

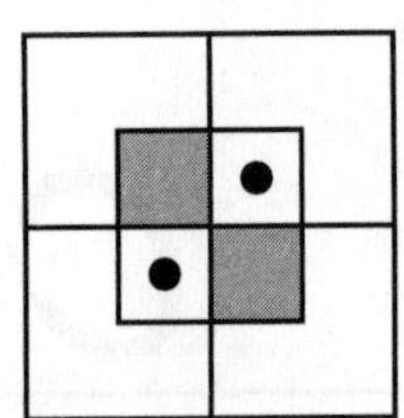

Order of rotation symmetry ________

6.

Order of rotation symmetry ________

Practice

Tell whether each number is divisible by 2, 3, 5, 6, 9, or 10.

7. 4,140 ________________

8. 324 ________________

Name Date Time

Lines of Symmetry

Use a transparent mirror to help you draw the missing half of each picture.

1.

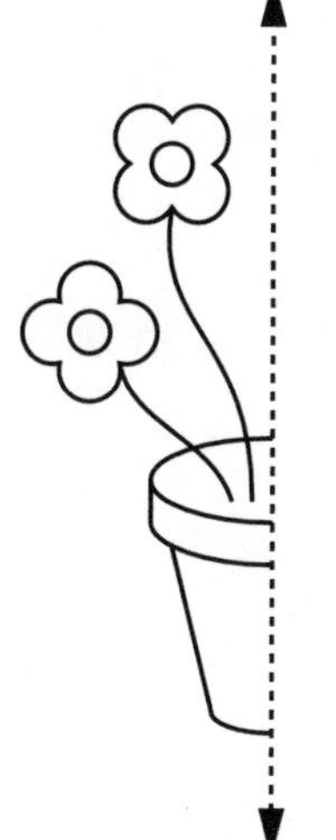

2.

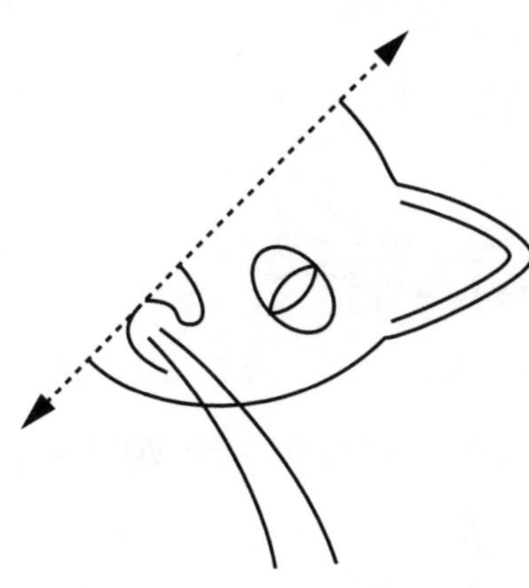

Use a transparent mirror to help you draw lines of symmetry for the following figures. Some figures have more than one line of symmetry; others may have none.

3.

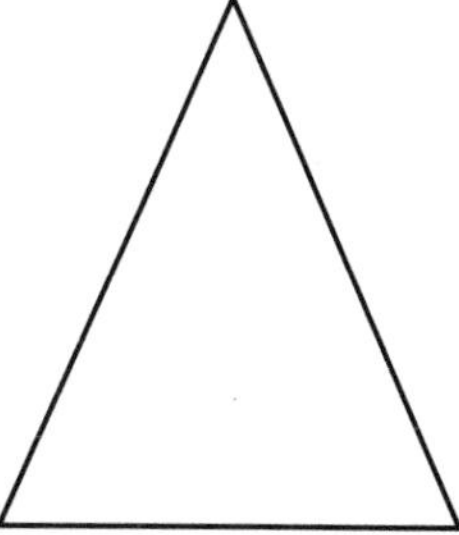

4.

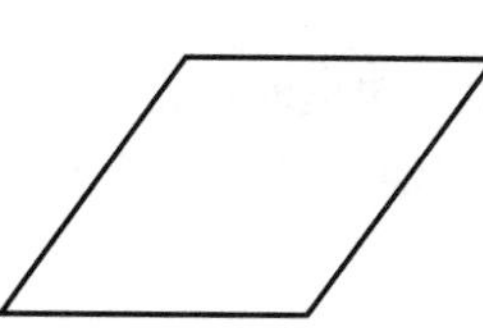

5.

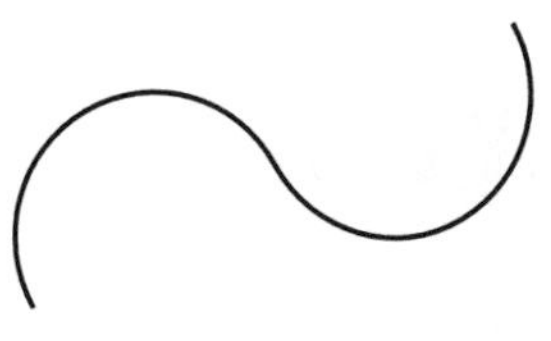

6.

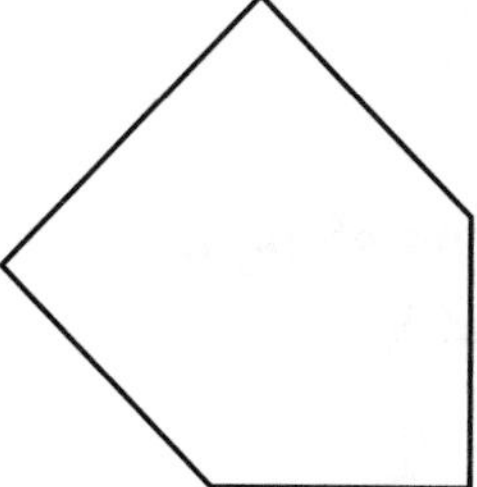

7.

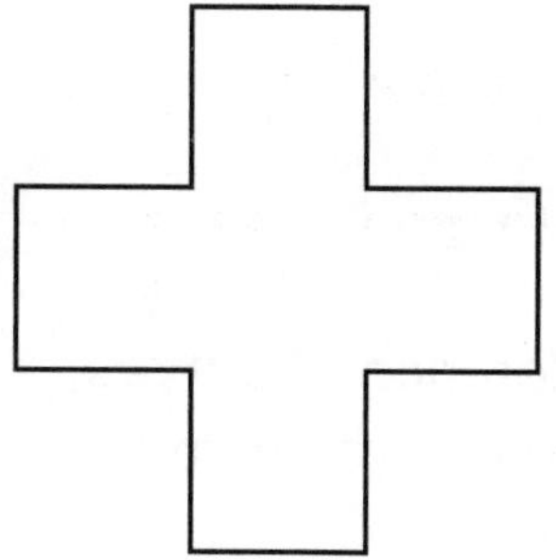

8.

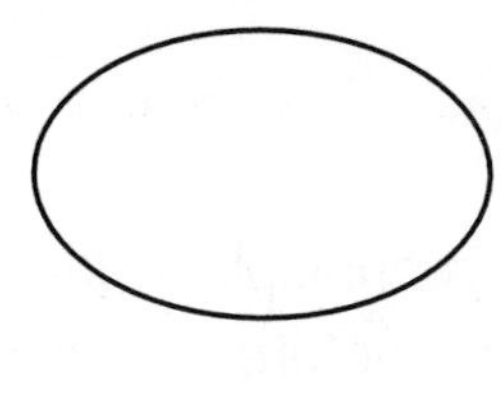

Name Date Time

A Topology Trick

Follow the procedure described below to tie a knot in a piece of string without letting go of the ends.

Step 1 Place a piece of string in front of you on a table or a desk.

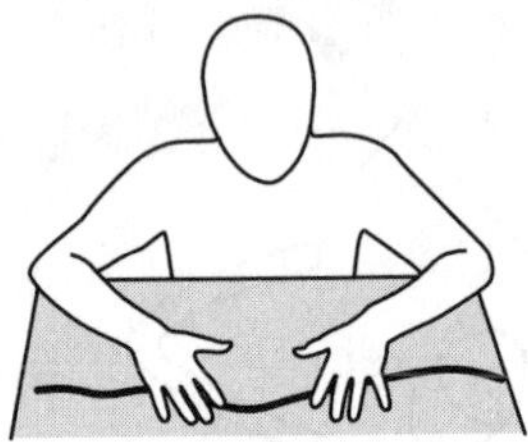

Step 2 Fold your arms across your chest.

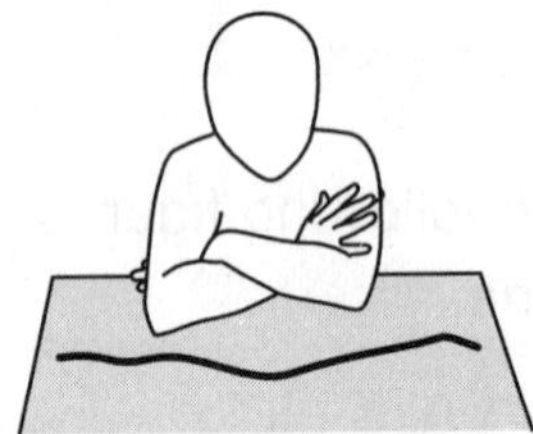

Step 3 With your arms still folded, grab the left end of the string with your right hand and the right end of the string with your left hand.

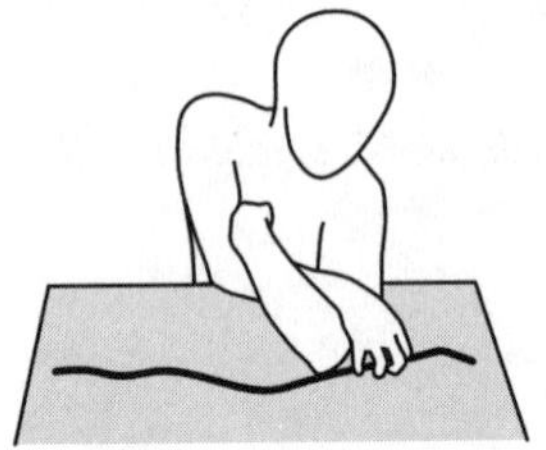

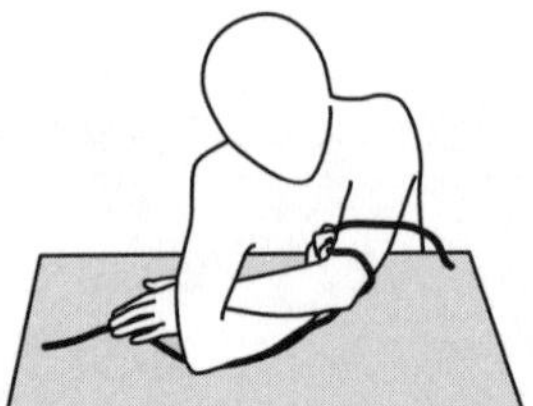

Step 4 Hold the ends of the string and unfold your arms. The string should now have a knot in it.

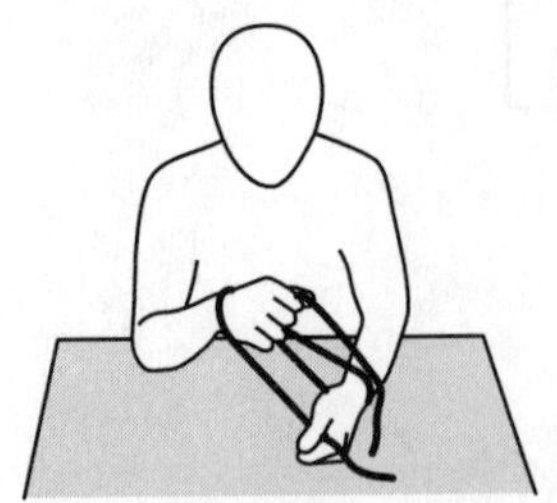

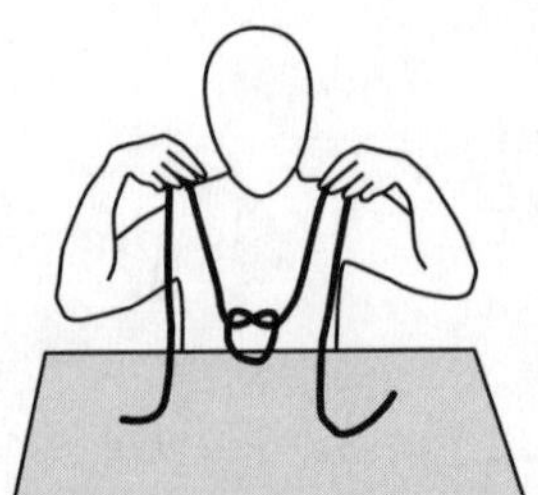

This trick works because of a principle in topology called **transference of curves.** Your arms had a knot in them before you picked up the string. When you unfolded your arms, you transferred the knot from your arms to the string.

Name Date Time

Rope Puzzle

1. Using a 4-foot length of rope, make a set of handcuffs by tying a loop at each end. Leave enough rope in the middle so you can step over the rope if you want or need to.

2. Before you and a partner each put on your set of handcuffs, loop them around each other so they are tied together as shown in the diagram below.

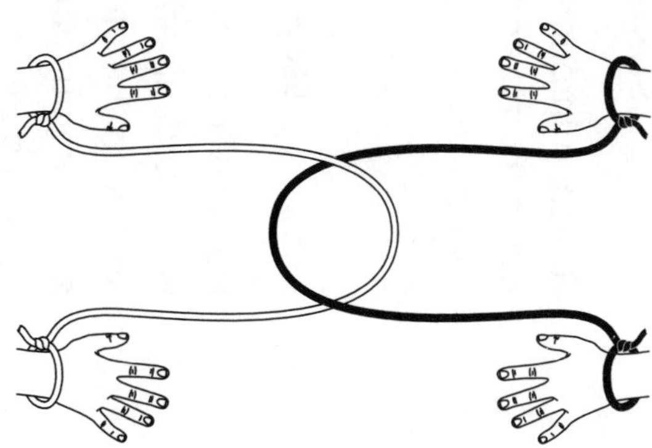

3. Stand within arms' reach of your partner. Without moving your feet, work to separate the two linked ropes while following these rules:

   - Do not remove your hands from the loops.
   - Do not cut or damage the rope in any way.

4. Be prepared to demonstrate the strategies and steps you used to separate the ropes.

LESSON 10•4

Rope Puzzle Solution

Steps 1–3

Start by moving your partner's rope along yours until it is lying on your arm. Make sure your partner's rope is not wrapped around your rope; it should only be touching your arm.

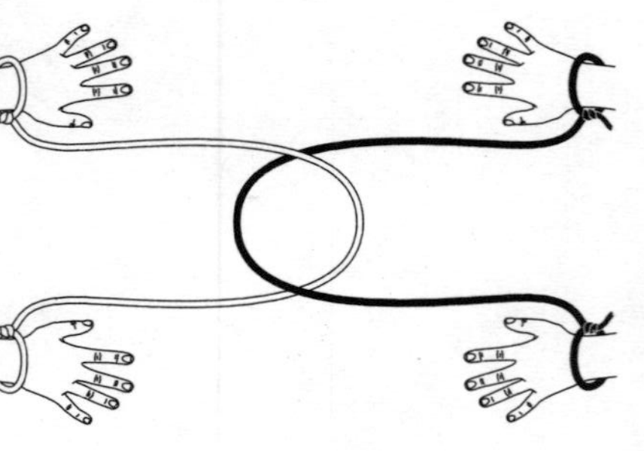

1

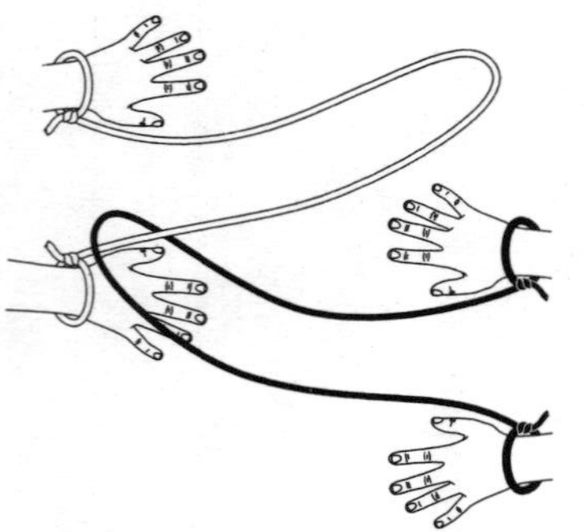

2

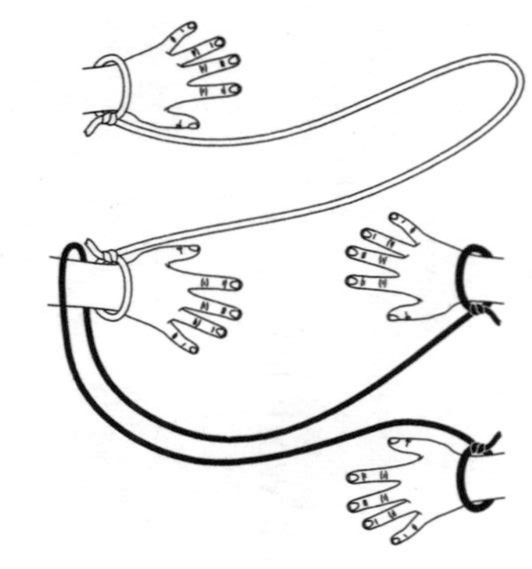

3

Steps 3a–3c

Reach in through your handcuff with a thumb and finger, and grab your partner's rope.

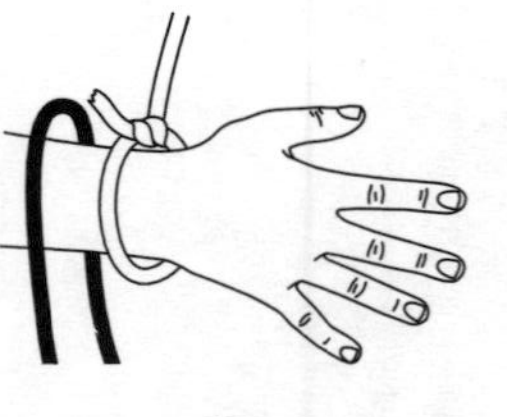

3a

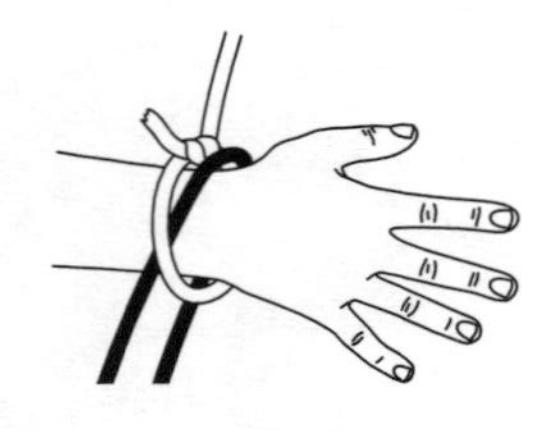

3b

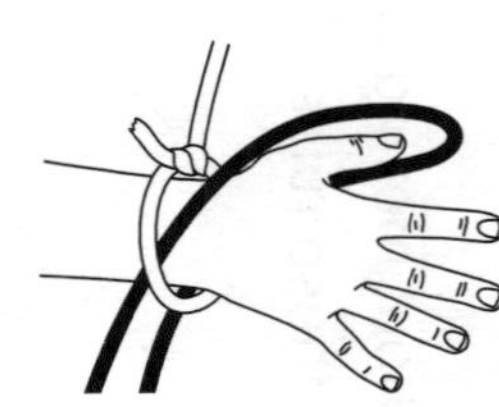

3c

Steps 3d–3e

Pull your partner's rope through your handcuff and over your hand so it is on the other side of your arm. Let your partner's rope go back through your handcuff. You should now be separated.

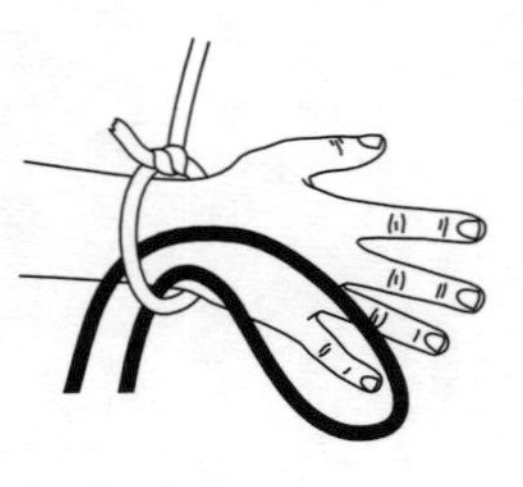

3d

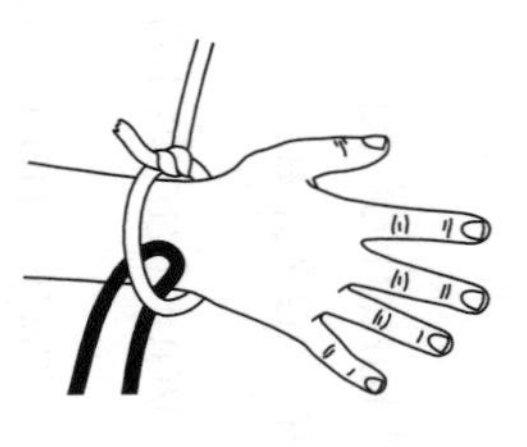

3e

Name Date Time

Topology Puzzles

Puzzle #1

Get a pencil and a piece of string. The string should be about $1\frac{1}{2}$ times the length of the pencil. You will also need a shirt or a jacket with a buttonhole.

Tie the two ends of the string together at the top of the pencil so the string forms a loop, as shown in Figure 1.

Figure out how to attach the pencil to the buttonhole, as shown in Figure 2.

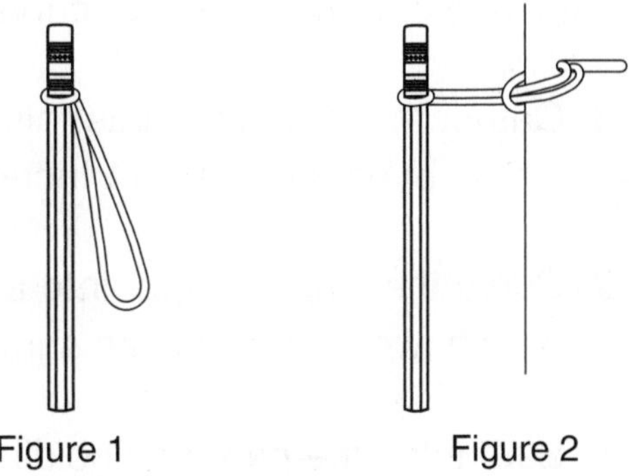

Figure 1 Figure 2

Puzzle #2

Get a pair of scissors, a piece of string, and a large button. The button must be larger than the finger holes in the scissors.

Tie the ends of the string to the holes in the button to form a large loop of string.

Figure out how to attach the button to the scissors, as shown in Figure 3.

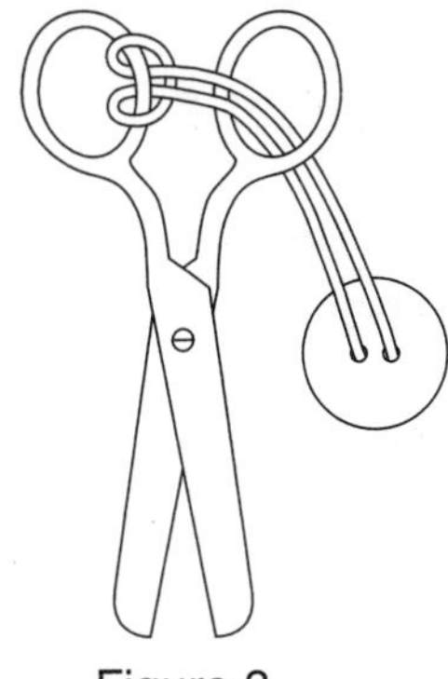

Figure 3

Explain how these puzzles involve topology.

____

____

____

____

____

Name Date Time

Another Topology Trick

Follow the procedure described below to perform another topology trick that works because of transference of curves.

Step 1 Gather the following materials: 2 to 8 large paper clips, a strip of paper $1\frac{1}{2}$ by 11 inches, and a rubber band.

Step 2 Curve the strip of paper into an S-shape. Attach two paper clips as shown at the right.

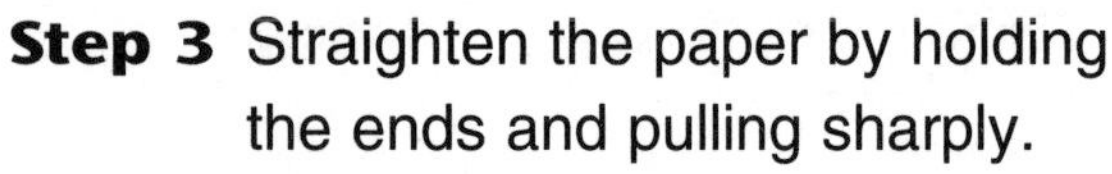

Step 3 Straighten the paper by holding the ends and pulling sharply.

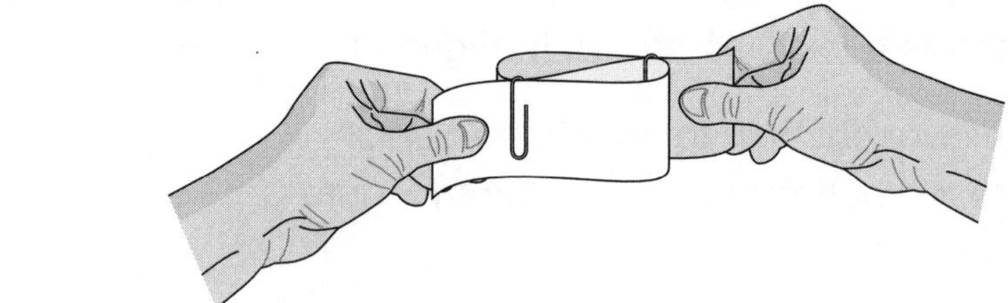

1. Describe your results.

____

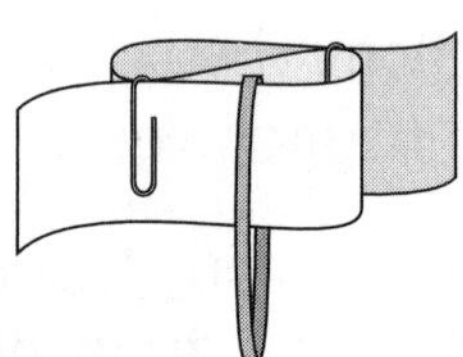

2. Add a rubber band as shown. Straighten the paper.

   Describe your results.

____

____

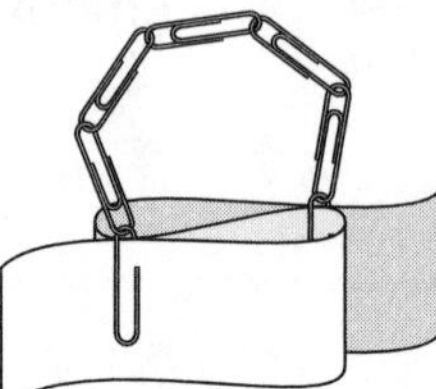

3. Try including a chain of paper clips as shown.

   Describe your results.

____

____

Practice

Find the LCM of each pair of numbers by dividing the product of the numbers by their GCF.

4. 15 and 20 ________
5. 10 and 50 ________
6. 21 and 63 ________
7. 17 and 29 ________

Name Date Time

Networks

A network is a set of points, called nodes, which are connected by segments, or paths.

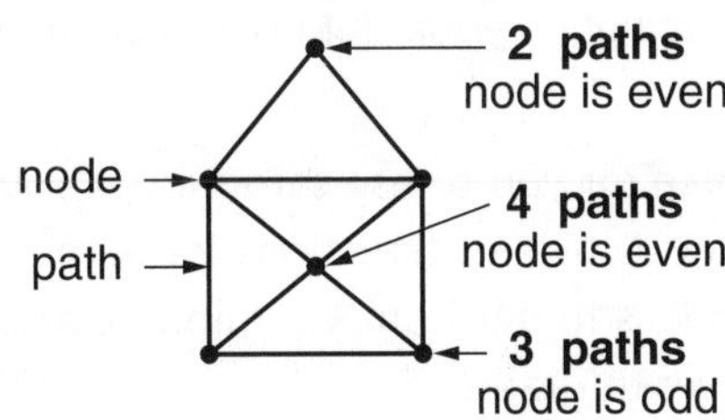

A node is odd if the number of paths leaving the node is odd. A node is even if the number of paths leaving the node is even.

A network is *traceable* if you can draw it without lifting your pencil or pen and without going over the same path twice.

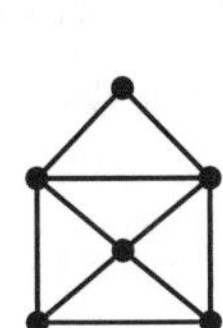

Figure A

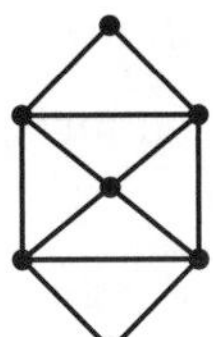

Figure B

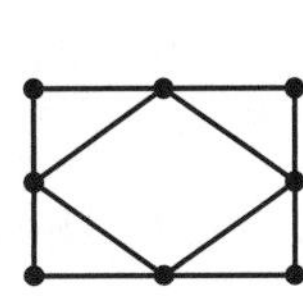

Figure C

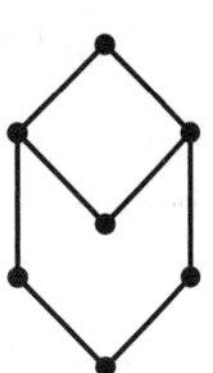

Figure D

1. Count the number of odd and even nodes in Figures A–D. Complete the table below.

Figure	Number of Odd Nodes	Number of Even Nodes	Is the Network Traceable? (Yes or No)
A			
B			
C			
D			

2. Use your table to complete the following two-part statement.

A network is traceable if there are:

a. only 2 ____________ nodes, or

b. all ____________ nodes.

3. Test the statements in Problem 2 by creating traceable and untraceable networks on a separate sheet of paper.

Name Date Time

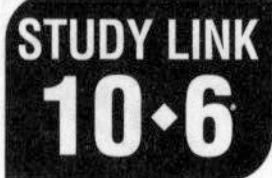

Family Letter

Congratulations!

By completing *Sixth Grade Everyday Mathematics,* your child has accomplished a great deal. Thank you for your support.

This Family Letter is intended as a resource for you to use throughout your child's vacation. It includes an extended list of Do-Anytime Activities, directions for games that you can play at home, a list of mathematics-related books to get from your library, and a preview of what your child might be learning in seventh grade.

Do-Anytime Activities

Mathematics means more when it is rooted in real-world situations. To help your child review many of the concepts learned in sixth grade, we suggest the following activities for you to do with your child over vacation. These activities will help your child build on the skills that he or she has learned this year and are good preparation for a seventh-grade mathematics course.

1. Practice quick recall of multiplication facts. Include extended facts, such as $70 * 8 = 560$ and $70 * 80 = 5,600$.
2. Practice calculating mentally with percents. Use a variety of contexts, such as sales tax, discounts, and sports performances.
3. Use measuring devices—rulers, metersticks, yardsticks, tape measures, thermometers, scales, and so on. Measure in both U.S. customary and metric units.
4. Estimate the answers to calculations, such as the bill at a restaurant or store, the distance to a particular place, the number of people at an event, and so on.
5. Play games like those in the *Student Reference Book.*
6. If you are planning to paint or carpet a room, consider having your child measure and calculate the area. Have him or her write the formula for area ($A = l * w$) and then show you the calculations. If the room is an irregular shape, divide it into separate rectangular regions and have your child find the area of each one.
7. Ask your child to halve, double, or triple the amount of ingredients needed in a particular recipe. Have your child explain how they calculated each amount.
8. Help your child distinguish between part-to-part and part-to-whole ratios in relation to the wins and losses of a favorite sports team. Ask him or her to decide which ratio is being used. For example, wins to losses (such as 5 to 15) or losses to wins (15 to 5) are part-to-part ratios. Part-to-whole ratios are used to compare wins to all games played (5 out of 20) or losses to all games played (15 out of 20).
9. Provide extra practice with the partial-quotients division algorithm by having him or her divide 3-digit numbers by 2-digit numbers, 4-digit numbers by 3-digit numbers, and so on. Ask your child to explain the steps of the algorithm to you as she or he works through them.

Building Skills through Games

The following section lists directions for games that can be played at home. Regular playing cards can be substituted for the number cards used in some games. Other cards can be made from 3" by 5" index cards.

Name That Number See *Student Reference Book* page 329.
This game provides practice in using order of operations to write number sentences. Two or three players need a complete deck of number cards.

Fraction Action, Fraction Friction See *Student Reference Book* page 317.
Two or three players gather fraction cards that have a sum as close as possible to 2, without going over. Students can make a set of 16 cards by copying fractions onto index cards.

Name That Number

Materials □ 4 each of number cards 0–10 and
□ 1 each of number cards 11–20

Players 2 or 3

Skill Naming numbers with expressions

Object of the game To collect the most cards

Directions

1. Shuffle the deck and deal five cards to each player. Place the remaining cards number-side down on the table between the players. Turn over the top card and place it beside the deck. This is the **target number** for the round.
2. Players try to match the target number by adding, subtracting, multiplying, or dividing the numbers on as many of their cards as possible. A card may only be used once.
3. Players write their solutions on a sheet of paper. When players have written their best solutions:
   - Each player sets aside the cards they used to match the target number.
   - Each player replaces the cards they set aside by drawing new cards from the top of the deck.
   - The old target number is placed on the bottom of the deck.
   - A new target number is turned over, and another round is played.
4. Play continues until there are not enough cards left to replace all the players' cards. The player who has set aside the most cards wins the game.

Fraction Action, Fraction Friction

Materials ☐ One set of 16 *Fraction Action, Fraction Friction* cards. The card set includes a card for each of the following fractions (for several fractions there are 2 cards): $\frac{1}{2}, \frac{1}{3}, \frac{2}{3}, \frac{1}{4}, \frac{3}{4}, \frac{1}{6}, \frac{1}{6}, \frac{5}{6}, \frac{1}{12}, \frac{1}{12}, \frac{5}{12}, \frac{5}{12}, \frac{7}{12}, \frac{7}{12}, \frac{11}{12}, \frac{11}{12}$.

☐ One or more calculators

Players 2 or 3

Skill Estimating sums of fractions

Object of the game To collect a set of fraction cards with a sum as close as possible to 2 without going over 2.

Directions

1. Shuffle the deck. Place the pile facedown between the players.
2. Players take turns.
   - On each player's first turn, he or she takes a card from the top of the pile and places it number-side up on the table.
   - On each of the player's following turns, he or she announces one of the following:

     Action This means the player wants an additional card. The player believes that the sum of the fraction cards he or she already has is *not* close enough to 2 to win the hand. The player thinks that another card will bring the sum of the fractions closer to 2, without going over 2.

     Friction This means the player does not want an additional card. The player believes that the sum of the fraction cards he or she already has *is* close enough to 2 to win the hand. The player thinks that there is a good chance that taking another card will make the sum of the fractions greater than 2.

   Once a player says *Friction,* he or she cannot say *Action* on any turn after that.
3. Play continues until all players have announced *Friction* or have a set of cards whose sum is greater than 2. The player whose sum is closest to 2 without going over 2 is the winner of that round. Players may check each other's sums on their calculators.
4. Reshuffle the cards and begin again. The winner of the game is the first player to win five rounds.

Vacation Reading with a Mathematical Twist

Books can contribute to learning by presenting mathematics in a combination of real-world and imaginary contexts. Teachers who use *Everyday Mathematics* in their classrooms recommend the titles listed below. Look for these titles at your local library or bookstore.

For problem-solving practice:

Math for Smarty Pants by Marilyn Burns, Little, Brown and Company, 1982.
Brain Busters! Mind-Stretching Puzzles in Math and Logic by Barry R. Clarke, Dover Publications, 2003.
Wacky Word Problems: Games and Activities That Make Math Easy and Fun by Lynette Long, John Wiley & Sons, Inc., 2005.
My Best Mathematical and Logic Puzzles by Martin Gardner, Dover Publications, 1994.
Math Logic Puzzles by Kurt Smith, Sterling Publishing Co., Inc., 1996.

For skill maintenance:

Delightful Decimals and Perfect Percents: Games and Activities That Make Math Easy and Fun by Lynette Long, John Wiley & Sons, Inc., 2003.
Dazzling Division: Games and Activities That Make Math Easy and Fun by Lynette Long, John Wiley & Sons, Inc., 2000.

For fun and recreation:

Mathamusements by Raymond Blum, Sterling Publishing Co., Inc., 1997.
Mathemagic by Raymond Blum, Sterling Publishing Co., Inc., 1992.
Kids' Book of Secret Codes, Signals, and Ciphers by E. A. Grant, Running Press, 1989.
The Seasons Sewn: A Year in Patchwork by Ann Whitford Paul, Browndeer Press, 1996.

Looking Ahead: Seventh Grade

Next year, your child will:

- increase skills with percents, decimals, and fractions.
- compute with fractions, decimals, and positive and negative numbers.
- continue to write algebraic expressions for simple situations.
- solve equations.
- use formulas to solve problems.

Thank you for your support this year. Have fun continuing your child's mathematical experiences throughout the summer!

Best wishes for an enjoyable vacation.

Project Masters

Name Date Time

PROJECT 2 **Modeling Distances in the Solar System** *cont.*

You probably need a different scale for distances of the planets from the Sun than for diameters of the planets. Discuss with your class what scale to use. Two important points to consider:

- How much space do you have to display the model? ____________
- How much space will be taken up by the Sun? ____________

Deciding on a Scale

8. In the scale we are using for distance, ____________ represents ____________.
9. In the model, my Planet Team's planet should be placed ____________ (how far?) from the Sun.

Building the Model

- First, the class should decide which part of the Sun to measure from.
- Then, working in teams, use a tape measure to place your planet the correct distance from the Sun.
- Finally, fill in as much information as you can on your team's Planet Information Label (*Math Masters*, p. 363). You will fill in the missing information later.

You can add details to the model by including some of the features of the solar system described on *Math Masters*, page 362. Record these details on the lines below.

Details/features of the solar system our team will add to the model:

____

____

____

____

Name Date Time

PROJECT 7 **Testing Paper Airplane Designs, Part 1**

Student-Designed Airplanes

1. Complete the following after you conduct test flights of student-designed paper airplanes.
   - a. Number of models tested ____________
   - b. Minimum distance ____________ feet
   - c. Median distance ____________ feet
   - d. Maximum distance ____________ feet

Schultz-Designed Airplanes

2. Complete the following after you conduct test flights of Schultz-designed airplanes.
   - a. Number of models tested ____________
   - b. Minimum distance ____________ feet
   - c. Median distance ____________ feet
   - d. Maximum distance ____________ feet

3. Select the 3 student-designed and 3 Schultz-designed airplanes that flew the farthest. Test these 6 planes again. Record the results in the table below.

Name of Designer	Distance	Rank (1st to 6th)
Student	feet	
Student	feet	
Student	feet	
Louis Schultz	feet	
Louis Schultz	feet	
Louis Schultz	feet	

Name Date Time

PROJECT 1 The Solar System

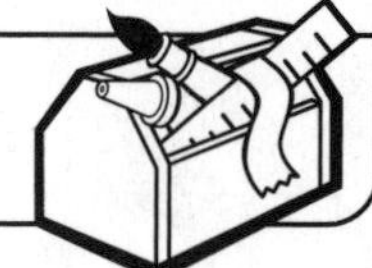

Our solar system consists of the Sun, 9 planets and their moons, and a large number of asteroids, comets, and meteors. The Sun is at the center of the solar system.

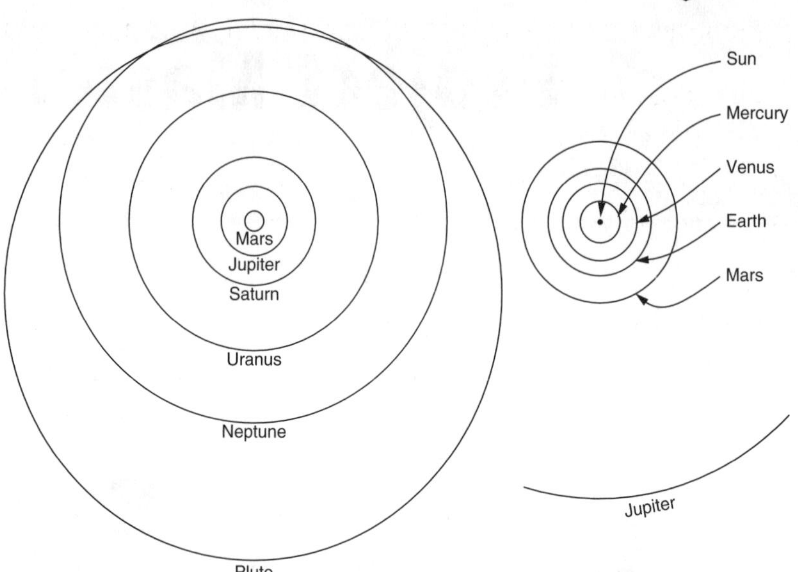

Astronomers estimate that the solar system formed between 4 and 5 billion years ago. A huge, slowly rotating cloud of particles pulled together to form the Sun. Planets, moons, and other objects formed from particles in the outer portion of the cloud.

From time to time, you can see Mercury, Venus, Mars, Jupiter, and Saturn in the night sky. For most of history, people thought these were the only planets other than Earth. Then, using increasingly powerful telescopes, astronomers spotted Uranus in 1781, Neptune in 1846, and Pluto in 1930. Astronomers might never have found Neptune and Pluto if they had not been guided by mathematical predictions that told them where to aim their telescopes.

The 4 planets closest to the Sun—Mercury, Venus, Earth, and Mars—are called the rocky dwarfs because they are small and made mostly of rock. Jupiter, Saturn, Uranus, and Neptune are huge balls of frozen gas and liquid with small solid cores. These planets are called the gas giants or Jovian planets. They have multiple moons and rings.

Knowledge of the solar system is growing rapidly. On July 29, 2005, Dr. Mike Brown and his colleagues announced the discovery of a tenth planet beyond Pluto. At that time, the planet's temporary name was 2003 UB313. The planet's permanent name, as well as information about its size and surface temperature, became available after this edition of *Everyday Mathematics* had already gone to press.

Name Date Time

Movement of the Planets

Today most people know that Earth revolves around the Sun.

Long ago, almost everyone believed that the entire universe revolved around Earth. That idea certainly corresponds to what we can see with our own eyes: Every day the Sun rises in the east and sets in the west. At night, the Moon, planets, and stars move steadily through the sky.

In the second century A.D., an Egyptian mathematician and astronomer named Claudius Ptolemaeus (Ptolemy) published a book called the *Almagest.* In it, he gave a mathematical description of the universe as **geocentric,** or Earth-centered. Ptolemy's theory of how the Sun, planets, and stars move through space was widely accepted for the next 1,400 years.

In 1543, the Polish astronomer Nicolaus Copernicus (1473–1543) described a different view of the universe in his book *On the Revolutions of the Celestial Spheres.* After 30 years of research, he concluded that the planets—including Earth—have a **heliocentric** movement: They actually revolve around the Sun. The apparent motion of heavenly bodies through the sky is due primarily to Earth's rotation. This idea had been proposed by Greek scholars as early as the third century B.C. but had been ignored.

Copernicus's theory did not perfectly explain the movement of all the planets that were known at the time, but it led scientists in a new direction. Astronomer Tycho Brahe (1546–1601) gathered large quantities of data in a search for the true laws of planetary motion. Although Brahe died before he could complete his theory, his assistant, Johannes Kepler (1571–1630) developed mathematical models that correctly explained the observed motions of the planets. Kepler showed that planetary orbits are elliptical (oval) rather than circular. He also demonstrated that the Moon is a satellite of Earth.

In *Everyday Mathematics,* you have developed mathematical models to describe situations, represent relationships, and solve problems. These models include number sentences and graphs. You are solving problems that are simpler than Kepler's, but you are following the same approach that he used. You can read more about problem solving on pages 258 and 259 in the *Student Reference Book.*

Name Date Time

Planet Data

The tables on this page and the next provide estimates of diameters and distances from the Sun, rounded to 2 **significant digits.** The data are presented in U.S. customary units and metric units. In your explorations, you can choose which units to work with.

The **diameter** of a **sphere** is the length of a line segment that passes through the center of the sphere and has **endpoints** on the sphere. Planets are not quite spheres, so an average diameter is used in the data tables.

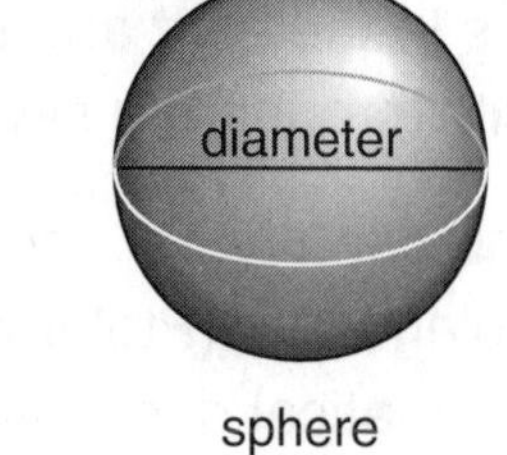

sphere

Planets move around the Sun in orbits that are **ellipses** (ovals), somewhat affected by the gravitational pulls of other planets. Estimates of average distances from the Sun are accurate enough for anything done in the *Sixth Grade Everyday Mathematics* solar system projects.

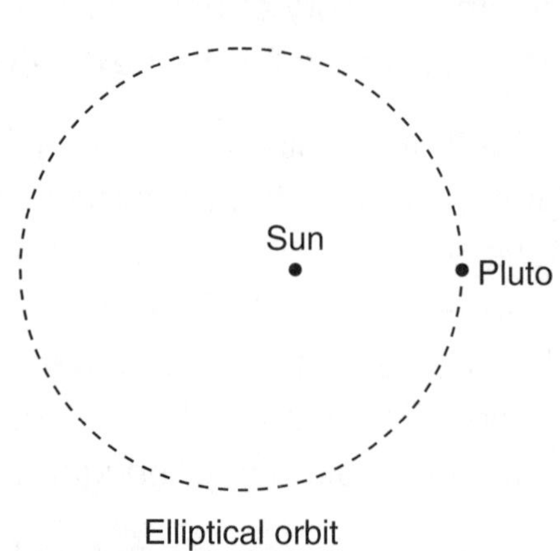

Elliptical orbit

Solar System Data Table 1

Planet	Average Diameter (Miles)	Average Distance from the Sun (Miles)	Surface Temperature (Degrees Fahrenheit)
Mercury	3,000	36,000,000 or $3.6 * 10^7$	−290 to 800
Venus	7,500	67,000,000 or $6.7 * 10^7$	850 to 910
Earth	7,900	93,000,000 or $9.3 * 10^7$	−130 to 140
Mars	4,200	140,000,000 or $1.4 * 10^8$	−190 to 80
Jupiter	89,000	480,000,000 or $4.8 * 10^8$	−240 to −150
Saturn	75,000	890,000,000 or $8.9 * 10^8$	−290 to −150
Uranus	32,000	1,800,000,000 or $1.8 * 10^9$	−350
Neptune	31,000	2,800,000,000 or $2.8 * 10^9$	−350
Pluto	1,400	3,700,000,000 or $3.7 * 10^9$	−350
Sun	860,000		5,400 to 36,000,000

Name Date Time

Planet Data *continued*

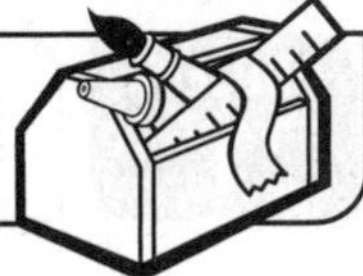

Solar System Data Table 2

Planet	Average Diameter (Kilometers)	Average Distance from the Sun (Kilometers)	Surface Temperature (Degrees Celsius)
Mercury	4,900	58,000,000 or $5.8 * 10^7$	−180 to 430
Venus	12,000	110,000,000 or $1.1 * 10^8$	450 to 490
Earth	13,000	150,000,000 or $1.5 * 10^8$	−90 to 60
Mars	6,800	230,000,000 or $2.3 * 10^8$	−90 to −10
Jupiter	140,000	780,000,000 or $7.8 * 10^8$	−150 to −100
Saturn	120,000	1,400,000,000 or $1.4 * 10^9$	−180 to −160
Uranus	51,000	2,900,000,000 or $2.9 * 10^9$	−200
Neptune	49,000	4,500,000,000 or $4.5 * 10^9$	−190
Pluto	2,300	5,900,000,000 or $5.9 * 10^9$	−230 to −220
Sun	1,400,000		3,000 to 20,000,000

Using Estimates and Comparing Big Numbers

Here is one strategy for comparing big numbers.

Problem Compare the distance of Earth from the Sun with the distances of Mars and Neptune from the Sun.

Think
Earth to Sun 150,000,000 km, or 150 million km
Mars to Sun 230,000,000 km, or 230 million km
Neptune to Sun 4,500,000,000 km, or 4,500 million km

Ask *About how many 150 millions are in 230 million? In 4,500 million?*

Another strategy is to compare distances in scientific notation. It is important to compare like powers of 10. Write equivalent names to make the division easier.

Think
Earth to Sun $1.5 * 10^8$ km, or $15 * 10^7$ km
Mars to Sun $2.3 * 10^8$ km, or $23 * 10^7$ km
Neptune to Sun $4.5 * 10^9$ km, or $45 * 10^8$ km, or $450 * 10^7$ km

Ask *About how many 15s are in 23? In 450?*

Name Date Time

Life on Other Planets

The unmanned Mariner 4 spacecraft flew past Mars on July 14, 1965, collecting the first close-up photographs of an inner solar-system planet. Since those first flyby images were taken, we have asked whether life ever arose on Mars. Life, as we understand it, requires water. Scientists believe that if life ever evolved on Mars, it did so in the presence of a long-standing supply of water.

Over 30 years ago, NASA launched two identical spacecraft (*Vikings 1 and 2*), each consisting of an orbiter and a lander. Each orbiter-lander pair flew together and entered Mars' orbit. After taking pictures, the orbiters separated and descended to the planet's surface for the purpose of data collection. The landers conducted three experiments designed to look for possible signs of life. While the experiments revealed unexpected chemical activity in the Martian soil, they provided no clear evidence for the presence of living microorganisms near the landing sites.

Exploration missions of the past decade have landed robotic rovers with far greater mobility than that of the *Viking* landers. The rovers carry a sophisticated set of instruments that collect and analyze surface samples. By studying rock and soil samples, scientists hope to determine whether water was involved in soil and rock formation and thereby identify areas on the planet that may have been favorable for life in the past.

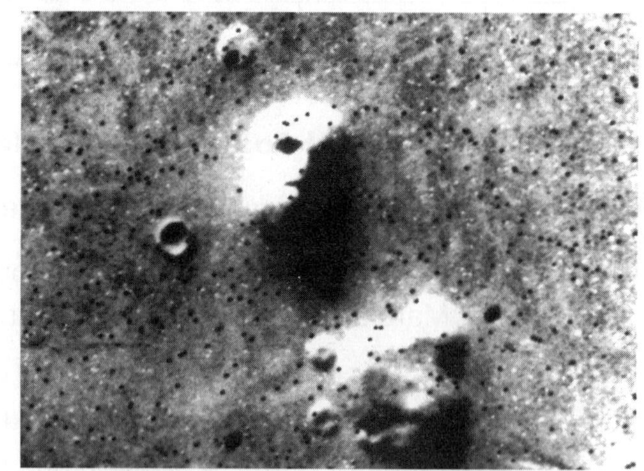

In 1976, the *Viking I* orbiter took the first photographs of the Cydonia region of Mars, showing an unusual mountain that seemed to resemble a face. Some people suggested that the face was a monument built by an extraterrestrial civilization. But scientists believed this resemblance was accidental, partly due to the angle of light at the time the photo was taken and partly due to the complicated image enhancement used to process the data that was available at the time.

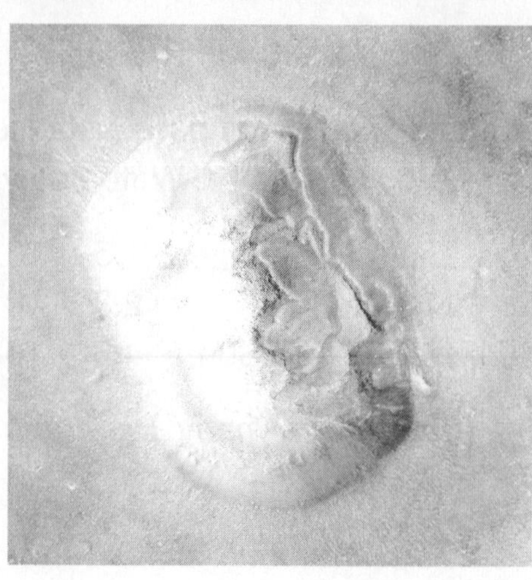

On May 28, 2001 the Mars Global Surveyor took a new photo of this feature. Although the landform has the same general shape as in earlier photographs, details provided by the higher-resolution photograph reveal the "face" to be a naturally formed hill.

Name Date Time

PROJECT 1

What Can You Learn from the Data Tables?

1. Look at the data on planet diameters on *Math Masters,* pages 352 and 353.

Describe any patterns you see. ______________________________

____

____

____

____

List some ideas or questions that the data suggest to you. ______________________________

____

____

____

____

____

2. Look at the data on average distance from the Sun. Are the planets evenly spaced?

____

Describe any patterns you see in the average-distance data. ______________________________

____

____

____

____

____

3. Look at the data on surface temperature. Is it likely that there is life on other planets today? Why or why not? ______________________________

____

____

For more information about life on other planets, read *Math Masters,* page 354.

Name Date Time

Data Analysis

One way to explore and understand a data table is to make another table that compares the same information to a common measure. Use Solar System Data Table 1 or 2 (pages 352 and 353) to fill in the table as described below.

1. Compare the diameters of other planets with the diameter of Earth. Use estimates. For example, the diameter of Mars (4,200 miles, or 6,800 kilometers) is about $\frac{1}{2}$ the diameter of Earth (7,900 miles or 13,000 kilometers).

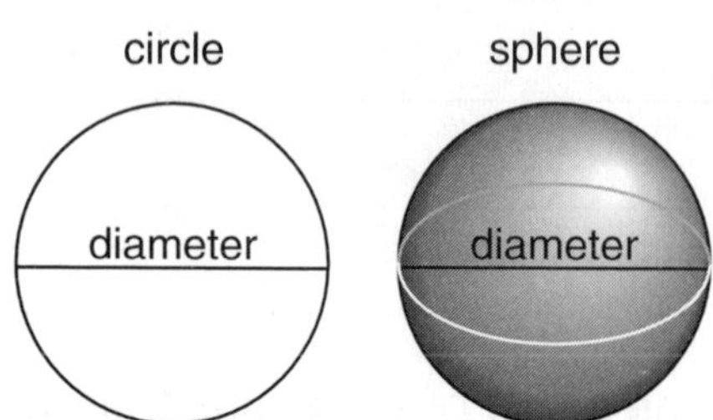

2. The average distance from Earth to the Sun is called one **astronomical unit.** This unit is important for measuring distances in the solar system.

   Compare each planet's distance from the Sun to Earth's distance from the Sun. Use estimates. For example, the distance of Jupiter from the Sun (480 million miles, or 780 million kilometers) is about 5 times the distance of Earth from the Sun (93 million miles, or 150 million kilometers).

How Do Other Planets Compare to Earth?

Planet	Diameter Compared to Earth's Diameter	Distance from Sun Compared to Earth's Distance from Sun
Mercury	About $\frac{3}{8}$ or $\frac{1}{2}$	About $\frac{1}{3}$
Venus		
Mars		
Jupiter		
Saturn		
Uranus		
Neptune		
Pluto		

Name Date Time

PROJECT 2

Starting the Model

1. Choose a Measurement System

In order to build a scale model of the solar system, the class needs to make some decisions.

◆ Will we measure in **U.S. customary units** (in. and mi) or in **metric units** (cm and km)?

Astronomers and astronauts use metric units. On the other hand, U.S. customary units may make the model easier to relate to personal references. For example, if the diameter of Earth is 1 inch (about the length of a toe), then the Sun's diameter is about 9 feet, almost twice the height of most sixth-grade students. Discuss the advantages and disadvantages of each measurement system. Then make a class decision.

We will use ______________________ units.

2. Choose a Scale

Now the class needs to make another decision.

◆ Which scale will we use to model the relative sizes of the Sun and the planets?

The **scale** tells how many units in the real solar system are represented by 1 unit in the scale model of the solar system. *Suggestions:*

◆ **U.S. Customary Units** You might let 1 inch represent 8,000 miles (1 inch to 8,000 miles, or 1 in.:8,000 mi). 8,000 miles is approximately the diameter of Earth. If the diameter of Earth is represented by 1 inch, about how many inches would represent the diameter of Jupiter?

____

◆ **Metric Units** You might let 1 centimeter represent 5,000 kilometers (1 centimeter to 5,000 kilometers, or 1 cm:5,000 km). These are easy numbers to work with and to remember.

We will use this scale for size: ______________________

3. Divide into Planet Teams

The class should divide into 8 Planet Teams, a team for each planet except Earth.

My Planet Team will model this planet: ______________________

Name Date Time

PROJECT 2

Modeling the Sizes of Planets and the Sun

1. My Planet Team's planet is ______________________________.

2. Its average diameter is ______________________________.

   (Remember to give the diameter in the same system of units—metric or U.S. customary—that you will use to build the model.)

3. In our scale model of planet size, ____________________ represents ______________________________.

4. How can you use the scale to figure out how large your planet should be in the model? Discuss with your teammates and write your answer below.

   ____
   ____
   ____
   ____
   ____
   ____
   ____

5. What will be the diameter of your planet in the model? ____________________

6. a. What will be the diameter of the Sun in the model? ____________________

   b. How many feet or meters is this? ____________________

Name Date Time

Making a Scale Model of Your Planet

To make a 2-dimensional scale model of your planet, your Planet Team needs a pencil, ruler, scissors, tape, compass, and colored construction paper.

If possible, use the chart at the right to select the color(s) of paper for your planet.

Planet	Color
Mercury	Orange
Venus	Yellow
Earth	Blue, brown, green
Mars	Red
Jupiter	Yellow, red, brown, white
Saturn	Yellow
Uranus	Green
Neptune	Blue
Pluto	Yellow

1. Use a ruler to draw a line segment equal in length to the diameter your planet should have in the model. If you are modeling Jupiter or Saturn, you may need to tape 2 sheets of paper together.

2. Find the **midpoint** (middle) of this line segment and mark a dot there.

3. Use a compass to draw a circle. The center of the circle should be at the midpoint you marked. Put the point of the compass on the dot. Put the pencil on one endpoint of the line segment and draw the circle.

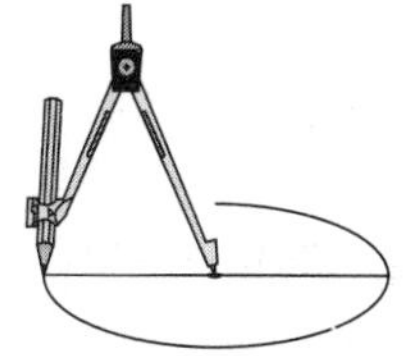

   If your compass is too small, tie a string around a pencil near the point. Hold the point of the pencil on one endpoint of the line segment. Pull the string tightly and hold it down at the dot (midpoint) on the line segment. Keeping the string tight, swing the pencil around to draw a circle.

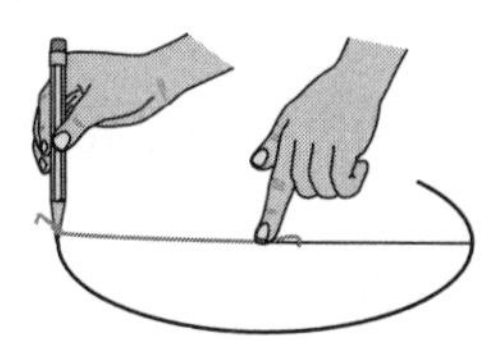

4. Cut out and label the circle.

5. Share your work with other Planet Teams.

Name Date Time

Modeling Distances in the Solar System

1. My Planet Team's planet is ______.

2. Its average distance from the Sun is ______.

3. Now that you have modeled the size of your planet, you need to figure out how far to place it from the Sun. How could you do this?

______

______

______

______

______

To model the distances between planets and the Sun, your class needs to make several decisions.

Finding a Scale

4. Can you use the same **scale** for distance that you used for size? This would provide an excellent picture of planetary sizes and distances but may not be possible. Why not? Discuss with your classmates.

______

______

5. If 1 inch represents 8,000 miles, how many inches from the Sun should Earth be placed? ______

6. How many feet is this? ______

7. Would a model of the entire solar system using this scale be possible anywhere in your school building? ______

Name _______________ Date _______________ Time _______________

Modeling Distances in the Solar System *cont.*

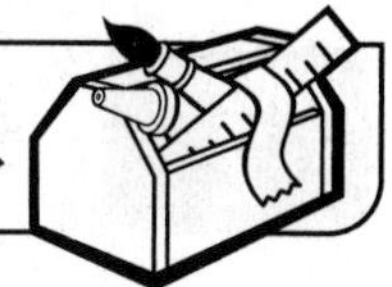

You probably need a different scale for distances of the planets from the Sun than for diameters of the planets. Discuss with your class what scale to use. Two important points to consider:

- How much space do you have to display the model? _______________
- How much space will be taken up by the Sun? _______________

Deciding on a Scale

8. In the scale we are using for distance, _______________ represents _______________.

9. In the model, my Planet Team's planet should be placed _______________ (how far?) from the Sun.

Building the Model

- First, the class should decide which part of the Sun to measure from.
- Then, working in teams, use a tape measure to place your planet the correct distance from the Sun.
- Finally, fill in as much information as you can on your team's Planet Information Label (*Math Masters,* p. 363). You will fill in the missing information later.

You can add details to the model by including some of the features of the solar system described on *Math Masters,* page 362. Record these details on the lines below.

Details/features of the solar system our team will add to the model:

____

____

____

____

Name Date Time

PROJECT 2 Some Solar System Features

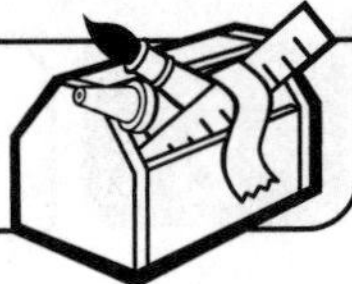

You can add more detail to the model by including some or all of the following celestial bodies.

Asteroids These are large pieces of rock that are too small to be considered planets. They range in size from big boulders to small mountains. Ceres, one of the largest asteroids, has a diameter of 580 miles, or 940 kilometers. Most asteroids are in what is known as the Asteroid Belt. The Asteroid Belt lies between Mars and Jupiter, about 180 to 270 million miles (290 to 430 million kilometers) from the Sun. To date, more than 18,000 asteroids have been identified in this region of the solar system. They can be represented in the model by small pen dots on pieces of paper or stick-on notes.

Moons Mars, Jupiter, Saturn, Uranus, and Neptune each have 2 or more moons. Mercury and Venus have no moons. The largest moons of Jupiter and Saturn are larger than Mercury and Pluto. Jupiter has at least 17 moons. Its 4 largest moons and their diameters are shown in the table.

Moon	Diameter
Ganymede	3,200 mi, or 5,300 km
Callisto	2,900 mi, or 4,800 km
Io	2,200 mi, or 3,600 km
Europa	1,900 mi, or 3,100 km

Saturn has at least 18 moons. The largest is Titan. Its diameter is 3,100 miles (5,200 kilometers). Earth's moon has a diameter of 2,200 miles (3,750 kilometers). It is slightly less than $\frac{1}{3}$ the size of Earth.

Rings Scientists have known for a long time that Saturn is surrounded by large, beautiful rings. When the *Voyager* spacecraft visited Jupiter, Neptune, and Uranus in the 1980s, scientists discovered that these planets also have rings, although they are considerably smaller than Saturn's. Saturn's rings are made up of frozen water particles ranging in size from tiny grains to blocks of ice that are 30 yards in diameter. The rings are only a few miles thick, but they extend from the planet for 50,000 miles (80,000 kilometers).

Name Date Time

PROJECT 2

Planet Information Label

Planet name: ________________

Average diameter: ________________

The planet's average diameter is about __?__ the diameter of Earth. ________________

Average distance from the Sun: ________________

How long would it take to fly from the planet to the Sun, assuming your rate of travel is 500 mph? ________________

Time sunlight takes to reach the planet: ________________

How long does it take the planet to orbit the Sun? ________________

Since 1776, this planet has orbited the Sun about __?__ times. ________________

What is the length of time it would take to reach the planet from Earth if you were to travel at a rate of 20,000 miles per hour? ________________

In our lifetime, humans might be able to travel 50,000 miles per hour in space. At this rate, how long would it take to reach the planet? ________________

Name Date Time

Conclusions

1. Suppose you had used the scale for planet diameters to also represent distances of planets from the Sun. Keep the same position for the Sun that you used in your model.

   a. How far away from your model Sun would Earth be? ____________

   b. Where in your school or town might Earth be located? ____________

   c. How far away from your model Sun would Neptune be? ____________

   d. Where in your school or town might Neptune be located? ____________

2. Suppose you had used the scale for distances of planets from the Sun to also represent the diameter of Earth.

   a. What would be the diameter of the model Earth? ____________

   b. If the model Earth were made with exactly that diameter, could you see it without a magnifying glass? (*Hint:* Pencil leads in some mechanical pencils are 0.5 mm, or about $\frac{2}{1,000}$ of an inch, thick.) ____________

3. Suppose you were explaining to someone how big the largest planet in the solar system is, compared to Earth.

   a. What would be an easy multiple to use? ____________

   b. What other comparison might you use to make the difference easier to understand (for example, the costs or sizes of two common objects)?

   ____

4. Similarly, suppose you were explaining how big the Sun is, compared to even the largest planet in the solar system.

   a. What would be an easy multiple to use? ____________

   b. What other comparison might you use to make the difference easier to understand?

   ____

5. Choose a fact you have learned about the solar system. Make up a question for a trivia game based on that fact.

   ____

Name Date Time

Travel Times between Earth and the Sun

Distances in the solar system are very large. For example, the average distance from Earth to the Sun is about 93,000,000 miles, or about 150,000,000 kilometers.

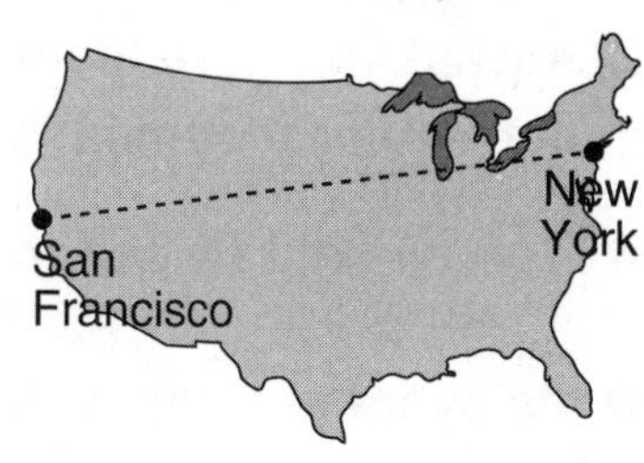

To understand distances in the solar system, it helps to compare them to distances you can understand more easily.

Distance from New York to San Francisco	about 3,000 miles (mi), or about 4,800 kilometers (km)
Time to fly by jet from New York to San Francisco	about 6 hours at 500 mi per hr, or about 6 hours at 800 km per hr
Speed of light	about 186,000 mi per sec, or about 298,000 km per sec

◆ To travel a distance equal to the distance from Earth to the Sun, about how many times would you need to cross the United States between New York and San Francisco?

About ______________ times

◆ If a plane flew at 500 miles per hour (800 kilometers per hour) without stopping, about how long would it take to travel the distance from Earth to the Sun?

About ______________ hours,

or ______________ days,

or ______________ years

◆ It takes sunlight about ______________ minutes to travel from the Sun to Earth.

Name Date Time

Estimate Travel Times

Use what you have learned about travel times between Earth and the Sun to make similar comparisons for your model planet.

- The planet I helped model is ______________.
- Its average distance from the Sun is ______________.
- This distance is equal to crossing the United States ______________ times.
- It would take about ______________ to fly this distance at 500 miles per hour.
- It takes sunlight about ______________ to reach this planet.

Add this information to your team's Planet Information Label.

Share your work with your classmates. Use their numbers to help you complete the following table.

Planet	Average Distance from Sun (Miles)	Number of Trips across U.S. to Equal Distance from Planet to Sun	Time to Fly the Distance from Planet to Sun (Years)	Time Sunlight Takes to Reach Planet (Minutes)
Mercury	36,000,000			
Venus	67,000,000			
Earth	93,000,000			
Mars	140,000,000			
Jupiter	480,000,000			
Saturn	890,000,000			
Uranus	1,800,000,000			
Neptune	2,800,000,000			
Pluto	3,700,000,000			

Name ______ Date ______ Time ______

Describe a Distance

1. The distance between Pluto and the Sun is very large. How could you describe this distance to help a friend understand it?

____

____

____

____

____

____

2. The **speed of light** is about 300,000,000 meters per second. At that rate, light can travel around the world about 7 times in 1 second.

a. Express the speed of light in scientific notation. ______________

b. Express the speed of light in centimeters per second.

The speed of light is about ______________ cm per second.

c. A **light-year** is the distance that light travels in 1 year. Explain how you would estimate the number of centimeters in a light-year.

____

____

____

____

____

____

____

____

Name Date Time

Spaceship Earth

To be a successful space traveler, you must be able to find your way back to Earth. This may not be easy. You do not feel it, but at this moment you are traveling through space at incredible speeds.

Earth spins around like a top. In 24 hours, it makes 1 complete **rotation.** At the equator, the distance around Earth is about 25,000 miles. In the middle of the United States, the distance is about 21,000 miles. This means that if you live in the middle of the United States, you travel about 21,000 miles every day.

21,000 miles
25,000 miles

At the same time Earth is rotating, it is moving in its orbit around the Sun. In 1 year, Earth makes 1 complete **revolution,** or trip, around the Sun. This trip is approximately 600,000,000 (or $6 * 10^8$) miles long.

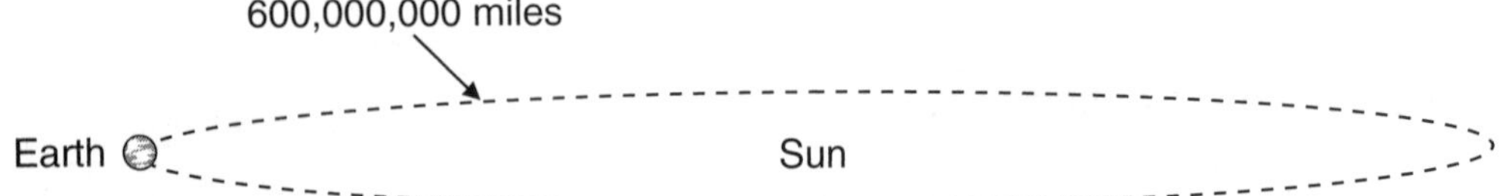

Movement of the Planets around the Sun

All the planets are in motion, rotating like tops and revolving around the Sun. Compared to Earth, some planets move fast, but others are quite slow. Understanding planetary motion is key for space travel. You must know where to aim the spaceship.

Solar System Data Table 3

Planet	Average Speed in Orbit: Miles per Earth Day	Time to Revolve Once around the Sun: Earth Days or Years	Time to Rotate Once: Earth Days or Hours
Mercury	2,600,000	88 days	59 days
Venus	1,900,000	223 days	243 days
Earth	1,600,000	365 days	24 hours
Mars	1,300,000	686 days	25 hours
Jupiter	700,000	12 years	10 hours
Saturn	520,000	29 years	11 hours
Uranus	360,000	84 years	16 hours
Neptune	290,000	165 years	18 hours
Pluto	250,000	249 years	6 days

Source: Richard Lewis. *The Illustrated Encyclopedia of the Universe,* Harmony Books, 1983.

Name Date Time

Rotating and Revolving with Earth

During 1 rotation of Earth, a person at the equator travels about 25,000 miles. The farther north of the equator a person is, the smaller the distance of rotation becomes.

City	Distance of One Rotation
Honolulu, HI	24,000 mi
Los Angeles, CA	21,000 mi
Philadelphia, PA	19,000 mi
Seattle, WA	17,000 mi
Anchorage, AK	13,000 mi

1. Estimate how many miles a person travels during 1 hour of rotation.

a. At the equator About ________ miles **b.** In Los Angeles About ________ miles

c. In Seattle About ________ miles **d.** In Anchorage About ________ miles

2. a. Estimate the distance of 1 rotation for your location. For example, if you live in Chicago—which is farther from the equator than Philadelphia but closer than Seattle—you might say 18,000 miles. About ______________ miles

b. How far have you rotated in the past hour? About ______________ miles

c. How far have you rotated in the past minute? About ______________ miles

3. Earth travels about 600,000,000 miles (in scientific notation: $6 * 10^8$) around the Sun in 1 year. Estimate how far Earth (with you on it) travels in its orbit around the Sun during various time periods. Complete the following statements.

a. In 1 month, Earth travels about ______________________________ miles.

b. In 1 day, Earth travels about ________________ miles.

c. In the past hour, Earth traveled about ________________ miles.

d. In the past minute, Earth traveled about ________________ miles.

Name Date Time

Movement of Planets around the Sun

Read the paragraph under Movement of the Planets around the Sun on *Math Masters,* page 368, and look at the information in Solar System Data Table 3. Then work with your Planet Team to complete the following.

1. Record some observations about the information in the table. For example, which planets rotate faster than Earth? About the same as Earth? Slower than Earth?

____

____

____

____

____

____

____

2. Since the Declaration of Independence was signed in 1776, about how many times has Earth revolved around the Sun? _______________

3. **a.** About how many times has your team's planet traveled around the Sun since 1776? _______________

   b. Share results with your classmates to complete the list below.

Approximate Number of Revolutions around the Sun Since 1776					
Mercury		Mars		Uranus	
Venus		Jupiter		Neptune	
Earth		Saturn		Pluto	

4. Use what you have learned to add information to your team's Planet Information Label.

Name Date Time

Minimum Distances

The constant movement of planets complicates space travel. Planets move at different speeds, so exact calculations are needed to figure out the directions spaceships should travel. Another challenge is that the distances between Earth and other planets are always changing.

Scientists use complex mathematical computer models to calculate the relationship of Earth to the other planets and to plot the data needed to send space probes to other planets. There are also some facts that we can use to make rough estimates of some things we might want to know for space travel.

All the planets except Pluto travel in nearly circular orbits, with the Sun at the center.

For all planets except Pluto, orbits are almost in the same plane. This means that when the planets pass each other on the same radius from the Sun, the minimum distance can be calculated from the information in the Solar System Data Tables on *Math Masters,* pages 352 and 353. This can be seen in the diagram below.

Earth revolves quickly around the Sun compared with all the planets except Mercury and Venus. This means that at least once every year, Earth and each of the outer planets line up on the same radius from the Sun, at the minimum distance. The times are predictable, too. It is harder to predict when Earth will line up with Mercury and Venus. (For Pluto the situation is even more difficult. You might want to take on the problem as a challenge, but it can't be done using only the information on these pages.)

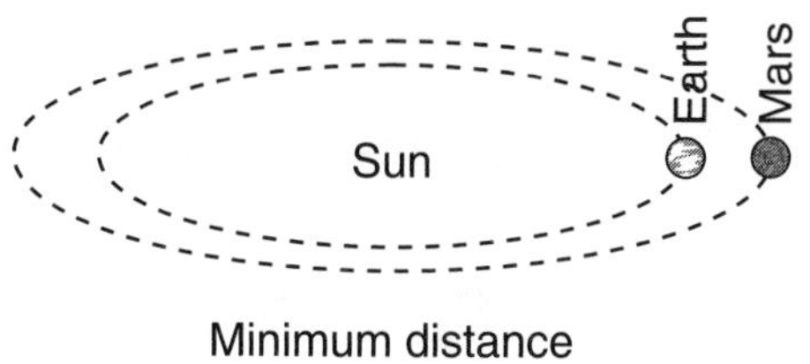

Minimum distance

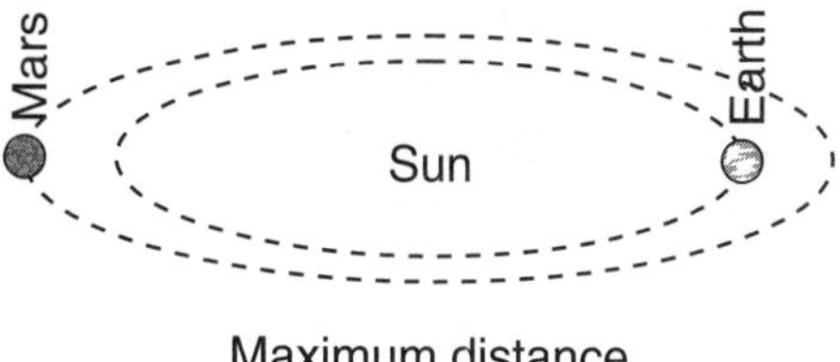

Maximum distance

Name Date Time

Minimum/Maximum Distances of Planets

Read Minimum Distances on *Math Masters,* page 371. Then work with your Planet Team, unless you are on the Pluto team. Your teacher will tell the Pluto team what to do.

Use the information on *Math Masters,* page 352 or 353 to estimate the distance between Earth and your planet when they are closest to each other. Round your estimate to 2 significant digits and write it in scientific notation. Share estimates with the other teams to fill in the estimated minimum distances in the table below. Then complete the Estimated Maximum Distance column. (*Hint:* Add Earth's distance from the Sun to each planet's distance from the Sun.)

Planet	Estimated Minimum Distance from Earth (mi or km)	Estimated Maximum Distance from Earth (mi or km)
Mercury		
Venus		
Mars		
Jupiter		
Saturn		
Uranus		
Neptune		

Summary

1. How would you describe to a friend the motion of Earth on its axis and around the Sun? ______________________

____

2. When you return from a space trip, will Earth be in the same place as when you left? ____________ Explain. ______________________

____

____

3. About how many times have you rotated and revolved since you were born?

Rotated: ____________ Revolved: ____________

Name ____________ Date ____________ Time ____________

Travel to Other Planets in Your Lifetime?

You have explored the solar system. You have learned about the size, distance, and motion of each planet. You are ready to offer an informed opinion on travel to other planets.

Fill in the basic facts about the planet you plan to visit. Then estimate the answers to the questions on the rest of this page and the next page. Work on your own, but consult with your teacher or classmates if you are unsure about what to do.

My planet ____________________

Here are some facts I know about this planet.
(This information is on *Math Masters,* pp. 352, 353, and 368.)

- Surface temperature ____________
- Average diameter ____________
- Average distance from the Sun ____________
- Earth days or years to orbit the Sun ____________

How Far Will You Need to Travel?

Estimated minimum distance from Earth
(See *Math Masters,* p. 372.) ____________

How Long Will It Take to Travel to Your Planet?

- Suppose a spaceship with people on it can travel at about 25,000 miles per hour. At this speed, how long will it take to reach your planet? ____________________
- If you could travel at 25,000 miles per hour, would it be possible to visit your planet and return to Earth in your lifetime? ____________________
- If not, how much faster would you need to travel? ____________ times faster
- At the faster speed, how long would it take to go to your planet and return? ____________________

Name Date Time

Travel to Other Planets in Your Lifetime? *cont.*

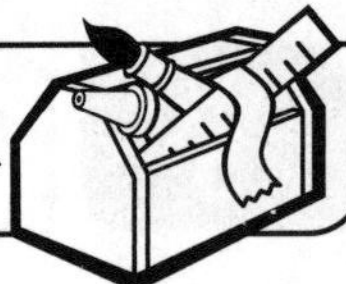

How long would your trip take if you could travel at

50,000 miles per hour? ________

100,000 miles per hour? ________

Write the results for your planet in the table below. Share your results with your classmates, and get information from them to complete as much of the table as possible.

Estimated Travel Time in Hours to the Planets			
Planet	**25,000 miles/hour**	**50,000 miles/hour**	**100,000 miles/hour**
Mercury			
Venus			
Mars			
Jupiter			
Saturn			
Uranus			
Neptune			
Pluto			

Try to complete the Planet Information Labels posted in the solar system model.

Name ________________ Date ________________ Time ________________

PROJECT 5

Travel to Other Planets in Your Lifetime? *cont.*

Conclusions

1. Do you think it might be possible to travel to your planet and return in your lifetime? Why or why not?

____

____

____

____

2. Which planets are most likely to be explored by humans? Why do you think so?

____

____

____

____

3. Some scientists believe that it makes sense to send people to explore other planets. Some scientists believe that other planets should be explored only with computers, cameras, and scientific instruments aboard space probes. Choose one of these positions, or one in between, and defend your choice.

____

____

____

____

4. If you were one of the first people to go on a trip to another planet, what items would you take to represent your beliefs and interests?

____

____

____

____

Name Date Time

PROJECT 5 Your Age on Another Planet

We use the time it takes Earth to make one trip around the Sun to keep track of our ages. When you tell someone how old you are, you are telling how many times Earth has traveled around the Sun since you were born.

1. a. Today my age is ______ years, ______ months, and ______ days.

b. I have been on Earth a total of about ____________ days.

Planet	Time to Orbit the Sun (Earth Days)
Mercury	88
Venus	223
Earth	365
Mars	686
Jupiter	4,380
Saturn	10,585
Uranus	30,660
Neptune	60,225
Pluto	90,885

Source: Universal Almanac

If you lived on a different planet, you would have a different age counted in the year of that planet. For example, on Venus, 1 year (the time it takes for Venus to travel around the Sun) equals 223 Earth days.

2. a. How many Earth days are there in a year on Mars? ________

b. How many Earth days are there in a year on Jupiter? ________

3. Estimate how old you would be today on the following planets by finding the number of times they have revolved around the Sun since you were born.

Venus ________ Mars ________ Jupiter ________

Name Date Time

PROJECT
6

Predicting Body Sizes

Anthropometry is the study of human body sizes and proportions. An **anthropometrist** gathers data on the size of the body and its components. Body-size data are useful to engineers, architects, industrial designers, interior designers, clothing manufacturers, and artists.

- Automotive engineers use body-size data to design vehicles and to set standards for infant and child safety seats.
- Architects take body-size data into account when designing stairs, planning safe kitchens and bathrooms, and providing access space for people who use wheelchairs.
- Clothing manufacturers use body-size data to create sewing patterns.

Not even identical twins are exactly alike. Body sizes and proportions differ depending on age, sex, and ethnic or racial attributes.

- There are no perfect rules that can be used to exactly predict one body measurement given another body measurement. For example, no rule can exactly predict a person's weight given the person's height, or height given arm length.
- There are imperfect rules and rules of thumb that can be useful in relating one body measurement to another.

This project investigates two such imperfect rules. The first rule is sometimes used to predict the height of an adult when the length of the adult's tibia is known. The **tibia** is the shinbone. When the measurements are in inches, the rule is

Height = (2.6 ∗ Length of Tibia) + 25.5

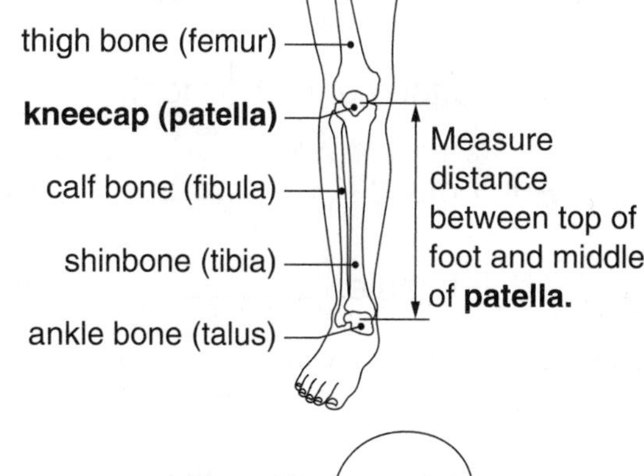
thigh bone (femur)
kneecap (patella)
calf bone (fibula)
shinbone (tibia)
ankle bone (talus)
Measure distance between top of foot and middle of patella.

The second rule relates the circumference of a person's neck to the circumference of the person's wrist.

Circumference of Neck = 2 ∗ Circumference of Wrist

As part of this project, you will collect some body-size data for an adult male, an adult female, and yourself.

Combine your data with data collected by your classmates. Then you will evaluate how helpful the rules are to predict body sizes for adults and sixth graders.

Measure around the neck.

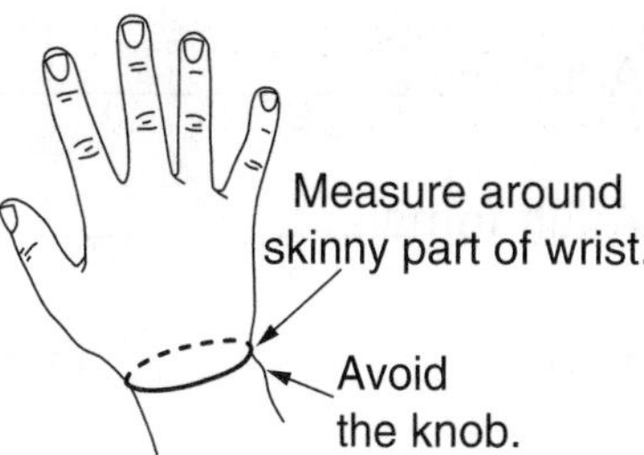
Measure around skinny part of wrist.
Avoid the knob.

Name Date Time

Anthropometry Project

Tibia and Height Data

1. The tibia is the shinbone. It is easiest to measure the tibia with a yardstick.

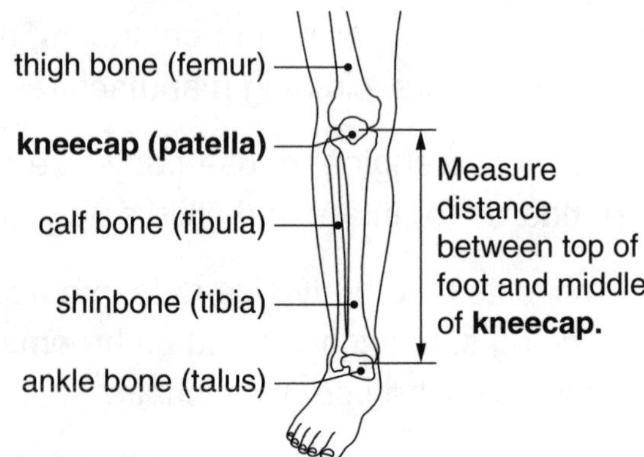

- ◆ Place the yardstick on the ankle so that one end is firmly against the top of the foot.
- ◆ The person being measured bends and straightens his or her knee while you feel the **patella (the kneecap)** and locate its top and bottom.
- ◆ The person being measured straightens the knee while you read the yardstick at the middle of the patella. Measure to the nearest $\frac{1}{4}$ inch.

You can also use a tape measure to measure the tibia. The person being measured should hold one end of the tape so you have a free hand to feel for the top and bottom of the patella.

Measure the tibia of two adults; then have one of them measure your tibia.

Tibia (to the nearest $\frac{1}{4}$ inch):

Adult male: _______________ inches

Adult female: _______________ inches

You: _______________ inches

2. Measure the height of the same two adults and your own height. Be sure that everyone removes her or his shoes before being measured.

Height (to the nearest $\frac{1}{2}$ inch):

Adult male: _______________ inches

Adult female: _______________ inches

You: _______________ inches

Name Date Time

PROJECT 6

Anthropometry Project *continued*

Neck and Wrist Data

Use a tape measure to measure both the neck and the wrist. If you don't have a flexible tape measure, use a piece of string and then measure the string length with a ruler.

3. Measure the neck as shown at the right. Be gentle!

Circumference of neck (to the nearest $\frac{1}{4}$ inch):

Adult male: ______________ inches

Adult female: ______________ inches

You: ______________ inches

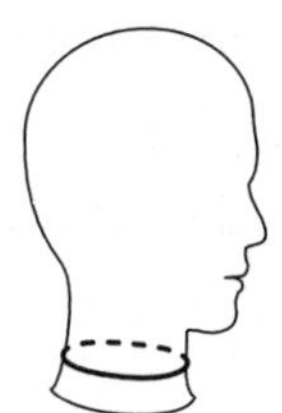

4. Measure the wrist around the thinnest part as shown at right.

Circumference of wrist (to the nearest $\frac{1}{8}$ inch):

Adult male: ______________ inches

Adult female: ______________ inches

You: ______________ inches

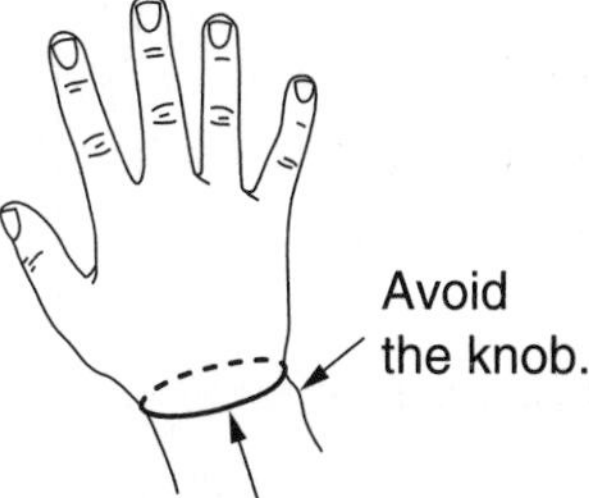
Avoid the knob.
Measure around skinny part of wrist.

Graph Your Data

Plot your data on 2 classroom graphs. These are the symbols to use:

- Open blue circles for adult male data
- Solid red circles for adult female data
- Solid black squares for data about you

Name Date Time

PROJECT 6 Anthropometry Project: Tibia and Height

1. The following rule is sometimes used to predict the height of an adult when the length of the adult's tibia is known. Measurements are in inches. (*Reminder:* Your tibia is your shinbone.)

$$\text{Height} = (2.6 * \text{Length of Tibia}) + 25.5$$

Do you think that this rule can exactly predict a person's height when the length of the person's tibia is known? ______________

Explain. ____

____

____

2. Use the rule in Problem 1 to complete the table. Find the predicted height for each tibia length. You may use your calculator.

Tibia Length	Height Predicted
11 in.	in.
14 in.	in.
19 in.	in.
$17\frac{1}{2}$ in.	in.

3. Your teacher will draw a **prediction line** on the grid where you plotted your research data. It passes through points that exactly follow the rule for predicting height given the tibia length. Use the prediction line to answer the following questions.

a. The predicted height for a person with a $15\frac{1}{4}$-inch tibia is about ________ inches.

b. The predicted height for a person with a ____________ -inch tibia is about 5 ft 0 in.

4. a. How closely does the prediction line approximate the actual data points for adult males? ____

Explain. ____

____

PROJECT 6

Anthropometry Project: Tibia and Height *cont.*

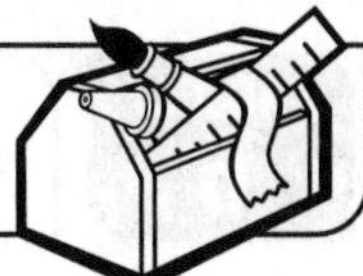

b. How closely does the prediction line approximate the actual data points for adult females? Explain.

____

____

____

____

c. How closely does the prediction line approximate the actual data points for students in your class? Explain.

____

____

____

____

5. Scientists can use a single bone from a human skeleton to estimate the height of an adult who lived many centuries ago. If they have a tibia, they can use the rule:

$$\text{Height} = (2.6 * \text{Length of Tibia}) + 25.5$$

a. The skeleton of a Neanderthal man who lived about 40,000 years ago contained a tibia about $14\frac{3}{4}$ inches long. Estimate the man's height. ________ in.

b. The tibia of a partial skeleton of a 20,000-year-old adult was reconstructed and found to be about $12\frac{1}{2}$ inches long. Estimate the person's height. ________ in.

6. Paul measured his baby sister's tibia (4 inches long) and then used the rule to estimate her height. "That's crazy!" said Paul when he saw the result.

a. What was Paul's estimate of his baby sister's height? ________ in.

b. Why did he say that the estimate was "crazy"? ________________________

____

Name Date Time

Anthropometry Project: Neck and Wrist

Use the neck and wrist data that you and your classmates collected on the graph posted in the classroom to answer the following questions about the wrist-to-neck rule.

Circumference of Neck =
2 ∗ Circumference of Wrist

1. How closely does the prediction line approximate the actual data points

for adult males? ____________________

for adult females? ____________________

for sixth graders? ____________________

The following passage is from *Gulliver's Travels* by Jonathan Swift. The setting is Lilliput, a country where the people are only 6 inches high.

"Two hundred seamstresses were employed to make me shirts … . The seamstresses took my measure as I lay on the ground, one standing at my neck, and another at my mid leg, with a strong cord extended, that each held by the end, while the third measured the length of the cord with a rule of an inch long. Then they measured my right thumb and desired no more; *for by a mathematical computation, that twice round the thumb is once round the wrist, and so on to the neck and the waist,* and by the help of my old shirt, which I displayed on the ground before them for a pattern, they fitted me exactly."

This passage provides three rules:

- Circumference of Wrist = 2 ∗ Circumference of Thumb
- Circumference of Neck = 2 ∗ Circumference of Wrist
- Circumference of Waist = 2 ∗ Circumference of Neck

2. Based on the data you and your classmates collected, how well do you think Gulliver's new clothes fit? Explain.

____

____

____

____

Name Date Time

PROJECT 6

Height-and-Tibia or Neck-and-Wrist Grid

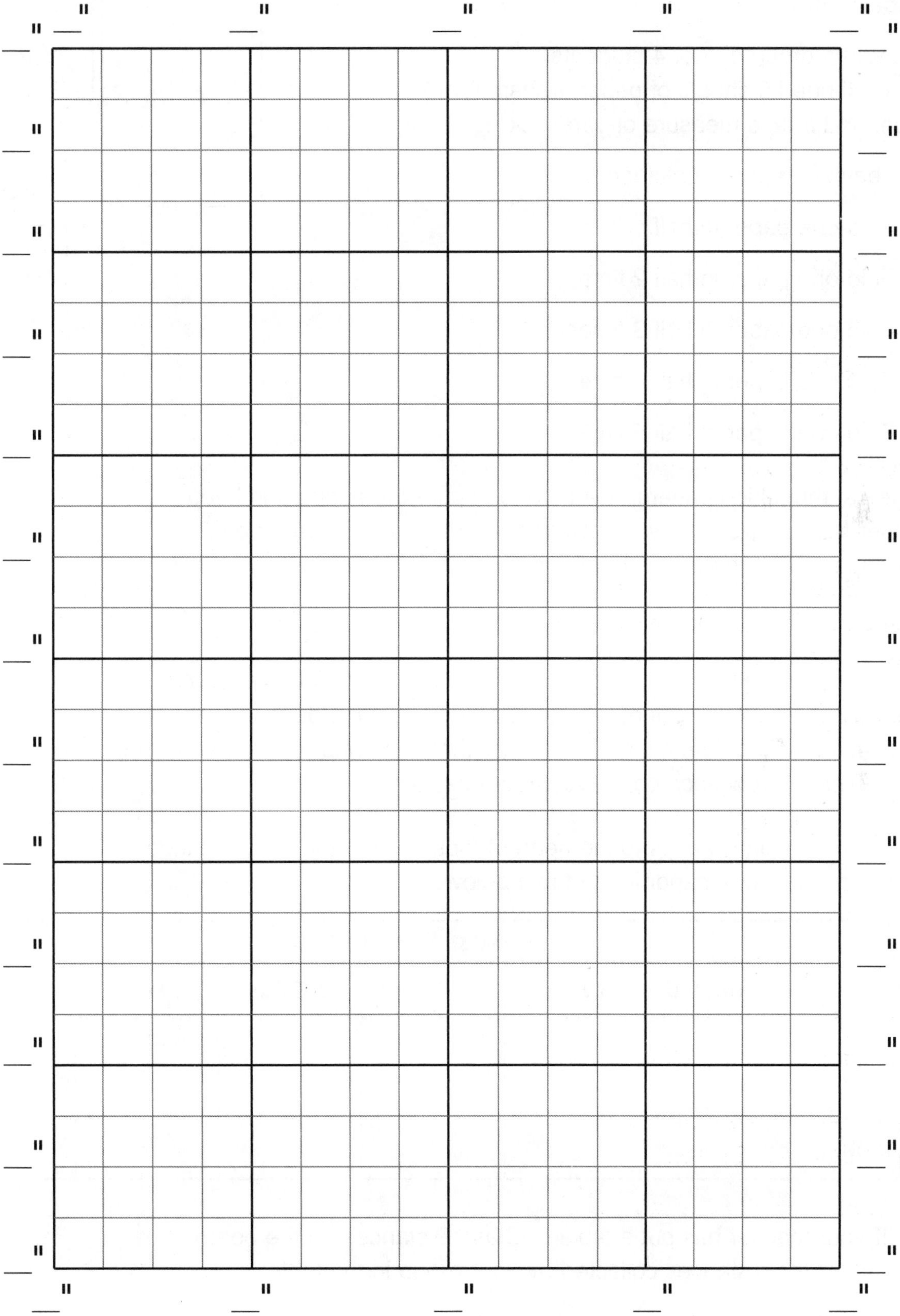

Name Date Time

How Far Can You Throw a Sheet of Paper?

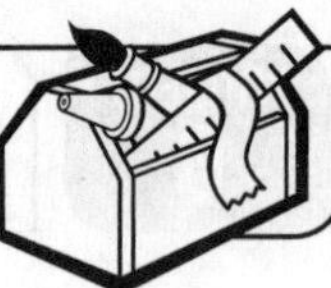

1. Paper Folding

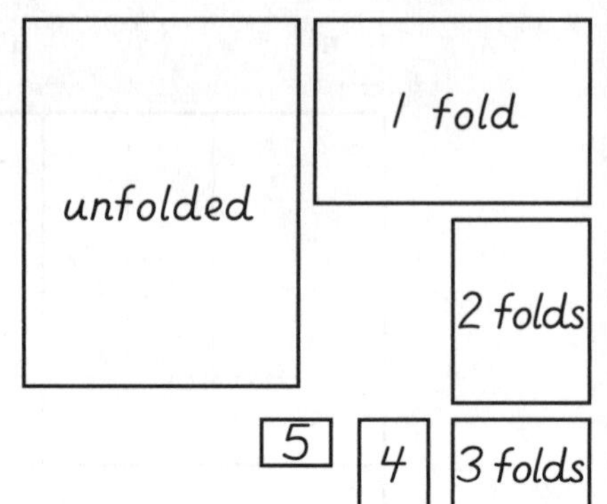

Work in a group of 3 or 4 students.
You will need 6 sheets of paper, transparent tape, and a tape measure or yardstick.

- Leave one paper unfolded.
- Fold one paper in half.
- Fold one paper in half 2 times.
- Fold one paper in half 3 times.
- Fold one paper in half 4 times.
- Fold one paper in half 5 times.

For each of the folded papers, use tape to secure the edges and keep the paper from unfolding. *Use no more than 3 inches of tape* for each folded paper. Write the number of folds on each folded paper.

2. Distance Testing

Agree on a baseline from which to throw each paper. Throw each paper (including the unfolded one) 3 times. Don't worry if the paper hits the floor, ceiling, or walls before it lands. You may throw the paper in any way you want. Try to throw each paper as far as possible.

a. Measure all distances to the nearest foot. Record the best distance for each kind of paper in the table below.

Group Distances

	Unfolded	1 Fold	2 Folds	3 Folds	4 Folds	5 Folds
Distance (to the nearest foot)						

b. If your teacher has put a table of Class Distances on the board, record the distances collected by your group in the table.

Name Date Time

How Far Can You Throw a Sheet of Paper? *cont.*

3. Use the data in the completed table of Group Distances to complete the table below.

Landmarks for Class Distances						
Landmark	**Unfolded**	**1 Fold**	**2 Folds**	**3 Folds**	**4 Folds**	**5 Folds**
Maximum						
Median						
Minimum						

4. Which paper(s) consistently traveled the longest distance? ____________

The shortest distance? ____________

How do you think the surface area of the paper, its shape, the method of throwing, and other factors affected how far the paper traveled?

____

____

____

____

____

____

5. Generations of students, much to the dismay of generations of teachers, have perfected a way of using the air to throw a sheet of paper a great distance. Can you describe how they do it?

____

____

____

____

____

____

How Far Can You Throw a Sheet of Paper? *cont.*

6. Graphing the Test Data

Use the results in the Landmarks for Class Distances table on *Math Masters,* page 385 to make a bar graph.

The graph should have 6 bars. Draw a bar for unfolded paper, a bar for 1 fold, a bar for 2 folds, and so on.

The height of each bar should be the maximum distance thrown. Mark the median and minimum distances on each bar as shown at the right.

Example

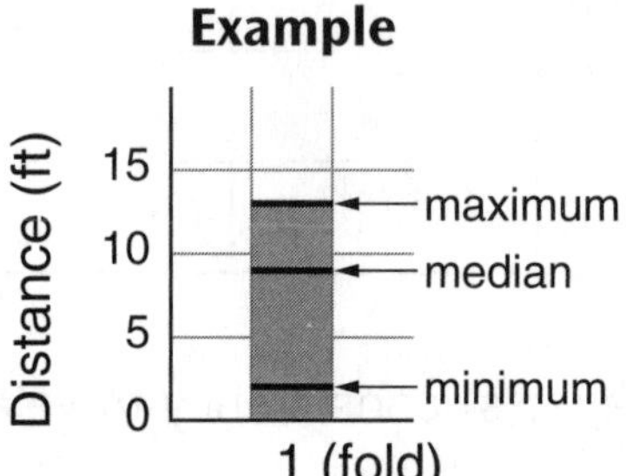

Landmarks for Class Distances

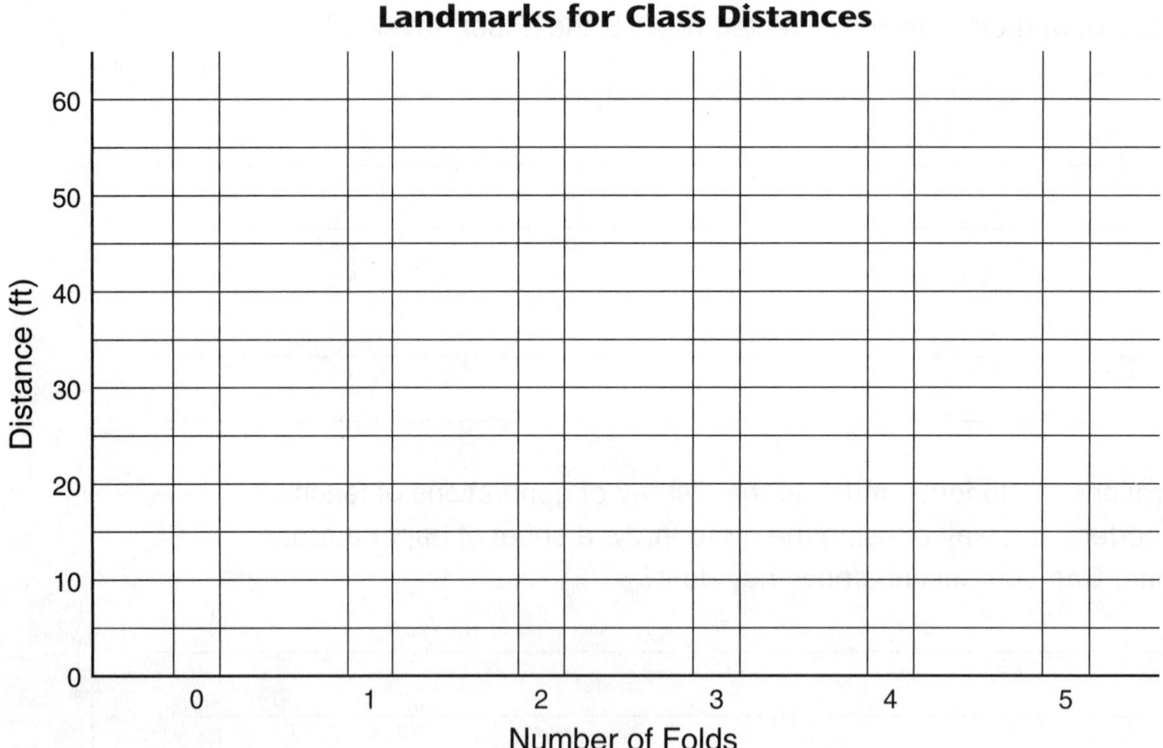

Name Date Time

PROJECT 7

Build a Paper Airplane

Design Objective To produce a paper airplane that will fly the greatest possible distance.

Rules

1. Your paper airplane design must be original.

2. Use $8\frac{1}{2}$"-by-11" paper or smaller. The paper must be of normal thickness. Do not use construction paper or card stock. You may construct your paper airplane out of this page, if you wish.

3. Assemble the plane only by folding, cutting, and taping. Do not use more than 3 inches of tape. You may cut the 3 inches of tape into any number of smaller pieces. Do not use glue or other adhesives, string, paper clips, or other objects.

You may need to try several different designs before you find a design that you believe will fly the greatest possible distance.

Good luck!

Name ____________ Date ____________ Time ____________

Testing Paper Airplane Designs, Part 1

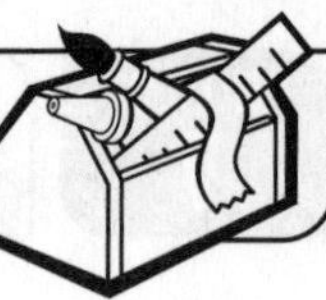

Student-Designed Airplanes

1. Complete the following after you conduct test flights of student-designed paper airplanes.

a. Number of models tested ____________

b. Minimum distance ____________ feet

c. Median distance ____________ feet

d. Maximum distance ____________ feet

Schultz-Designed Airplanes

2. Complete the following after you conduct test flights of Schultz-designed airplanes.

a. Number of models tested ____________

b. Minimum distance ____________ feet

c. Median distance ____________ feet

d. Maximum distance ____________ feet

3. Select the 3 student-designed and 3 Schultz-designed airplanes that flew the farthest. Test these 6 planes again. Record the results in the table below.

Name of Designer	Distance	Rank (1st to 6th)
Student	feet	
Student	feet	
Student	feet	
Louis Schultz	feet	
Louis Schultz	feet	
Louis Schultz	feet	

Name Date Time

First International Paper Airplane Competition

The First International Paper Airplane Competition was held during the winter of 1966–67 and was sponsored by *Scientific American* magazine. The 11,851 entries (about 5,000 from children), from 28 different countries, were original designs for paper airplanes. They were entered into one of the following categories:

- Duration aloft (The winning designs flew for 9.9 and 10.2 seconds.)
- Distance flown (The winning designs flew 58 feet, 2 inches and 91 feet, 6 inches.)
- Aerobatics (stunts performed in flight)
- Origami (the traditional Japanese art or technique of folding paper into a variety of decorative or representational forms)

The Leonardo

Contestants were permitted to use paper of any weight and size. The smallest entry received, entered in the distance category, measured 0.08 inch by 0.00003 inch. However, this entry was found to be made of foil, not paper. The largest entry received, also entered in the distance category, was 11 feet long. It flew 2 times its length when tested.

Scientific American awarded a winner's trophy to two designers, a nonprofessional and a professional, in each category. Nonprofessionals were people not professionally involved in air travel. Professionals were "people employed in the air travel business, people who build non-paper airplanes, and people who subscribe to *Scientific American* because they fly so much." The winners received a trophy called *The Leonardo,* named after Leonardo da Vinci (1452–1519), whom *Scientific American* refers to as the Patron Saint of Paper Airplanes.

Self-portrait of Leonardo da Vinci done in red chalk

Da Vinci, known for many accomplishments in the fields of painting and sculpture, was also an architect, engineer, and inventive builder. Studying the flight of birds, da Vinci believed that it would be possible to build a flying apparatus that would enable humans to soar through the air. He designed several wing-flapping machines, suggested the use of rotating wings similar to those of the modern helicopter, and invented the air screw, which is similar to the modern propeller.

More information about the First International Paper Airplane Competition, as well as templates and directions for making each of the winning designs, can be found in *The Great International Paper Airplane Book,* by Jerry Mander, George Dippel, and Howard Gossage (Simon and Schuster, 1971).

Name Date Time

A Winning Paper Airplane Design

The design plan shown below was submitted by Louis Schultz, an engineer. Schultz's paper airplane flew 58 feet, 2 inches and was a winner in the distance category for nonprofessionals. The professional winner in the distance category was Robert Meuser. His paper airplane flew 91 feet, 6 inches.

1. Follow the directions below to make an accurate copy of the design plan on an $8\frac{1}{2}$"-by-11" sheet of paper.

a. Use a ruler to find the midpoints at the top and bottom of the paper. Mark these points. Draw a center line connecting the midpoints to match the subsequent labels.

b. Mark 2 points that are $\frac{1}{4}$ inch away from the midpoint at the top of the paper.

c. Use a protractor to make two 45° angles as shown. Mark them with dashed lines.

d. Use a protractor to make two 82° angles as shown. Mark them with dashed lines.

Louis Schultz's Paper Airplane Design Plan

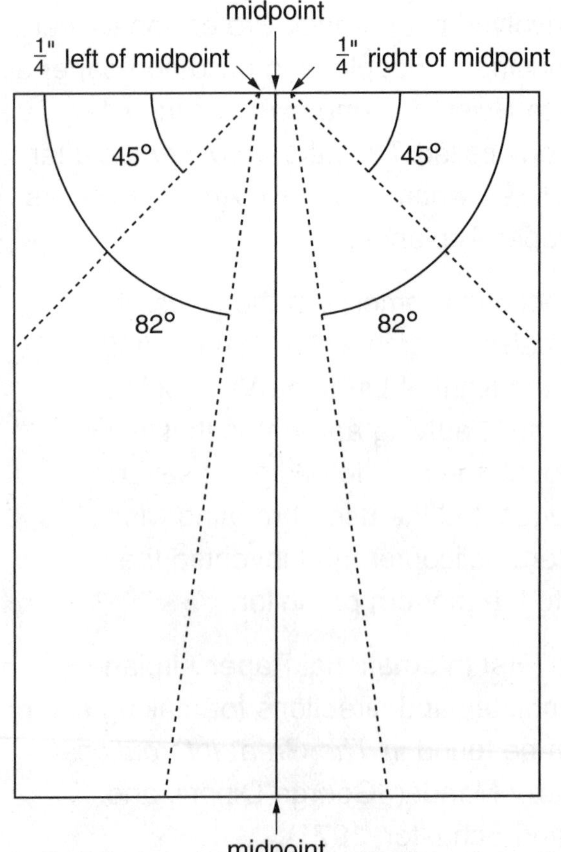

Name Date Time

A Winning Paper Airplane Design *cont.*

2. Assemble the paper airplane as shown below. Be very careful to make precise folds. Make the folds on a table. When making a fold, first press down on the paper with your finger. Then go over this fold with a pen or a ruler on its side. It is important that you *do not* use your fingernails to make folds. (Using your fingernail causes more than one fold to be made in a small area. This fold will move as you attempt to make the rest of the plane.)

a. Fold the paper back and forth along the center line to get a sharp crease. Then unfold.

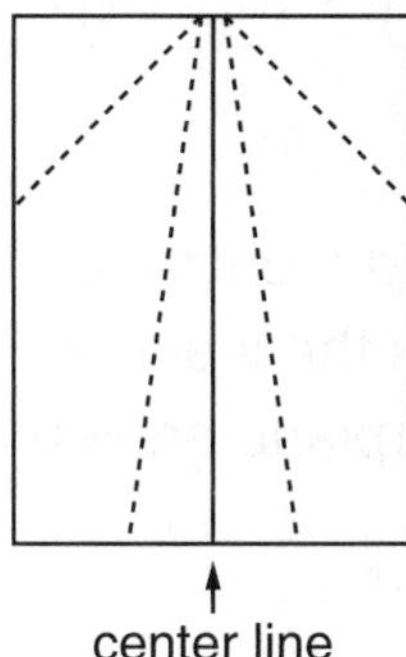

b. Fold corners along the dashed lines as shown. Use a small piece of tape to secure each corner, as shown in the sketch.

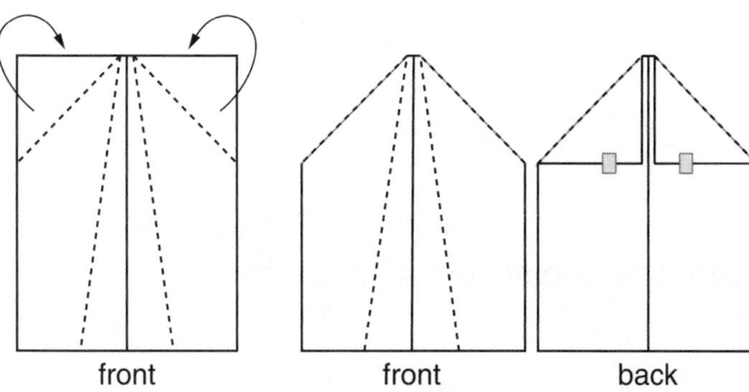

c. With the back side of the paper facing you, fold the right side of the paper toward the center so that the edges highlighted in the sketch meet. Use a small piece of tape to secure the flap in the position shown in the sketch. Do the same to the other side.

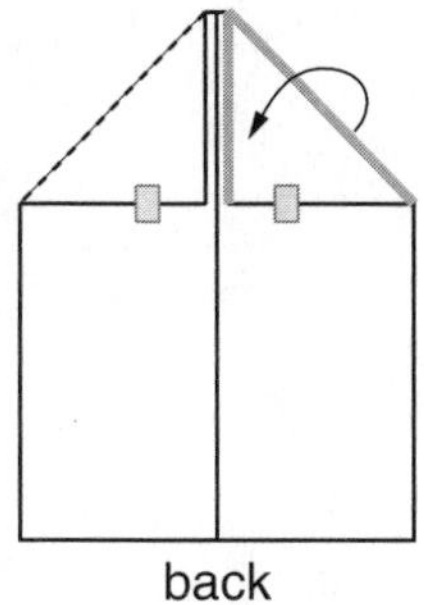

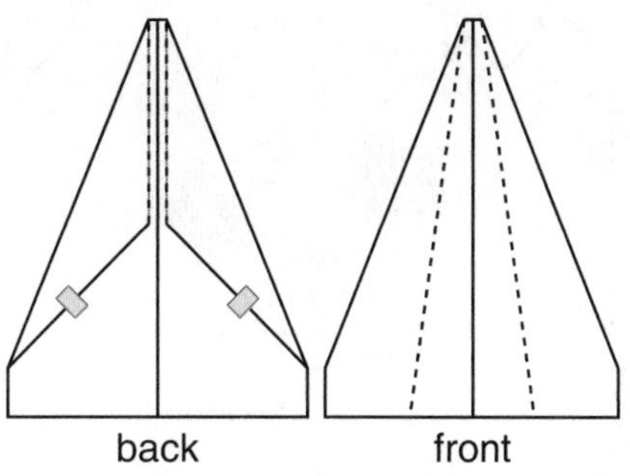

A Winning Paper Airplane Design *cont.*

d. Flip the paper to the front side. Fold in half along the center line so that the front side is now inside. Your paper airplane should look like this.

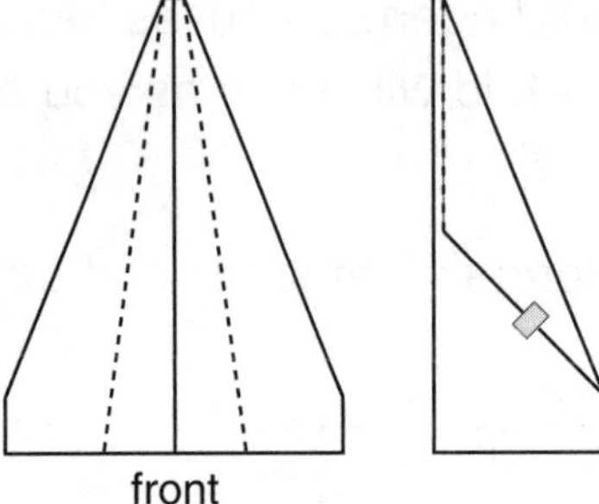

e. Take the top flap of the paper and fold it outward along the dashed lines. (Look for these dashed lines on the inside of the plane.) Do the same to the other flap. Your paper airplane should now look like this.

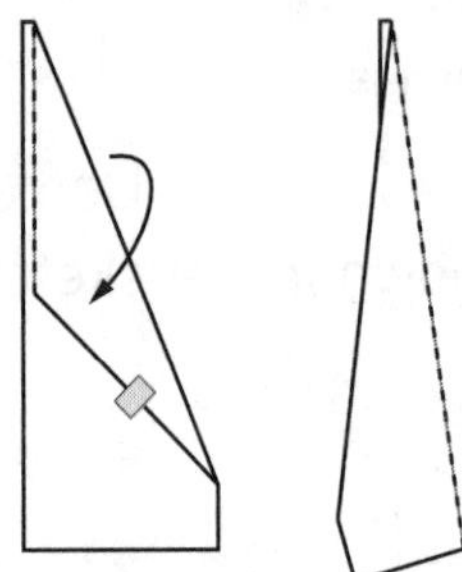

f. Tape the wings together on top of the airplane. Then tape the bottom as shown, making sure to secure all loose flaps.

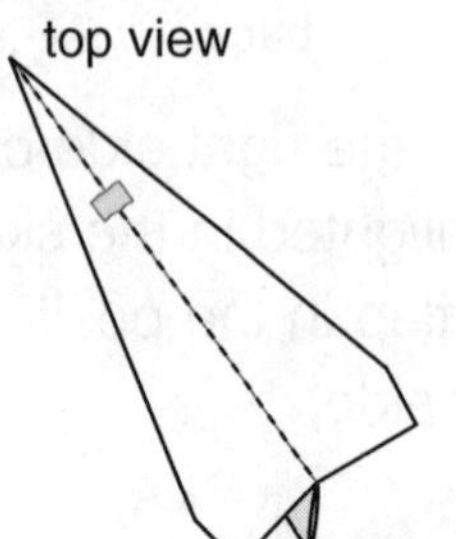

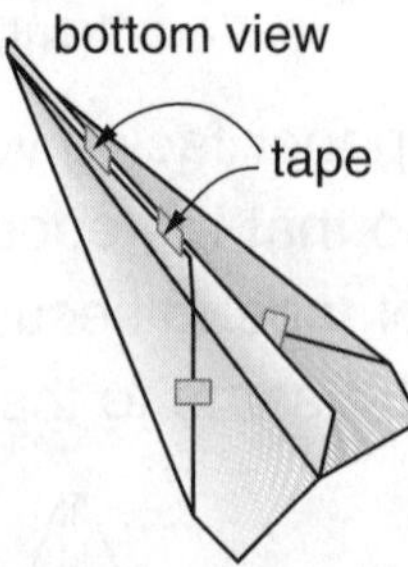

Name Date Time

PROJECT 7

Testing Paper Airplane Designs, Part 2

1. Draw a bar graph below to show the distance traveled by each of the 6 planes as recorded in the table on *Math Masters,* page 388.

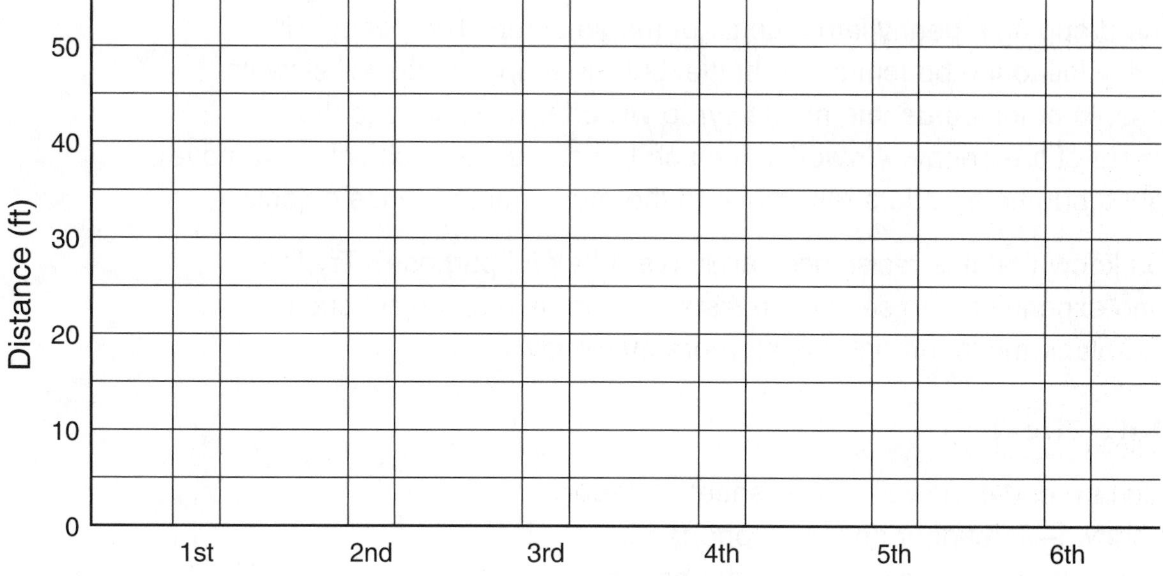

Name ________ ________ ________ ________ ________ ________

2. Describe the test-flight results. Did student-designed airplanes perform better or worse than airplanes built using Schultz's design?

____

____

____

____

3. Which do you think works best for distance:

a. a paper airplane that uses air to assist the motion of the paper?

b. a piece of paper, folded very tightly (like the 5-fold paper), which cuts through the air? Explain.

____

____

____

____

Name Date Time

Experiments with Air

Air is a real substance, just as water, earth, and maple syrup are real substances. Because air is a substance, it offers **resistance,** or opposition, to the movement of objects through it.

Imagine dropping a penny into a bottle of maple syrup. The penny will eventually fall to the bottom of the bottle, but the maple syrup will slow its progress. In other words, the maple syrup will offer resistance to the movement of the penny. Air works in much the same way—objects can move through it, but the air offers resistance to the movement of those objects.

Did you know that this resistance can serve a helpful purpose? Try the following experiments to see how resistance can help an object such as an airplane move through the air more efficiently.

The Kite Effect

1. Hold one end of an $8\frac{1}{2}$"-by-11" sheet of paper as shown—forefinger on top, supported by the thumb and second finger on the bottom. Notice that the paper in the illustration is tilted slightly, so the opposite end of the paper is a bit higher than the end being held.

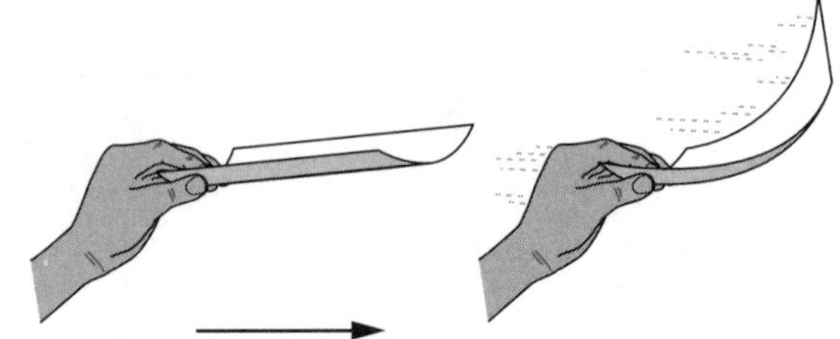

2. Push the paper directly forward as shown.

   You will notice that the end of the paper that is opposite the end you are holding tilts up. When the tilted surface of the paper pushes against the air, the air pushes back. This partially slows the paper down and partially lifts it up.

The sheet of paper has some of the characteristics of an airplane wing. The wings of an airplane are set at an angle so the front edge is higher than the back edge. In this way, the lower surface of the airplane wing uses the air resistance to achieve a small amount of lift.

Name Date Time

Experiments with Air *continued*

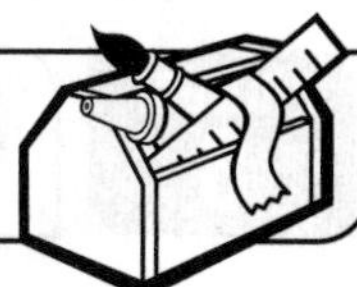

The Vacuum Effect

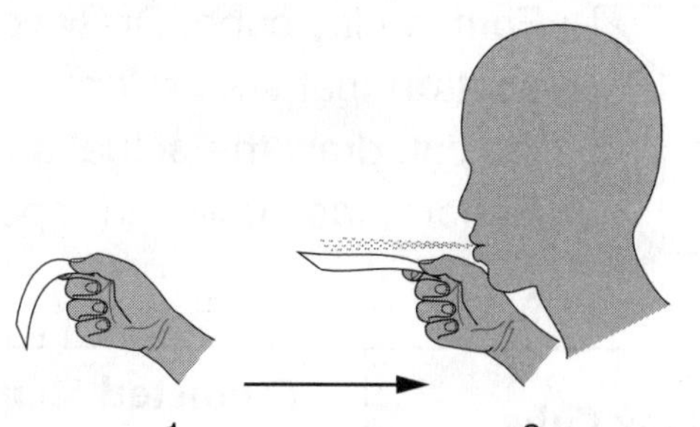

1. Hold the small end of a 2"-by-6" strip of paper between your thumb and forefinger as shown—thumb on top. The paper should fall in a curve.

2. Blow across the top of the paper as shown.

As you blow across the top of the paper, notice that the end of the paper that is opposite the end you are holding tilts up. Air rushing over the upper surface of the paper causes the air pressure on the upper surface to decrease. When the air pressure on the upper surface becomes less than the air pressure on the lower surface, the higher pressure underneath lifts the paper.

This sheet of paper has some of the characteristics of an airplane wing. Only the lower surface of an airplane wing is flat; the upper surface is curved, or arched. In this way, the upper surface of an airplane wing also uses air resistance to achieve lift. The kite effect and the vacuum effect contribute to the total lift of an airplane. However, the vacuum effect is responsible for about 80% of it.

Additional Sources of Information about Paper Airplanes

Here are three books about paper airplanes:

- *The Best Paper Airplanes You'll Ever Fly* by the editors of Klutz (Klutz, 1998).
- *The Great International Paper Airplane Book* by Jerry Mander, George Dippel, and Howard Gossage (Simon and Schuster, 1971, and Galahad Books, 1998).
- *The World Record Paper Airplane Book* by Ken Blackburn and Jeff Lamers (Workman, 1994).

You may also want to search the Internet for "paper airplanes."

Name Date Time

PROJECT 8

Cross Sections of a Clay Cube

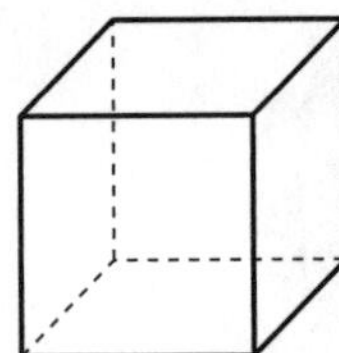

Form a clay cube. Draw your prediction of the shape of the **cross section** that will be formed by the first cut shown below. After making the cut, draw the actual shape and describe (name) the shape. Re-form the cube and repeat these steps for the other cuts.

Clay Cube	Predicted Shape of Cross Section	Actual Shape of Cross Section	Description of Shape
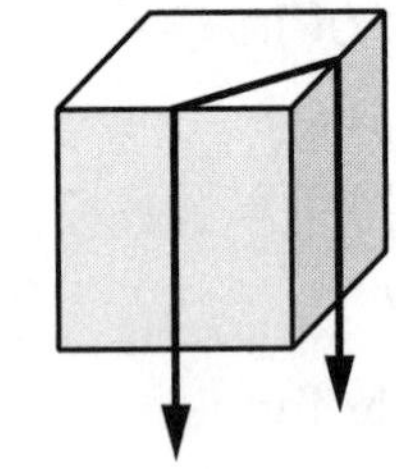			
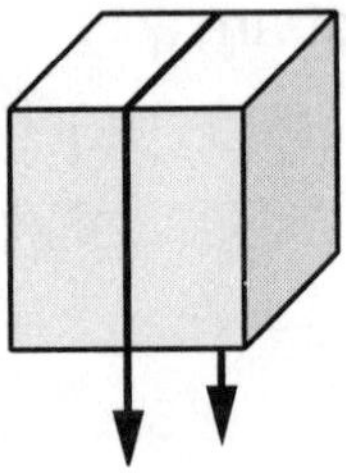			
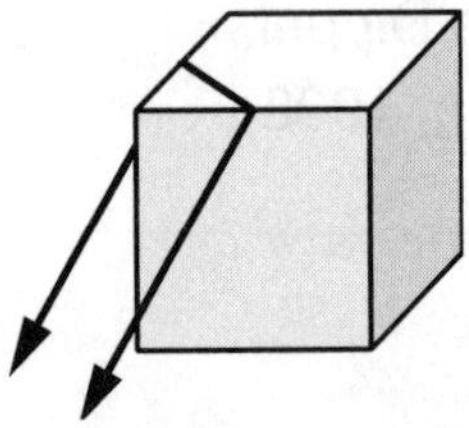			
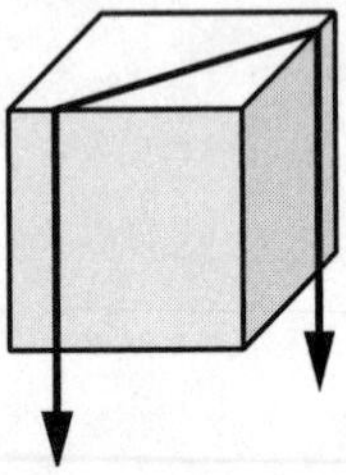			

Name Date Time

Cross Sections of a Clay Cylinder

Form a clay cylinder. Draw your prediction of the shape of the cross section that will be formed by the first cut shown below. After making the cut, draw the actual shape and describe (name) the shape. Re-form the cylinder and repeat these steps for the other cuts.

Clay Cylinder	Predicted Shape of Cross Section	Actual Shape of Cross Section	Description of Shape

Name Date Time

Cross Sections of a Clay Cone

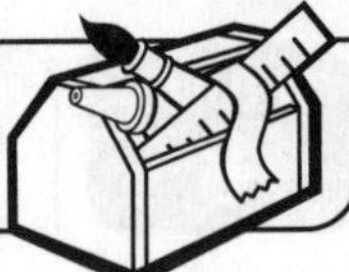

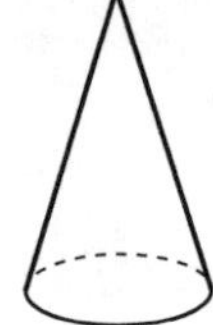

Form a clay cone. Draw your prediction of the shape of the cross section that will be formed by the first cut shown below. After making the cut, draw the actual shape and describe (name) the shape. Re-form the cone and repeat these steps for the other cuts.

Clay Cone	Predicted Shape of Cross Section	Actual Shape of Cross Section	Description of Shape

Name Date Time

Cross Sections of a Clay Pyramid

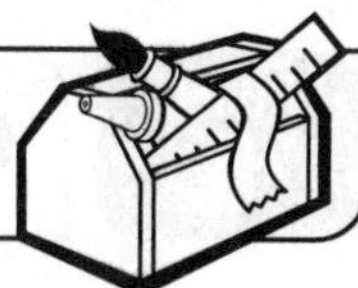

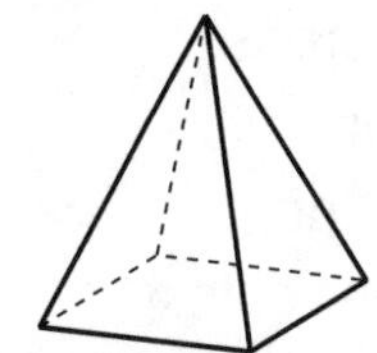

Pyramid with square base

Form a clay pyramid with a square base. Draw your prediction of the shape of the cross section that will be formed by the first cut shown below. After making the cut, draw the actual shape and describe (name) the shape. Re-form the pyramid and repeat these steps for the other cuts.

Clay Pyramid	Predicted Shape of Cross Section	Actual Shape of Cross Section	Description of Shape

Name Date Time

Cross Sections of a Clay Torus

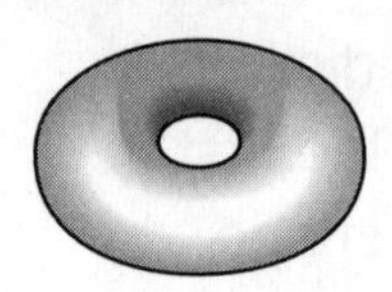
Torus (doughnut)

Form a clay torus. Draw your prediction of the shape of the cross section that will be formed by the first cut shown below. After making the cut, draw the actual shape and describe (name) the shape. Re-form the torus and repeat these steps for the other cuts.

Clay Torus	Predicted Shape of Cross Section	Actual Shape of Cross Section	Description of Shape

Name Date Time

PROJECT 8

Cross Sections of a Clay Prism

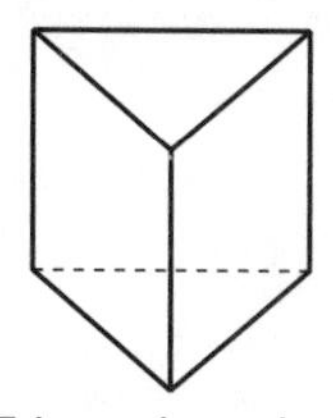
Triangular prism

Form a clay triangular prism. Draw your prediction of the shape of the cross section that will be formed by the first cut shown below. After making the cut, draw the actual shape and describe (name) the shape. Re-form the triangular prism and repeat these steps for the other cuts.

Clay Prism	Predicted Shape of Cross Section	Actual Shape of Cross Section	Description of Shape

Teaching Aid Masters

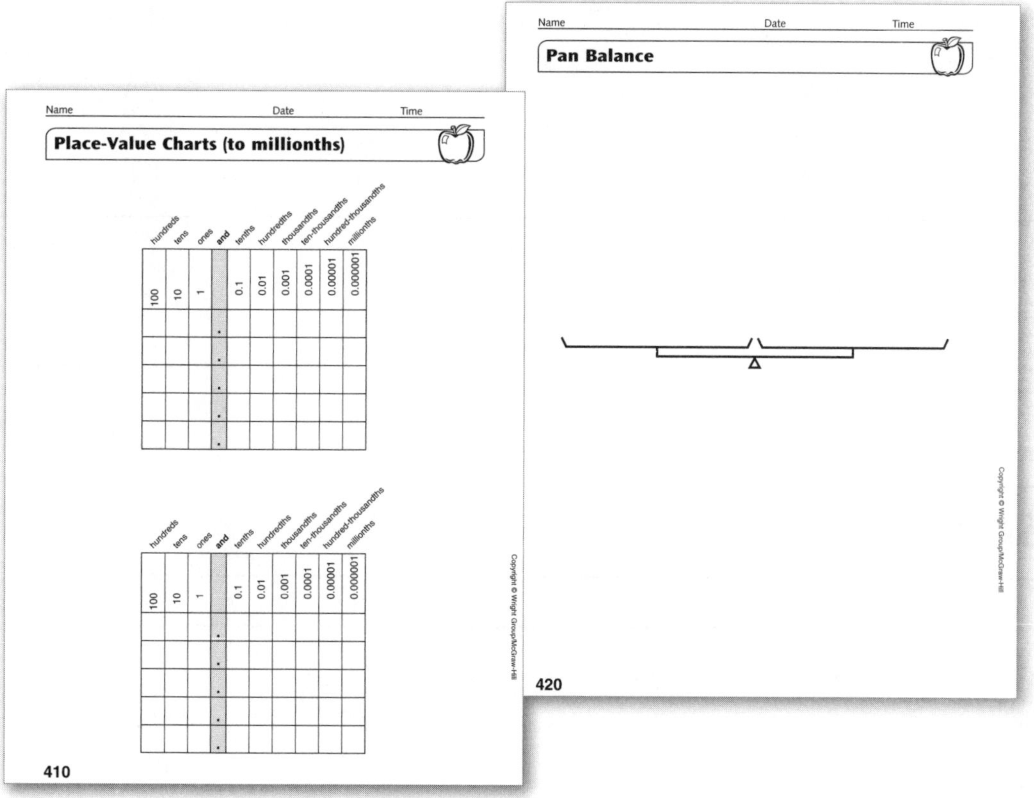

Name Date Time

Exit Slip

Name Date Time

Exit Slip

Name Date Time

Math Boxes

Name Date Time

Geometry Template

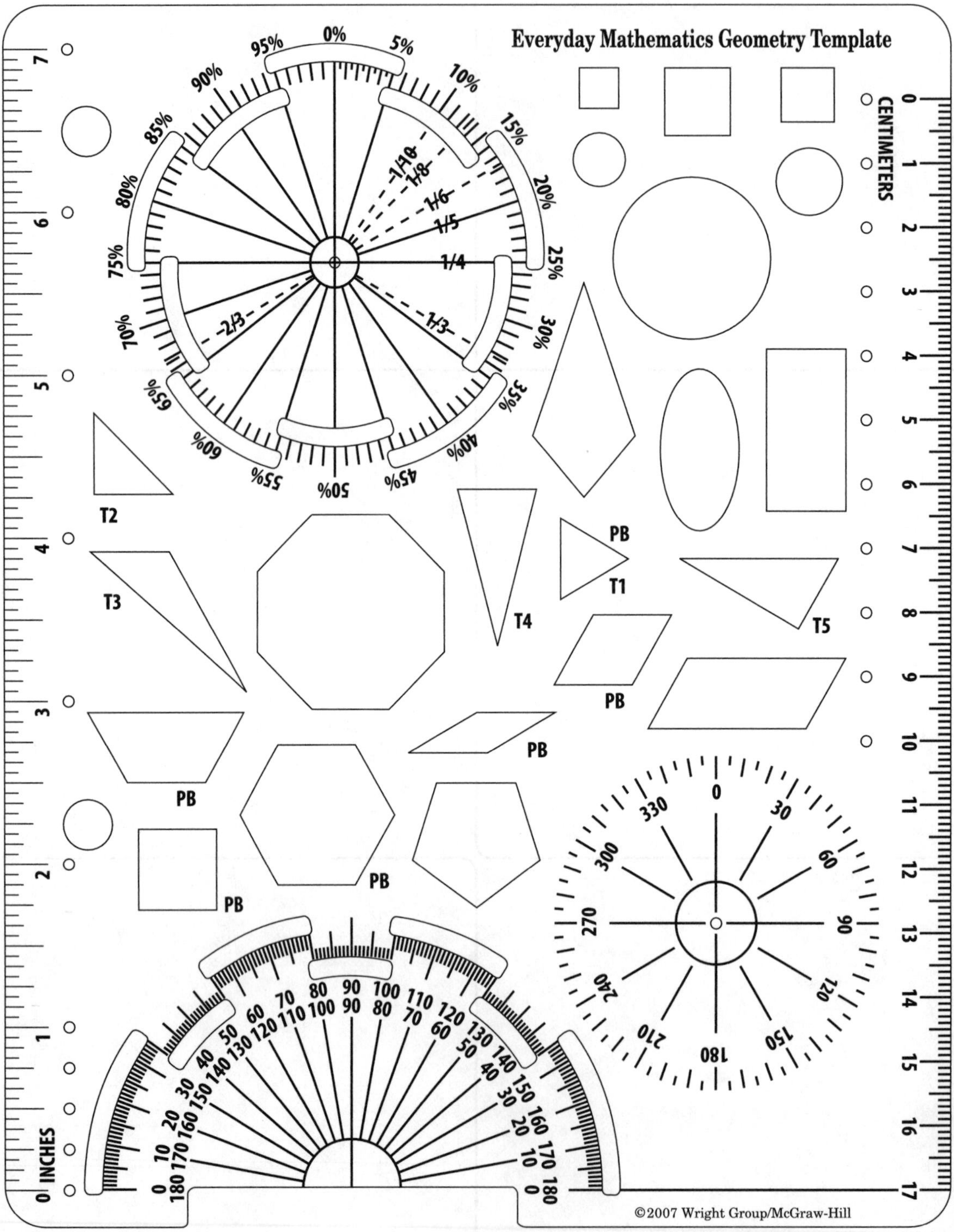

Everyday Mathematics Geometry Template

T2 T3 T4 T1 T5 PB PB PB PB PB PB PB

INCHES 0 1 2 3 4 5 6 7

CENTIMETERS 0 1 2 3 4 5 6 7 8 9 10 11 12 13 14 15 16 17

0% 5% 10% 15% 20% 25% 30% 35% 40% 45% 50% 55% 60% 65% 70% 75% 80% 85% 90% 95%

1/10 1/8 1/6 1/5 1/4 1/3 2/3

0 30 60 90 120 150 180 210 240 270 300 330

0 10 20 30 40 50 60 70 80 90 100 110 120 130 140 150 160 170 180

180 170 160 150 140 130 120 110 100 90 80 70 60 50 40 30 20 10 0

Name Date Time

$\frac{1}{4}$-inch Grid Paper

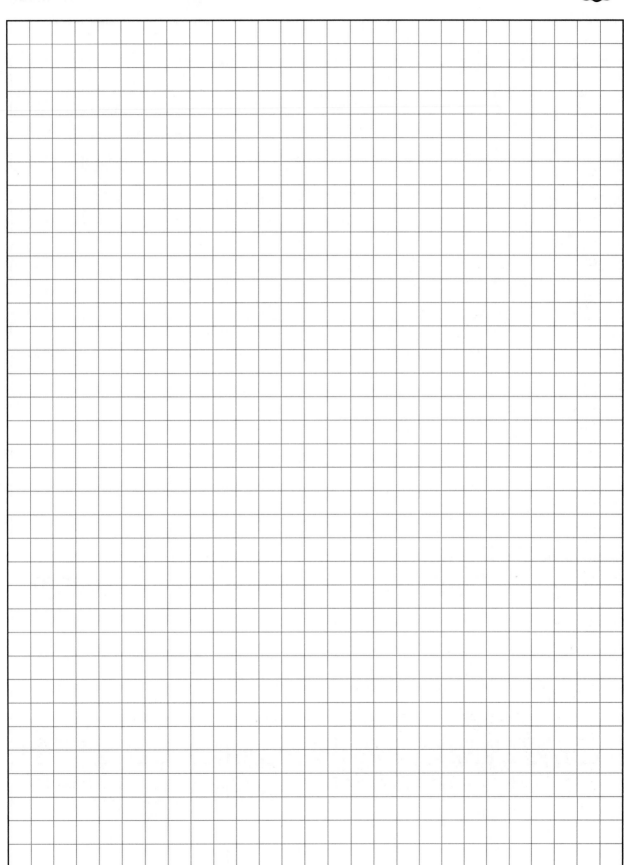

Name Date Time

1-centimeter Grid Paper

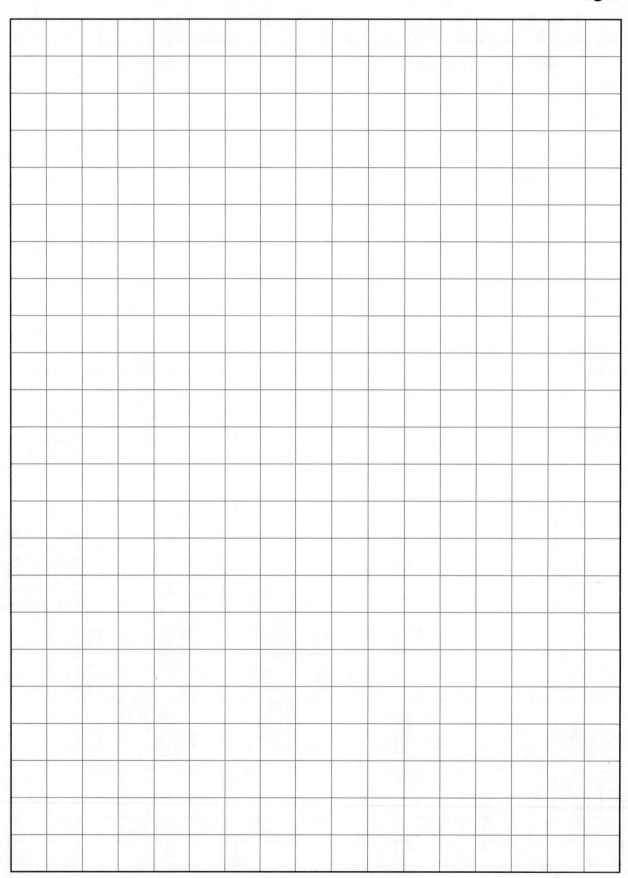

Name Date Time

15-Digit Place-Value Charts

trillions			,	billions			,	millions			,	thousands			,	ones		
100,000,000,000,000	10,000,000,000,000	1,000,000,000,000		100,000,000,000	10,000,000,000	1,000,000,000		100,000,000	10,000,000	1,000,000		100,000	10,000	1,000		100	10	1
			,				,				,				,			
			,				,				,				,			
			,				,				,				,			
			,				,				,				,			
			,				,				,				,			
			,				,				,				,			

__ __ __ , __ __ __ , __ __ __ , __ __ __ , __ __ __
H T O trillion, H T O billion, H T O million, H T O thousand, H T O

__ __ __ , __ __ __ , __ __ __ , __ __ __ , __ __ __
H T O trillion, H T O billion, H T O million, H T O thousand, H T O

__ __ __ , __ __ __ , __ __ __ , __ __ __ , __ __ __
H T O trillion, H T O billion, H T O million, H T O thousand, H T O

__ __ __ , __ __ __ , __ __ __ , __ __ __ , __ __ __
H T O trillion, H T O billion, H T O million, H T O thousand, H T O

Name Date Time

Place-Value Charts (to millionths)

hundreds	tens	ones	and	tenths	hundredths	thousandths	ten-thousandths	hundred-thousandths	millionths
100	10	1		0.1	0.01	0.001	0.0001	0.00001	0.000001
			.						
			.						
			.						
			.						
			.						

hundreds	tens	ones	and	tenths	hundredths	thousandths	ten-thousandths	hundred-thousandths	millionths
100	10	1		0.1	0.01	0.001	0.0001	0.00001	0.000001
			.						
			.						
			.						
			.						
			.						

Name Date Time

Base-10 Grid: Flat (1.0)

Name Date Time

Base-10 Grid: Longs and Units

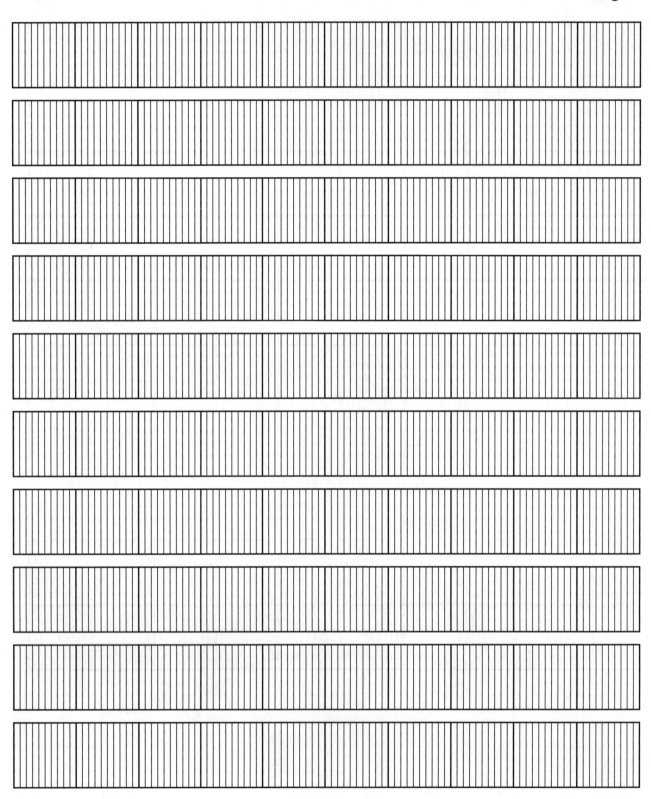

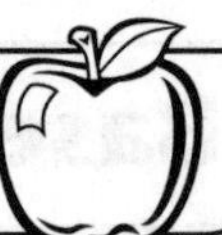

Name Date Time

Base-10 Grid: Units (0.001)

Name Date Time

Computation Grid

Name Date Time

Lattice Multiplication Grids

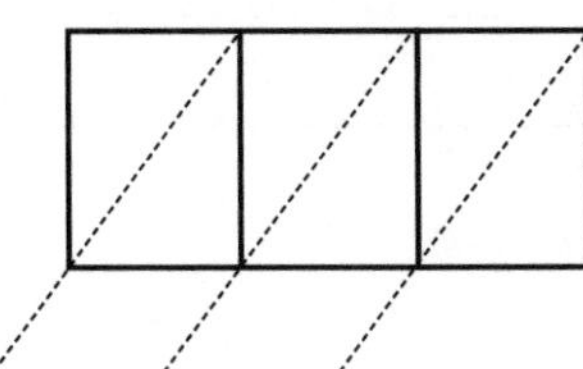
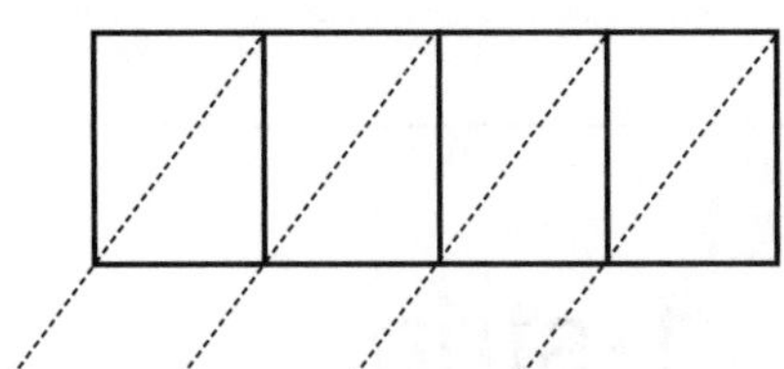

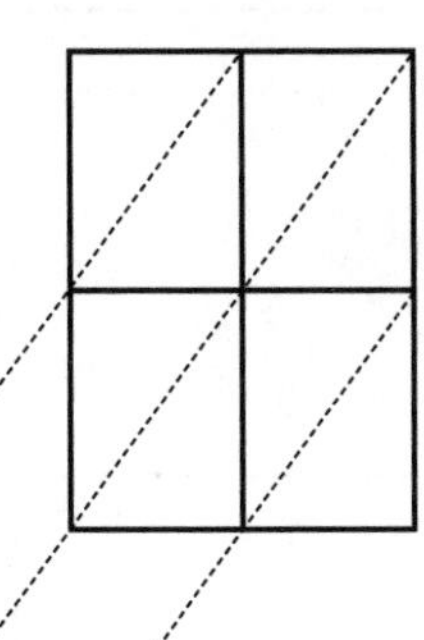
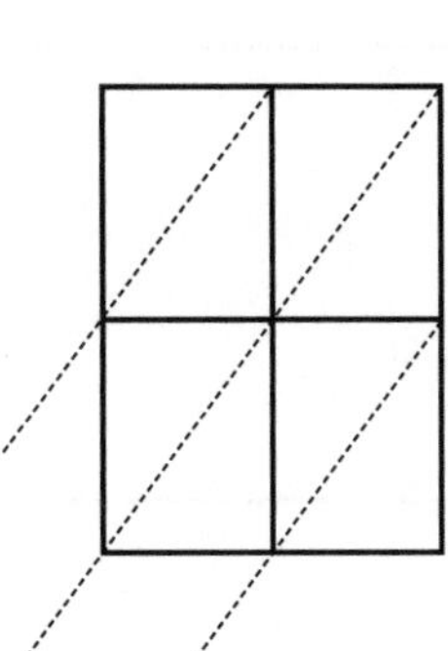
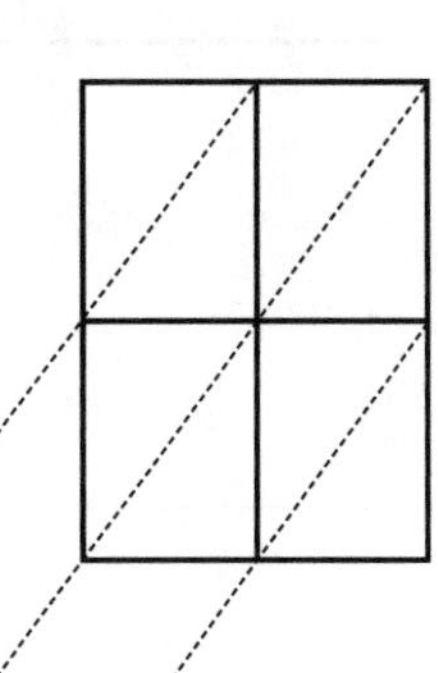
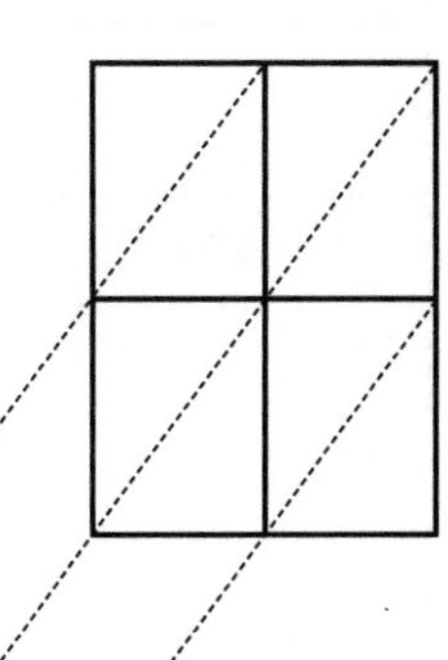

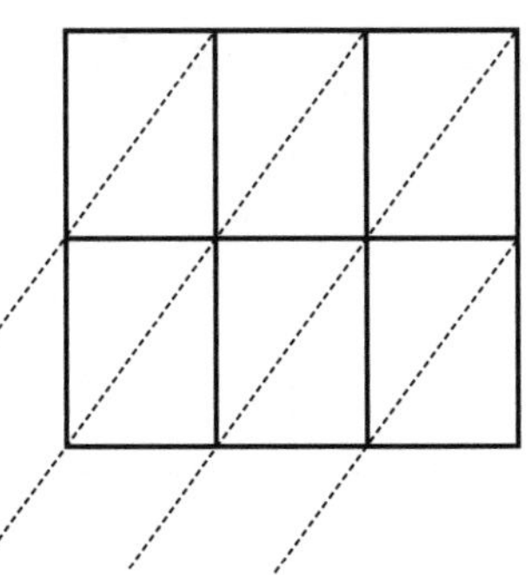
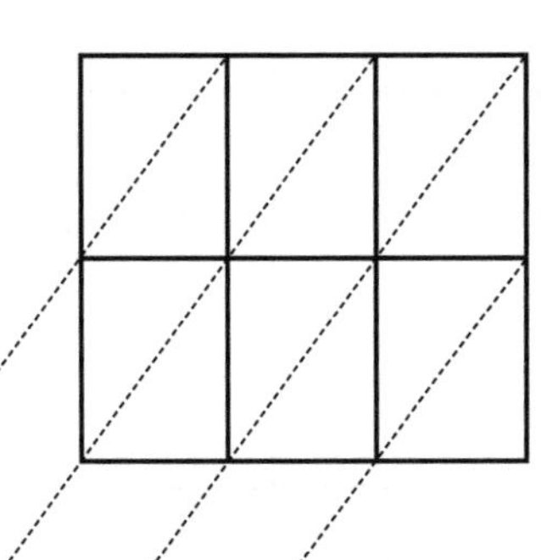
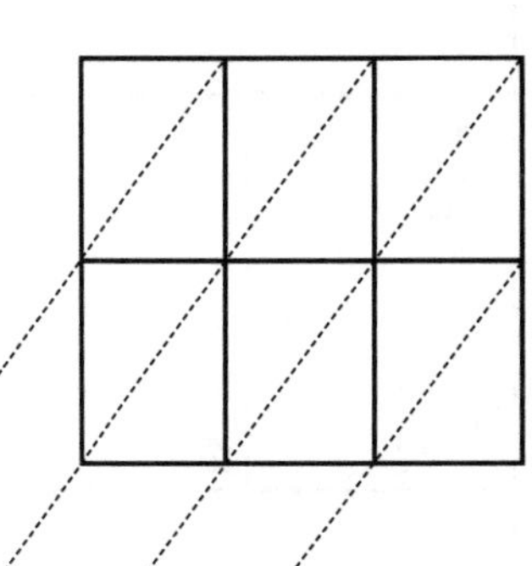

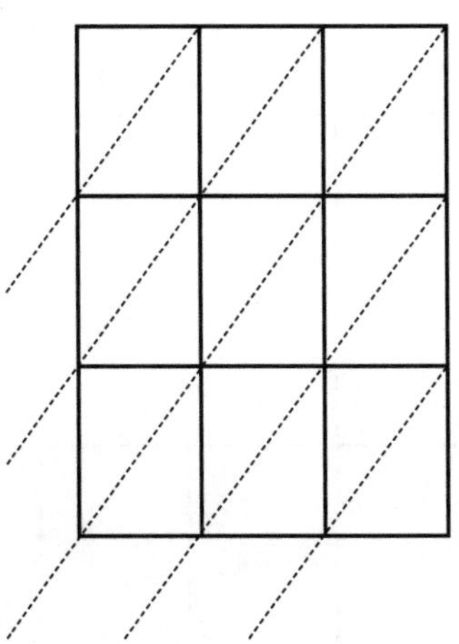
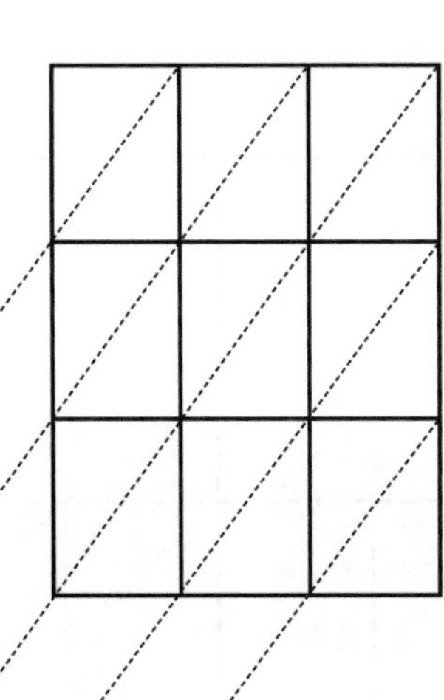
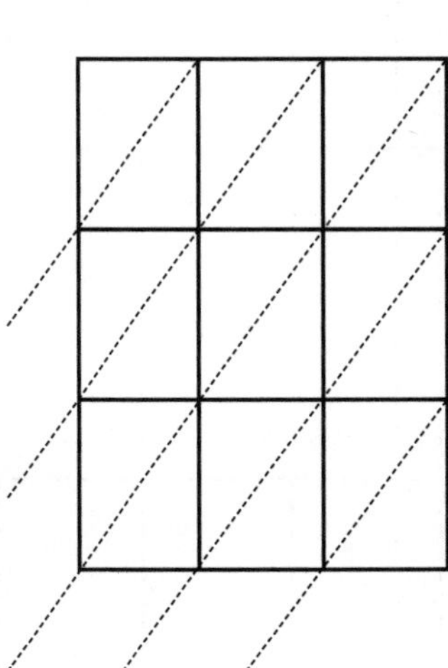

Name Date Time

Fraction Strips

1-strip

Name Date Time

Coordinate Grid

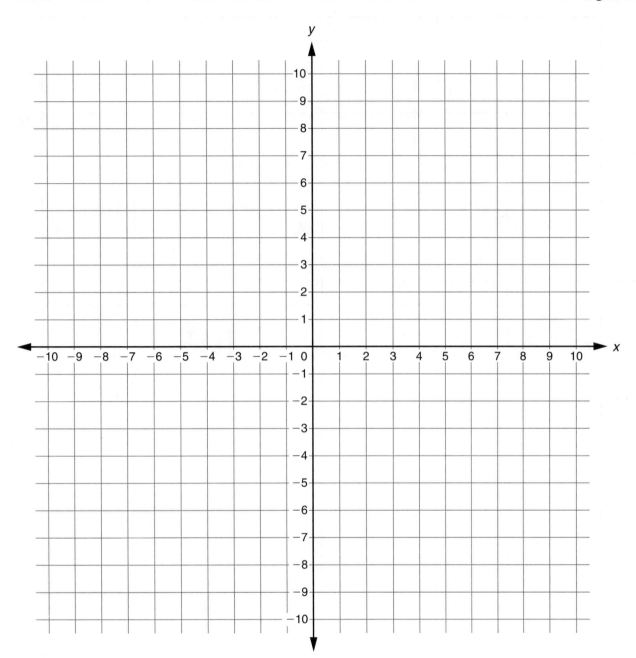

y

10
9
8
7
6
5
4
3
2
1

−10 −9 −8 −7 −6 −5 −4 −3 −2 −1 0 1 2 3 4 5 6 7 8 9 10 x

−1
−2
−3
−4
−5
−6
−7
−8
−9
−10

Name Date Time

Graph Paper (1 in.)

Name Date Time

Dot Paper (1 cm)

Name Date Time

Pan Balance

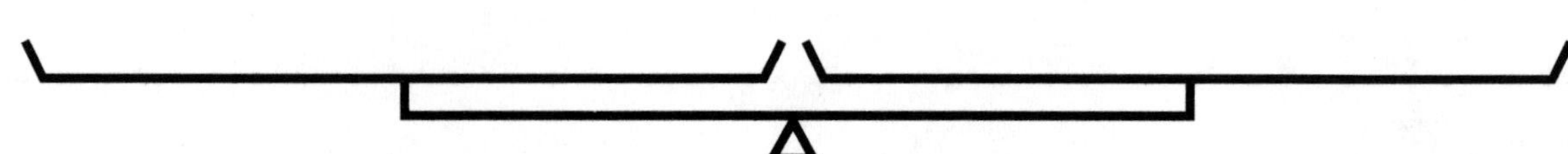

Name Date Time

Solving Equations

Solve the following equations.

1. Original equation

Operation

Check

2. Original equation

Operation

Check

3. Original equation

Operation

Check

4. Original equation

Operation

Check

5. Original equation

Operation

Check

6. Original equation

Operation

Check

Name Date Time

Venn Diagram

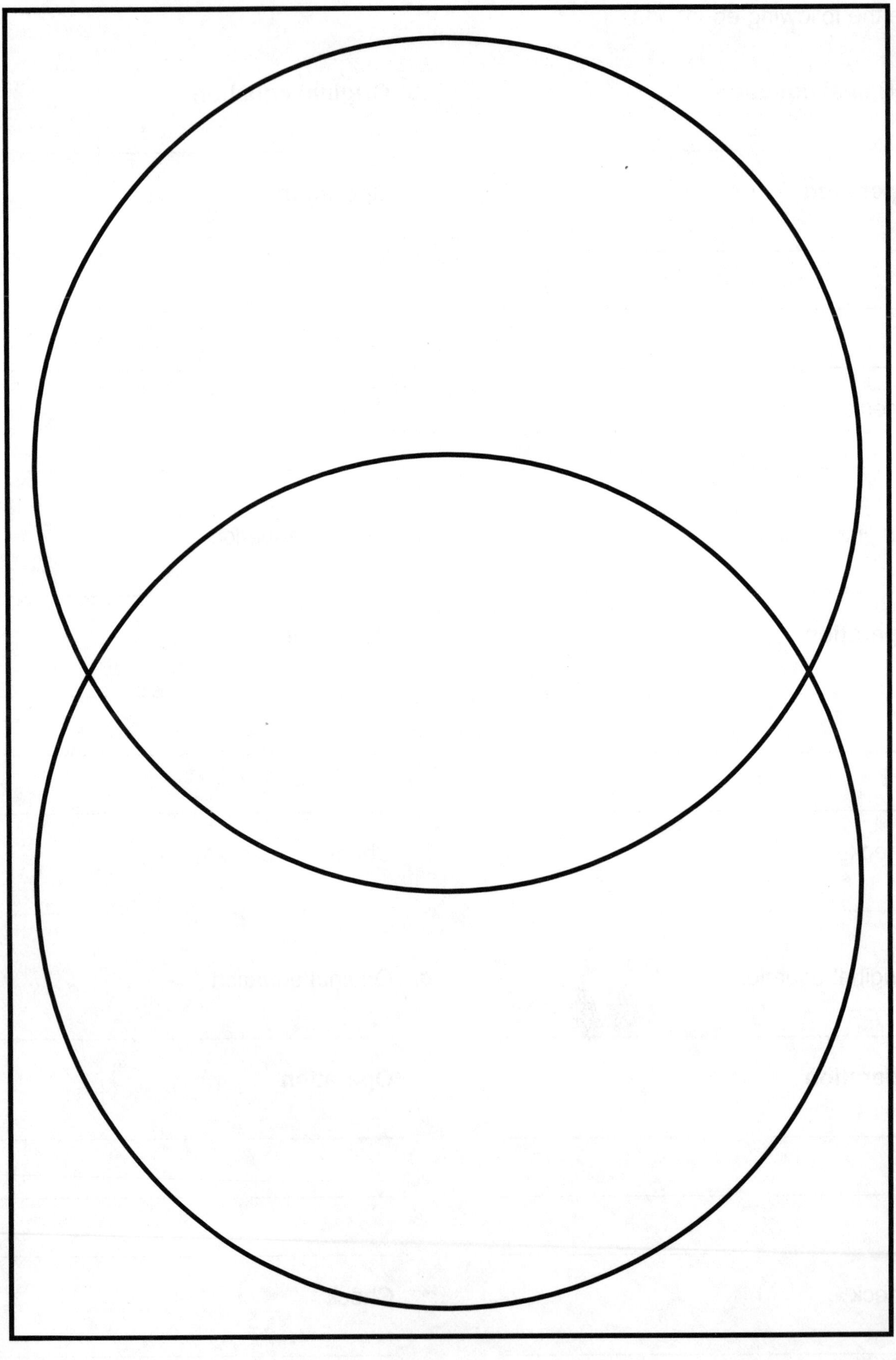

Name Date Time

A Golden Rectangle

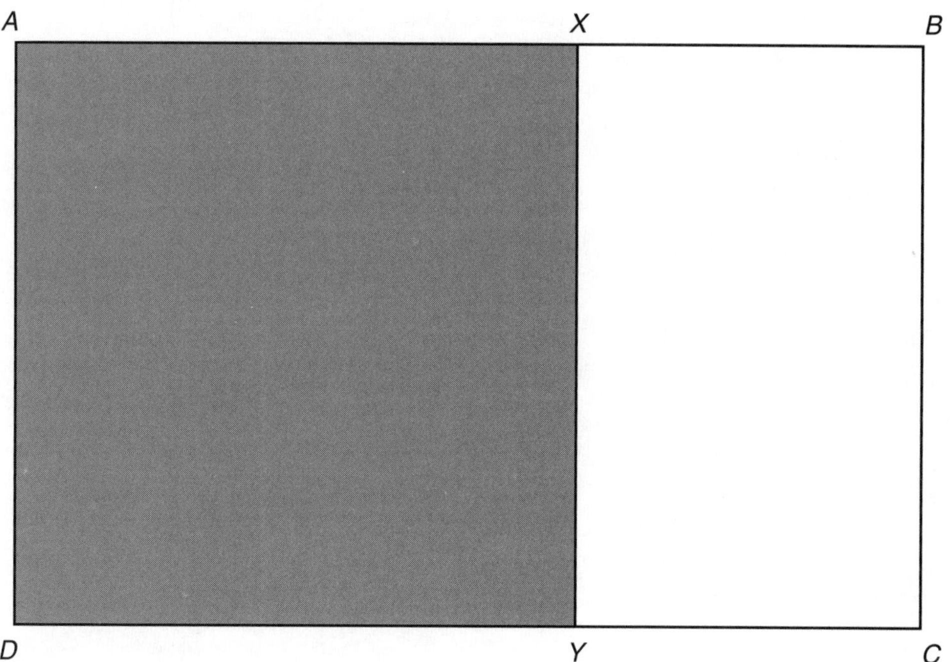

Game Masters

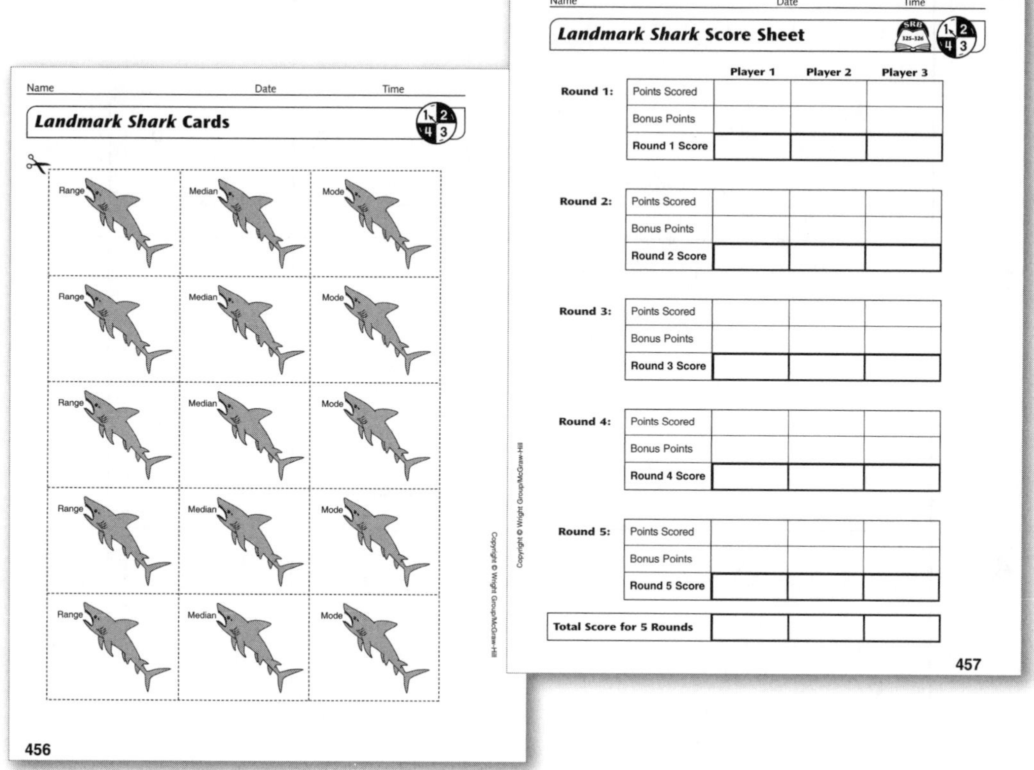

Name Date Time

Landmark Shark Cards

Range	Median	Mode
Range	Median	Mode
Range	Median	Mode
Range	Median	Mode
Range	Median	Mode
Range	Median	Mode

Copyright © Wright Group/McGraw-Hill

456

Name Date Time

Landmark Shark Score Sheet

SRB 325–326

		Player 1	Player 2	Player 3
Round 1:	Points Scored			
	Bonus Points			
	Round 1 Score			
Round 2:	Points Scored			
	Bonus Points			
	Round 2 Score			
Round 3:	Points Scored			
	Bonus Points			
	Round 3 Score			
Round 4:	Points Scored			
	Bonus Points			
	Round 4 Score			
Round 5:	Points Scored			
	Bonus Points			
	Round 5 Score			
Total Score for 5 Rounds				

Copyright © Wright Group/McGraw-Hill

457

Name Date Time

Angle Tangle Record Sheet

Round	Angle	Estimated measure	Actual measure	Score
1		_____ °	_____ °	
2		_____ °	_____ °	
3		_____ °	_____ °	
4		_____ °	_____ °	
5		_____ °	_____ °	
			Total Score	

Name Date Time

Build-It Card Deck

$\frac{5}{9}$	$\frac{1}{3}$	$\frac{11}{12}$	$\frac{1}{12}$
$\frac{7}{12}$	$\frac{3}{8}$	$\frac{1}{4}$	$\frac{1}{5}$
$\frac{2}{3}$	$\frac{3}{7}$	$\frac{4}{7}$	$\frac{3}{4}$
$\frac{3}{5}$	$\frac{4}{5}$	$\frac{7}{9}$	$\frac{5}{6}$

Name Date Time

Build-It Gameboard

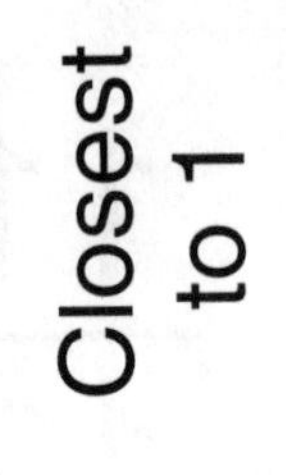

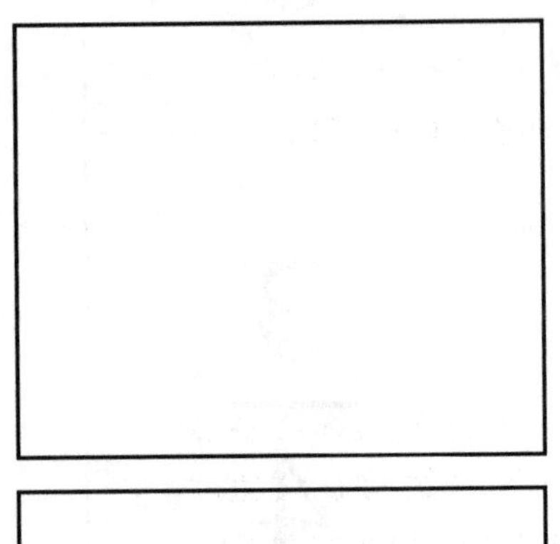

Closest to 1

Closest to 0

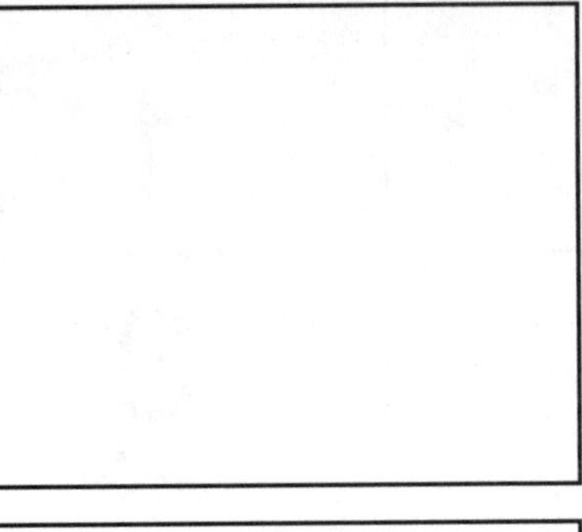

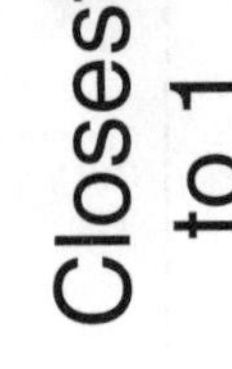

Closest to 1

Closest to 0

Name Date Time

Credits/Debits Game

Materials ☐ recording sheets (*Math Masters,* p. 430)
☐ 1 complete deck of number cards

Players 2

Object of the Game To have the most money at the end of 10 draws.

Directions

1. Shuffle the deck and lay it facedown between the players.
2. The black-numbered cards are the credits (+), and the blue- (or red-) numbered cards are the debits (−).
3. Each player begins with a bottom line of +\$10. As credits and debits are recorded, players will adjust the bottom line.
4. Players take turns. On your turn, do the following.
   - Draw a card. The card tells you the dollar amount and whether it is a credit or debit to the bottom line. Record the credit or debit in the Change column.
   - Use the credit or debit to adjust the bottom line.
   - Record the result in the table.

Example 1: Cleo has a Start balance of +\$10. He draws a blue (or red) 12. This is a debit of \$12, so he records −\$12 in the Change column. He adds −\$12 to the bottom line: \$10 + (−\$12) = −\$2. Cleo then records −\$2 in the End, and next start column. He also records −\$2 in the Start column on the next line.

Example 2: Aisha has a Start balance of +\$20. She draws a black 9. This is a credit of \$9, so she records +\$9 in the Change column, and she adds \$9 to the bottom line: \$20 + \$9 = \$29. Aisha then records +\$29 in the End, and next start column. She also records +\$29 in the Start column of the next line.

Scoring

At the end of 10 draws each, the player with the most money is the winner of the round. If both players have negative dollar amounts, the player whose amount is closer to 0 wins.

Name Date Time

Credits/Debits Game Recording Sheets

Player 1 ______________

Recording Sheet

	Start	Change	End, and next start
1	+$10		
2			
3			
4			
5			
6			
7			
8			
9			
10			

Player 2 ______________

Recording Sheet

	Start	Change	End, and next start
1	+$10		
2			
3			
4			
5			
6			
7			
8			
9			
10			

–22 –21 –20 –19 –18 –17 –16 –15 –14 –13 –12 –11 –10 –9 –8 –7 –6 –5 –4 –3 –2 –1 0 1 2 3 4 5 6 7 8 9 10 11 12 13 14 15 16 17 18 19 20 21 22

Name Date Time

Credits/Debits Game (Advanced Version)

Record Sheet

	Start	Change		End, and next start
		Addition or Subtraction	Credit or Debit	
1				
2				
3				
4				
5				
6				
7				
8				
9				
10				

Name Date Time

Record Sheet

	Start	Change		End, and next start
		Addition or Subtraction	Credit or Debit	
1				
2				
3				
4				
5				
6				
7				
8				
9				
10				

Name Date Time

Divisibility Dash

Record Sheet

Player 1

Round	Cards in your hand	Divisor	2-digit or 3-digit multiples
1			
2			
3			
4			
5			
6			
7			
8			
9			
10			

Name Date Time

Divisibility Dash

Record Sheet

Player 1

Round	Cards in your hand	Divisor	2-digit or 3-digit multiples
1			
2			
3			
4			
5			
6			
7			
8			
9			
10			

Name ______________________ Date ______________ Time ______________

Doggone Decimal

For each round, circle the Target Number. Then complete the number sentence by recording the numbers formed and the product of those numbers.

Player 1

Target Number 0.1 1 10 100

Number Sentence ________ * ________ = ________

Target Number 0.1 1 10 100

Number Sentence ________ * ________ = ________

Target Number 0.1 1 10 100

Number Sentence ________ * ________ = ________

Target Number 0.1 1 10 100

Number Sentence ________ * ________ = ________

Name ______________________ Date ______________ Time ______________

Doggone Decimal

For each round, circle the Target Number. Then complete the number sentence by recording the numbers formed and the product of those numbers.

Player 2

Target Number 0.1 1 10 100

Number Sentence ________ * ________ = ________

Target Number 0.1 1 10 100

Number Sentence ________ * ________ = ________

Target Number 0.1 1 10 100

Number Sentence ________ * ________ = ________

Target Number 0.1 1 10 100

Number Sentence ________ * ________ = ________

Name Date Time

Electoral Vote Map

WA
Washington
11

MT
Montana
3

ND
North Dakota
3

OR
Oregon
7

ID
Idaho
4

SD
South Dakota
3

WY
Wyoming
3

NE
Nebraska
5

NV
Nevada
5

UT
Utah
5

CO
Colorado
9

KS
Kansas
6

CA
California
55

AZ
Arizona
10

NM
New Mexico
5

OK
Oklahoma
7

TX
Texas
34

AK
Alaska
3

HI
Hawaii
4

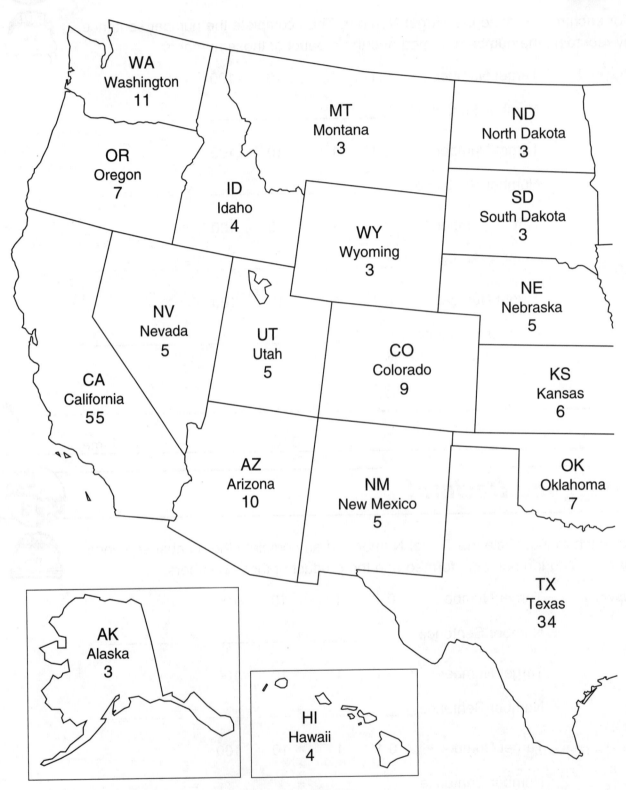

NOTE: Alaska and Hawaii are not drawn to scale.

Name Date Time

Electoral Vote Map *continued*

Minnesota
MN
10

WI
Wisconsin
10

MI
Michigan
17

IA
Iowa
7

IL
Illinois
21

IN
Indiana
11

OH
Ohio
20

MO
Missouri
11

KY
Kentucky
8

TN 11
Tennessee

AR
Arkansas
6

MS
Mississippi
6

AL
Alabama
9

LA
Louisiana
9

GA
Georgia
15

FL
Florida
27

SC
South
Carolina
8

NC
North Carolina
15

VA
Virginia
13

WV
West
Virginia
5

PA
Pennsylvania
21

NY
New York
31

VT
3

Vermont*

ME
Maine
4

NH
4

New Hampshire*

MA

Massachusetts*
12

RI
Rhode Island*
4

CT

Connecticut*
7

NJ

New Jersey*
15

DE
Delaware*
3

MD

Maryland*
10

DC
District of Columbia*
3

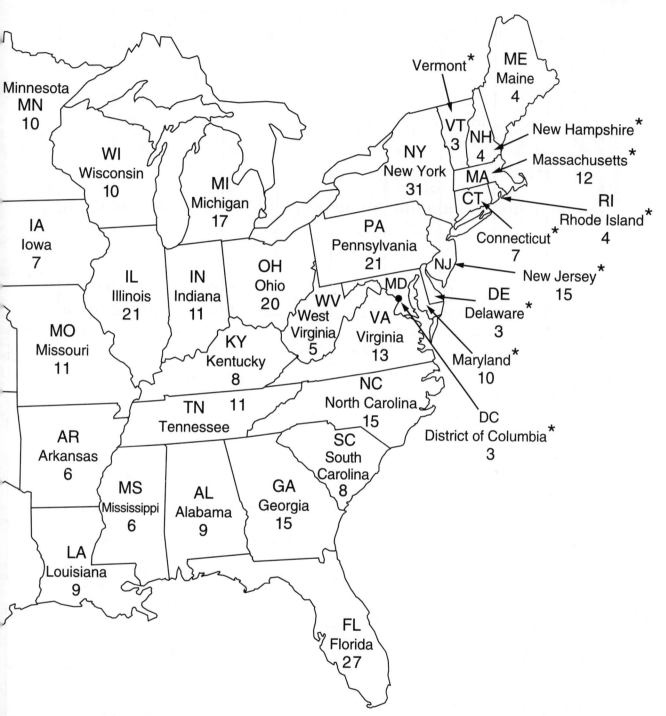

*If your marker does not fit on the state, put your marker on the state's name.

Name Date Time

Exponent Ball Gameboard

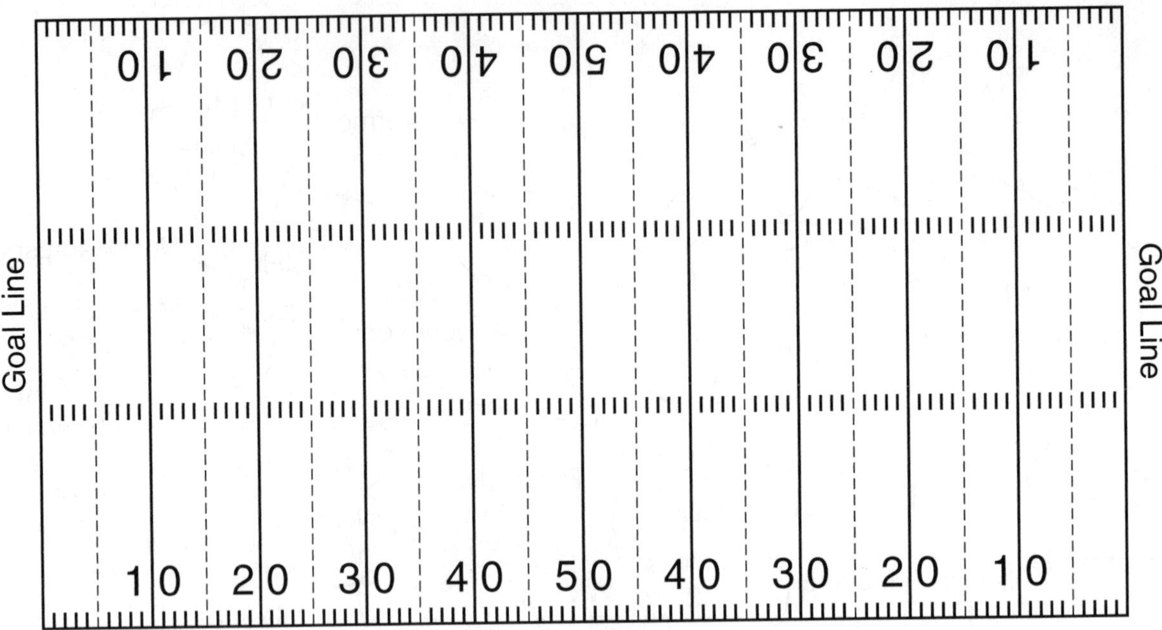

Table 1: Runs

Value of Roll	Move Ball	Chances of Gaining on the Ground
1	−15 yd	−15 yards: 1 out of 6, or about 17%
2 to 6	+10 yd	10 yards or more: 5 out of 6, or about 83%
8 to 81	+20 yd	20 yards or more: 4 out of 6, or about 67%
In the 100s	+30 yd	30 yards or more: 13 out of 36, or about 36%
In the 1,000s	+40 yd	40 yards or more: 7 out of 36, or about 19%
In the 10,000s	+50 yd	50 yards: 1 out of 18, or about 6%

Table 2: Kicks

Value of Roll	Move Ball	Chances of Kicking
1	+10 yd	10 yards or more: 6 out of 6, or 100%
2	+20 yd	20 yards or more: 5 out of 6, or about 83%
3	+30 yd	30 yards or more: 4 out of 6, or about 67%
4	+40 yd	40 yards or more: 3 out of 6, or 50%
5	+50 yd	50 yards or more: 2 out of 6, or about 33%
6	+60 yd	60 yards or more: 1 out of 6, or about 17%

Name Date Time

Factor Captor Grid 1 (Beginning Level)

1	2	2	2	2	2
2	3	3	3	3	3
3	4	4	4	4	5
5	5	5	6	6	7
7	8	8	9	9	10
10	11	12	13	14	15
16	18	20	21	22	24
25	26	27	28	30	32

Name Date Time

Factor Captor Grid 2 (Advanced Level)

1	2	2	2	2	2	3
3	3	3	3	4	4	4
4	5	5	5	5	6	6
6	7	7	8	8	9	9
10	10	11	12	13	14	15
16	17	18	19	20	21	22
23	24	25	26	27	28	30
32	33	34	35	36	38	39
40	42	44	45	46	48	49
50	51	52	54	55	56	60

Name Date Time

Frac-Tac-Toe Number-Card Board

NUMERATOR PILE

PLACE CARDS
NUMBER-SIDE DOWN.

WHEN ALL CARDS ARE USED, SHUFFLE AND REPLACE.

→

NUMERATOR PILE

PLAY EACH CARD
NUMBER-SIDE UP.

DENOMINATOR PILE

PLACE CARDS
NUMBER-SIDE DOWN.

WHEN ALL CARDS ARE USED, JUST REPLACE. DO NOT SHUFFLE!

→

DENOMINATOR PILE

PLAY EACH CARD
NUMBER-SIDE UP.

Name Date Time

2-4-8 Frac-Tac-Toe (Decimals)

If you use a standard deck of playing cards:

- Use queens as zeros (0).
- Use aces as ones (1).
- Discard jacks and kings.

If you use an Everything Math Deck, discard cards greater than 10.

Use different color counters or coins as markers. If you use coins, one player is HEADS and the other player is TAILS.

Numerator Pile

All remaining cards

Denominator Pile

Two each of the 2, 4, and 8 cards

> 2.0	0 or 1	> 1.5	0 or 1	> 2.0
1.5	0.125	0.25	0.375	1.5
> 1.0	0.5	0.25 or 0.75	0.5	> 1.0
2.0	0.625	0.75	0.875	2.0
> 2.0	0 or 1	1.125	0 or 1	> 2.0

Name Date Time

3-6-9 Frac-Tac-Toe (Decimals)

If you use a standard deck of playing cards:

- Use queens as zeros (0).
- Use aces as ones (1).
- Discard jacks and kings.

If you use an Everything Math Deck, discard cards greater than 10.

Use different color counters or coins as markers. If you use coins, one player is HEADS and the other player is TAILS.

Numerator Pile

All remaining cards

Denominator Pile

Two each of the 3, 6, and 9 cards

> 1.0	0 or 1	$0.\overline{1}$	0 or 1	> 1.0
$0.1\overline{6}$	$0.\overline{2}$	$0.\overline{3}$	$0.\overline{3}$	$0.\overline{4}$
> 2.0	$0.\overline{5}$	> 1.0	$0.\overline{6}$	> 2.0
$0.\overline{6}$	$0.\overline{7}$	$0.8\overline{3}$	$0.\overline{8}$	$1.\overline{3}$
> 1.0	0 or 1	$1.\overline{6}$	0 or 1	> 1.0

Name Date Time

2-4-8 Frac-Tac-Toe (Percents)

If you use a standard deck of playing cards:

- Use queens as zeros (0).
- Use aces as ones (1).
- Discard jacks and kings.

If you use an Everything Math Deck, discard cards greater than 10.

Use different color counters or coins as markers. If you use coins, one player is HEADS and the other player is TAILS.

Numerator Pile

All remaining cards

Denominator Pile

Two each of the 2, 4, and 8 cards

> 200%	0% or 100%	> 150%	0% or 100%	> 200%
150%	$12\frac{1}{2}\%$	25%	$37\frac{1}{2}\%$	150%
> 100%	50%	25% or 75%	50%	> 100%
200%	$62\frac{1}{2}\%$	75%	$87\frac{1}{2}\%$	200%
> 200%	0% or 100%	$112\frac{1}{2}\%$	0% or 100%	> 200%

Name Date Time

3-6-9 Frac-Tac-Toe (Percents)

If you use a standard deck of playing cards:

- Use queens as zeros (0).
- Use aces as ones (1).
- Discard jacks and kings.

If you use an Everything Math Deck, discard cards greater than 10.

Use different color counters or coins as markers. If you use coins, one player is HEADS and the other player is TAILS.

Numerator Pile

All remaining cards

Denominator Pile

Two each of the 3, 6, and 9 cards

> 100%	0% or 100%	11.1%	0% or 100%	> 100%
$16\frac{2}{3}\%$	22.2%	$33\frac{1}{3}\%$	33.3%	44.4%
> 200%	55.5%	> 100%	66.6%	> 200%
$66\frac{2}{3}\%$	77.7%	$83\frac{1}{3}\%$	88.8%	$133\frac{1}{3}\%$
> 100%	0% or 100%	$166\frac{2}{3}\%$	0% or 100%	> 100%

Name Date Time

2-4-5-10 Frac-Tac-Toe (Decimals)

If you use a standard deck of playing cards:

- Use queens as zeros (0).
- Use aces as ones (1).
- Discard jacks and kings.

If you use an Everything Math Deck, discard cards greater than 10.

Use different color counters or coins as markers. If you use coins, one player is HEADS and the other player is TAILS.

Numerator Pile

All remaining cards

Denominator Pile

Two each of the 2, 4, 5, and 10 cards

> 1.0	0 or 1	> 2.0	0 or 1	> 1.0
0.1	0.2	0.25	0.3	0.4
> 1.5	0.5	> 1.5	0.5	> 1.5
0.6	0.7	0.75	0.8	0.9
> 1.0	0 or 1	> 2.0	0 or 1	> 1.0

Name Date Time

2-4-5-10 *Frac-Tac-Toe* (Percents)

If you use a standard deck of playing cards:

- Use queens as zeros (0).
- Use aces as ones (1).
- Discard jacks and kings.

If you use an Everything Math Deck, discard cards greater than 10.

Use different color counters or coins as markers. If you use coins, one player is HEADS and the other player is TAILS.

Numerator Pile

All remaining cards

Denominator Pile

Two each of the 2, 4, 5, and 10 cards

> 100%	0% or 100%	> 200%	0% or 100%	> 100%
10%	20%	25%	30%	40%
> 100%	50%	> 200%	50%	> 100%
60%	70%	75%	80%	90%
> 100%	0% or 100%	> 200%	0% or 100%	> 100%

Name Date Time

Fraction Action, Fraction Friction Card Deck

$\frac{1}{2}$	$\frac{1}{3}$	$\frac{2}{3}$	$\frac{1}{4}$
$\frac{3}{4}$	$\frac{1}{6}$	$\frac{1}{6}$	$\frac{5}{6}$
$\frac{1}{12}$	$\frac{1}{12}$	$\frac{5}{12}$	$\frac{5}{12}$
$\frac{7}{12}$	$\frac{7}{12}$	$\frac{11}{12}$	$\frac{11}{12}$

Name Date Time

Fraction Capture Gameboard

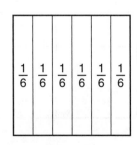

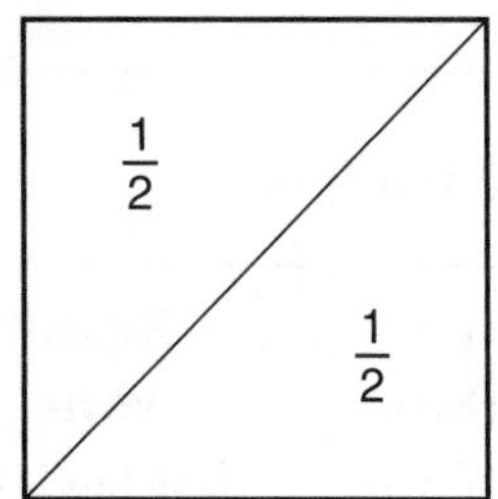

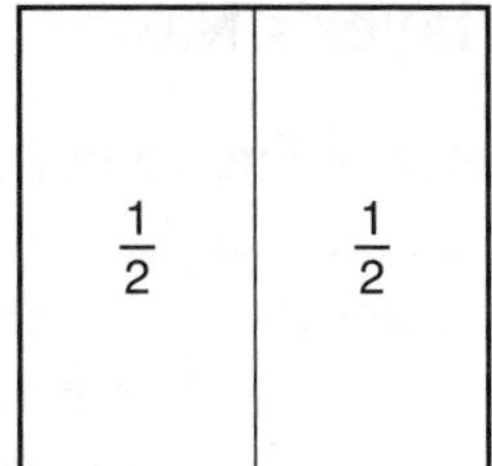

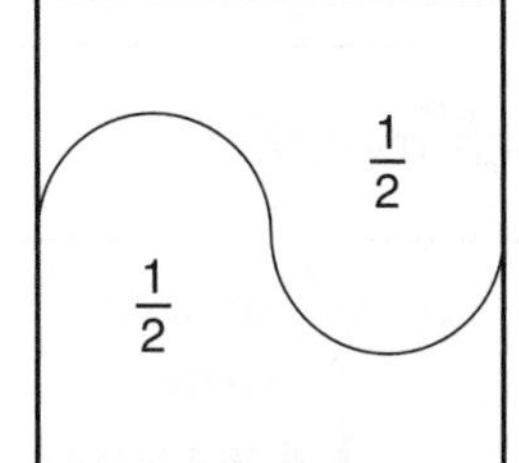

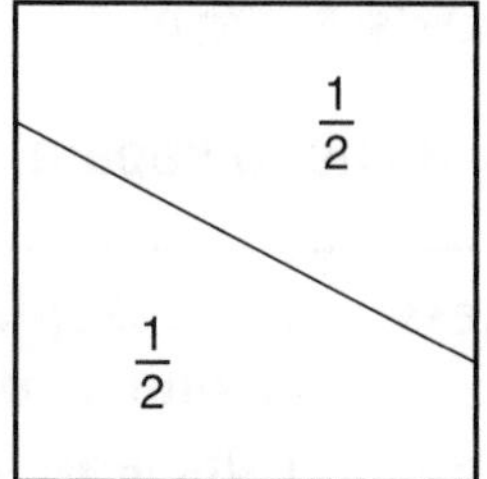

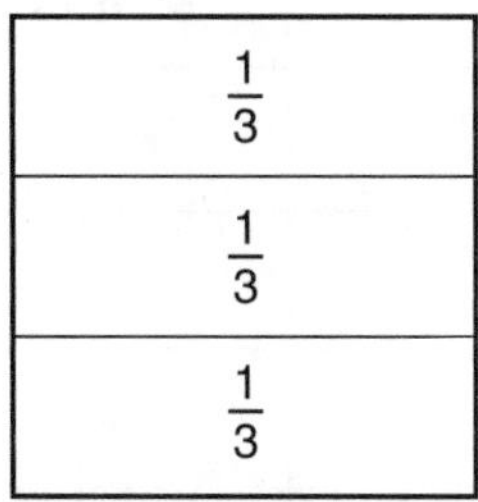

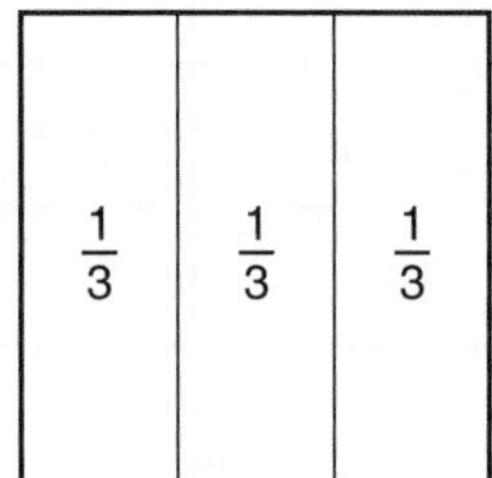

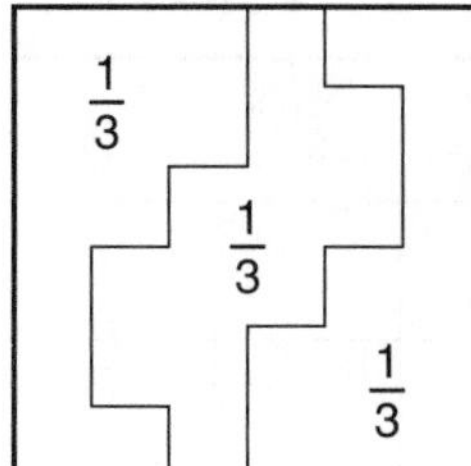

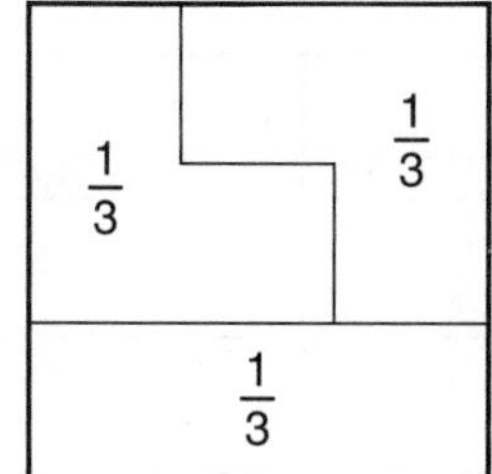

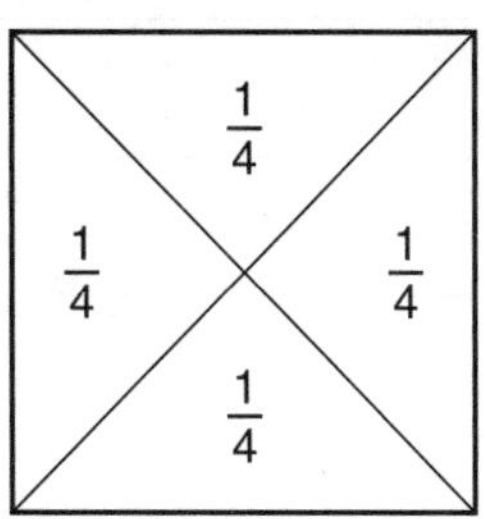

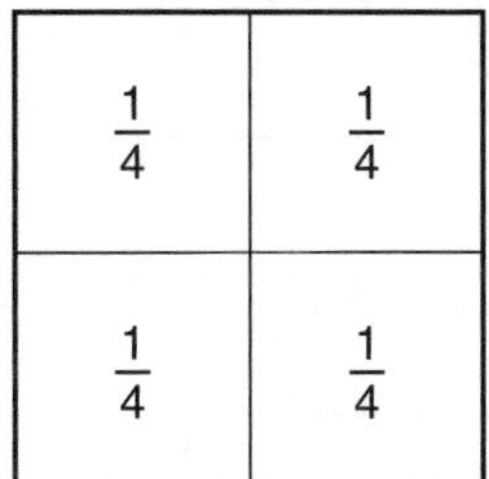

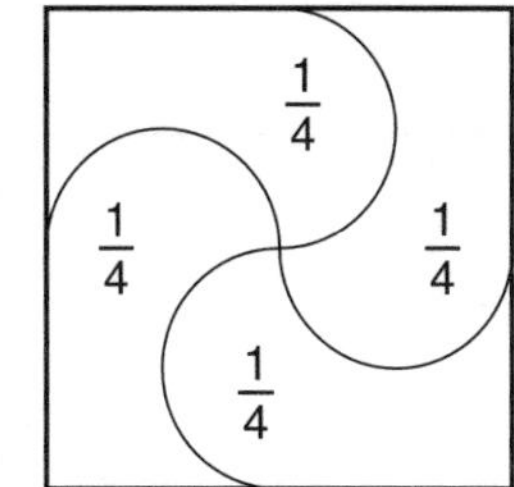

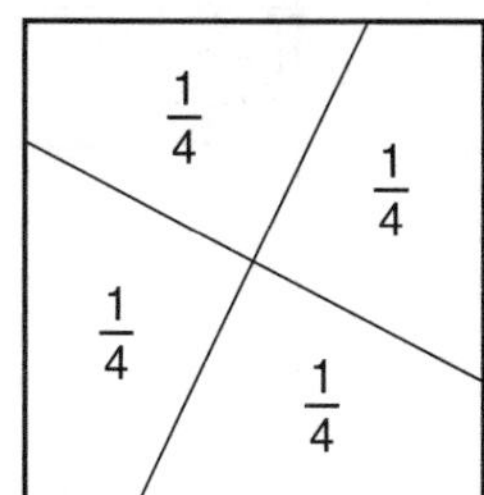

$\frac{1}{5}$ $\frac{1}{5}$ $\frac{1}{5}$ $\frac{1}{5}$ $\frac{1}{5}$

$\frac{1}{5}$
$\frac{1}{5}$
$\frac{1}{5}$
$\frac{1}{5}$
$\frac{1}{5}$

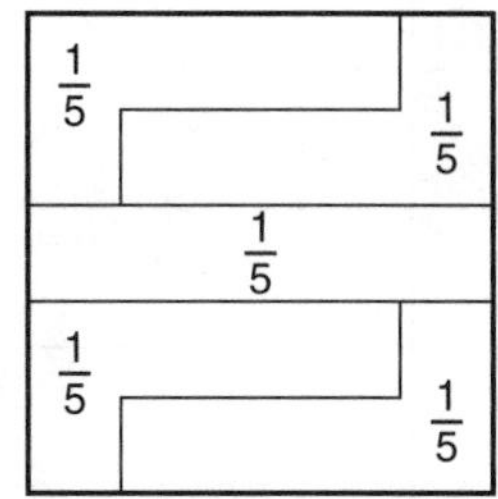

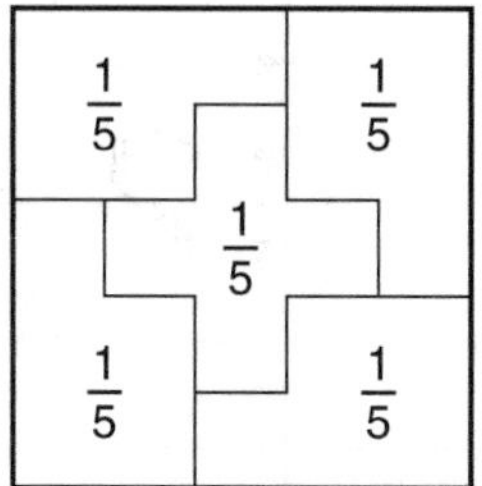

$\frac{1}{6}$	$\frac{1}{6}$
$\frac{1}{6}$	$\frac{1}{6}$
$\frac{1}{6}$	$\frac{1}{6}$

$\frac{1}{6}$ $\frac{1}{6}$ $\frac{1}{6}$ $\frac{1}{6}$ $\frac{1}{6}$ $\frac{1}{6}$

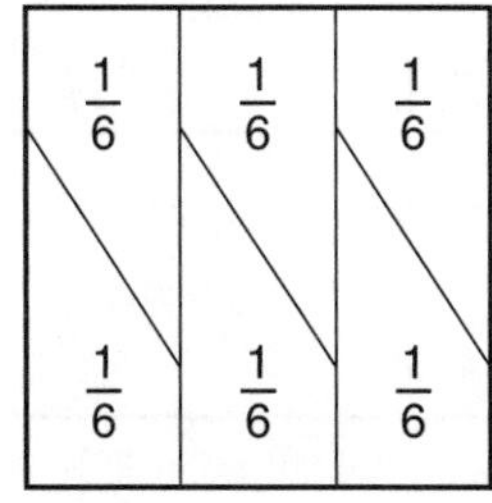

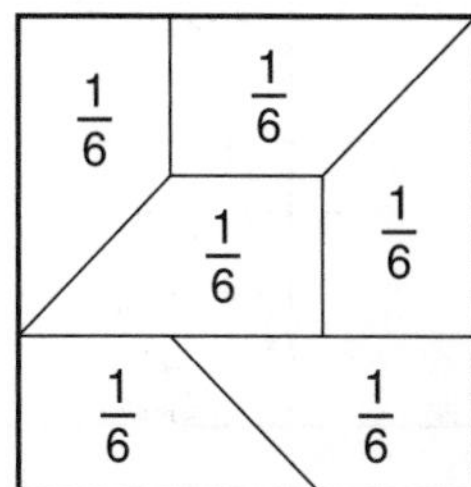

Name Date Time

Getting to One Record Sheets

Player's Name ____________________

Draw a line to separate each round.

Guess	**Display on calculator** (to nearest 0.01)	**Result** Write: **L** if too large **S** if too small **✔** if exact

Player's Name ____________________

Draw a line to separate each round.

Guess	**Display on calculator** (to nearest 0.01)	**Result** Write: **L** if too large **S** if too small **✔** if exact

Name Date Time

Grab Bag

Materials

Per partnership or team:

- ☐ 1 deck of *Grab Bag* cards (*Math Masters,* pp. 450 and 451)
- ☐ 1 *Grab Bag* Record Sheet (*Math Masters,* p. 452)
- ☐ 3 six-sided dice

Players 2, or two teams of 2

Object of the game To score more points by calculating the expected probability of events.

Directions

1. Shuffle the deck of *Grab Bag* cards and place it problem-side down on the table.

2. Players (or teams) take turns. When it is your turn:

   - Draw a card and place it problem-side up on the table. Two quantities are missing from each card. They are shown with the variables x and y.

   - Roll the 3 dice and substitute the numbers rolled for variables x and y in the following way:

     (i) Replace x with the number shown on one of the dice.

     (ii) Replace y with the sum of the numbers on the other two dice.

   - Solve the problem and give an answer. The opposing player (or team) checks the answer. Your score for the round is calculated as follows.

     10 points: if the event is unlikely (probability is less than $\frac{1}{2}$)

     30 points: if the event is likely (probability is greater than $\frac{1}{2}$)

     50 points: if the event is 50-50 (probability is exactly $\frac{1}{2}$)

3. The player (or team) with the highest score after 5 rounds wins.

Hint: Use a strategy when replacing x and y with the dice numbers to earn the most points possible for that turn.

Name Date Time

Grab Bag Cards

Lina has a bag of ribbons. She has 2 red, 2 blue, x pink, and y green ribbons.

What is the probability that she will pick a green ribbon without looking?

Mario has a bag of art pencils. He has 3 purple, 1 white, x green, and y yellow pencils.

What is the probability that he will pick a yellow pencil without looking?

Kenji has a bag of marbles. She has 6 striped, 1 clear, x solid, and y swirl marbles.

What is the probability that she will pick a swirl marble without looking?

There are 2 grape, 2 cherry, x apple, and y peach jelly beans in a bag.

Without looking, what is the probability of picking a peach jelly bean?

There are 3 clear, 3 blue, x white, and y orange beads in a bag.

Without looking, what is the probability of picking an orange bead?

There are 5 lemon, 2 strawberry, x cherry, and y grape lollipops in a bag.

Without looking, what is the probability of picking a grape lollipop?

A bag of markers has 1 yellow, 2 green, x pink, and y blue markers.

Kendra picks a blue marker from the bag. She puts the marker back in the bag.

Without looking, what is the probability that Kendra will pick a blue marker again?

A bag of erasers has 3 pink, 3 white, x blue, and y red erasers.

Cyrus picks a red eraser from the bag. He puts the red eraser back in the bag. Without looking, what is the probability that Cyrus will pick a red eraser again?

A bag of plastic buttons has 2 green, 3 gray, x black, and y white buttons.

Amir picks a white button from the bag. He puts the white button back in the bag.

Without looking, what is the probability that Amir will pick a white button again?

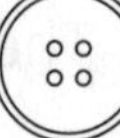

Name Date Time

Grab Bag Cards *continued*

Teresa has a bag of 2 red, 6 green, *x* white, and *y* blue centimeter cubes.

If she picks a cube out of the bag without looking, what is the probability that it will be blue?

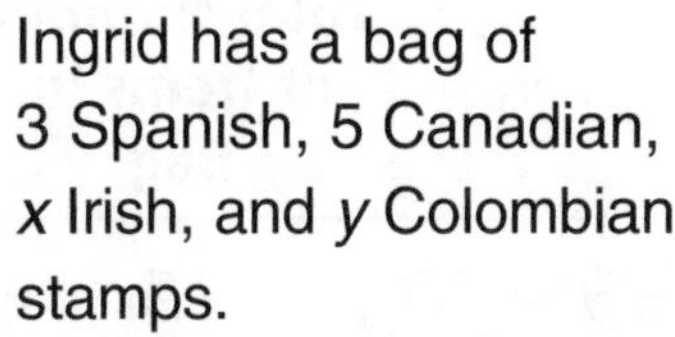

Ingrid has a bag of 3 Spanish, 5 Canadian, *x* Irish, and *y* Colombian stamps.

If she picks 1 stamp out of the bag without looking, what is the probability that it will be Colombian?

Boris has a bag of 1 red, 5 black, *x* orange, and *y* green toy cars.

If he picks 1 car out of the bag without looking, what is the probability that it will be green?

Jesse has a bag of painted blocks: 2 with flowers, 3 with leaves, *x* with animals, and *y* with dots.

Without looking, what is the probability that he will pull a block with dots from the bag?

Victor has a bag of family photos: 3 of his parents, 4 of his brothers, *x* of his cousins, and *y* of his grandma.

Without looking, what is the probability that he will pull a picture of his grandma from the bag?

Simone has a bag of playing cards: 1 diamond, 4 hearts, *x* spades, and *y* clubs.

Without looking, what is the probability that she will pull a club card from the bag?

There are 1 green, 2 blue, *x* red, and *y* yellow paper clips in a bag.

Without looking, what is the probability of picking a yellow paper clip?

There are 3 orange, 2 blue, *x* green, and *y* pink dice in a bag.

Without looking, what is the probability of picking a pink die?

There are 2 green, 2 purple, *x* gold, and *y* silver crayons in a bag.

Without looking, what is the probability of picking a silver crayon?

Name Date Time

Grab Bag Record Sheet

Round	Number of Items Given on Card		*x*	*y*	Total Number of Items in Bag	Probability of Event Occurring	Score
Sample	2	2	1	$6 + 4 = 10$	15	$\frac{10}{15}$, or $\frac{2}{3}$	30
1							
2							
3							
4							
5							
						Total Score	

Name Date Time

Grab Bag Record Sheet

Round	Number of Items Given on Card		*x*	*y*	Total Number of Items in Bag	Probability of Event Occurring	Score
Sample	2	2	1	$6 + 4 = 10$	15	$\frac{10}{15}$, or $\frac{2}{3}$	30
1							
2							
3							
4							
5							
						Total Score	

Greedy Score Sheets

Name ____________________

Greedy Score Sheet	
Round	**Score**
1	
2	
3	
4	
5	
6	
Total Score	

Name ____________________

Greedy Score Sheet	
Round	**Score**
1	
2	
3	
4	
5	
6	
Total Score	

Name ____________________

Greedy Score Sheet	
Round	**Score**
1	
2	
3	
4	
5	
6	
Total Score	

Name ____________________

Greedy Score Sheet	
Round	**Score**
1	
2	
3	
4	
5	
6	
Total Score	

Name Date Time

High-Number Toss Record Sheet

Hundred-Millions	Ten-Millions	Millions	,	Hundred-Thousands	Ten-Thousands	Thousands	,	Hundreds	Tens	Ones

Player 1 ______________________ (Name) **Player 2** ______________________ (Name)

Round	Player 1	>, <, =	Player 2
Sample	1 3 2 | 6 132,000,000	>	3 5 6 | 4 3,560,000
1	___ ___ ___ | ___ __________		___ ___ ___ | ___ __________
2	___ ___ ___ | ___ __________		___ ___ ___ | ___ __________
3	___ ___ ___ | ___ __________		___ ___ ___ | ___ __________
4	___ ___ ___ | ___ __________		___ ___ ___ | ___ __________
5	___ ___ ___ | ___ __________		___ ___ ___ | ___ __________

Name Date Time

High-Number Toss (Decimal Version) Record Sheet

Circle the winning number for each round. Fill in the Score column each time you have the winning number.

Player 1 ______________________ **Player 2** ______________________
(Name) (Name)

Round	Player 1	Player 2	Score
Sample	0. 6 5 4	0. 7 5 3	0.753 − 0.654 0.099
1	0.___ ___ ___	0.___ ___ ___	
2	0.___ ___ ___	0.___ ___ ___	
3	0.___ ___ ___	0.___ ___ ___	
4	0.___ ___ ___	0.___ ___ ___	
5	0.___ ___ ___	0.___ ___ ___	
		Total Score	

Name Date Time

Landmark Shark Cards

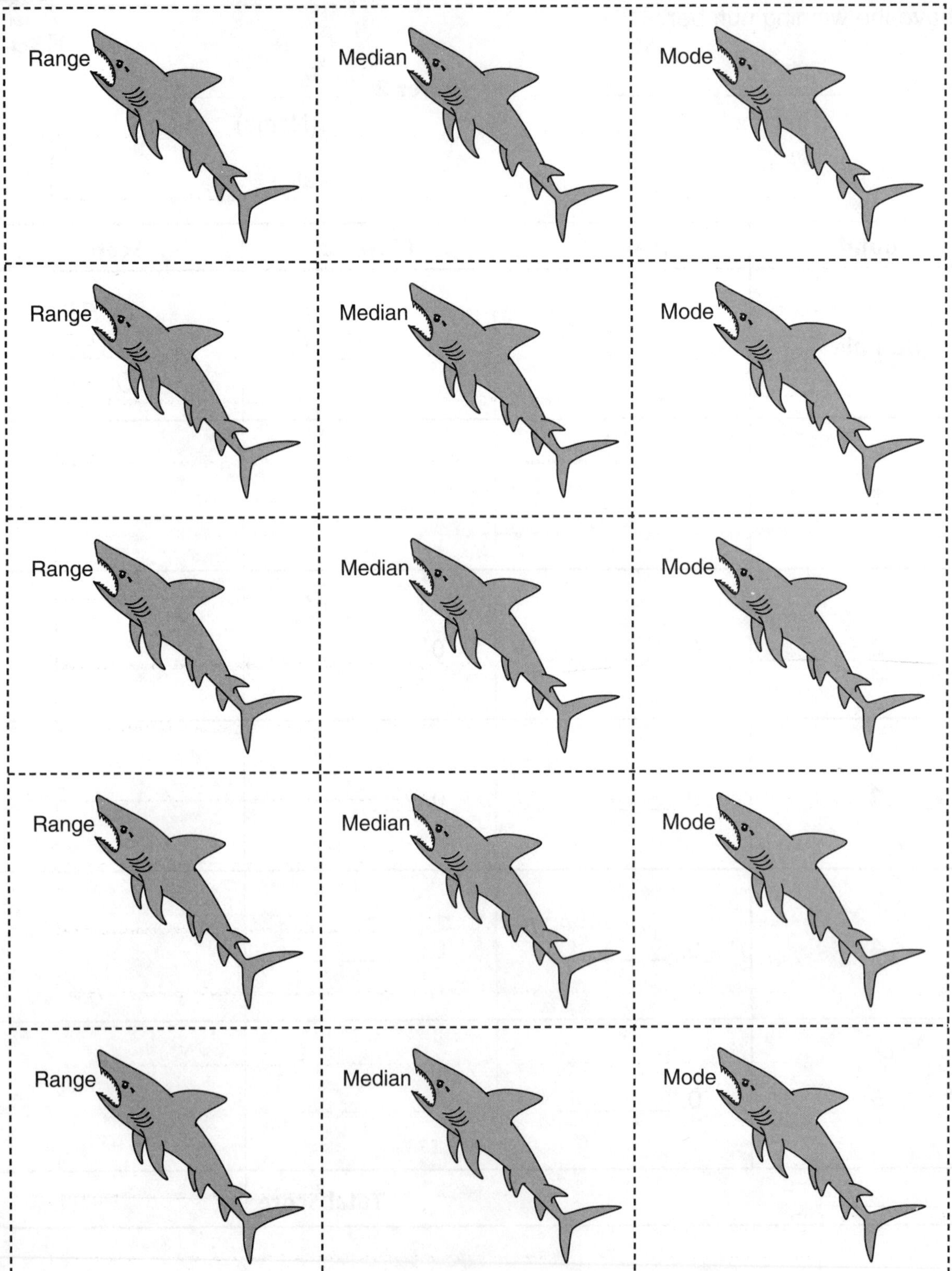

Range	Median	Mode
Range	Median	Mode
Range	Median	Mode
Range	Median	Mode
Range	Median	Mode

Name Date Time

Landmark Shark Score Sheet

SRB 325–326

		Player 1	Player 2	Player 3
Round 1:	Points Scored			
	Bonus Points			
	Round 1 Score			
Round 2:	Points Scored			
	Bonus Points			
	Round 2 Score			
Round 3:	Points Scored			
	Bonus Points			
	Round 3 Score			
Round 4:	Points Scored			
	Bonus Points			
	Round 4 Score			
Round 5:	Points Scored			
	Bonus Points			
	Round 5 Score			
Total Score for 5 Rounds				

Name Date Time

Mixed-Number Spinner

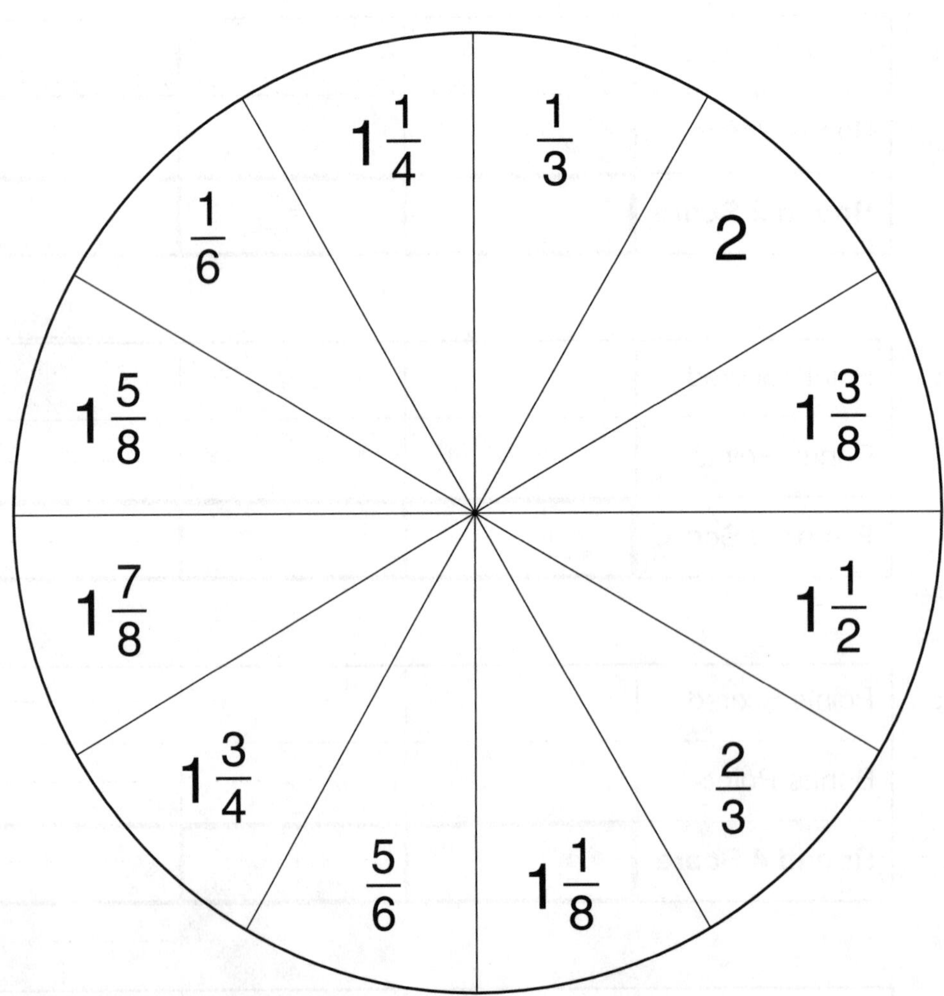

Name ______________________ Date ______________ Time ______________

Mixed-Number Spin Record Sheet

Materials ☐ *Math Masters,* page 458
☐ large paper clip

Players 2

Object of the Game To be the first player to generate 10 true number sentences using fractions and mixed numbers.

Directions

1. Each player writes his or her name in one of the boxes below.

2. Take turns spinning. When it is your turn, write the fraction or mixed number you spin in one of the blanks below your name.

3. The first player to complete 10 true sentences is the winner.

[ ] Name	[ ] Name
______ + ______ < 3	______ + ______ < 3
______ + ______ > 3	______ + ______ > 3
______ − ______ < 1	______ − ______ < 1
______ − ______ $> \frac{1}{2}$	______ − ______ $> \frac{1}{2}$
______ + ______ > 1	______ + ______ > 1
______ + ______ < 1	______ + ______ < 1
______ + ______ < 2	______ + ______ < 2
______ − ______ $= 3$	______ − ______ $= 3$
______ − ______ > 1	______ − ______ > 1
______ + ______ $> \frac{1}{2}$	______ + ______ $> \frac{1}{2}$
______ + ______ < 3	______ + ______ < 3
______ + ______ > 2	______ + ______ > 2

Name Date Time

Multiplication Wrestling

Materials ☐ 4 each of number cards 0–9 (from the Everything Math Deck, if available)

Players 2

Object of the Game To get the largest product of two 2-digit numbers.

Directions

Shuffle the deck of cards and place it facedown. Each player draws 4 cards and forms two 2-digit numbers. There are many possible ways to form 2-digit numbers using 4 cards. Each player should form two numbers whose product is as large as possible.

Example:

Player 1:
Draws 4, 5, 7, 8
Forms 75 and 84

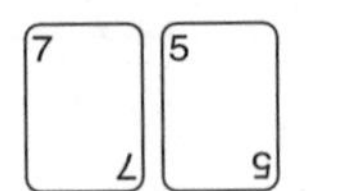

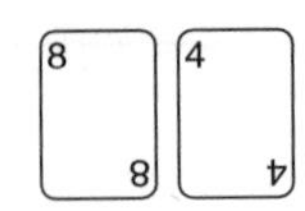

Player 2:
Draws 1, 4, 6, 9
Forms 64 and 91

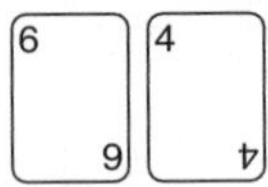

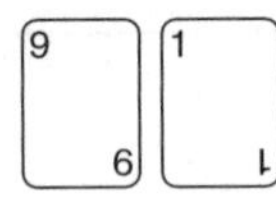

Each player creates 2 wrestling teams by writing each number as a sum of tens and ones.

Player 1: 75 ∗ 84	**Player 2:** 64 ∗ 91
Team 1 Team 2	Team 1 Team 2
(70 + 5) ∗ (80 + 4)	(60 + 4) ∗ (90 + 1)

Then each player's 2 teams wrestle. Each member of Team 1 (70 and 5) is multiplied by each member of Team 2 (80 and 4). The 4 products are then added.

Player 1:		**Player 2:**	
Teams: (70 + 5) ∗ (80 + 4)		Teams: (60 + 4) ∗ (90 + 1)	
Products:	70 ∗ 80 = 5,600	Products:	60 ∗ 90 = 5,400
	70 ∗ 4 = 280		60 ∗ 1 = 60
	5 ∗ 80 = 400		4 ∗ 90 = 360
	5 ∗ 4 = 20		4 ∗ 1 = 4
Total: (add 4 products)	5,000	Total: (add 4 products)	5,000
	1,200		700
	+ 100		120
	6,300		+ 4
			5,824

Scoring

The player with the larger product wins the round and receives 1 point. To begin a new round, each player draws 4 new cards to form 2 new numbers. A game consists of 3 rounds.

Name Date Time

Multiplication Wrestling Scorecard

Players' Names		
Round 1		
Round 2		
Round 3		
Total		

Players' Names		
Round 1		
Round 2		
Round 3		
Total		

Players' Names		
Round 1		
Round 2		
Round 3		
Total		

Players' Names		
Round 1		
Round 2		
Round 3		
Total		

Name ______________________ Date ______________ Time ______________

Name That Number Record Sheet

Round 1

Target Number: ________ My Cards: ______ ______ ______ ______ ______

My Solution (number sentence): ______________________________

Number of cards used: ________

Round 2

Target Number: ________ My Cards: ______ ______ ______ ______ ______

My Solution (number sentence): ______________________________

Number of cards used: ________

- -

Name ______________________ Date ______________ Time ______________

Name That Number Record Sheet

Round 1

Target Number: ________ My Cards: ______ ______ ______ ______ ______

My Solution (number sentence): ______________________________

Number of cards used: ________

Round 2

Target Number: ________ My Cards: ______ ______ ______ ______ ______

My Solution (number sentence): ______________________________

Number of cards used: ________

Name Date Time

Number Top-It (10-digit Whole Numbers)

Materials ☐ number cards 0–9 (4 of each)

☐ *Number Top-It* Game Mat (*Math Masters,* p. 464)

☐ *Top-It* Record Sheet (*Math Masters,* p. 478)

Players 2 to 4

Object of the game To make the largest 10-digit number.

Directions

1. Shuffle the cards. Place the deck, number-side down, on the playing surface.
2. Each player uses a row of boxes on the *Number Top-It* Game Mat.
3. In each round, players take turns turning over the top card from the deck and placing it on any one of their empty boxes. Each player takes 10 turns and places 10 cards on his or her row of the game mat.
4. At the end of each round, players read their numbers aloud and compare them to the other players' numbers. The player with the largest number for the round scores 1 point. The player with the next larger number scores 2 points, and so on.
5. Players play 5 rounds for each game. Shuffle the deck between each round. The player with the smallest total number of points at the end of 5 rounds wins the game.

Example: Paulina and Armando played 10-digit *Number Top-It*. The result for one complete round of play is shown below.

***Number Top-It* Game Mat**

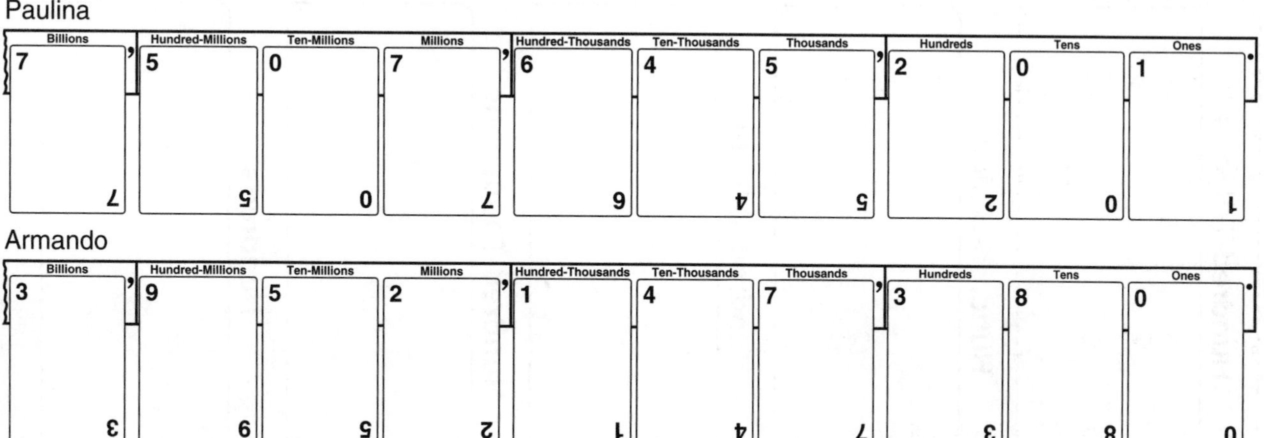

Paulina's number is larger than Armando's number for this round. Paulina scores 1 point for this round and Armando scores 2 points.

Name Date Time

Number Top-It Game Mat

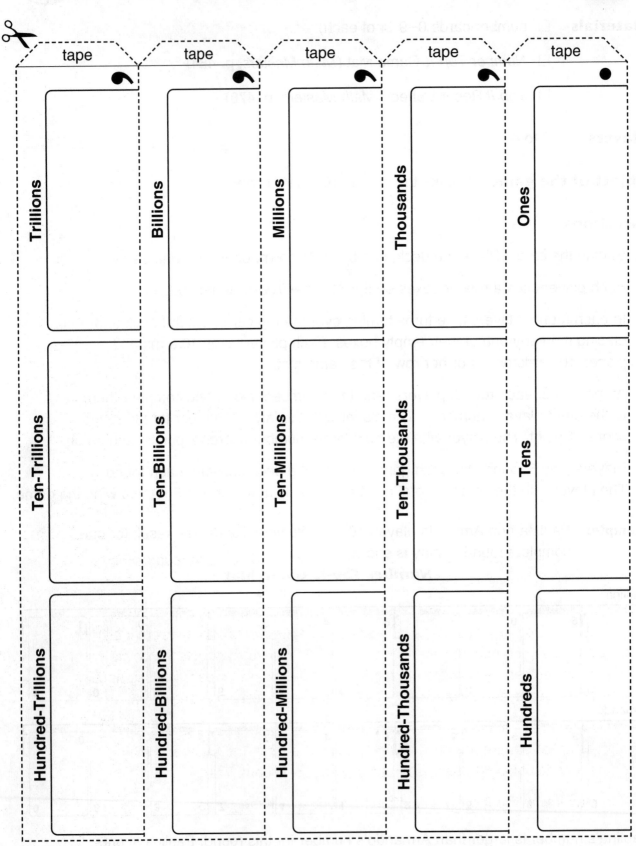

tape	tape	tape	tape	tape
,	,	,	,	.
Trillions	Billions	Millions	Thousands	Ones
Ten-Trillions	Ten-Billions	Ten-Millions	Ten-Thousands	Tens
Hundred-Trillions	Hundred-Billions	Hundred-Millions	Hundred-Thousands	Hundreds

Name Date Time

Over and Up Squares

Materials
- ☐ 1 *Over and Up Squares* gameboard and record sheet
- ☐ 1 color pencil per player (different color for each player)
- ☐ 2 six-sided dice

Players 2

Object of the game

To score the most points by connecting ordered pairs on a grid.

Directions

1. Player 1 rolls two dice and uses the numbers to make an ordered pair. Either number can be used to name the *x*-coordinate (over) of the ordered pair. The other number is used to name the *y*-coordinate (up) of the ordered pair. After deciding which ordered pair to use, the player uses a color pencil to plot the point.
2. Player 1 records the ordered pair and the score in the record sheet. A player earns 10 points each time an ordered pair is plotted correctly.
3. Player 2 rolls the dice and decides how to make an ordered pair. If both possible ordered pairs are already plotted, the player rolls the dice again. (Variation: If both possible ordered pairs are already plotted, the player can change one or both of the numbers to 0.)
4. Player 2 uses the other color pencil to plot the ordered pair and records his or her score on the record sheet.
5. Players continue to take turns rolling dice, plotting ordered pairs, and recording the results. If, on any player's turn, two plotted points are next to each other on the same side of one of the small grid squares, the player connects the points with a line segment. A player scores an additional 10 points for each line segment. Sometimes a player may draw more than one line segment in a single turn.
6. If a player draws a line segment that completes a grid square (so that all 4 sides of the square are drawn), that player shades in the square. A player earns an additional 50 points each time a square is completed.
7. The player with the most points after 10 rounds wins the game.

Name Date Time

Over and Up Squares Gameboard and Record Sheet

Player 1 ______________________

Round	Over (*x*-coordinate)	,	Up (*y*-coordinate)	Score
1				
2				
3				
4				
5				
6				
7				
8				
9				
10				
			Total Score	

Scoring	
Ordered pair	10 points
Line segment	10 points
Square	50 points

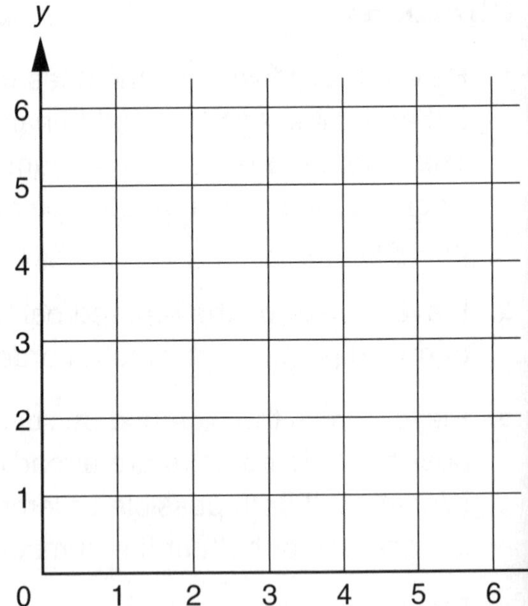

Player 2 ______________________

Round	Over (*x*-coordinate)	,	Up (*y*-coordinate)	Score
1				
2				
3				
4				
5				
6				
7				
8				
9				
10				
			Total Score	

Name Date Time

Percent/Sector Match Up

Materials ☐ 1 set of Percent/Sector tiles

Players 2 or 3

Object of the game

To match percents and the shaded sectors that represent them.

Directions

1. Shuffle the tiles and lay them facedown on a playing surface. The backs of the 12 percent tiles should have the percent symbol (%) showing. The backs of the sector tiles are blank. Arrange the tiles into a 6-row-by-4-column array, keeping them facedown.
2. Players take turns. At each turn, a player turns over a percent tile and a sector tile. If the tiles match, the player keeps the tiles. If the tiles do not match, the player turns the tiles facedown.
3. The game ends when all tiles have been taken. The player with the most tiles wins.

   (Variation: If the selected percent tile and sector tile add up to 100%, the player keeps the tiles.)

Name Date Time

Percent/Sector Tiles

%	%	%	%
%	%	%	%
%	%	%	%